Alan and Holly Bass

Prealgebra with Study Skills

Second Preliminary Edition

Taken from:
Prealgebra
by Alan Bass and Holly Bass

Cover Art: Courtesy of Photodisc/Getty Images, brandxpictures

Taken from:

Prealgebra
by Alan Bass and Holly Bass
Copyright © 2016 by Pearson Education, Inc.
Published by Prentice Hall
Upper Saddle River, New Jersey 07458

Pearson Learning Solutions, 501 Boylston Street, Suite 900, Boston, MA 02116
A Pearson Education Company
www.pearsoned.com

Printed in the United States of America

1 2 3 4 5 6 7 8 9 10 VOCR 17 16 15 14 13 12

000200010271699550

RM/TY

ISBN 10: 1-256-85502-2
ISBN 13: 978-1-256-85502-6

NOTE TO STUDENTS

This textbook is a customized preliminary edition featuring a comprehensive Prealgebra textbook to be published in the upcoming year. **As a preliminary edition, this book will contain editor's notes and other draft materials.**

In order that the main edition may be of the greatest value to classes, you send constructive criticism on this preliminary edition:

- suggestions for improving the book
- supplementing and applying the material
- especially successful topics
- things that you have and/or would find useful.

You will all have a part in making the main edition better as it will represent the experience and the best thought and effort of those who have used this book.

Thank you!

Alan and Holly Bass

Mail suggestions and comments to: abass@sdccd.edu.

Prealgebra with Study Skills

By Alan and Holly Bass

San Diego Mesa College

Table of Contents

Chapter 6. Ratios, Proportions, and Square Roots   434

Chapter 7. Percent   498

Topics:
- Introduction
- Features of the Book
- Icons
- Study Tips

Introduction

Welcome to Prealgebra! This textbook will help meet the challenge of succeeding in math and in college. We have created this textbook to make it easy for you to take advantage of the resources that have been developed to help you succeed.

To be honest, many Prealgebra students are burned out on math. Many of them think that they are "just not math people". Many of them are returning students who have not seen any math at all in a very long time. Many of them have math anxiety. If you identify with any of these ideas but know you need to succeed in this course, you have come to the right place. We have created a textbook that helps students meet these obstacles head on.

The key to being successful in math is NOT in having a high intelligence. The key to being success in math is having an intelligent approach. That is, math is not at all impossible to master if you have the proper tools. This means managing your time wisely to make sure you are committed to the course. This means staying organized. This means taking the time to prepare adequately for exams. If you can do these things you can succeed, period.

In a nut-shell, the phrase "Study Skills" refers to a student's ability to "work hard" and "work smart" in a college course.

Good Study Skills are the number one most important factor in a student passing a college math class...not "being smart", not having a "math brain"...STUDY SKILLS!

To get started, you need to honestly reflect on your current study habits.

#1. You Current Study Habits.
Write a response using the following questions as prompts. This response should take up about half a page of writing.

• What is your approach to homework and studying in math class?

_____
_____
_____

• What are the things that you do that you know are effective?

_____
_____
_____

• What are the things that you don't do that you know you should? That is, what areas of your studying that need improving?

_____
_____
_____

Your Course Syllabus

Ultimately, your instructor is the authority on how your Prealgebra class will run. So the first and most important in getting started is to understand you course syllabus. A syllabus is an outline of what the course covers and all the professor's policies from grading to attendance. Professors usually go over the syllabus on the first day of class.

Syllabus Quiz

#2. What is your instructor's name?

_____

#3. How can you contact your instructor?

_____

#4. What materials are required for the course?

_____

#5. What is the best way to contact your professor?

_____

#6. Does your professor have office hours? If so, when are they?

_____

#7. How many absences are you allowed before you may be dropped?

_____

#8. What are the different kinds of grades you will get in the class (Exams, Homework, Group Work, etc.)?

_____

#9. Do you know the date of your first test? If so, when is it?

_____

#10.   What is the date of your final exam?

_____

Features of the Book

To make best use of any textbook you should be familiar of the features

Topics and Are You Ready

Each section of this book is broken up into *topics*. Let's look at the beginning of a typical section.

These are the topics that will be covered in the section

This is a short quiz that will help you prepare for the material in the section

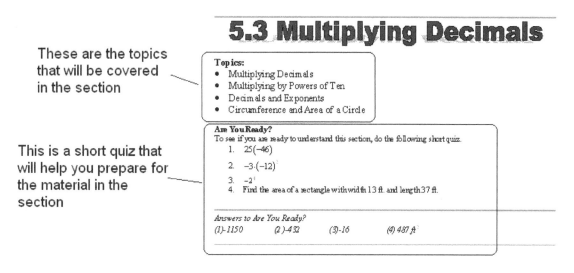

5.3 Multiplying Decimals

Topics:
- Multiplying Decimals
- Multiplying by Powers of Ten
- Decimals and Exponents
- Circumference and Area of a Circle

Are You Ready?
To see if you are ready to understand this section, do the following short quiz.
1. $25(-46)$
2. $-3 \cdot (-12)$
3. -2^4
4. Find the area of a rectangle with width 13 ft. and length 37 ft.

Answers to Are You Ready?
(1) -1150   (2) -432   (3) -16   (4) 487 ft

Are You Ready?
Math builds on itself. To properly understand whatever chapter you are working on you have to understand topics from previous chapters. For each section we have created a short exercise set that will help you review important topics from previous chapters.

Integrated Homework

To help you understand each topic as you read through the book, and to make referencing as easy as possible, we have integrated the homework. Integrated homework means that rather put all the homework at the end of each section we have mixed it into the text after each topic. After each topic there is a set of exercises for you to try. A stop sign will point out these exercise sets. As you go through the book, this icon will let you know when it's time to get to work!

Putting it ALL Together

The exercise set at the end of the section is called **Putting it ALL Together**. This set contains exercises of all kinds from the section.

Exercise Set - Putting it ALL Together

Vocabulary Check: Fill in each blank with a word from our Vocabulary Checklist to the right. Each word is used exactly once.

1. Reversing the order of a product does not change the result. For example, $11 \cdot 4 = 4 \cdot 11$. This is called _____

2. In division, the number zero cannot be used as a _____.

Vocabulary Checklist:
factors
product
area
dividend
divisor
quotient
the commutative property of mult
the associative property of multip

 # QUIZ YOURSELF

Using the textbook examples and your notes to do homework is smart and important. But we need to make sure that do problems without that kind of help. So, at the end of each section there will be a set of about 10 quiz exercises after the title "Quiz Yourself". This exercise set is a practice quiz to help you ensure that you can do math without help and to prepare you for quizzes in class or an exam. To make sure you are ready for class, you should try these exercises without any help from the book or your notes.

 # TEST YOURSELF

Preparing for exams is an important study skill. At the end of each chapter there will be a set of about 40 exam exercises after the title "Test Yourself". This exercise set is a practice exam to help you prepare for you in-class exam. To make sure you are ready for exam, you should try these exercises without any help from the book or your notes.

Succeed in Math!
Succeeding in math and college takes hard work and, more importantly, smart work. To help you study smart, we have placed Succeed in Math boxes like the one below through out the book with useful study tips.

I'll be giving you tips throughout the book to help you SUCCEED IN MATH! Our first tip is all about getting ready for the course.

Icons

Let's look at the symbols used in the book. These symbols point out everything from when to use a calculator to special video material to study tips so it is important that you are familiar with them. The following table explains all of the icons we will be using.

Icon	Description
STOP	Indicates a set of homework exercises.
	This icon indicates there is a video that explains how to do this topic or question.
	Indicates a Succeed in Math study tip or study skills material.
	Indicates a calculator should be used for this exercise.

Take the following quiz to make sure you understand what the different icons represent.

Icon Quiz - Beside each icon give a short explanation for what it means.

#11.

Icon	Description
STOP	

Feature Quiz

#12.   What is the purpose of the Quiz Yourself exercises at the end of each section?

#13.   What is the purpose of the Test Yourself exercises at the end of each chapter?

#14.   What does "Integrated Homework" mean?

#15.   What is the purpose of the Are You Ready exercises?

Study Tips

You are starting down the road to success. To help get you on your way here are some general study tips.

- **You are not in high school anymore.** In high school teachers tend to be more flexible and lenient about assignments and grading. In college, professors have high standards for graded and expect you to perform as such. Be prepared!
- **Go to class.** For many students being in college represents a new level of social freedom. This can make it tempting to skip class. Avoid the temptation. Besides learning the material in class, you'll also receive information from the professors about what to expect on tests, changes in due dates, etc.
- **Meet your professor.** Take the time to meet your professor one on one. Professors can seem intimidating but generally people who are in education are here because they want to help people like you. And they enjoy getting to know their students. Meet your professor in her office or after class, tell her your concerns about the course, what your academic goals are. She may have some good advice for you.
- **WANT TO SUCCEED!** You have to want it! Wanting to succeed in your math course will force you to think about what it takes to do it, and that's good.
- **Find your schools tutor center.** Most schools have a tutor center where students can get free tutoring in math. Your professor probably knows where the tutor center is and what the hours are.
- **Take responsibility for yourself.** You are responsible for your success in this class. Not your professor, not the school, not anyone but you. Being an adult means taking responsibility for everything that happens to you. It is good to keep this in mind as you start getting grades and turning in assignments.
- **Look for other students in your class who want to succeed.** They are there. Study with them. Find out what they do to get good grades. Connect yourself to a study group. Successful students tend to study in groups.
- **Be prepared to feel overwhelmed.** You have a lot going on in your life right now. Expect to have moments where it seems a bit too much. The key is in being prepared to do what it takes to be successful. This book will have tips to help you along the way.

Finally, let's think about what your goal is for this course. It is an important process to reflect on what you want out of such a major undertaking as a college class. What is your goal for this course? It could be "Get an "A"!" or it could be "To pass". Regardless it is important that you know what you want to accomplish at the outset.

#16. What is your goal for this course?

_____

Good. Time to get into Prealgebra! Work hard! Work smart!

Chapter 1 - From Basic Math to Prealgebra

Prealgebra

This chapter is a review of some of the most important things you have learned about Basic Math along with some other ideas that will lead you into Prealgebra.

What's Inside?!

Review how to perform the four basic operations…

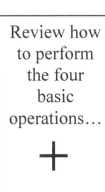

Courtesy of Fotolia

We'll talk about how to get yourself prepared for this course so you can… SUCCEED IN MATH!

PLUS! Learn how scientists use variables to help track the path of a rocket!

$$vt - gt^2 = 165(2) - 16(2)^2$$
$$= 266$$

Courtesy of Fotolia

1.1 Whole Numbers

Topics:
- Place Value and Naming Numbers
- Number Lines
- Rounding
- Reading Tables and Graphs

Place Value and Naming Numbers

Whole numbers refers to the following set of numbers:

Whole Numbers:
$$0, 1, 2, 3, 4, 5, 6, 7, 8, 9, 10, 11, 12, \ldots$$

The three dots at the end of the list indicate that the list of whole numbers goes on forever. We use whole numbers to count and measure.

- A football team has 11 players on the field at one time.
- The average American spends 152 minutes per day using a cell phone.
- The Apple Corporation profited $4,310,000,000 for the year 2010.

We use 10 digits (0, 1, 2, 3, 4, 5, 6, 7, 8, and 9) to make whole numbers. The number 152 has three digits: 1, 5, and 2. The number 13,908 has five digits. We label the digits in a whole number by their position in the number, called the *place value*.

The position of a digit in a whole number is called its **place value**.

We also separate the digits into groups of three, called *periods*. Here is a chart that shows the place value system.

[PN: Can we have a merged cell above each period giving the periods name like "thousands period, millions period, etc.]

Hundred Trillion	Ten-Trillions	Trillions	Hundred-Billion	Ten-Billions	Billions	Hundred-Millions	Ten-Millions	Millions	Hundred-Thousands	Ten-Thousands	Thousands	Hundreds	Tens	Ones
		9,	3	2	0,	8	7	1,	5	6	3,	8	0	2

We can use this place value chart as reference to determine the place value of a given digit in a whole number.

Example 1: In the number 5,347,095 in what place value is the digit 3?

Solution: Using the chart as a reference we see the 3 is in the hundred-thousands place.

We use the place value system above and separate the whole number into periods to read the number.

45,102,560 is read

"forty-five million, one hundred two thousand, five hundred sixty"
[PN: arrows point out each period]

To read a whole number:
1. Start at the right and separate the number into periods using commas.
2. Read the number from the left using the comma as an indicator to state the place value (trillions, billions, millions, thousands).
3. Continue this process for each period the whole number contains.

Note that it is not necessary to state the last period by saying ones.

Example 2: Write the following whole numbers in words.
a) 16,492   b) 3,467,012

Solution: [PN: arrows pointing out each period]

a) 16,492 is read "sixteen thousand, four hundred ninety two".

b) 3,467,012 is read "three million, four hundred sixty seven thousand, twelve".

It is an important real-world skill to be able to hear a number read and know how it is written in digits.

Example 3: Where in the World? An astronomy professor giving a lecture says "the distance between the orbital paths of Earth and Mars is *forty eight million, six hundred eighty thousand* miles". Write the number referred to as a whole number.

Solution: "*forty eight million, six hundred eighty thousand* miles" is 48,680,000 miles.

STOP Exercise Set - Place Value and Naming Numbers

Write each phrase as a whole number.
1. five thousand three hundred sixty-five
2. twenty-six thousand, seven hundred eighty-two
3. four hundred five thousand

4.   twelve million, fifteen thousand, nine hundred forty-two

Write the following numbers in words.
5.   312
6.   709
7.   72,601
8.   203,918
9.   21,305,297
10. 1,088,513

Number Lines

Most people are visual learners. That means they understand information best when they can see a picture to represent it. In math, we use number lines to help us visualize numbers and understand concepts. This is a number line…

To graph a number on a number line, we put a point at that number. For example, we could graph the whole numbers 4 and 7 by putting points at those numbers.

Example 4: Graph the whole numbers 3, 8, and 1 on a number line.

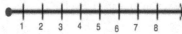

Solution: We draw a number line and put a point at the numbers 3, 8, and 1.

When graphing large numbers on a number line, it is common to use a *scale* other than one.

The **scale** on the number line is the distance between each tic mark.

This number line has a scale of 25.

A scientist may have to use this scale to deal with larger numbers that involve temperature.

The most common numbers used for scaling are 1, 5, 10, 25, 50 and 100 unless the numbers are very large.

Example 5: Where in the World?
The following list of numbers gives the successive world records for the longest jump on a motorcycle. Graph the numbers on a number line using a scale of 25.

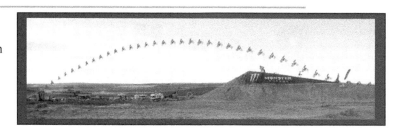

Jumper	Distance
John Sumpter	125 feet
Ernest Murillo	201 feet
John Floyd	277 feet
Dana Littlewood	322 feet
Jesse Gaither	390 feet

Solution:
The axis is scaled to 50 and each jump is labeled with a point. Note that not every point falls on a tic mark, so we approximate where it should be on the number line in relation to the tic marks.

STOP Exercise Set - Number Lines

Graph the following whole numbers on a number line. Use the scale indicated.

11. 1, 5, 0, 11, Scale: 1

12. 2, 6, 7, 10, Scale: 1

13. 15, 25, 40, 70, Scale: 10

14. 30, 50, 70, 80, Scale: 10

15. 150, 30, 200, 265, Scale: 50

16. 23, 57, 98, 129, 159, Scale: 25

17. The following table gives the temperature reached in a science experiment. Graph the temperature settings on a number line using a scale of 5.

Experiment Number	Temperature Setting
#1	5 degrees
#2	15 degrees
#3	20 degrees
#4	35 degrees

18. The following table gives height, in meters, of several buildings in New York City. Graph the numbers using a scale of 25.

Building	Height
Empire State	380
Park Avenue	190
Wall Street	280
M&M Headquarters	180
Carnegie Hall	230

Rounding

In everyday life it is common to estimate a number rather than use it exactly. You probably do this with your checking account balance. Your account may have a balance of $319, and you may note that you have about $300 in your account. When you do this you have *rounded* your balance *to the nearest hundreds*. A number line can help explain why we round this way.

On a number line, 319 is closer to 300 than 400.

Here is the procedure for rounding a whole number to a given place value:

To Round a Number to a Given Place Value:

Look at the place value just to the right of the place value where you want to round:

- If that digit is 5 or higher round up by adding 1 to the given place value.
- If that digit is less than 5 round down by leaving the number in the place value the same.
- In both cases replace the digits to the right of the rounded place value with zeros.

Trillions	Hundred-Billions	Ten-Billions	Billions	Hundred-Millions	Ten-Millions	Millions	Hundred-Thousands	Ten-Thousands	Thousands	Hundreds	Tens	Ones
9	3	2	0	8	7	1	5	6	3	8	0	2

Example 6: Round each number to the place value given.
a.) 5,249 to the nearest hundred.
b.) 149,704,179 to the nearest million.

Solution:

a.) To round to the nearest hundreds we look at the value in the tens place.   5249

Since the value in the tens place is less than five, we round down by leaving the digit in the hundreds place unchanged and putting zeros in the place values after.   5200

b.) To round to the nearest million we look at the value in the hundred-thousands place. $149,704,179$

Since the value in the hundred-thousands place is more than five, we round up by adding one to the millions place and putting zeros after. $150,000,000$

Rounding is particularly useful for applications and everyday life.

Example 7: Where in the World? The state of California covers 163,696 square miles. Round this value to the nearest ten-thousands place.

Solution: To the nearest ten-thousand, California is 160,000 square miles.

Estimate each number by rounding to the place value given.

19. 35 ; ten
20. 578 ; hundred
21. 219,645 ; ten-thousand
22. 4,504,913 ; hundred
23. 894,479 ; thousand
24. 235,671,009 ; millions

25. Last year, Pavel drove a total of 36,781 miles for work. Round this value to the nearest thousands place.

26. Rachel has to fly to Boston for work on a regular basis. In the past three months, she has flown 9,237 miles. Round this value to the nearest hundreds place.

Reading Tables and Graphs

As with graphing numbers on a number line, tables and graphs are another way to visualize information and organize whole numbers. If you pick up a newspaper or look at a news website, you will probably see tables giving important data. Here are some examples of tables and graphs.

Tables

A table is a very popular way to organize information. Both of the tables below give the same information: they show a family's house-hold spending over a period of several months. The first column or row of numbers gives the month while the second column or row gives the spending for that month.

Month	Spending
April	$3,470
May	$3,215
June	$5,307
July	$2,925

Month	April	May	June	July
Spending	$3,470	$3,215	$5,307	$2,925

Many of the exercises we do in math involve reading information off a table. Tables are so popular because at a glance you have a lot of information. This makes it easy to compare the numbers. When making your monthly budget, you might use a very similar table.

Example 8: According to the table above, what was the family's spending for the month of July?

Month	April	May	June	July
Spending	$3,470	$3,215	$5,307	$2,925

Solution: Using the table above we see the spending for July was $2,925.

Bar Graphs

Bar graphs are a fantastic way to visualize information. Bar graphs do not usually give exact values but are useful for showing patterns. The bar graph to the right gives a company's profit over several years. The *axis* on the bottom represents the years. The profit for each year is found by seeing how high the bar for that year goes up. The scale for the profit is on the left.

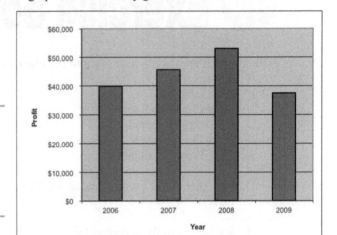

Example 9: According to the bar graph about how much profit did the company make in 2007?

Solution: The bar for the year 2007 looks like it is about half way between, so we'll say the company's profit for the year 2007 was about $45,000.

Line Graphs

Line graphs connect the dots between given data to show patterns in the graph instead of using bars. This line graph shows jet-ski sales for a boating store. From this line graph, we can tell that sells were going up from April to May and down from January to February. This ability to show patterns is the best feature of the line graphs.

Example 10: According to the line graph, in which month did the company sell the most jet-skis?

Solution: The month with the highest sells would be the one that has the highest point. This would be the May.

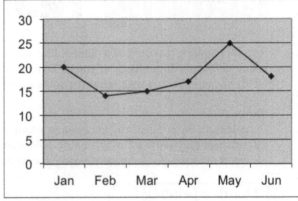

STOP Exercise Set - Reading Tables and Graphs

The following bar graph gives the number of jet skies sold by Pacific Water Sports. Answer the questions that follow.

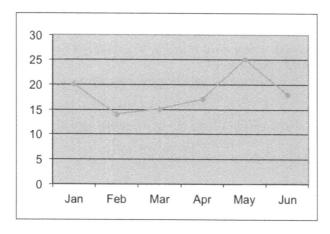

27. How many jet skies were sold in March?
28. How many jet skies were sold in June?
29. In which month did they sell the most? How many were sold that month?
30. In which month did they sell the least? How many were sold that month?

A survey is given to 100 people about their preference for brand of car. Answer the questions that follow.

Company	Toyota	GM	Volkswagen	Ford	Honda
Frequency of Preference	30	24	8	19	19

31. Which car company was the most popular? How many people in the survey preferred it?
32. Which car company was the least popular? How many people in the survey preferred it?
33. The two American companies are GM and Ford. How many votes did the get combined?
34. Which two companies had the same number of votes?

A large sample of everyday household waste is processed to measure the different materials it contains. The following line graph shows the type of trash and how many pounds of it there were. Answer the questions that follow.

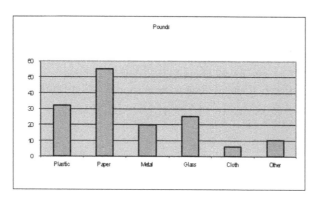

35. How many pounds of glass were found?
36. How many pounds of paper were found?
37. What type of material was there the most of?
38. Plastic and glass are the easiest materials to recycle. How many pounds were there of these two materials combined?

Exercise Set - Putting It ALL Together

Vocabulary. Fill in each blank with a word from our Vocabulary Checklist to the right. Each word is used exactly once.

Vocabulary Checklist:
whole numbers
digit
place value
scale

39. _____ refers to the following list of numbers: 0, 1, 2, 3, 4, 5, 6, 7, 8…

40. The _____ on a number line is the distance between each tic mark.

41. The position of a digit in a whole number is called its _____.

42. In the number 130,907,256 in what place value is the 3?

43. In the number 45,681,341 in what place value is the 6?

44. In the number 56,804,671 what digit is in the ten-thousands place?

45. In the number 655,482,907 what digit is in the millions place?

Write each phrase as a whole number.
46. five hundred two
47. seven hundred thirteen
48. thirteen thousand, forty-three
49. four thousand, seven hundred five
50. eleven million, seventy-six
51. fifty-five million, three hundred fifteen thousand

Write the following numbers in words.
52. 35
53. 79
54. 741
55. 309

56. 45,001
57. 712,411
58. 4,823,915
59. 18,090,423

Write the word name for the number given in each sentence.
60. The radius of the moon is 1,738 km.
61. The radius of the Earth is 6,371 km.
62. The Moon is 384,403 kilometers from the Earth.
63. The Moon is 238,857 miles from the Earth.
64. The space shuttle Endeavour cost about $1,700,459,650 to make.
65. The total weight of propellants used on a space shuttle weigh 1,607,185 pounds.

Round to the given place value.
66. 7,823 ; hundred
67. 18,909 ; ten
68. 713,311 ; thousand

69. 8,012,734 ; ten thousand
70. 4,856,965 ; hundred-thousand
71. 34,719,200 ; million

72. The state of California covers 53,818 square miles. Round this value to the nearest thousand.

73. The state of Texas covers 268,601 square miles. Round this value to the nearest thousands place.

74. The University of North Carolina at Wilmington has a budget for instruction per term of $78,498,237. Round this number to the nearest ten-thousands.

75. North Carolina State University has a budget for their library per year of $29,484,084. Round this number to the nearest millions.

76. Draw a number line with a scale of 1 and use it to graph the numbers 2, 0, 5, and 8.
77. Draw a number line with a scale of 1 and use it to graph the numbers 4, 6, 1, and 3.
78. Draw a number line with a scale of 10 and use it to graph the numbers 25, 40, 35, and 60.
79. Draw a number line with a scale of 5 and use it to graph the numbers 15, 0, 30, and 25.
80. Draw a number line with a scale of 20 and use it to graph the numbers 20, 80, 160, 240.
81. Draw a number line with a scale of 100 and use it to graph the numbers 700, 50, 350, and 450.

82. The following table gives the prices for several different guitars. Use a number line with a scale of 100 to graph each of the prices.

Guitar	Price
Razorback	$250
Truckster	$600
Rebop	$365
Hell's Bell	$975

83. The Big Three US carmakers are GM, Ford and Chrysler. In the table below are the profits for 2005 for these car companies. Use a number line with a scale of 20 to graph their profits.

Car Company	Profit in 2005 in billions
GM	193
Ford	178
Chrysler	57

84. In the table below is the number of Wal-mart stores by state. Use a number line with a scale of 30 to graph each number.

State	Number of Walmart stores
Washington	193
California	176
Kansas	58
Wisconson	83
Virginia	91
North Carolina	136
Florida	203
Texas	338

85. In the table below is the amount of investment in billions in IT Equipment, Software, Services, & Staff. Use a number line with a scale of 50 starting at 700 to graph the amount of investment.(source : http://www.businessweek.com/technology/tech_stats/ITinvest051027.htm)

Year	Investment in IT Equipment, Software, Services&Staff(in billions)
2004	$708
2005	$755

2006	$806
2007	$825
2008	$865
2009	$935
2010	$1024

The following tables gives sales in the entertainment industry for different types of media in the year 2006. Answer the questions that follow.

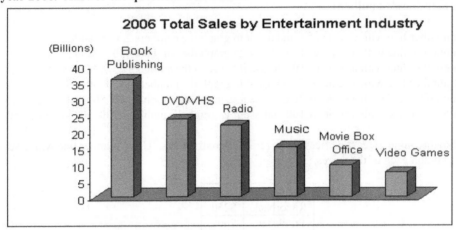

Source: www.beneaththecover.com

86. About how many billions of dollars did the entertainment industry make in music?
87. About how many billions of dollars did the entertainment industry make in radio?
88. What category is generating the most sales? About what were the sales for this category?
89. What category is generating the least sales? About what were the sales for this category?

The following line shows the temperature in New York City over a six-day visit. Answer the questions that follow.

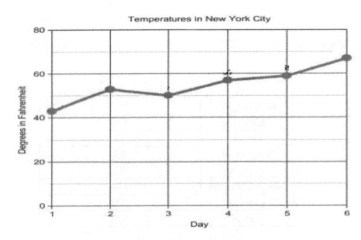

90. About what was the temperature on day three of the trip?
91. About what was the temperature on day five of the trip?
92. Which day had the highest temperature? What was the temperature for that day?
93. Which day had the lowest temperature? What was the temperature for that day?

1.1 QUIZ YOURSELF:

To make sure you are ready for the EXAM, try these problems without any help. Give yourself about 20 minutes and don't check the answers until you have completely finished.

1. Write the whole number in words: 305,023
2. Write the phrase as a whole number: twelve million, three hundred fifteen
3. Round to the nearest hundred: 17,912
4. The distance around the earth is about 24,859 miles. Round this to the nearest thousand.
5. Draw a number line with a scale of 25 and use it to graph the numbers:
    0, 50, 125, 250, 375, 525
6. The following table gives the numbers of students enrolled in different community colleges. Which school has the most students enrolled and how many attend that school?

College	Enrollment
Mesa	23,575
City	18,671
AB Tech	14,250
Haywood	25,809
Miramar	7,537

7. The following table gives the number of common dolphins seen off the coast of Santa Barbara, California over a period of years. In which year were the most dolphins seen? About how many dolphins were seen in the year 1999?

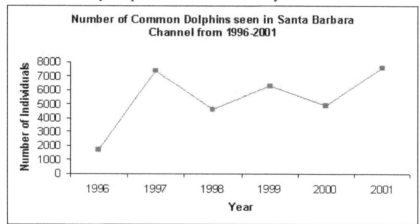

Answers to this Quiz Yourself are on page 639.

I'll be giving you tips throughout the book to help you SUCCEED IN MATH! Our first tip is all about getting ready for the course.

Succeed in Math!   Getting Ready!

Welcome to college Prealgebra. As you begin to dive into homework there are certain things you can do to make sure you are ready to tackle the course and succeed.

In a nut-shell, the phrase "Study Skills" refers to a student's ability to "work hard" and "work smart" in a college course.

Good Study Skills are the number one most important factor in a student passing a college math class...not "being smart", not having a "math brain"...STUDY SKILLS!

Exercise: Your Study Habits
What have you done in math classes in the past that you know will help you succeed in this course?

_____
_____
_____

What do you do in math classes that you know needs improving?

_____
_____
_____

The first and most important in getting started is to understand you course syllabus. A syllabus is an outline of what the course covers and all the professor's policies from grading to attendance. Professors usually go over the syllabus on the first day of class.

Exercise: Syllabus Quiz - Use your syllabus to answer the following questions.

1. What materials are required for the course?
2. What is the best way to contact your professor?
3. Does your professor have office hours? If so, when are they?
4. How many absences are you allowed before you may be dropped?
5. What are the different kinds of grades you will get in the class (Exams, Homework, Group Work, etc.)?
6. What is the date of your first test?
7. What is the date of your final exam?

1.2 Adding and Subtracting Whole Numbers

Topics:
- Adding Whole Numbers
- Geometry: Finding Perimeter
- Subtracting Whole Numbers
- Properties of Addition and Subtraction

Adding Whole Numbers

You and two of your friends are pooling your money together to order pizza and wings for the Super Bowl. You have $8, one of your friends has $12 and the other friend has $15. The total amount is found using addition … $\$8 + \$12 + \$15 = \$35$.

Addition is the process of finding a sum. Two or more numbers being added are called **addends** and the result is called the **sum** (or **total**).

$$8 + 12 + 15 = 35$$

[PN: arrows]

Addends   Sum or Total

To add numbers with several digits we normally stack them together and line up their place values. Having the place values lined up allows us to add each number's digit for that place value to get the total for that place value. If the sum of the numbers in a place value exceeds 9 we carry to the next place value.

To Add Two or More Whole Numbers:
- Stack the numbers, lining up their place values.
- Starting with the ones place, add the digits in each place value.
- If the result for any place value is more than 9, *carry* the extra digit to the top in the next place value.

$$98 + 146 \quad \rightarrow \quad \begin{array}{r} 98 \\ + 146 \\ \hline \end{array} \rightarrow \quad \begin{array}{r} 98 \\ + 146 \\ \hline 244 \end{array}$$

[PN: mark up the last one with carries]

Good Question: Why do we 'carry' a digit to the next place value?

Answer: We line up the place values so we are adding the ones together, the tens together, the hundreds together and so on. When we add 8 + 6, we now have 14 ones OR 1 ten and 4 ones. When we add 9 tens with 4 tens, we now have 13 tens which is 130 OR 1 hundred and 3 tens... the 'extra' digit really belongs in the next place value.

$$98$$
$$+146$$
$$244$$

Example 1: Add.

a) $4,579 + 745$ b) $8,709 + 886 + 6,308$

Solution: [PN: I failed miserably at marking these up to reflect the steps.]

a) In the last example we rewrote the sum each time to show what was being done in each step. Normally we do all the work on one expression like below.

Rewrite the sum stacked and proceed as before, carrying when necessary.

$$\begin{array}{r} 4579 \\ +745 \\ \end{array}$$

- The sum for the ones places is $9 + 5 = 14$ so we record a 4 in the ones place and carry 1.
- The sum for the tens place is $1 + 7 + 4 = 12$: record 2 and carry 1.
- The sum for the hundreds place is $1 + 5 + 7 = 13$: record 3 and carry 1.
- The sum for the thousands place is $1 + 4 = 5$: record 5.

The sum is 5,324.

b) The process is the same for adding more than two numbers. We just have to keep track of more numbers being added in each place value.

Rewrite the sum stacked and proceed as normal:

$$\begin{array}{r} 8709 \\ +886 \\ 6308 \\ \end{array}$$

- The sum for the ones places is $9 + 6 + 8 = 23$ so we record a 3 in the ones place and carry 2.
- The sum for the tens place is $2 + 0 + 8 + 0 = 10$: record 0 and carry 1.
- The sum for the hundreds place is $1 + 7 + 8 + 3 = 19$: record 9 and carry 1.
- The sum for the thousands place is $1 + 8 + 6 = 15$.

The sum is 15,903.

Recall that we discussed estimating (rounding) in the previous section. It is a common skill in real-world situations to round when adding, since it allows us to get a quick and fairly accurate idea of the total before we get an exact sum.

Example 2: Where in the World? A music producer has sold the following number of songs on i-tunes:

"Party Down on 1st Street" - 137,987 sells
"Big Hair Nightmare" - 9,504 sells
"Pocket Full of Zen" - 54,215 sells

She wants to get a quick estimate of how many songs have been sold. Estimate the total sells by rounding each number to the nearest thousand and then adding.

$$
\begin{array}{r}
137,987 \rightarrow 138,000 \\
9,504 \rightarrow +10,000 \\
54,215 \rightarrow \underline{+54,000} \\
202,000
\end{array}
$$

So the producer has sold about 202,000 songs.

STOP Exercise Set - Adding Whole Numbers

Add.

1. $56+92$
2. $89+13$
3. $617+59$
4. $237+907$

5. $7029+4776$
6. $3543+6571$
7. $249+57+805$
8. $6253+98+796$

9. A salesman travels for his company. His daily mileage for a one week period is 357 miles on Monday, 689 miles on Tuesday, 214 miles on Wednesday, 298 miles on Thursday and 171 miles on Friday. Estimate his total mileage by rounding to the nearest hundred. Then find the exact mileage.

10. Medhi spent $65, $89, $37 and $51 for groceries one month. Estimate his total grocery bill for the month by rounding to the nearest ten. Then find the exact total.

Geometry: Finding Perimeter

When enclosing a space, like your backyard with fencing, you need to find the total distance around the space. This total distance is called the *perimeter*.

> ### The **perimeter** of a geometric object is the distance around the object.

Perimeter is measured using linear units such as inches, feet or miles. It is important to take note of the units being used so you can include them in your total measurement.

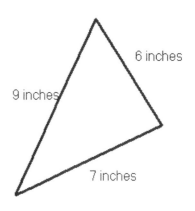

A triangle has three sides. So to get the total distance around a triangle we add the side lengths together:

$$9 \text{ inches } + 6 \text{ inches } + 7 \text{ inches } = 22 \text{ inches}$$

So the perimeter of the triangle shown is 22 inches.

To find the perimeter of an object: Add up the lengths of its sides.

Remember to always include the units (feet, miles, meters, etc.) in your answer.

Example 3: Find the perimeter of the following object.

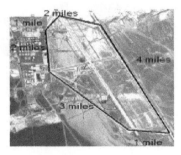

Solution: Adding the sides we get $13 + 8 + 9 + 12 = 42$, so the perimeter is 42 feet.

Example 4: Where in the World? The following picture shows an overhead shot of an airport. Security has the lengths for each strip highlighted and wants to know the total distance around this area. What is the perimeter of the highlighted area.

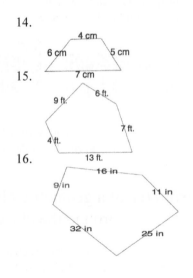

Solution: Adding the sides up we get $4 + 1 + 3 + 2 + 1 + 2 = 13$, so the perimeter is 13 miles.

STOP Exercise Set - Perimeter

Find the perimeter of the following objects.

11.

5 units
8 units

12.

4 units
10 units

13.

7 ft.   4 ft.
10 ft.

14.

4 cm
6 cm   5 cm
7 cm

15.

6 ft.
9 ft.
7 ft.
4 ft.
13 ft.

16.

16 in
9 in   11 in
32 in   25 in

Subtracting Whole Numbers

Tonya wants to find how many course units she needs before receiving her degree. She needs a total of 60 units and has 36, so she can find the *difference* between 60 and 36 units. The difference is found using subtraction... $60 \text{ units} - 36 \text{ units} = 24 \text{ units}$.

Subtraction is the process of finding the difference between two numbers. The first number in the difference is called the **minuend,** the second is called the **subtrahend**. The result of subtraction is called the **difference**.

$$60 \quad - \quad 36 \quad = 24$$

$$[PN : arrows]$$

minuend subtrahend difference

Subtraction is closely related to addition. Every subtraction statement has a corresponding addition statement.

$$
\begin{array}{ccc}
15 & & 9 \\
\underline{-9} & \to & \underline{+6} \\
6 & & 15
\end{array}
$$

This gives us a way to check our work. As with addition, to subtract larger numbers we usually stack them and line up their place values. Having the place values lined up allows us to subtract each numbers' digit for that place value to get the difference. If the number on top is smaller, we *borrow* from the place value before it.

To subtract two whole numbers:

- Stack the numbers, lining up their place values. For subtraction the larger number must always be on top.
- Starting with the ones place, find the difference between the digits in each place value.
- If the top digit is smaller, borrow from the next highest place value.

$$
653 - 37 \quad \to \quad
\begin{array}{r}
653 \\
-\ \ 37 \\
\hline
\end{array}
\quad \to \quad
\begin{array}{r}
653 \\
-\ \ 37 \\
\hline
616
\end{array}
$$

[PN: mark up the last one with borrowing]

Good Question: Why do we 'borrow' a digit from the place value before if the top digit is smaller?

Answer: This is a very similar idea to carrying when we add. We line up the place values so we are subtracting the ones, the tens, the hundreds and so on. When we subtract 3 – 7, we do not have enough ones to take 7 away. However, if we take 1 of the tens, then there are 4 tens left and our 3 ones become 13 ones. Then we can subtract 13 – 7 = 6. So, borrowing from the next higher place value gives us to subtract when necessary.

$$\begin{array}{r} 653 \\ -\ 37 \\ \hline 616 \end{array}$$

Example 5: Subtract.

a) 62 – 47

b) 7,316 – 842

Solution: [PN: I failed miserably at marking these up to reflect the steps.]

a) Rewrite the subtraction stacked.

$$\begin{array}{r} 62 \\ -\ 47 \\ \hline \end{array}$$

Here is the borrow step. We can't take 7 away from 2 so we borrow from the ten's place and rewrite the 2 as 12.

$$\begin{array}{r} 62 \\ -\ 47 \\ \hline \end{array}$$

Now we can subtract in each place value.

$$\begin{array}{r} 62 \\ -\ 47 \\ \hline 15 \end{array}$$

b) In the last example we rewrote the difference each time to show what was being done in each step. Normally we do all the work on one expression like below.

Rewrite the subtraction stacked. Notice that the hundreds place is involved in borrowing twice.

$$\begin{array}{r} 7316 \\ -\ 842 \\ \hline 6474 \end{array}$$

The next example combines the real world data in a bar graph with subtraction.

Example 6: Where in the World? The following table gives the average salary for nurses in several different cities. What is the difference between the salary for nurses living in New York and Boston?

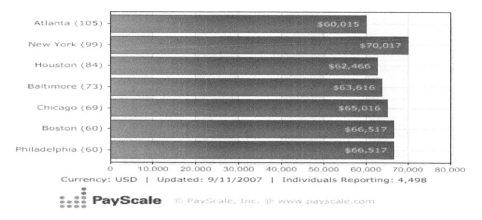

Solution: Reading the table we see that the average salary for New York is $70,017 and in Boston it is $66517. So we subtract these two. Remember with subtraction the larger number always goes on top.

$$
\begin{array}{r}
70017 \\
-66517 \\
\hline
3500
\end{array}
$$
So the salary difference is $3,500.

STOP Exercise Set - Subtracting Whole Numbers

Subtract.

17. $78 - 32$
18. $67 - 15$
19. $957 - 34$

20. $3,489 - 520$
21. $11,241 - 2,493$
22. $629,417 - 481,026$

The following table gives the average salary for teachers in different states. Answer the questions that follow.

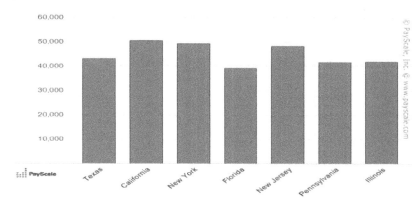

23. About what is the difference between the salaries for teachers in California versus Florida?
24. About what is the difference between the salaries for teachers in New Jersey versus Illinois?

Properties of Addition and Subtraction

The operations addition and subtraction have certain important properties. These properties are used so often that we take them for granted, but they are particularly important as we move closer to studying Algebra. The first property holds only for addition and is called *commutativity*.

With addition, changing the order of addends does not change the sum. This is called **the commutative property of addition**.

$$8 + 6 = 6 + 8$$

Example 7: Find the sum $\begin{array}{r}549\\+1498\end{array}$ and $\begin{array}{r}1498\\+549\end{array}$. Comment on the result.

Solution: $\begin{array}{r}549\\+1498\\\hline 2047\end{array}$ $\begin{array}{r}1498\\+549\\\hline 2047\end{array}$

Both of the additions give the same sum of 2047.

It is important to note that subtraction is NOT commutative. $7 - 3 = 4$. If we change the order on this subtraction we get $3 - 7$ which cannot be done since you can't take 7 away from 3. So $7 - 3 \neq 3 - 7$ (The symbol $\neq$ means "does not equal"). Subtraction is not commutative.

Another property of addition is called *associativity*. Notice that the sum $5 + 8 + 2$ can be found two ways. We use parentheses to show which addition should be done first. This is called *grouping*.

By adding $5 + 8$ first... $\underbrace{(5+8)}_{13} + 2$ or by adding $8 + 2$ first... $5 + \underbrace{(8+2)}_{10}$. The sum is the same in both

$$15 \qquad\qquad\qquad 15$$

cases. The point is that with addition, it doesn't matter which is done first.

Three numbers being added can be regrouped with the same result. This is called **the associative property of addition**.

$$(4 + 8) + 3 = 4 + (8 + 3)$$

Example 8: Find the sums $(49+157)+63$ and $49+(157+63)$. Comment on the results.

Solution: We find each sum doing the addition inside parentheses first.

$(49+157)+63$:
$$\begin{array}{r} 49 \\ +157 \\ \hline 206 \end{array} \qquad \begin{array}{r} 206 \\ +63 \\ \hline 269 \end{array}$$
[PN: arrow to next]

$49+(157+63)$:
$$\begin{array}{r} 157 \\ +63 \\ \hline 220 \end{array} \qquad \begin{array}{r} 220 \\ +49 \\ \hline 269 \end{array}$$
[PN: arrow to next]

The result of each sum is the same.

Like the commutative property, the associative property applies for addition but not subtraction. Notice that regrouping with subtraction gives a different result:

$$\underbrace{(9-5)}_{4}-3 \text{ gives a different answer from } 9-\underbrace{(5-3)}_{2}$$
$$1 \qquad\qquad\qquad\qquad\qquad\qquad 7$$

Finally, our last property holds for both addition and subtraction and has to do with the number zero. Notice that when we add or subtract zero, the sum or difference is just the same number we began with.

If zero is added or subtracted to a number the result is the original number. This property of is called **the identity property of zero**.

$$16+0=16 \qquad\qquad 7-0=7$$

Example 9: Find each sum or difference.
a) $469+0$ b) $5{,}913-0$

Solution: We are just making we under the identity property of zero.

a) $469+0=469$ b) $5{,}913-0=5{,}913$

Here is a summary of the properties we have discussed for easy reference.

Properties of Addition	**Example**
Commutative Property	$6+14=14+6$
Associative Property	$(3+4)+7=3+(4+7)$
Zero as the Identity	$8+0=8$
Properties of Subtraction	**Example**
Zero as the Identity	$13-0=13$

Good Question: I don't really see the point of all these properties. I know how to add and subtract, isn't that enough?

Answer: Understanding these properties is an important part of moving from Basic Math to the more complex ideas of Algebra. It is true that these rules are generally taken for granted, that is, we don't talk about them much but we use them all the time. This next example shows one important practical way they are used.

Example 10: Where in the World? A business owner needs to quickly tally her sales over the last few minutes, the receipts are for $6, $12, $4, $8, $3, and $7. What is the total?

Solution: To find the tally we need to add the dollar amounts. The tendency with a sum like $6+12+4+8+3+7$ is to move from left to right. But the commutative and associative properties together tell us we can add the numbers in whatever order we want. It is quickest to look for numbers that add together easily.

$$6+12+4+8+3+7$$

[PN: arrows to indicate grouping]

$$10+20+10$$

$$40$$

So the tally is $40.

Tell which property is being used in the following example.

25. $913+84=84+913$

26. $(4+16)+7=4+(16+7)$

27. $839+0=839$

28. $16-0=16$

29. Rewrite using the associative property of addition: $5+(15+9)$

30. Rewrite using the commutative property of addition: $23+99$

31. Rewrite using the commutative property of addition: $18+(2+21)$

32. Rewrite using the associative property of addition: $(19+10)+20$

Exercise Set - Putting it ALL Together

Vocabulary Check: Fill in each blank with a word from our Vocabulary Checklist to the right. Each word is used exactly once.

33. The _____ says means that if zero is added or subtracted from a number the result is just the original number.

34. In geometry the distance around an object is called its _____.

Vocabulary Checklist:
addition
addends
sum (or total)
perimeter
subtraction
minuend
subtrahend
difference
the commutative property of addition
the associative property of addition
the identity property of zero

35. For the addition $5+9=14$, the numbers 5 and 9 are called _____ and 14 is called the
_____ or _____ .

36. Having $3+7$ and $7+3$ result in the same sum. This illustrates the _____ property
of addition.

37. The process of finding a difference is called _____ .

38. In the subtraction $18-11=9$, the number 18 is called the _____ , 11 is called the
_____ , and 9 s called the _____ .

39. Having $(6+3)+5$ and $6+(3+5)$ results in the same sum. This illustrates the
_____ property of addition.

40. The process of finding a sum or total is called _____ .

Add or Subtract.

41.
$$\begin{array}{r} 65 \\ +34 \\ \hline \end{array}$$

42.
$$\begin{array}{r} 64 \\ -55 \\ \hline \end{array}$$

43.
$$\begin{array}{r} 822 \\ -629 \\ \hline \end{array}$$

44.
$$\begin{array}{r} 287 \\ +192 \\ \hline \end{array}$$

45.
$$\begin{array}{r} 4,501 \\ -299 \\ \hline \end{array}$$

46.
$$\begin{array}{r} 782 \\ -71 \\ \hline \end{array}$$

47.
$$\begin{array}{r} 24,819 \\ +18,203 \\ \hline \end{array}$$

48.
$$\begin{array}{r} 403,289 \\ +912,711 \\ \hline \end{array}$$

49. $7,089-0$
50. $781+0$
51. $0+918$
52. $1,001-0$
53. $381+602$
54. $1,945-473$
55. $912-56$
56. $44+33+6+10$
57. $12+20+30+8$
58. $15+34+25+7+23$

59. $77+18+102+10+33$
60. $752+12,491$
61. $6,308-1,867$
62. $501,723-78,215$
63. $15,891+603,512$
64. $88,405-32,913$
65. $792,111-199,999$
66. $78,040,640+2,557,757$

Estimate the sum or difference by rounding to the place value given *before* you perform the operation.
67. $89-34$; tens place
68. $728+1,934$; hundreds place
69. $513-47$; tens place
70. $29,517-5,088$, thousands place
71. $768,005+3,019$; thousands place
72. $5,671,902+12,783,001$, hundred thousands place

73. Micah sold his house for $289,500. He bought it 6 years ago for $195,900. How much did he make on the house?

74. Debra and Alberto are taking a cross country trip and will drive a total of 3,834 miles. If they have already traveled 1,781 miles, how many miles do they have on their trip?

75. LaTonya has $6,732 in her checking account. She pays her bills of $847, $231, $88, and $37. She then deposits her paycheck for $456. How much money does she have in her account now?

76. Over one month a salesperson made $891 the 1st week, $1,290 the 2nd week, $945 the 3rd week, and $1567 the 4th week. How much did she make for the month?

Estimate the answers by rounding to the given place value. Also give the exact answer.

77. Summer is training for her first triathlon and goes shopping for all the necessary items. She buys a bike for $789, a helmet for $39, a tri-suit for $79, a wetsuit for $159 and a new pair of running shoes for $114. How much did she invest for her new favorite sport? Round to the nearest ten.

78. A company that manufactures two products has made a profit of $36,985 from the first product and $57,314 from the second. What is the difference between the two profits? Round to the nearest thousand.

79. Lin has $3685 in her checking account. She spends $825 on her rent. How much is left in her account? Round to the nearest thousand.

80. Eduardo goes shopping and spends $118 at a music store, $289 at a sports store and $322 at a computer store. What is the total spent for the trip? Round to the nearest ten.

81. The following tables gives the monthly profit for an electronic store. Estimate the total profit by rounding each month's profit to the nearest thousand.

Month	Profit
March	$15,709
April	$12,406
May	$9,046
June	$16,689

82. The following table gives the monthly profit for a store that sells recreational vehicles. Estimate the total profit by rounding each month's profit to the nearest thousand.

Month	Profit
August	$4,209
September	$13,716
October	$12,964
November	$10,073

Find the perimeter of the following figures.

83.

84.

85.

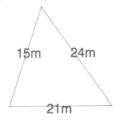

86.

87.

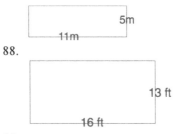

88.

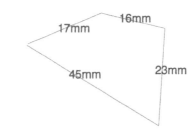

89.

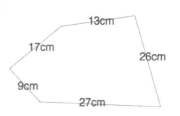

90.

91. Eamon is fencing in his backyard for his new puppy. His backyard measures 30 ft by 45 ft. How many feet of fencing does he need?

92. Miguel is putting up crown molding in his dining room, which measures 8 ft by 10 ft. How many linear feet of crown molding should he purchase?

The following table gives the number of Starbucks Coffee stores in various states. Answer the questions #91 through #96 that follow.

State	Number of Starbucks
Florida	375
Nevada	193
California	2010
Texas	604
New York	384
Washington	559
Georgia	168
Source: www.statemaster.com	

93. Which state given has the most number of Starbucks? How many does it have?
94. In order, list the top three states for most number of Starbucks.
95. How many Starbucks do the states New York and Washington have combined?
96. How many Starbucks are in California and New York combined?
97. What is the difference between the number Starbucks in Florida and Georgia?
98. What is the difference between the number Starbucks in New York and Nevada?

The following bar graph gives the yearly laptop sales for an electronics store. Answer the questions that follow.

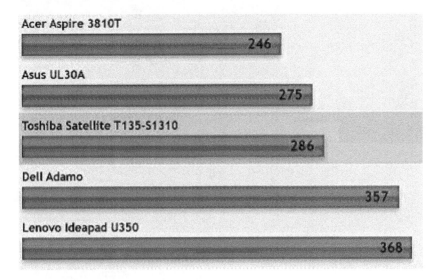

99. What was the difference in sales between Asus and Lenovo?
100. What was the difference in sales between Acer and Dell?
101. What were the combined sales for Toshiba and Lenovo?
102. What were the combined sales for Asus and Dell?

103. Find the sum $\begin{array}{r} 719 \\ +2701 \\ \hline \end{array}$ and $\begin{array}{r} 2701 \\ +719 \\ \hline \end{array}$. Comment on the result.

104. Find the sum $\begin{array}{r} 3201 \\ +\ 702 \\ \hline \end{array}$ and $\begin{array}{r} 702 \\ +3201 \\ \hline \end{array}$. Comment on the result.

105. Find the sums $(845+21)+79$ and $845+(21+79)$. Comment on the results.
106. Find the sums $(175+225)+99$ and $175+(225+99)$. Comment on the results.

Exercise Set - Chapter 1 Review

107. Graph the numbers 3, 6, 2, and 0 on a number line.
108. Round 439 to the nearest tens place.
109. Add. $467+39$
110. Write "five thousand fifty-two" as a whole number.
111. Rewrite using the commutative property of addition: $34+(26+77)$

1.2 QUIZ YOURSELF:

To make sure you are ready for the EXAM, try these problems without any help. Give yourself about 20 minutes and don't check the answers until you have completely finished.

1. Add. $49 + 74 + 14$
2. Add. $3967 + 919$
3. Subtract. $2781 - 697$
4. Name the property. $15 + 8 + 5 = 15 + 5 + 8$
5. For two concerts, attendance is counted at 15,783 and 23,082. Estimate the total attendance for both concerts by rounding to the nearest thousand.
6. Find the perimeter.

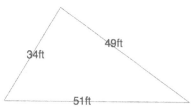

7. The following bar graph gives the results of a survey given to employees about their evaluations. How many of the employees either "agree" or "strongly agree"?

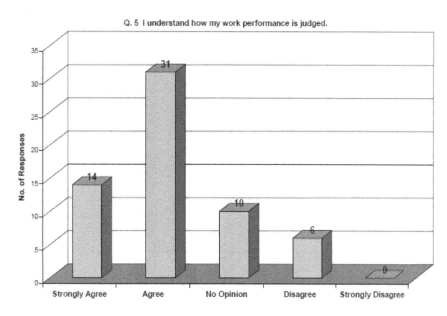

Answers to this Quiz Yourself are on page 639.

1.3 Multiplying and Dividing Whole Numbers

Topics:

- Multiplying Whole Numbers
- Geometry: Finding Area
- Dividing Whole Numbers
- Properties of Multiplication and Division

Multiplying Whole Numbers

Jin is starting a new running regime and has ran 5 miles 4 times the first week. To find the total number of miles he runs, we could add $5 + 5 + 5 + 5$ or use multiplication, which is shorthand for repeated addition...

$$4 \cdot 5 = \underbrace{5 + 5 + 5 + 5}_{\text{add 5 four times}} = 20$$

$$5 \cdot 4 = 20$$

[PN: arrows]

factors product

Numbers being multiplied are called **factors**. The result of a multiplication is called the **product**.

In Algebra, to indicate multiplication, we use a dot as in $4 \cdot 5$ or parentheses as in $4(5)$ but almost never a cross as in 4×5.

The products of smaller numbers are usually memorized using a multiplication table.

Succeed in Math!
It may be a good idea
to keep a multiplication
table handy. You can
easily print one out from
the internet.

To find the product of larger numbers we stack whole numbers to multiply similar to addition and subtraction. Consider the product $3527(48)$.

Line up place values. Multiply the first digit in the bottom by each digit in the top factor. The ones place in each product is recorded and the excess is carried to the next place value to be added to the next product.

$$\begin{array}{r} 3527 \\ \times 48 \\ \hline 2416 \end{array}$$

Repeat the process for the next digit in the bottom factor putting the first result directly under that digit.

$$\begin{array}{r} 3527 \\ \times 48 \\ \hline 2416 \\ 14108 \end{array}$$

Now add each of the rows. The product is $3527 \cdot 48 = 169,296$.

$$\begin{array}{r} 3527 \\ \times 48 \\ \hline 2416 \\ 14108 \\ \hline 169296 \end{array}$$

To multiply larger whole numbers together:

- Line up place values with the number with the least digits on bottom.
- Multiply the ones digit of the bottom number with the top number.
- Multiply the tens digit of the bottom number with the top number. Since we are multiplying by ten, the result should start in the 10's place.
- Repeat until all the digits in the bottom number have been multiplied to the top number.
- Add up all the individual products.

Example 1: Multiply.

a) $245 \cdot 712$ b) $7 \cdot 4 \cdot 15$ c) $42,073 \cdot 800$

Solution:

a) This multiplication has three rows to multiply.
- Multiply 2 by 245.
- Multiply 1 by 245.
- Multiply 7 by 245.
- Sum it all up.

Our final answer is 174,440.

$$\begin{array}{r} 245 \\ \times 712 \\ \hline 174440 \end{array}$$

b) To multiply more than two numbers we move from left to right. So we multiply $7 \cdot 4$ first.

$$\begin{array}{l} 7 \cdot 4 \quad \cdot 15 \\ = 28 \quad \cdot 15 \end{array}$$

Now we multiply $28 \cdot 15$.
- Multiply 5 by 28.
- Multiply 1 by 28.
- Sum it all up.

Our final answer is 420.

$$\begin{array}{r} 28 \\ \times 15 \\ \hline 420 \end{array}$$

c) Doing this multiplication the long way we notice two rows of nothing but zeros. This leads to a short cut when a one of the factors has these *trialing zeros*.

$$\begin{array}{r} 4073 \\ \times 800 \\ \hline \end{array}$$

Write the trialing zero at the end and bring straight down in the answer.

$$\begin{array}{r} 4073 \\ \times 800 \\ \hline \end{array}$$

Example 2: Where in the World? Jay makes \$18 per hour at his job. If he has worked 36 hours this week, what will be his pay before taxes are taken out?

Solution: To get the pay we would find 18 added up 36 times, but this can be done by multiplication.

$$\underbrace{18+18+18+\cdots+18+18}_{\substack{\text{36 times since he} \\ \text{worked 36 hours}}} = 18 \cdot 36 = 648$$

So his pay will be \$648.

1. $27 \cdot 313$
2. $101 \cdot 79$
3. $2345 \cdot 230$
4. $4209 \cdot 108$
5. $12 \cdot 5 \cdot 23$
6. $8 \cdot 5 \cdot 19$

7. Sekou is a math tutor and is paid \$15 per hour. If he works 24 hours in a month, what is his monthly pay before taxes are taken out?

8. Alexis works for a pharmaceutical company entering data for trial drugs. If she makes \$35 per hour and works 38 hour week, what is her yearly pay before taxes are taken out? (There are 52 weeks in a year.)

Geometry: Finding Area

Recall that the perimeter of an object is the distance around the object. Another important measurement for geometric objects is *area*.

The **area** of an object measures how much space it takes up.

Area is measured in square units. One square unit is the amount of space taken up by a square that has sides of length 1 unit. Here are a few examples…

Actual Sizes

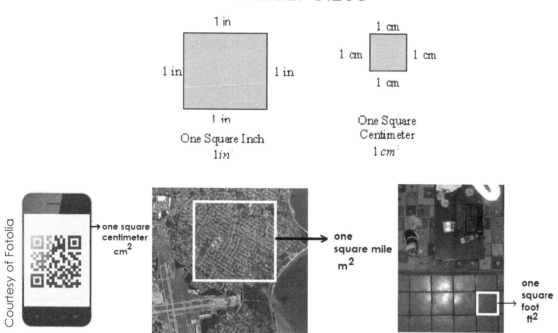

We abbreviate square units by putting the squared symbol above the linear measurement.

$$\text{square feet} \rightarrow ft^2$$

$$\text{square centimeters} \rightarrow cm^2$$

$$\text{square miles} \rightarrow mi^2$$

Example 3: What unit would most likely be used to measure the area of the following objects: square inches (in^2), square feet (ft^2), or square miles (mi^2)?

a) The total amount of floor space in a house.
b) The area of the state of New York.
c) The area of the display on a cell phone.

Solution:

a) Houses are typically measured using square feet $\left(ft^2\right)$.

b) To measure the area of an entire state we would use square miles $\left(mi^2\right)$.

c) A cell phone screen would be measured in square inches (in^2).

To show the connection between area and multiplication, suppose we wanted to know how much space is taken up by a rectangle. How many square centimeters does this rectangle take up?

One way to find out would be to divide the sides into centimeters. Now, every square on the grid represents one square centimeter.

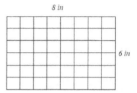

Next, we can count up the total number of square inches by noting that there are 6 squares in each column. So the total area is 48 square centimeters or $48cm^2$. Notice that this is the same as the product $6 \cdot 8 = 48$. This is always true for rectangles and squares.

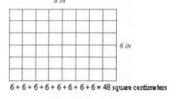

To find the area of a rectangle: Multiply the *length* by the *width*.

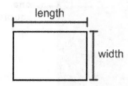

$$\text{Area} = \text{length} \cdot \text{width}$$

In fact, multiplication is almost always involved when we wish to find area. As another example, recall that a parallelogram is an object where opposite sides is parallel. We can find the area of a parallelogram by multiplying its base and its height.

To find the area of a parallelogram: Multiply the *base* by the *height*.

$$\text{Area} = \text{base} \cdot \text{height}$$

Example 4: Find the area of each object. Make sure to include units with your answer.

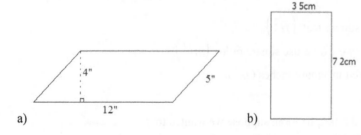

Solution:
a) Remember, the area of a parallelogram is the product of its base and height, not just the sides.

$$\begin{aligned}\text{Area} &= \text{base} \cdot \text{height} \\ &= 12 \cdot 4 \\ &= 48\end{aligned}$$

Since the sides are measured in inches the area will be measured in *square inches*.	$48\,in^2$

a) The area of a rectangle is the product of its length and width.	Area = length · width =35·72 = 2520

Since the sides are measured in centimeters the area will be measured in *square centimeters*.	$2520\,cm^2$

Example 5: Where in the World? A professional basketball court is 94 feet wide and 50 feet long. To replace the floor of the court it costs about $15 per square foot. What would be the total cost of replacing the entire floor of the court?

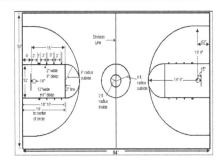

Solution: First we need to know how many square feet the court covers. Since the court is a rectangle we can find the area by multiplying its length by its width: $94 \cdot 50 = 4700$. So the court is 4700 square feet. Since each square foot costs $15 to refloor we multiply 4700 by $15: $4700 \cdot 15 = 70500$. So it will cost about $70,500 to refloor the basketball court.

STOP Exercise Set - Geometry: Finding Area

What unit would most likely be used to represent each area: square inches (in^2), square feet (ft^2), or square miles (mi^2)?

   9.   The area of a large lake.
  10.   The area of dance floor.
  11. The area of a business card.
  12. The area of a rug.

Find the area of each figure.

13.

15.

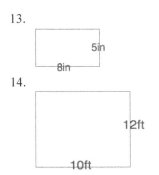

14.

16.

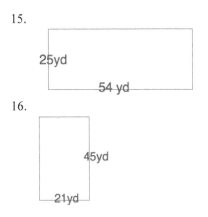

17.

19.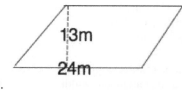

18.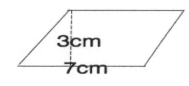

20.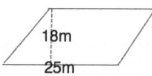

21. The parking lot shown to the right needs to be repaved. What will the charge be if it costs $15 per square yard?

22. An artist charges $8 per square foot to put a mural on a wall. How much will she charge to put a mural on the wall pictured below?

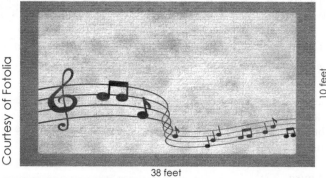

Courtesy of Fotolia

10 feet

38 feet

Dividing Whole Numbers

At the local state fair, each ride takes 3 tickets. If you bought a pack of 15 tickets, to decide how many rides you could go on you could…

- Subtract: $15 - 3 = 12$, $12 - 3 = 9$, $9 - 3 = 6$, $6 - 3 = 3$, $3 - 3 = 0$
- Divide: $15 \div 3 = 5$

In either case, you would get to ride 5 rides. Division is the process of repeated subtraction.

In division the number being divided is called the **dividend**, the number we are dividing by is called the **divisor**, and the result is called **quotient**.

$15 \div 3 = 5$

[PN: arrows]

dividend   divisor   quotient

To indicate division we use a division symbol $15 \div 3 = 5$, a division bar $3\overline{)15}$ with a 5 or a fraction bar $\dfrac{15}{3} = 5$.

If your friend bought a packet of 20 tickets then 20 divided by 3 is 6 with 2 left over. The part that is left over is called the *remainder*. Performing division we usually express the idea this way: $3\overline{)\,20}$ with $6\,R\,2$.

To divide larger numbers, we use a process called *long division*. The dividend is placed in a division bar with the divisor on the outside. The quotient goes on top as we perform division.

$$695 \div 14 \;\rightarrow\; 14\overline{)695} \quad \text{[PN: arrows point out divisor, quotient, etc.]}$$

Example 6: Divide $695 \div 14$.

Think "how many times will 14 divide 69?" $14\overline{)695}$

We can guess 6. Record 6 above the 69, multiply $6 \cdot 14 = 84$, put 84 under 69 and subtract. Since we can't subtract our estimate was too large. $14\overline{)695}$

The correct guess is 4. Record a 4 above the 69 and multiply $4 \cdot 14 = 56$, put 56 under 69 and subtract. $14\overline{)695}$

Next we bring the number down from the next place value in the dividend and repeat the process. $14\overline{)695}$

Think "how many times will 14 divide 135?" The correct guess is 9 so we multiply $9 \cdot 14 = 126$, 126 under 135 and subtract. $14\overline{)695}$

Since there are no more numbers to bring down this difference is our remainder. $14\overline{)695}$ with $49\,R\,9$

Example 7: Where in the World? A computer programmer is storing files on a CD. One CD can hold 650 megabytes of data. If each file is 45 megabytes, how many files can the CD hold? How many megabytes will be leftover?

Solution: We want to see how many 45 megabyte files will fit onto a 650 megabyte CD. This is a classic division problem: $650 \div 45$.

$$\begin{array}{r} 14R20 \\ 45\overline{)650} \end{array}$$

This means the CD will hold 14 files and have 20 megabytes left over.

STOP Exercise Set - Dividing Whole Numbers

Divide. If there is a remainder give the remainder with the answer.

23. $15 \div 3$

24. $28 / 7$

25. $\dfrac{144}{12}$

26. $13\overline{)221}$

27. $\dfrac{1863}{15}$

28. $1405 \div 23$

29. $2365 \div 11$

30. $18\overline{)2808}$

31. $32\overline{)6709}$

32. $\dfrac{23,851}{13}$

Properties of Multiplication and Division

We find certain patterns in multiplication and addition that come up a lot in math. Notice, for example, that like with addition the order of two numbers being multiplied can be reserved.

$4 \cdot 6 = \underbrace{4+4+4+4+4+4}_{\text{add 4 six times}} = 24$ and $6 \cdot 4 = \underbrace{6+6+6+6}_{\text{add 6 four times}} = 24$, so $4 \cdot 6 = 6 \cdot 4$. This is always true for multiplication.

With multiplication, changing the order of the factors does not change the product. This is called **the commutative property of multiplication**.

$$6 \cdot 8 = 8 \cdot 6$$

Notice that, like subtraction, division is not commutative: $14 \div 2 \neq 2 \div 14$.

Example 8: Find each multiplication as it is written. Comment on the result.

$$\begin{array}{r} 17 \\ \times 24 \\ \hline \end{array} \qquad \begin{array}{r} 24 \\ \times 17 \\ \hline \end{array}$$

Solution: $\begin{array}{r} 17 \\ \times 24 \\ \hline 408 \end{array} \qquad \begin{array}{r} 24 \\ \times 17 \\ \hline 408 \end{array}$

The result is the same for each product.

Multiplication, like addition is also *associative*. Recall that we use parentheses to indicate what operation to do first. But with three numbers being multiplied the grouping doesn't matter.

$$(\underbrace{12 \cdot 5}) \cdot 3 = 12 \cdot (\underbrace{5 \cdot 3})$$
$$\begin{array}{cc} 60 \quad \cdot 3 & 12 \cdot \quad 15 \\ 180 & 180 \end{array}$$

This is always true for multiplication.

Three numbers being multiplied can be regrouped with the same result. This is called **the associative property of multiplication**.

$$(2 \cdot 5) \cdot 4 = 2 \cdot (5 \cdot 4)$$

Example 9: Find each multiplication as it is grouped. Comment on the result.

$$(3 \cdot 11) \cdot 4 \qquad 3 \cdot (11 \cdot 4)$$

Solution:
$$\begin{array}{ll} (3 \cdot 11) \cdot 4 & 3 \cdot (11 \cdot 4) \\ = (33) \cdot 4 & = 3 \cdot (44) \\ = 132 & = 132 \end{array}$$

The result is the same for each product.

Again, like subtraction, division is not associative: $18 \div (6 \div 3) \neq (18 \div 6) \div 3$

In the last section, we called zero *the identity for addition and subtraction* because adding or subtracting zero doesn't change a number. The identity for multiplication and division is one.

$$7 \cdot 1 = 7 \qquad 1 \cdot 45 = 45 \qquad 12 \div 1 = 12 \qquad \frac{5}{1} = 5$$

Notice there is a difference between $\frac{5}{1}$ and $\frac{1}{5}$. The division $\frac{5}{1} = 5$ represents division *by* 1. For $\frac{1}{5}$ we are dividing by 5, this means dealing with fractions or decimal numbers which doesn't come until later chapters.

If a number is multiplied or divided by 1 the result is the original number. This property is called **the identity property of one**.

$$14 \cdot 1 = 14 \qquad\qquad 35 \div 1 = \frac{35}{1} = 35$$

Notice that any number multiplied by zero gives zero as a result.

The product of zero and any number is zero.

$$18 \cdot 0 = 0$$

Example 10: Find each product.

a) $0 \cdot 7$ b) $6 \cdot 3 \cdot 14 \cdot 0$

Solution:

a) $0 \cdot 7 = 0$

b) Normally we multiply from left to right. But no matter how many factors there are in a product, if one of the factors is zero the entire product is zero. $6 \cdot 3 \cdot 14 \cdot 0 = 0$

There are two cases to consider for division involving zero: dividing zero by another number and dividing a number by zero.

Zero as a dividend:

Notice that every division statement has a corresponding multiplication statement.

$$\frac{18}{6} = 3 \rightarrow 6 \cdot 3 = 18 \qquad\qquad \frac{63}{7} = 9 \rightarrow 7 \cdot 9 = 63$$

If zero is the dividend in a quotient, what should the result be?

$\dfrac{0}{7} = ? \rightarrow 7 \cdot ? = 0$ In this case the question mark "?" should be replaced with the number zero.

Zero divided by any other number is zero.

$$0 \div 9 = \frac{0}{9} = 0$$

Zero as a divisor:

What about dividing a number by zero? Let's look at rewriting division as multiplication to see what the result might be.

$\dfrac{13}{0} = ? \rightarrow 0 \cdot ? = 13$ In this case there is no number that can replace the question mark to have the statement

make sense. This shows that zero cannot be a divisor.

Division by zero is undefined. That is, an answer does not exist.

$$5 \div 0 \text{ is undefined}$$

$$\frac{5}{0} \text{ is undefined}$$

Example 11: Find each quotient or write "undefined".

a) $0 \div 17$ b) $41 \div 0$ c) $\dfrac{1}{0}$ d) $\dfrac{0}{9}$

Solution:
a) Here, zero is the dividend, so $0 \div 17 = 0$.
b) Here, zero is the divisor, so $41 \div 0$ is undefined.
c) Here, zero is the divisor, so $\dfrac{1}{0}$ is undefined.

d) Here, zero is the dividend, so $\dfrac{0}{9} = 0$.

Here is a summary of the properties we have discussed for easy reference.

Properties of Multiplication	Example
Commutative Property	$6 \cdot 3 = 3 \cdot 6$
Associative Property	$(3 \cdot 5) \cdot 4 = 3 \cdot (5 \cdot 4)$
One as the Identity	$15 \cdot 1 = 15$
Properties of Division	**Example**
One as the Identity	$23 \div 1 = \dfrac{23}{1} = 23$
Properties of Zero	**Example**
Multiplying by Zero	$7 \cdot 0 = 0$
Dividing Zero	$0 \div 8 = \dfrac{0}{8} = 0$
Division by Zero	$6 \div 0$ or $\dfrac{6}{0}$ is undefined

STOP **Exercise Set - Properties of Multiplication and Division**

In each case, indicate which of the following properties is being demonstrated:
The Commutative Property, The Associative Property, One as the Identity, Multiplying by Zero, Dividing Zero, or Dividing by Zero

33. $154 \cdot 0 = 0$
34. $45 \cdot 12 = 12 \cdot 45$
35. $0 / 14 = 0$
36. $\dfrac{21}{1} = 21$

37. $(15 \cdot 25) \cdot 4 = 15 \cdot (25 \cdot 4)$
38. $57 \div 0$ is undefined

Exercise Set - Putting it ALL Together

Vocabulary Check. Fill in each blank with a word from our Vocabulary Checklist to the right. Each word is used exactly once.

Vocabulary Checklist:
factors
product
area
dividend
divisor
quotient
the commutative property of multiplication
the associative property of multiplication
the identity property of one

39. Reversing the order of a product does not change the result. For example, $11 \cdot 4 = 4 \cdot 11$. This is called _____.

40. In division, the number zero cannot be used as a _____.

41. _____ is a measure how much space an object take up measured in square units like square feet or square inches.

42. The product of any number and the one is always the number. This is called _____.

43. In the division $168 \div 4 = 42$ the number 168 is referred to as the _____.

44. The result of a multiplication is called a _____ and the result of a division is called a _____.

45. _____ states that when multiplying three numbers the grouping does not change the overall product.

46. Number being multiplied together are called _____.

47. What are two other ways to express the multiplication 3×7?

48. What are two other ways to express the division $2\overline{)154}$?

49. Without finding the result, rewrite the addition as multiplication: $5+5+5+5+5+5$

50. Without finding the result, rewrite the addition as multiplication: $12+12+12+12$

Multiply or divide if possible. If a division has a remainder, give the remainder with the answer.

51. $6 \cdot 18$
52. Find 54 times 9.
53. $8 \cdot 14$
54. $68 \div 4$
55. $947 \div 5$
56. $713(42)$
57. Find the quotient of 60 and 4.
58. $615 \cdot 24$
59. $0 \div 5$
60. $\dfrac{762}{4}$
61. Find the product of 15 and 23.
62. $12\overline{)5,891}$

63. $32\overline{)40,972}$
64. $415 \cdot 253$
65. $\dfrac{578}{0}$
66. Divide 5886 by 9.
67. $13,981 \cdot 0$
68. $15,970 \cdot 214$
69. $20,915(325)$
70. $14 \cdot 3 \cdot 25$
71. $21 \cdot 4 \cdot 6$
72. $14 \cdot 5 \cdot 20$
73. $5 \cdot 9 \cdot 4 \cdot 8 \cdot 0$
74. $8(5)(0)(3)(2)$

75. $9(5)(2)(6)$ 76. $8(6)(7)(5)(3)$

In the text we mentioned that for every division statement there is a corresponding multiplication. For example, $18 \div 3 = 6$ corresponds to $6 \cdot 3 = 18$. For exercises 77 to 82, a division statement is given. Write the corresponding multiplication statement.

77. $35 \div 5 = 7$

78. $\dfrac{16}{4} = 4$

79. $45 \div 1 = 45$

80. $\dfrac{147}{7} = 21$

81. $\dfrac{3887}{23} = 169$

82. $35400 \div 236 = 150$

In each of the following real-world scenarios you will have to decide whether to multiply or divide. Make sure to include units with your answer.

83. There are 3 feet in 1 yard. How many feet are there in 18 yards?

84. There are 12 inches in 1 foot. How many inches are there in 8 feet?

85. There are 152 ounces of Orange Juice in a container. If one serving is 8 ounces, how many servings are in the container?

86. Wayne wants to run 7 miles every day. How many days will it take him to run 203 miles?

87. After the Tour de France the winner usually divides his $400,000 prize evenly among his 8 teammates and takes nothing for himself. How much will each teammate get?

88. When a speaker talks at a conference they often like to know how many people might be attending. Suppose a conference room has 28 rows and each row has 12 seats. How many seats are there?

89. The band Green Day's last tour was selling out venues that have about 35,000 seats. If they played 18 shows, about how many people did they play to on the whole tour?

90. Cane works at landscaping for $16 an hour. If he works 36 hours in week, how much will his pay be?

91. Marcela oversees information storage on mainframe computers. He mentions that they can store a total of 7,800 terra-bytes of information on 12 mainframes. How many terra-bytes does each mainframe hold?

92. A shipping manager knows that each box can hold 17 pounds of merchandise. How pounds could be shipped if the manager has 60 boxes?

93. The average salary for a paralegal is about $53,400 per year. What is the monthly pay? (Hint: there are 12 months in one year.)

94. Estimate the product $586 \cdot 713$ by rounding each factor to the nearest hundred.

95. Estimate the product $683 \cdot 390$ by rounding each factor to the nearest hundred.

Recall that the perimeter is the distance around an object (measured in inches, feet, miles, etc.) and that area is the amount of space the object takes up (measured in square inches, square feet, square miles, etc.) Find the perimeter and area of each object.

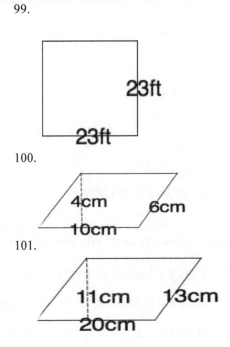

96.

3ft
8ft

97.

14in
15in

98.

6yd
6yd

99.

23ft
23ft

100.

4cm   6cm
10cm

101.

11cm   13cm
20cm

The following set of exercises involves performing all four operations: addition, subtraction, multiplication, and division. Perform the indicated operation.

102. $461 + 988$

103.
$$\begin{array}{r} 3173 \\ +1589 \\ \hline \end{array}$$

104.
$$\begin{array}{r} 742 \\ -248 \\ \hline \end{array}$$

105. $1{,}549 - 947$

106. $512 \cdot 64$

107.
$$\begin{array}{r} 785 \\ \times 37 \\ \hline \end{array}$$

108. $\dfrac{744}{24}$

109. $7868 \div 14$

Exercise Set - Chapter 1 Review

110. Graph the numbers 23, 75, 19, and 51 on a number line using a scale of 10.
111. Estimate the sum $4,590 + 13,214$ by rounding the nearest hundred.
112. Subtract. $751 - 389$
113. Find the perimeter.

9ft

6ft

114. True or false? $7 < 7$

 # 1.3 QUIZ YOURSELF:

To make sure you are ready for the EXAM, try these problems without any help. Give yourself about 20 minutes and don't check the answers until you have completely finished.

Multiply or divide, if possible.

1. $7 \cdot 12$
2. $175 \div 15$
3. $11\overline{)4681}$
4. $1355(24)$
5. $47 \cdot 0$
6. $\dfrac{13}{0}$

7. Jin is a general contractor who has 6,975 pounds of steel framing in storage. If it takes 75 pounds of steel to frame one shed, how many sheds can be framed with the steel in storage?

8. Light travels at a speed of about 186,000 miles per second. About how many miles does light travel in one minute? (Hint: There are 60 seconds in one minute.)

9. Find the perimeter and area of the following rectangle.

5ft

13ft

Answers to this Quiz Yourself are on page 639.

1.4 Exponents and the Order of Operations

Topics:
- Introduction to Exponents
- Geometry: Area of a Square
- The Order of Operations
- More About Grouping Symbols

Introduction to Exponents

In the previous section, we studied multiplication as repeated addition and division as repeated subtraction. *Exponents* are shorthand for repeated multiplication.

$$4^3 = \underbrace{4 \cdot 4 \cdot 4}_{\substack{\text{three} \\ \text{factors of 4}}} = 64$$

An **exponent** is a number written just above the right side of a number to indicate repeated multiplication of that number.

The **base** of an exponent is the number being multiplied.

The expression b^n is read "b to the nth power".

$$b^n = \underbrace{b \cdot b \cdots b \cdot b}_{n \ \ times}$$

base   *exponent*

this is called exponent form

this is called expanded form

$$4^3 = 4 \cdot 4 \cdot 4$$

It is very important to get comfortable with exponents. In the next couple of examples, we will just focus on converting between expanded form and exponential form.

Example 1: Rewrite each multiplication in exponential form. Indicate the base and the exponent and write out how the expression would be read.

a) $3 \cdot 3 \cdot 3 \cdot 3$ b) $2 \cdot 5 \cdot 5 \cdot 2 \cdot 2 \cdot 5 \cdot 2$

Solution: In each case, the exponent represents the number of times the number is being multiplied.

> The commutative and associative properties of multiplication are what allow us to rearrange these factors.

a) $3 \cdot 3 \cdot 3 \cdot 3 = 3^4$ The base is 3 and the exponent is 4, read "3 to the fourth power".

b) $2 \cdot 5 \cdot 5 \cdot 2 \cdot 2 \cdot 5 \cdot 2 = 2 \cdot 2 \cdot 2 \cdot 2 \cdot 5 \cdot 5 \cdot 5 = 2^4 \cdot 5^3$. The bases are 2 with an exponent of four and 5 with an exponent of three, read " 2 to the fourth power times 5 cubed".

Example 2: Rewrite each exponential statement in expanded form.

a) 35^5 b) $2^2 \cdot 15^3$

Solution: In each case, we write the base multiplied to itself the number of times indicated by the exponent.

a) $35^5 = 35 \cdot 35 \cdot 35 \cdot 35 \cdot 35$

b) $2^2 \cdot 15^3 = 2 \cdot 2 \cdot 15 \cdot 15 \cdot 15$

Finally, we are often required to find the result of an exponent.

Example 3: Find the following.

a) 7^3 b) $3^2 \cdot 2^4$

Solution: These are just multiplication problems.

a) $7^3 = 7 \cdot 7 \cdot 7 = 343$

b) $3^2 \cdot 2^4 = 3 \cdot 3 \cdot 2 \cdot 2 \cdot 2 \cdot 2 = 144$

The two most common exponents used in math are the second power, as in 5^2, and the third power, as in 4^3. These two powers have special names:

- "To the second power" is called "squared". So 5^2 is read "5 squared".
- "To the third power" is called "cubed". So 4^3 is read "4 cubed".

STOP Exercise Set - Introduction to Exponents

Rewrite each multiplication in exponential form. Indicate the base and the exponent and write out how the expression would be read.

1. $6 \cdot 6$
2. $18 \cdot 18 \cdot 18$
3. $21 \cdot 21 \cdot 21 \cdot 21$
4. $9 \cdot 9 \cdot 9 \cdot 9 \cdot 9 \cdot 9 \cdot 9$
5. $2 \cdot 2 \cdot 7 \cdot 7 \cdot 7 \cdot 9 \cdot 9$
6. $6 \cdot 6 \cdot 13 \cdot 6 \cdot 13 \cdot 7 \cdot 13 \cdot 13$

Rewrite each exponential statement in expanded form.

7. 8^2
8. 7^3
9. 5^4
10. 17^5
11. $3^3 \cdot 8^2$
12. $5^6 \cdot 11^3$

Find the following.

13. 4^2
14. 9^2
15. 2^4
16. 3^3
17. 6^4
18. 5^3
19. $10^2 \cdot 2^5$
20. $5^2 \cdot 3^3$

Geometry: Area of a Square

A square is a rectangle for which all four sides are equal in length. Since it is a rectangle, the area is:

Area of rectangle = length · width

Area of a square = side · side

To find the area of a square: Raise the side length to the second power or square the side length.

$$\text{Area} \ = \ (\text{side})^2$$

Remember that area is measured in square units such as square inches (in^2) or square miles (mi^2).

Example 4: Where in the World?
A new computer monitor design has a screen that is a square with sides of 20 inches.
Find the area of the screen.

Solution: The area of a square is given by the square of its side length.

$$\begin{aligned}
\text{Area} \ &= \ (\text{side})^2 \\
&= (20)^2 \\
&= 400
\end{aligned}$$

Since the units used in the figure are inches, the area of the square is 400 square
inches or 400 in^2 .

Courtesy of Fotolia

20 in

20 in

STOP Exercise Set - Geometry: Area of a Square

Find the area of each square.

21.

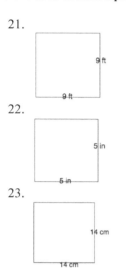

9 ft

9 ft

22.

5 in

5 in

23.

14 cm

14 cm

24.

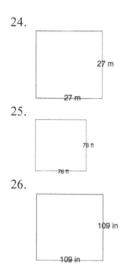

27 m

27 m

25.

78 ft

78 ft

26.

109 in

109 in

27. A square picture frame is 15 inches on one side. What is the area of the frame?

28. A square table top is 38 inches per side. What is the area of the table?

SUCCEED IN MATH!

Does music move you? If you want to listen to music while you study math, that's great! IT can help. But try finding music that has NO lyrics like classical music or some groovy funk or jazz.

Courtesy of Fotolia

The Order of Operations

The expression $5 + 3 \cdot 2$ has two operations.

$$5 + 3 \cdot 2$$

Addition   Multiplication

So which operation should be done first? Multiplication or addition? You get a different result depending on which you do first.

$$5 + 3 \cdot 2$$
Add first: $= 8 \cdot 2$
$= 16$

$$5 + 3 \cdot 2$$
Multiply first: $= 5 + 6$
$= 11$

To avoid this confusion, there is a universal order in which we do the operations in an expression.

The Order of Operations:

- Perform operations inside **grouping symbols** like parentheses first.
- Evaluate any **exponents** in the expression.
- Perform **multiplication** and **division** moving left to right.
- Perform **addition** and **subtraction** from left to right.

Example 5: Find the following.

a) $3 + 4 \cdot 7$ b) $25 \div (17 - 12)$ c) $25 - 3(2 + 5) + 3^3$

Solution:

a) There are no parentheses in the expression. And there are no exponents. There is multiplication, so we perform it first.

$3 + 4 \cdot 7$
$= 3 + 28$

Addition is done last.

$= 31$

b) Since there are parentheses in the expression, we do the operation inside them first.

$25 \div (17 - 12)$
$= 25 \div (5)$

Finally we divide.

$= 5$

c) The operation inside parentheses is done first.

$25 - 3(2 + 5) + 3^3$

$= 25 - 3(7) + 3^3$

The exponent is performed next.

$= 25 - 3(7) + 27$

Now we multiply.

$= 25 - 21 + 27$

$25 - 3(2 + 5) + 3^3$

It is tempting to subtract $25 - 3$ as the first step in this problem but the addition/subtraction step comes LAST!

Last we add and subtract form left to right. $= 4 + 27$

$= 31$

Example 6: Where in the World?

Olga is ordering trailer parts for her boat shop. She orders three hitch balls for $16 each, five gear cranks for $12 each and seven joint plates for $8 each. Give an expression that will find the total cost and use the order of operations to find the total cost.

Solution:

Finding the total cost will involve the operations multiplication and addition. Here is a summary of the important information along with the translation into an expression that we can evaluate:

three hitch balls : $16 each, five gear cranks : $12 each, seven joint plates : $8 each

$$3(16) + 5(12) + 7(8)$$

$$48 + 60 + 56$$

$$164$$

So the expression is $3(16) + 5(12) + 7(8)$ and the total cost is $164.

In each scenario, indicate what two operations are to be used and which operation should be done first.

29. $16 + 15 \div 3$

30. $3 \cdot 8 - 12$

31. $3^3 + 12$

32. $3 + 63 \div 7$

33. $36 \div 3 \cdot 4$

34. $3(18 - 4)$

35. $(15 + 71) \cdot 3 \div 3$

36. Chad is buying new stuff for his Playstation. He buys four controllers for $35 each and five games for $50 each. Find the expression that will be used to calculate his total cost and find the total cost.

37. A catering service charges a flat fee of $65 plus $23 per person. A party is thrown where there are a total of 50 guests. Give the expression that will be used to find the total cost of renting the truck and find the total cost.

More About Grouping Symbols

While parentheses are the most common grouping symbols, all of the following symbols can be used as grouping symbols.

Parentheses ( )   Brackets [ ]   Braces { }   Division Bar ——

Consider the following expression.

$$2\left(11+\left(5(3+2)+15\right)-7\right)$$

Using only parentheses for this expression, makes this expression look confusing. So if more than one pair of grouping symbols needs to be used in an expression, we can use different kinds of grouping symbols to avoid any confusion.

Using different grouping symbols for the expression makes it easier to see which grouping symbols go together.

$$2\{11+[5(3+2)+15]-7\}$$

If more than one pair of grouping symbols appears in an expression start working inside the inner most pair.

Example 7: Find the following.

a.) $18+\{7[16-5]-34\}$ b.) $\dfrac{16+32}{2(10-8)}$

Solution:

a.) $18+\{7[16-5]-34\}$

Begin with the innermost grouping symbol, the brackets. We subtract first.	$18+\{7[16-5]-34\}$ $=18+\{7[11]-34\}$
Still working inside the braces, we multiply.	$=18+\{77-34\}$
Subtract inside the braces.	$=18+\{43\}$
Finally we add.	$=51$

b.) $\dfrac{16+32}{2(10-8)}$

As mentioned earlier, the division bar is treated as a grouping symbol. So $16+32$ and the $2(10-8)$ are found separately before we divide.

Since the expressions are to be found separately first, we perform an operation on each of them. Addition on top and subtraction on bottom.	$\dfrac{16+32}{2(10-8)}$ $=\dfrac{48}{2(2)}$
Multiply on the bottom.	$=\dfrac{48}{4}$
Now we divide.	$=12$

Example 8: Where in the World?

The *average* of a set of numbers is the value that best represents the "expected value" of that set of numbers. We find an average by finding the sum of the numbers and then divided by the numbers of numbers, using a division bar as a grouping symbol.

A math student has the following test scores: 83, 90, 75, 70. Find the average of the test scores.

Solution: An average is usually set up using a division bar as a grouping symbol.

$$\frac{\text{sum of the test scores}}{\text{number of test scores}}=\frac{83+90+75+70}{4}$$

Find the sum on top.

$$=\frac{320}{4}$$

Perform the division. $= 80$

So the student's average test score is 80.

STOP Exercise Set - More About Grouping Symbols

Find the following.

38. $2(17-9)+5(7+16)$

39. $6(27-26)^4+3(12-8)$

40. $3\left[6+(17-14)^3\right]-15$

41. $4\left[(31-26)^2-12\right]+89$

42. The following numbers are the temperature (in degrees) for Charlotte, North Carolina over a five day period: 63, 71, 69, 78, 74 . Find the average of the temperatures.

43. Hyun is an English student who takes weekly quizzes that are worth tens points. Here are her quiz grades so far: 7, 7, 6, 5, 9, 8. Find her average quiz grade.

Exercise Set - Putting It ALL Together

Vocabulary Check: Fill in each blank with a word from our Vocabulary Checklist to the right. Each word is used exactly once.

Vocabulary Checklist:
exponent
base

44. In the expression 6^3 the number 3 represents repeated multiplication and is called an _____.

45. The _____ in an exponential form indicates that number that is being repeatedly multiplied.

Find the following.

46. 6^2	49. 3^3	52. 14^2	55. $3^2 \cdot 10^2$
47. 43^2	50. 1^4	53. $2^2 \cdot 5^2$	56. $1^3 \cdot 2^2 \cdot 3^3$
48. 2^4	51. 12^3	54. $2^3 \cdot 4^2$	57. $2^2 \cdot 4^3 \cdot 5$

58. Sometimes a power of 2 is called a "square". For example, 5^2 is read as "five squared". List the results for the first six squares: $1^2, 2^2, 3^2, 4^2, 5^2, 6^2 =$ ____,____,____,____,____,____ .

59. Sometimes a power of 3 is called a "cube". For example, 4^3 is read as "four cubed". List the results for the first six cubes: $1^3, 2^3, 3^3, 4^3, 5^3, 6^3 =$ ____,____,____,____,____,____ .

Find the following.

60. $3 \cdot 4 + 2 \cdot 5$

61. $12 - 5 \cdot 2$

62. $9 + 3 \cdot 5$

63. $72 \div 6 - 5$

64. $\dfrac{55 - 13}{20 - 2 \cdot 3}$

65. $99 \div 11 \cdot 3 + 2^2$

66. $15 \div 5 \cdot 3 + 1$

67. $12 \cdot 4 \div 6 + 3$

68. $4(16 - 4) + 5(11 + 9)$

69. $(24 - 15) - 3^2$

70. $8 \cdot 3 \div 4 + 8 \cdot 7$

71. $6(67 - 34) + 2 \cdot 7 \div 14$

72. $7^2 - \left[3(9 - 4) + 1^5\right]$

73. $(15 + 4 \cdot 3) - 3^3$

74. $600 \div (3 \cdot 5^2) + 18 \cdot 4$

75. $5^3 + \left[84 - 3(8 + 11)\right]$

76. $74 - \left(4^3 - 3^3\right)$

77. $\left(7^3 - 7^2\right) - 6 \cdot 7 + 1^3$

78. $74 - (4 - 3)^3$

79. $3^4 \div 3^3 + 7(12 - 9)$

80. $28 \cdot 6 - 5^3 \div 5^2$

81. $(13 - 7)^3 + (57 - 46)^2$

82. $97 + 4\left[3(4 + 1)^2 - 2 \cdot 5\right]$

83. $3 \cdot 10^2 - 5 \cdot 4^2 + 23$

84. $17 + (23 - 18)^2 - 24$

85. $16 \cdot 3 + (14 - 11) \cdot (37 - 29)^2$

86. $144 \div 2^4 + 21 \cdot 3 - 10$

87. $4 \cdot 5^2 + \left[17 + 3(89 - 88)^6 + 4 \cdot 5\right]$

88. $2 \cdot (625 \div 5^2) + 16 \cdot 5 - 5$

In the following exercises work has been done on some order of operations expressions but in each exercise a common mistake has been made. Explain the mistake and rework the problem correctly.

89. $5 + 3 \cdot 2$

    $= 8 \cdot 2$

    $= 16$

90. $7 \cdot 8 - 4$

    $= 7 \cdot 4$

    $= 28$

91. $36 \div 9 \cdot 4^2 + 1$

    $= 36 \div 36^2 + 1$

    $= 1^2 + 1$

    $= 1 + 1$

    $= 2$

92. $21 - 4(1 + 2)$

    $= 17(1 + 2)$

    $= 17(3)$

    $= 51$

93. $100 \div 5^2 + 6 \cdot 11$

    $= 20^2 + 6 \cdot 11$

    $= 400 + 6 \cdot 11$

    $= 400 + 66$

    $= 466$

Set up an expression and simplify.

94. Renting a dump truck costs a flat fee of $45 plus $14 per hour. Suppose the truck is rented for 8 hours. Give the expression that will be used to find the total cost of renting the truck and find the total cost.

95. A computer supply store orders five power chords for $15 each, twelve thumb drives for $10 each, and three wireless keyboards for $25 each. Find the expression that will be used to calculate the total cost and find the total cost.

96. Vince is buying art prints. The prints are $75 and he wants to buy 10 of them. Because he spending more than $500 he will get a $100 discount. Give the expression that will be used to find his total charge and find the total charge.

97. Katie has taken 5 exams in her Western Civilization class this semester. Her scores are 85, 96, 87, 94, and 83. What is Katie's average on her exams?

98. Afy took 7 exams in her chemistry and scored 86 on two of them, 89 on three of them, a 95 and a 68. What is Afy's average on her exams?

99. Fernando is waiting tables and kept track of his tips for one week. He reported that during his weekday shifts he made $86, $65, $93, and $112. Friday and Saturday night he made $168 each night. Sunday brunch he made $134. What is the average he made per night?

TRUE/FALSE

100. An exponent is shorthand for repeated addition.
101. In the order of operations, addition is always done before subtraction.
102. In the order of operations, multiplication is always done before division.
103. 4^2 is often read as "four cubed".

104. When writing a textbook it is very important to be aware of how many pages are making up each section. The following table gives the number of pages in certain sections of the original manuscript for this book. Find the average number of pages for the sections given.

Section	Number of Pages
1.1 Whole Numbers	14
4.1 Fraction Basics	17
5.2 Adding/Subtracting Decimals	9
6.4 Proportions	8
7.2 Percent Statements	12

105. An amateur cyclist is thinking about going pro and needs to know how many miles per day, on average he has been biking. Find the average number of miles biked per day from the following table that gives the miles per day over one week.

Day	Miles Biked
Monday	75
Tuesday	61
Wednesday	87
Thursday	0
Friday	105
Saturday	83
Sunday	79

Exercise Set - Chapter 1 Review

106. Multiply. 64(120)
107. Add. 546 + 98
108. Round 156,769 to the nearest ten-thousand.
109. Write "seven hundred five" as a whole number.
110. Divide. 312 ÷ 12

 # 1.4 QUIZ YOURSELF:

To make sure you are ready for the EXAM, try these problems without any help. Give yourself about 20 minutes and don't check the answers until you have completely finished.

1. Write $8 \cdot 8 \cdot 8$ using exponents.
2. Write $2^3 \cdot 7^4$ in expanded form.
3. Evaluate 3^4.
4. Evaluate $3^3 \cdot 7^2$.
5. $36 \div 3^2 + 47$
6. $4(67 - 34) + 3(23 - 19)$
7. $14 \cdot 6 \div 21 + 37$
8. $\dfrac{12 \cdot 3}{4^2 - 2 \cdot 6}$

9. The following is a set of SAT scores taken from four students: 750, 820, 1020, 810. Find the average.

10. Audio books can be purchased online for a flat, one time fee of $19 plus $13 per book purchased. If 10 books are purchased, give the expression that will used to find the total charge and find the total charge.

Answers to this Quiz Yourself are on page 639.

1.5 Factoring

Topics:
- Tests For Divisibility
- Factorizations Of A Number
- Prime And Composite Numbers
- Prime Factorizations
- Multiples

Tests For Divisibility

Carmelina is planning a party with 102 guests. She does not want any empty chairs at each of the tables. Should she rent tables that sit 4 people or 6 people if she doesn't want any empty chairs? To see which option is better she needs to know whether 102 is divisible by 4 or 6.

A number is **divisible** by another if it can be divided without a remainder.

$$\begin{array}{r} 25R2 \\ 4\overline{)102} \end{array}$$ The number 102 is not divisible by 4 because the division has a remainder.

The number 102 is divisible by 6 since the division has no remainder. $\begin{array}{r} 17 \\ 6\overline{)102} \end{array}$

So, Carmelina should rent tables that sit 6 people per table.

Example 1: Use long division to determine if the number 582 is divisible by 6 and/or 13.

Solution: A quick check with long division shows that 582 is divisible by 6, but not by 13.

$$\begin{array}{r} 97 \\ 6\overline{)582} \end{array} \qquad\qquad \begin{array}{r} 44R10 \\ 13\overline{)582} \end{array}$$

There are shortcuts for telling if a number is divisible by another without having to do long division to check. Here are some tests for divisibility.

Tests for Divisibility

A number is divisible by...	If...
2	...it is an even number (ends with 0, 2, 4, 6, or 8).
3	...the sum of the digits is divisible by 3.
4	...the last 2 digits are divisible by 4.
5	...the last digit is 0 or 5.
6	...the number is divisible by both 2 and 3.
8	...the last three digits are divisible by 8.
9	...the sum of the digits is divisible by 9.
10	...the number ends in 0
12	...the number is divisible by both 3 *and* 4

Example 2: Use the tests for divisibility to determine if each statement is true or false.
a) 468 is divisible by 9
b) 761 is divisible by 5
c) 1026 is divisible by 12

Solution:
a) According to the tests, 468 is divisible by 9 if the sum of its digits is: 4 + 6 + 8 = 18. 18 is divisible by 9, so 468 is also divisible by 9. TRUE.

b) 761 does not end in 0 or 5, so it is not divisible by 5. FALSE.

c) For this number, we must check to see if it is divisible by 3 and 4.
Check 3: 1 + 0 + 2 + 6 = 9, which is divisible by 3, so 1026 is divisible by 3.
Check 4: The last two digits are 26, which is not divisible by 4, so it is not divisible by 4. So 1026 is not divisible by 12. False

Example 3: Where in the World? Carmelina is planning a party for 102 guests. Should you rent tables that sit 4 people or 6 people if she doesn't want any empty chairs?

Solution:
102 is not divisible by 4 since the last two digits are not divisible by 4.

102 is divisible by 2, since it ends in 2 AND 102 is divisible by 3 since 1+0+2=3 and 3 is divisible by 3. This means 102 is divisible by 6.

Carmelina should rent tables that sit 6, since 102 is divisible by 6.

STOP Exercise Set - Tests For Divisibility

1. Use long division to determine if 588 is divisible by 7.
2. Use long division to determine if 756 is divisible by 12.
3. Use long division to determine if 1705 is divisible by 3.
4. Use long division to determine if 327 is divisible by 23.

Use the divisibility tests to determine if each statement is true or false.
5.   702 is divisible by 6.
6.   357 is divisible by 5.
7.   2114 is divisible by 4.
8.   40524 is divisible by 9.
9.   21648 is divisible by 12.
10. 108743 is divisible by 10.

Factorizations of a Number

Throughout all of math, certain topics involve rewriting a number as the product (multiplication) of two smaller numbers called *factors*. This process is called *factoring*.

To **factor** a number means to write it as the product of two or more numbers.

Here are several ways to factor the number 36.

$$36 = 1 \cdot 36 \qquad 36 = 2 \cdot 18$$

$$36 = 3 \cdot 2 \cdot 6 \qquad 36 = 4 \cdot 9$$

Recall that the numbers in a product are also called factors. So the word factor is both a noun and a verb.

Definition: Factor
1.) *verb* – To write a number as the product of two or more numbers. We could factor 36 by writing $36 = 9 \cdot 4$.
2.) *noun* – A number in a product. In the product $9 \cdot 4$, 9 and 4 are the factors.
[PN Can we make this look like a page from a dictionary?]

The factored form of a number is called a **factorization**.

Here are some factorizations of the number 36:

$$1 \cdot 36 \qquad 2 \cdot 18 \qquad 6 \cdot 6 \qquad 4 \cdot 9 \qquad 2 \cdot 2 \cdot 3 \cdot 3$$

Example 4: Show two factorizations for each number if possible.
a) 32   b) 13

Solution:
a) There are several ways to factor 32, but we were only asked for two.

$$32 = 4 \cdot 8 \qquad\qquad 32 = 2 \cdot 16$$

b) There is only one way to factor the number 13. That is to write it as itself times 1.

$$13 \cdot 1$$

This makes 13 a special type of number called *prime* which we will discuss as the next topic.

In Beginning Algebra, you will be asked to factor polynomials. A critical part of this process is shown in example 5. Understand it now to make life easier next semester.

Example 5: Find a factorization of 36 so that the sum of the factors is 15.

Solution: We are looking for factors (multiplication) of 36 that result in a sum (addition) of 15. Let's look at all the ways to factor 36.

Factorizations of 36	Sum of the Factors
$1 \cdot 36$	$1 + 36 = 37$
$6 \cdot 6$	$6 + 6 = 12$
$4 \cdot 9$	$4 + 9 = 13$
$3 \cdot 12$	$3 + 12 = 15$
$2 \cdot 18$	$2 + 18 = 19$

$\rightarrow$ Since we are looking for a sum of 15, these are the factorization we want.

So the two factors of 36 that add up to 15 are 3 and 12.

The **multiples** of a number are the values we get from multiplying the number by the natural (counting) numbers.

So the multiples of a number are the numbers we get by multiplying that number by 1,2,3,4,5,6,… Every number has an infinite number of multiples.

Here are the multiples of 5:
$$5 \cdot 1 = 5, \ 5 \cdot 2 = 10, \ 5 \cdot 3 = 15, \ 5 \cdot 4 = 20, \ 5 \cdot 5 = 25, \ 5 \cdot 6 = 30,...$$

So, written in a list the multiples of 5 are 5, 10, 15, 20, 25, 30, 35, 40, 45, 50, 55, 60, 65, 70...

In general, to find the **nth multiple** of a number, multiple the number by n.

Example 6:
a.) What is the 15th multiple of 8?   b.) What is the 34th multiple of 23?

Solution:
a.) We could make a long list until we get to the 15th multiple but that number is just going to be $8 \cdot 15$, so we just multiply: $8 \cdot 15 = 120$.

b.) The 34th multiple of 23 will be $34 \cdot 23 = 782$.

Show two different factorizations for each number if possible.

11. 35   13. 64   15. 100
12. 49   14. 23   16. 144

17. Find a factorization of 6 so that the sum of the factors is 5.
18. Find a factorization of 16 so that the sum of the factors is 10.

19. Find a factorization of 24 so that the sum of the factors is 14.
20. Find a factorization of 36 so that the sum of the factors is 13.

List the first 6 multiples for the following numbers.
21. 14
22. 25
23. 101
24. 234

25. What is the 22nd multiple of 19?
26. What is the 35th multiple of 47?

Prime and Composite Numbers

In Example 3 we noted that the only way to factor the number 13 is by writing $13 \cdot 1$. Some numbers can be factored into the product of smaller numbers and some cannot.

A **composite number** is a number that can be factored into the product of two smaller numbers.

A **prime number** is a number that can only be factored as the product of itself and 1.

The numbers 0 and 1 are considered neither prime nor composite.

The number 24 is *composite* because it can be written as the product of smaller numbers like $4 \cdot 6$. The number 13 is *prime* because the only way to factor it is $1 \cdot 13$.

Here is a list of the prime numbers less than 100:
2, 3, 5, 7, 11, 13, 17, 19, 23, 29, 31, 37, 41, 43,
47, 53, 59, 61, 67, 71, 73, 79, 83, 89, 97

Example 7: Of the following numbers, which are prime and which are composite? If a number is composite, show one factorization other than 1 and itself.

14, 17, 35, 39, 53

Solution: As you work more in math you will get familiar with the first few primes numbers. Using the list above as a reference we have...

17 and 53 are prime numbers.

14, 35, and 39 are composite numbers:

$14 = 2 \cdot 7$ $35 = 5 \cdot 7$ $39 = 3 \cdot 13$

Good Question: If you don't have the list of prime numbers in front you, is there a way to quickly tell if a number is prime?

Answer: That's where the rules for divisibility come in. For example, if a number is divisible by 3 then it can be written as a product involving 3 and you know it's not prime. If you need to know if a number is prime, start testing to see if it is divisible by any numbers.

STOP Exercise Set - Prime and Composite Numbers

Identify each number as prime or composite. If it is composite, show one factorization for the number that shows it is composite.

27. 13   28. 15   29. 27   30. 23   31. 91   32. 81

Prime Factorizations

Putting together the ideas of factoring and prime numbers, we now discuss prime factorizations.

The **prime factorization** of a number is the factorization that involves only prime numbers.

Look at these factorizations of the number 90:

$$9 \cdot 10 \qquad 3 \cdot 3 \cdot 10 \qquad 2 \cdot 3 \cdot 3 \cdot 5 \qquad 2 \cdot 45$$

Of all these factorizations, the following is the only one that involves only primes, so it is the prime factorization of 90.

$$90 = 2 \cdot 3 \cdot 3 \cdot 5 = 2 \cdot 3^2 \cdot 5$$

Note that we can use exponents to express a repeated factor.

In general, to find the prime factorization of a number we just factor and keep factoring the resulting factors until there are only primes.

Example 8: Find the prime factorization of each number.
a) 99   b) 126

Solution: With finding prime factorizations, factor by what ever you see first and keep factoring until you know all the factors are prime.

a)
$$99 = 11 \cdot 9$$
$$= 11 \cdot 3 \cdot 3$$
$$= 3^2 \cdot 11$$

b)
$$126 = 2 \cdot 63$$
$$= 2 \cdot 3 \cdot 21$$
$$= 2 \cdot 3 \cdot 3 \cdot 7$$
$$= 2 \cdot 3^2 \cdot 7$$

Professors, tutors, and other students will have lots of shortcuts to save themselves from having to rewrite all the factors in every step, like factor trees. Find whatever method works best for you, just be sure it is mathematically correct!

We need to make a connection between prime factorizations and multiples. Look at the prime factorization $7 \cdot 5 \cdot 2 \cdot 3$ and consider the following question:

Is $7 \cdot 5 \cdot 2 \cdot 3$ a multiple of 14? The answer is yes. And how do we know? Using the commutative property of multiplication, we can rewrite the product as $7 \cdot 5 \cdot 2 \cdot 3 = 7 \cdot 2 \cdot 5 \cdot 3$ OR $14 \cdot 5 \cdot 3$. Since $7 \cdot 5 \cdot 2 \cdot 3$ can be written as 14 times a number, then yes it is a multiple of 14.

$7 \cdot 5 \cdot 2 \cdot 3$

[PN: arrows]   This shows that $7 \cdot 5 \cdot 2 \cdot 3$ is actually a multiple of 14.

$14 \cdot 15$

For the same reason, $7 \cdot 5 \cdot 2 \cdot 3$ is also a multiple of 6 since $7 \cdot 5 \cdot 2 \cdot 3 = 6 \cdot 35$ and a multiple of 10 since $7 \cdot 5 \cdot 2 \cdot 3 = 10 \cdot 21$.

Example 9: Answer the following questions.
a.) Is $3 \cdot 5 \cdot 3 \cdot 11$ a multiple of 6?
b.) Is $5 \cdot 2 \cdot 13 \cdot 3 \cdot 7$ a multiple of 42?

Solution:
a.) $3 \cdot 5 \cdot 3 \cdot 11$ is not a multiple of 6. The primes necessary to get a product of 6 are not present, so it can not write it as 6 times a number
b.) $5 \cdot 2 \cdot 13 \cdot 3 \cdot 7$ is a multiple of 42 since the prime factors can be multiplied to get 42 times a number, as shown to the right.

$2 \cdot 13 \cdot 3 \cdot 7$

$42 \cdot 13$

STOP Exercise Set - Prime Factorizations

Find the prime factorization of each number.
33. 36
34. 84
35. 132
36. 105
37. 156
38. 153
39. 171
40. 1000

41. Is $2 \cdot 3 \cdot 3 \cdot 5 \cdot 7$ a multiple of 15?
42. Is $5 \cdot 3 \cdot 11 \cdot 3$ a multiple of 55?
43. Is $5 \cdot 2 \cdot 7 \cdot 3$ a multiple of 12?
44. Is $3 \cdot 5 \cdot 11 \cdot 7$ a multiple of 70?

Exercise Set - Putting It ALL Together

Vocabulary Check: Fill in each blank with a word from our Vocabulary Checklist to the right. Each word is used exactly once.

Vocabulary Checklist:
divisible
factor (noun)
factor (verb)
factorization
composite number
prime number
prime factorization
multiples

45. To _____ a number means to rewrite as the product of two or more numbers.

46. $3 \cdot 8$ is just one _____ of the number 24.

47. Since the number 45 can be factored as $5 \cdot 9$ it is an example of a
_____.

48. To get the _____ of a number we factor until it is the product of all prime numbers.

49. A _____ is a number that can only be factored as the product of one and itself.

50. The number 72 is not _____ by 5 because when you divide you have a remainder.

51. If we take the number 7 and start multiplying by 1, 2, 3, 4, 5, 6, and so on we will be finding the _____ of 7.

52. Because 18 can be written as $2 \cdot 9$, the number 9 is a _____ of 18.

Determine if the following numbers are prime or composite. If they are composite, give a factorization of the number other than $1 \cdot$ *the number*.

53. 77
54. 91
55. 278
56. 59
57. 1086
58. 517

Use the tests for divisibility or division if necessary to decide if the following numbers are divisible by the given number(s).

59. 916; 2, 3, 4, 5, 6, 7, 8, 9, 10
60. 4032; 2, 3, 4, 5, 6, 7, 8, 9, 10
61. 1260; 2, 3, 4, 5, 6, 7, 8, 9, 10
62. 13,851; 2, 3, 4, 5, 6, 7, 8, 9, 10
63. 345; 3, 5, 15
64. 912; 2, 3, 4, 12
65. 252; 3, 7, 21
66. 231; 2, 7, 14
67. 660; 5, 11, 55

Find the prime factorization of the following numbers.

68. 52	71. 264	74. 635	77. 4071
69. 96	72. 352	75. 408	78. 2010
70. 155	73. 585	76. 980	79. 6080

80. What is the 31st multiple of 8?
81. What is the 45th multiple of 18?
82. What is the 45th multiple of 18?

83. What is the 57th multiple of 9?
84. What is the 33rd multiple of 231?
85. What is the 64th multiple of 198?

86. Is $3 \cdot 7 \cdot 7 \cdot 7$ a multiple of 49
87. Is $2 \cdot 2 \cdot 11 \cdot 23$ a multiple of 22?
88. Is $5 \cdot 19 \cdot 3$ a multiple of 45?

89. Is $2 \cdot 2 \cdot 3 \cdot 29 \cdot 3$ a multiple of 36?
90. Is $2 \cdot 3 \cdot 7 \cdot 11 \cdot 17$ a multiple of 77?
91. Is $2 \cdot 3 \cdot 5 \cdot 7 \cdot 7$ a multiple of 100?

92. Find two factors of 45 whose sum is 18.
93. Find two factors of 48 whose sum is 19.
94. Find two factors of 72 whose sum is 17.

95. Find two factors of 81 whose sum is 30.
96. Find two factors of 105 whose sum is 22.
97. Find two factors of 132 whose sum is 23.

Exercise Set - Chapter 1 Review

98. How many digits does the number 1,350 have?
99. Multiply. 8(6)(10)

100. Write 5^3 in expanded form.
101. Evaluate. $4 + 2(6-3)$
102. Add. $59 + 162$

 # 1.5 QUIZ YOURSELF:

To make sure you are ready for the EXAM, try these problems without any help. Give yourself about 20 minutes and don't check the answers until you have completely finished.

Use the divisibility tests to determine if the following numbers are divisible by 2, 3, 4, 5, 6, 9, or 10.

1. 1080
2. 907,209

Which of the following are prime and which are composite?

3. 49
4. 4,071

5. Find two factorizations for 48.
6. Find the prime factorization for 168.
7. Find the prime factorization for 1155.
8. Find the 54th multiple of 7.
9. Find two factors of 24 whose sum is 11.
10. Is $2 \cdot 5 \cdot 11 \cdot 23 \cdot 29$ a multiple of 30?

Answers to this Quiz Yourself are on page 639.

1.6 A Review Of Basic Fractions

Topics:
- Understanding Fractions
- Simplifying Fractions
- Multiplying and Dividing Fractions
- Adding and Subtracting Fractions

Understanding Fractions

Fractions are used to represent part of a whole.   In the picture to the right, four parts make the whole and three parts are shaded. So the *fraction* of the picture that is shaded is 3 out of 4, represented as $\frac{3}{4}$.

A **fraction** is a number that is used to represent part of a whole. The top number in a fraction is called the **numerator**. The bottom number is called the **denominator**.

$$\frac{3}{4} = \frac{\text{part}}{\text{whole}} = \frac{\text{numerator}}{\text{denominator}}$$

Example 1: Identify the numerator and denominator in each fraction and draw a picture to represent the fraction.

a) $\frac{3}{5}$ b) $\frac{7}{8}$

Solution: In each case, the denominator shows us how many equal parts to draw and the numerator tells us how many of them to shade in. We can use either boxes or circles to represent the fractions, but boxes are usually easier to draw.

a) The numerator is 3. The denominator is 5.

b) The numerator is 7. The denominator is 8.

Here is an example of how fractions are used to represent real-world information.

Example 2: Where in the World?
An English class has 35 students. Of the 35 students, 28 of them have already turned in their portfolio assignment. What fraction of the students have turned in the assignment?

Solution: In this case, the "whole" would be the total number of students, which is 35. And the "part" would be the number of students that have turned in the assignment, which is 28. We know 28 out of 35 students have turned in the assignment. The fraction of students that have turned in the assignment is $\frac{28}{35}$.

 # Exercise Set - Understanding Fractions

For each fraction, identify the numerator and denominator. Then draw a picture to represent the fraction.

1. $\frac{3}{7}$ 3. $\frac{3}{4}$

2. $\frac{9}{10}$ 4. $\frac{5}{8}$

5. At a factory, 500 parts are inspected and of them, 23 are found to have defects. What fraction of the parts had defects?

6. Antwon took a math test with 25 problems. He got 3 of the problems *wrong*. What fraction of the problems did he get *correct*?

Simplifying Fractions

It is possible for two fractions that look different to represent the same quantity. To illustrate, consider the pictures below.

The same quantity can be represented using several different fractions. This illustrates the idea of *equivalent fractions*.

> ## Two or more fractions are called **equivalent fractions** if they represent the same amount.

Given a fraction we can often find an equivalent fraction that has smaller numerator and denominator.

The Fundamental Principle of Fractions
If the numerator and denominator have a common factor, this factor can be removed without changing the value of the fraction.

$$\frac{10}{15} = \frac{2\cdot 5}{3\cdot 5} = \frac{2\cdot \cancel{5}}{3\cdot \cancel{5}} = \frac{2}{3}$$

Example 3: Fill in the blank to complete each factorization and write an equivalent fraction.

$$\frac{21}{35} = \frac{\boxed{}\cdot 7}{\boxed{}\cdot 5} = \frac{\boxed{}}{\boxed{}}$$

Solution: $\dfrac{21}{35} = \dfrac{\boxed{3}\cdot 7}{\boxed{7}\cdot 5} = \dfrac{\boxed{3}}{\boxed{5}}$

Good Question: Why does the Fundamental Principle of Fractions work? Why can I just remove a common factor from the numerator and denominator?

Answer: This Fundamental Principle works because of the way we multiply fractions, as we will study in more detail soon:

$$\frac{10}{15} = \frac{2\cdot 5}{3\cdot 5} = \frac{2}{3}\cdot\frac{5}{5} = \frac{2}{3}\cdot 1 = \frac{2}{3}$$

So, using the above principle, we are really just removing a factor of 1, which does not change the value according to the multiplicative identity of one.

The last example showed that $\dfrac{21}{35}$ and the simplified fraction $\dfrac{3}{5}$ are equivalent. Since the fraction $\dfrac{3}{5}$ has no common factors (other than 1) in the numerator and denominator, it is considered to be in *lowest terms*.

> ## Removing a common factor from the numerator and denominator of a fraction is called **simplifying a fraction**. A fraction in **lowest terms** has no common factors in the numerator and denominator other than 1.

Of course, it is possible that the numerator and denominator of a fraction have several factors in common. So we use prime factorizations to make sure we find them all.

To simplify a fraction to lowest terms:
1. Prime factor the numerator and denominator.
2. Remove any common factors.
3. Multiply the remaining factors in the numerator and denominator.

Example 4: Simplify each fraction to lowest terms.

a) $\dfrac{22}{55}$ b) $\dfrac{15}{45}$

Solution:

a) Prime factor the numerator and denominator. $\dfrac{22}{55} = \dfrac{2 \cdot 11}{5 \cdot 11}$

Now remove the common factor of 11. $= \dfrac{2 \cdot \cancel{11}}{5 \cdot \cancel{11}}$

There are no remaining factors to multiply. $= \dfrac{2}{5}$

c) Prime factor the numerator and denominator. $\dfrac{15}{45} = \dfrac{3 \cdot 5}{3 \cdot 3 \cdot 5}$

Now remove the common factors 3 and 5. $= \dfrac{\cancel{3} \cdot \cancel{5}}{\cancel{3} \cdot 3 \cdot \cancel{5}}$

Recall that even if all your common factors are
removed there is still a factor of 1. So we write a 1 $= \dfrac{1}{3}$
in the numerator.

> Be careful! If all prime factors are removed from the numerator, there is still a factor of 1:
> $$\dfrac{5}{10} = \dfrac{\cancel{5} \cdot 1}{\cancel{5} \cdot 2} = \dfrac{1}{2}$$

In applications, having a fraction in lowest terms usually makes it easier to visualize what the information means.

Example 5: Where in the World? A company has 24 employees. Last month, 18 of them traveled on job related business trips. Write the fraction of employees who took a business trip and reduce the fraction to lowest terms.

Solution: 18 out of 24 took a trip, so we have the fraction $\dfrac{18}{24}$. Now we can reduce it to lowest terms.

- Factor the numerator and denominator to primes. $\dfrac{18}{24} = \dfrac{\cancel{2} \cdot \cancel{3} \cdot 3}{\cancel{2} \cdot 2 \cdot 2 \cdot \cancel{3}}$
- Cross out common factors as soon as they have the prime factorization, as we have done here.
- Multiply the remaining factors from the "marked up" fraction, as we have done here. $= \dfrac{3}{4}$

So, $\dfrac{3}{4}$ or "three-fourths" of the employees had a business trip last month.

STOP Exercise Set -Simplifying Fractions

Fill in each blank to complete the factorization and write an equivalent fraction.

7. $\dfrac{14}{22} = \dfrac{2 \cdot \square}{\square \cdot 11} = \dfrac{\square}{\square}$

8. $\dfrac{15}{21} = \dfrac{\square \cdot 5}{\square \cdot 3} = \dfrac{\square}{\square}$

Simplify each fraction to lowest terms.

9. $\dfrac{6}{8}$

10. $\dfrac{12}{15}$

11. $\dfrac{14}{21}$

12. $\dfrac{21}{56}$

13. $\dfrac{20}{25}$

14. $\dfrac{45}{75}$

15. In a class of 42 students, 36 pass a test. Write the fraction of students who passed the test and express the fraction in lowest terms.

16. A survey of 100 people finds that 68 of them prefer a PC to Mac. Write the fraction of people who prefer a PC and reduce the fraction to lowest terms.

Multiplying and Dividing Fractions

We now turn to performing operations on fractions. In this section, we will focus on how to multiply, divide, add, and subtract fractions. Later, in Chapter 4, we will look at *why* we operate on fractions the way we do. But for now, let's focus on the *how*.

Multiplying Fractions
$$\frac{A}{B} \cdot \frac{C}{D} = \frac{A \cdot C}{B \cdot D}$$

So to multiply two fractions, multiply the numerators and denominators separately. To get you familiar with this we will begin examples where we don't have to worry about simplifying the final answer.

Example 6: Multiply.

a) $\dfrac{5}{7} \cdot \dfrac{3}{4}$ b) $\dfrac{2}{13} \cdot 4$

Solution: In each case we multiply the numerators and denominators of each fraction.

a) $\dfrac{5}{7} \cdot \dfrac{3}{4}$

Write the multiplication as a single fraction. $\dfrac{5}{7} \cdot \dfrac{3}{4} = \dfrac{5 \cdot 3}{7 \cdot 4}$

Perform the multiplication to get the final answer. $= \dfrac{15}{28}$

b) $\dfrac{2}{13} \cdot 4$

For this problem, recall that any whole number can be rewritten as a fraction with 1 as the denominator. In this case, $4 = \dfrac{4}{1}$.

Write the whole number 4 as a fraction. $\dfrac{2}{13} \cdot 4 = \dfrac{2}{13} \cdot \dfrac{4}{1}$

Write the multiplication as a single fraction. $= \dfrac{2 \cdot 4}{13 \cdot 1}$

Perform the multiplication to get the final answer. $= \dfrac{8}{13}$

> Recall that any whole number can be rewritten as a fraction with 1 as the denominator: $b = \dfrac{b}{1}$.

Often, we must simplify a final answer into lowest terms. To do this, start looking for common factors in the numerator and denominator before you actually multiply the factors together.

Example 7: Multiply and simplify the final answer to lowest terms, if possible.

a) $\dfrac{2}{5} \cdot \dfrac{7}{10}$ b) $\dfrac{5}{6} \cdot \dfrac{7}{15}$

Solution: For each problem, we begin looking for common factors after we rewrite the multiplication as a single fraction.

a) Rewrite the multiplication as a single fraction. $\dfrac{2}{5} \cdot \dfrac{7}{10} = \dfrac{2 \cdot 7}{5 \cdot 10}$

Notice that there is common factor of 2 in the numerator and denominator. $= \dfrac{\cancel{2} \cdot 7}{5 \cdot \cancel{2} \cdot 5}$

Remove the common factor. $= \dfrac{7}{5 \cdot 5}$

Multiply the factors remaining.	$= \dfrac{7}{25}$

b) Rewrite the multiplication as a single fraction. $\quad \dfrac{5}{6} \cdot \dfrac{7}{15} = \dfrac{5 \cdot 7}{6 \cdot 15}$

Notice that there is common factor of 5 in the
numerator and denominator. $\qquad\qquad\qquad = \dfrac{\cancel{5} \cdot 7}{6 \cdot 3 \cdot \cancel{5}}$

Remove the common factor. $\qquad\qquad\qquad\qquad = \dfrac{7}{3 \cdot 6}$

Multiply the factors left. $\qquad\qquad\qquad\qquad = \dfrac{7}{18}$

To divide fractions we use reciprocals.

$$\text{The fractions } \ \frac{a}{b} \ \text{ and } \ \frac{b}{a} \ \text{ are called } \textbf{reciprocals}.$$

Example 8: Find the reciprocal of each fraction or whole number.

a) $\dfrac{2}{13}$ $\qquad$ b) 7

Solution:

a) The reciprocal of $\dfrac{2}{13}$ is $\dfrac{13}{2}$.

b) We rewrite 7 as the fraction $\dfrac{7}{1}$ to get a reciprocal of $\dfrac{1}{7}$.

Here is the rule for dividing fractions.

Dividing Fractions

$$\frac{A}{B} \div \frac{C}{D} = \frac{A}{B} \cdot \frac{D}{C} = \frac{A \cdot D}{B \cdot C}$$

So to divide fractions we take the reciprocal of the second fraction and change the operation to multiplication. Again, in Chapter 4 we will look at *why* this works. For now, we will focus on *how* to perform the operation.

Example 9: Divide the fractions and simplify the final answer to lowest terms, if possible.

a) $\dfrac{2}{5} \div \dfrac{4}{15}$ $\qquad$ c) $\dfrac{21}{32} \div 14$

Solution: For each problem, we begin looking for common factors right after we rewrite the division as multiplication as a single fraction.

a) Rewrite the division as a multiplication.

$$\frac{2}{5} \div \frac{4}{15} = \frac{2}{5} \cdot \frac{15}{4}$$

Rewrite the multiplication as a single fraction.

$$= \frac{2 \cdot 15}{5 \cdot 4}$$

Notice that there is common factor of 2 and 5 in the numerator and denominator. We can remove these factors.

$$= \frac{\cancel{2} \cdot 3 \cdot \cancel{5}}{\cancel{5} \cdot \cancel{2} \cdot 2}$$

Remove the common factor.

$$= \frac{3}{2}$$

b) Rewrite the division as a multiplication.

$$\frac{21}{32} \div 14 = \frac{21}{32} \cdot \frac{1}{14}$$

Rewrite the multiplication as a single fraction.

$$= \frac{21 \cdot 1}{32 \cdot 14}$$

Notice that there is common factor of 7 in the numerator and denominator. Also, we do not bother writing the prime factorization of 32 since it 32 does not have 3 or 7 as a factor.

$$= \frac{3 \cdot \cancel{7}}{32 \cdot 2 \cdot \cancel{7}}$$

Remove the common factor.

$$= \frac{3}{32 \cdot 2}$$

Multiply the remaining factors.

$$= \frac{3}{64}$$

 # Multiplying and Dividing Fractions Homework

Multiply or divide. Simplify your final answer if necessary.

17. $\dfrac{3}{4} \cdot \dfrac{2}{5}$

18. $\dfrac{1}{3} \cdot \dfrac{7}{8}$

19. $\dfrac{5}{6} \cdot \dfrac{7}{8}$

20. $\dfrac{2}{15} \div \dfrac{3}{5}$

21. $\dfrac{5}{6} \div \dfrac{5}{9}$

22. $\dfrac{9}{28} \div \dfrac{3}{4}$

Adding and Subtracting Fractions

Suppose two cakes are sliced into five pieces each. If there is one slice left over from one cake and two slices left over from the other, the combined leftovers could be represented as follows:

$$\frac{1}{5} \quad + \quad \frac{2}{5} \quad = \quad \frac{3}{5}$$

This represents the basic process for adding fractions. Note that the number of parts that make a whole (the denominator) does not change. Also, to add or subtract fractions the denominators must be the same.

Adding Fractions

$$\frac{A}{B} + \frac{C}{B} = \frac{A+C}{B}$$

Subtracting Fractions

$$\frac{A}{B} - \frac{C}{B} = \frac{A-C}{B}$$

So to add or subtract fractions with a common denominator we keep the denominator the same and just add or subtract the numerators.

Example 10: Add or subtract.

a) $\frac{3}{7} + \frac{2}{7}$

b) $\frac{15}{19} - \frac{12}{19}$

Solution: In each of case we keep the same denominator and add or subtract the numerators.

a) Keep the denominator the same and *add* the numerators.

$$\frac{3}{7} + \frac{2}{7} = \frac{3+2}{7}$$

$$= \frac{5}{7}$$

b) Keep the denominator the same and *subtract* the numerators.

$$\frac{15}{19} - \frac{12}{19} = \frac{15-12}{19}$$

$$= \frac{3}{19}$$

As mentioned before you should *always* simplify your answer if possible. First, add or subtract. Then check your answer to see if there is a common factor in the numerator and denominator to reduce the fraction.

Example 11: Add or subtract and reduce the final answer to lowest terms, if possible.

a) $\dfrac{12}{70} + \dfrac{33}{70}$ b) $\dfrac{25}{22} - \dfrac{3}{22}$

Solution:

a) Keep the denominator the same and *add* the numerators.

$$\dfrac{12}{70} + \dfrac{33}{70} = \dfrac{12 + 33}{70}$$

Make sure to add the numbers in the numerator *before* you start to reduce the fraction.

$$= \dfrac{45}{70}$$

Factor the numerator and denominator to look for common factors. Remove the common factor of 5.

$$= \dfrac{3 \cdot 3 \cdot 5}{7 \cdot 5 \cdot 2}$$

Multiply the remaining factors to get the final answer.

$$= \dfrac{9}{14}$$

b) Keep the denominator the same and *subtract* the numerators.

$$\dfrac{25}{22} - \dfrac{3}{22} = \dfrac{25 - 3}{22}$$

Make sure to subtract the numbers in the numerator *before* you start to reduce the fraction.

$$= \dfrac{22}{22}$$

Since the numerator and denominator are the same the fraction reduces to 1.

$$= 1$$

STOP Exercise Set - Adding and Subtracting Fractions

Add or subtract and simplify the final answer to lowest terms, if necessary.

23. $\dfrac{2}{5} + \dfrac{1}{5}$ 28. $\dfrac{23}{24} - \dfrac{10}{24}$

24. $\dfrac{2}{9} + \dfrac{3}{9}$ 29. $\dfrac{5}{51} - \dfrac{2}{51}$

25. $\dfrac{3}{7} - \dfrac{1}{7}$ 30. $\dfrac{8}{35} + \dfrac{6}{35}$

26. $\dfrac{7}{12} - \dfrac{2}{12}$ 31. $\dfrac{14}{95} + \dfrac{11}{95}$

27. $\dfrac{8}{15} - \dfrac{6}{15}$ 32. $\dfrac{27}{120} + \dfrac{35}{120}$

Exercise Set - Putting It ALL Together

Vocabulary Check: Fill in each blank with a word from our Vocabulary Checklist to the right. Each word is used exactly once.

33. _____ states that a factor common to the numerator and denominator can be removed.

Vocabulary Checklist:
fraction
numerator
denominator
the fundamental principle of fractions
equivalent fractions
simplifying a fraction
lowest terms
reciprocal

34. The part of a fraction that represents how many parts make a whole is called the _____ of the fraction.

35. The fraction $\frac{5}{7}$ is called the _____ of the fraction $\frac{7}{5}$.

36. $\frac{1}{2}$ and $\frac{5}{10}$ are called _____ because they represent the same quantity.

37. A fraction is in _____ when all factors common of numerator and denominator have been removed. This process is called _____ .

38. The number in the top of a fraction is called the _____ of the fraction.

39. A _____ is a number that is used to represent part of a whole.

What fraction is being represented in each picture?

40.

41.

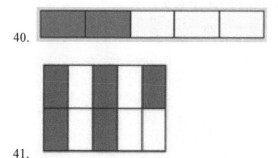

42. What two equivalent fractions are represented in the four pictures below?

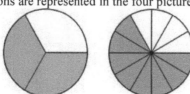

43. What four equivalent fractions are represented in the four pictures below?

44. What three equivalent fractions are represented in the pictures below?

45. What three equivalent fractions are represented in the pictures below?

46. What fraction has a denominator of 15 and numerator of 9?
47. What fraction has a denominator of 16 and a numerator of 7?

Simplify each fraction to lowest terms, if possible.

48. $\dfrac{12}{24}$ 52. $\dfrac{28}{72}$ 56. $\dfrac{72}{136}$

49. $\dfrac{3}{9}$ 53. $\dfrac{51}{85}$ 57. $\dfrac{30}{102}$

50. $\dfrac{28}{36}$ 54. $\dfrac{60}{65}$ 58. $\dfrac{81}{117}$

51. $\dfrac{25}{75}$ 55. $\dfrac{6}{61}$ 59. $\dfrac{294}{525}$

Determine whether each pair of fractions are equivalent by simplifying each fraction to lowest terms.

60. $\dfrac{6}{14}$ and $\dfrac{10}{35}$ 62. $\dfrac{40}{90}$ and $\dfrac{44}{99}$

61. $\dfrac{4}{12}$ and $\dfrac{6}{9}$ 63. $\dfrac{14}{30}$ and $\dfrac{21}{45}$

Perform the indicated operation. Simplify your final answer to lowest terms if necessary.

64. $\dfrac{2}{3} \cdot \dfrac{4}{5}$

65. $\dfrac{1}{5} \cdot \dfrac{3}{7}$

66. $\dfrac{5}{6} \div \dfrac{8}{9}$

67. $\dfrac{8}{9} \div \dfrac{7}{3}$

68. $\dfrac{3}{5} \cdot \dfrac{4}{9}$

69. $\dfrac{2}{3} \div \dfrac{1}{6}$

70. $\dfrac{12}{13} \cdot \dfrac{3}{4}$

71. $\dfrac{9}{10} \cdot \dfrac{5}{8}$

72. $\dfrac{6}{7} \div \dfrac{15}{14}$

73. $\dfrac{21}{33} \cdot \dfrac{11}{14}$

74. $\dfrac{8}{9} - \dfrac{2}{9}$

75. $\dfrac{17}{24} - \dfrac{5}{24}$

76. $\dfrac{9}{32} + \dfrac{5}{32}$

77. $\dfrac{6}{7} \cdot \dfrac{7}{6}$

78. $\dfrac{19}{30} + \dfrac{11}{30}$

79. $\dfrac{14}{19} + \dfrac{5}{19}$

80. $\dfrac{22}{45} - \dfrac{4}{45}$

81. $\dfrac{17}{60} - \dfrac{11}{60}$

82. $\dfrac{43}{54} - \dfrac{16}{54}$

83. $\dfrac{34}{105} + \dfrac{11}{105}$

84. $\dfrac{87}{94} - \dfrac{25}{94}$

85. $\dfrac{15}{34} + \dfrac{2}{34}$

86. $\dfrac{25}{36} \cdot \dfrac{12}{45}$

87. $\dfrac{8}{15} \div \dfrac{8}{15}$

88. $\dfrac{5}{9} \cdot 18$

89. $\dfrac{14}{15} \cdot 30$

90. $\dfrac{15}{26} \cdot \dfrac{13}{45}$

91. How could you use a visual illustration to convince a fellow student that $\dfrac{1}{8} + \dfrac{3}{8} = \dfrac{1}{2}$?

92. How could you use a visual illustration to convince a fellow student that $\dfrac{1}{6} + \dfrac{1}{6} = \dfrac{1}{3}$?

93. Of 45 students in a math class, 9 received an "A" on the last exam. What fraction of the students *did not* receive an A on the last exam? Simplify your answer if possible.

94. A marathon race is about 26 miles. If 4 of those miles are uphill, what fraction of the race is *not* uphill? Simplify your answer if possible.

95. A researcher at Apple takes sample of album sales by genre and gets the following results.

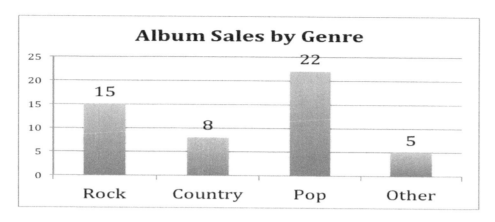

a.) How many albums are in the total sample?
b.) What fraction of the albums sold were rock albums?
c.) What fraction of the albums sold were pop albums?

96. A website that sells smart phone apps is researching what is most popular. A sample of apps sold is taken.

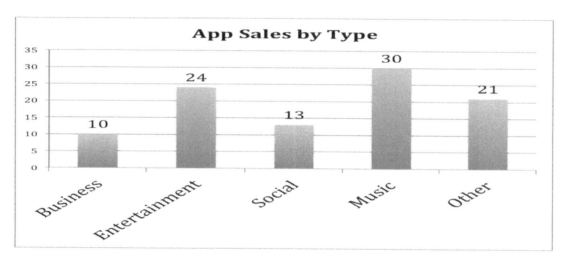

a.) How many apps are in the total sample?
b.) What fraction of the apps sold were for social networking?
c.) What fraction of the apps sold were for entertainment?

For each statement, answer TRUE or FALSE.

97. To add two fractions simply add the numerators and the denominators separately.
98. Fractions being multiplied do not have to have the same denominator.
99. To divide fractions we take the reciprocal of *both* fractions and change the operation to multiplication.

100. The Fundamental Principle of Fractions can be expressed as $\dfrac{a \cdot c}{b \cdot c} = \dfrac{a}{b}$.

Exercise Set - Chapter 1 Review

101. Estimate the difference $472 - 387$ by rounding to the nearest ten.
102. Find two factors of 24 that add up to 11.
103. Find the prime factorization of 54.
104. Multiply. $352 \cdot 23$

105. Use the order of operations to evaluate. $(5-3)(8-1)+5$

1.6 QUIZ YOURSELF:

To make sure you are ready for the EXAM, try these problems without any help. Give yourself about 15 minutes and don't check the answers until you have completely finished.

1. What fraction is represented in the picture below? Identify the numerator and denominator.

2. Simplify. $\dfrac{48}{72}$

Perform the indicted operation. Simplify your final answer if possible.

3. $\dfrac{3}{19}+\dfrac{11}{19}$

4. $\dfrac{5}{14}\cdot\dfrac{4}{10}$

5. $\dfrac{11}{24}-\dfrac{2}{24}$

6. $\dfrac{2}{13}+\dfrac{1}{2}$

7. At production factory, 150 parts are sampled. Of these, 140 were found to *not* have a defect. What fraction of the parts *did* have a defect? Simplify your answer if possible.

Answers to this Quiz Yourself are on page 639.

1.7 Introduction to Variables, Expressions, and Equations

Topics:
- Introduction To Variables and Expressions
- Introduction to Equations

Introduction To Variables and Expressions

Suppose you get a job making $11 per hour. Given the number of hours you work in a week we can use multiplication to determine your pay.

Hours Worked	Pay
10	$11(10) = $110
23	$11(23) = $253
40	$11(40) = $440

Since the number of hours you work may change from week to week, we call it a *variable*. In algebra, we often use a letter to represent numbers like this: h = number of hours worked .

A **variable** is a letter that represents a number that is unknown or that changes.

Here are examples of other variables in math applications:
- t = time (measured in seconds, minutes, or or hours)
- W = width of a rectangle (measured in feet, inches, or meters, etc)
- m = number of miles a customer drives a rental car

And sometimes we just the generic variable x = some unknown number .

If the variable h represents how many hours you work in a certain week for $11 per hour then the multiplication $11(h)$ will give her pay for a given week. The multiplication $11(h)$ is an example of an *expression*.

An **expression** is a series of operations, numbers, and/or variables.

Here are some other examples of algebraic expressions:

$$15a \qquad x+5 \qquad 2w+2l \qquad \frac{y+4}{5} \qquad mx+b$$

In an algebraic expression, each variable represents a number. When you look at an expression, keep in mind that there are several ways to represent the operations multiplication and division.

Common Ways to Represent Division		
Division Sign	A Division Bar	A Fraction Bar
$x \div 3$	$x/3$	$\dfrac{x}{3}$

Common Ways to Represent Multiplication		
A Dot	Parentheses	No Symbol
$5 \cdot r$	$5(r)$	$5r$

Earlier we supposed that if you get paid \$11 per hour we can use the expression $11h$ to find your total pay where h represents the number of hours you work. If, for a certain week, you work 20 hours we can find your pay by letting $h = 20$ and performing the multiplication: $11h = 11(20) = 220$. This process is called *evaluating an expression*.

SUCCEED IN MATH! If you succeed in college you will make MUCH more than \$11 an hour!!

To **evaluate an expression** means to substitute a value for the variable(s) and perform the operations involved to get a number.

Example 1: Evaluate each expression for the variable value(s) given.

a) $23 - m$ for $m = 20$ b) $x^2 + 3x$ for $x = 11$

Solution:

a) Since we are given $m = 20$ we substitute 20 in for m then perform the operation.

$$23 - m = 23 - 20$$
$$= 3$$

b) Since we are given $x = 11$ we substitute 11 in for x. Notice that there are x appears twice in the expression, so we substitute 11 into both places. To evaluate this expression we use the order of operations: grouping symbols, exponents, multiplication and division, then addition and subtraction. Also, notice that putting the variable in parentheses in our first step helps clarify the meaning of each operation.

$$x^2 + 3x = (11)^2 + 3(11)$$
$$= 121 + 3(11)$$
$$= 121 + 33$$
$$= 154$$

In section 1.1, we introduced tables in the context of applications. It is convenient to fill in tables to evaluate expressions.

Example 2: The tables below give variable values and an expression to be evaluated. Fill in each table.

b	$b^2 + 7b$
2	
0	
5	

Solution: We are asked to evaluate the expression for three values of b.
We can put use the table to evaluate the expression for each value. Here is the result.

b	$b^2 + 7b$
2	$= (2)^2 + 7(2) = 4 + 7(2) = 4 + 14 = 18$
0	$= (0)^2 + 7(0) = 0 + 7(0) = 0 + 0 = 0$
5	$= (5)^2 + 7(5) = 25 + 7(5) = 25 + 35 = 60$

Completing the tables above helps organize data as we saw in section 1.1 and will be useful with several topics in the future.

In our examples so far, we had only one variable. However, often there are several variables in an expression. Hence we substitute in more than one variable value when evaluating.

Example 3: Evaluate each expression for the variable value(s) given.

a.) $mx + b$ for $m = 3$, $b = 7$, and $x = 2$

b.) $b^2 - 4ac$ for $a = 1$, $b = 6$, and $c = 4$

Solution: These expressions have more than one variable value to substitute. As mentioned before, notice that putting the variable value in parentheses in the first step helps clarify the meaning of each operation.

a.) We are given $m = 3$, $b = 7$, and $x = 2$ so we substitute these values in for the variables.

$$mx + b = 3(2) + 7$$
$$= 6 + 7$$
$$= 13$$

b.) We are given $a = 1$, $b = 6$, and $c = 4$ so we substitute these values in for the variables.

$$b^2 - 4ac = (6)^2 - 4(1)(4)$$
$$= 36 - 4(1)(4)$$
$$= 36 - 16$$
$$= 20$$

Example 4: Where in the World? If a rocket is fired straight up, then to find out how high (in feet) it will be after 2 seconds a scientist would have to evaluate the expression $vt - gt^2$ for $g = 16$, $v = 165$, and $t = 2$. Evaluate the expression for the values given.

We are given $g = 16$, $v = 165$, and $t = 2$, so we substitute these values in for the variables.

$$\begin{aligned} vt - gt^2 &= 165(2) - 16(2)^2 \\ &= 165(2) - 16(4) \\ &= 330 - 64 \\ &= 266 \end{aligned}$$

Evaluate each expression for the variable value(s) given.

1. $x + 8$, for $x = 5$
2. $3y$, for $y = 12$
3. $17 + 4b$, for $b = 2$
4. $3x + 7$, for $x = 8$
5. $x^2 - 3x$, for $x = 7$
6. $a^2 + 7a - 11$, for $a = 9$

7. $2x + 5y$ for $x = 0$ and $y = 3$
8. $4x - y$ for $x = 6$ and $y = 8$
9. $mx + b$, for $m = 2, x = 1, b = 23$
10. $mx + b$, for $m = 6, x = 17, b = 119$

The tables below give variable values and an expression to be evaluated. Fill in each table.

11.

y	$y^2 + 3y$
4	
0	
3	

12.

x	$\dfrac{3}{4}x + 1$
0	
4	
8	

13. To find the perimeter of a rectangle you can use the expression $2L + 2W$. Evaluate the expression $2L + 2W$ for $L = 18$ and $W = 35$.

14. To find the number of games that can be played between x sports teams you use the expression $x^2 - x$. Evaluate the expression $x^2 - x$ for $x = 10$.

Introduction to Equations

Again, suppose the expression $11h$ represents your pay for working h hours in a week. If you need to make \$248 a certain week, we would need to find the solution to the equation $11 \cdot h = 248$ to find out how many hours you must work·

An **equation** is a statement that two expressions are equal.

The statement $6 + 4 = 2 \cdot 5$ is another example of an equation. It is important that you can distinguish between an expression and an equation. By definition an equation must have an equals sign " $=$ " where an expression does not.

Examples of Expressions	Examples of Equations
$3(5) + (4)^2$	$3 + 7 = 2 \cdot 5$
$x + 5$	$5y = 10$
$mx + b$	$x + 4 = 9$

Example 5: Identify whether each is an expression or an equation.

a) $3^2 - 4$ b) $3 + 1 = 8 \div 2$

c) $2a + 1 = 7$ d) $b^2 - 4ac$

Solution: Since an equation is a statement about equality, it must have an equals sign $(=)$.

a) $3^2 - 4$ is an expression since it does not contain an equals sign.

b) $3 + 1 = 8 \div 2$ is an equation since it contains an equals sign.

c) $2a + 1 = 7$ is an equation since it contains an equals sign.

d) $b^2 - 4ac$ is an expression since it does not contain an equals sign.

An equation can be true or false. To decide if an equation is true or false, use the order of operations to simplify the expression on each side separately. If the simplified values are equal, the equation is true. If not, the equation is false.

This equation is true:

$$18 \div 3 = 10 - 4$$
$$6 = 6 \quad \text{True}$$

This equation is false:

$$3(5) = 7 + 3$$
$$15 = 10 \quad \text{False}$$

Example 6: In each case, indicate whether the equation is true or false by simplifying the expressions on each side.

a) $4 \cdot (5 + 2) = 2(14)$ b) $\dfrac{3}{5} + \dfrac{1}{5} = \dfrac{3}{5} \cdot \dfrac{1}{5}$

Solution: At each step we use the order of operations to simplify each side. It is important to remember to do each side *separately*.

a)
$$4 \cdot (5+2) = 2(14)$$

Left Side: Add inside the parenthesis. $\qquad 4 \cdot (7) = 28 \qquad$ Right Side: Multiply.

Left Side: Multiply. $\qquad\qquad\qquad 28 = 28$

Since we get the same value on each side, this equation is TRUE.

b) This equation involves fraction addition on the left and fraction multiplication on the right.
$$\frac{3}{5} + \frac{1}{5} = \frac{3}{5} \cdot \frac{1}{5}$$

Left Side: Add in the numerators, keep the denominator the same. $\qquad \dfrac{4}{5} = \dfrac{3}{25} \qquad$ Right Side: Multiply the numerators and denominators.

Since we did not get the same value on each side, this equation is FALSE.

If an equation has a variable, then whether or not the equation is true depends on the value of the variable.

The equation $x + 4 = 9$ is TRUE if $x = 5$ because $5 + 4 = 9$ is TRUE.

The equation $x + 4 = 9$ is FALSE if $x = 3$ because $3 + 4 = 9$ is FALSE.

This brings us to our next definition.

The **solution to an equation** is the value of the variable that makes the equation true.

So $x = 5$ is the solution to the equation $x + 4 = 9$.

The solution to an equation is not always obvious. For example, $x = 3$ is the solution to the equation $2x + 5 = 14 - x$. Why? Because when we substitute 3 in for x we get a true equation:

$$2x + 5 = 14 - x$$
$$2(3) + 5 = 14 - 3$$
$$6 + 5 = 11 \quad \text{True}$$

We call this process "checking a solution".

To check a solution to an equation:
Substitute the given value into the equation then use the order of operations to simplify each side separately to check if the equation is true.

Example 7: Determine whether the given number is the solution to the equation.
a) $x - 11 = 5$, $x = 14$ b) $d + 3 = 3d - 7$, $d = 5$

Solution: In each case we substitute in the variable value given and see if the resulting equation is true.

a) Since we were given $x = 14$ we substitute 14 in for x.

$$x - 11 = 5$$
$$14 - 11 = 5$$

The left hand side does not equal the right hand side, so $x = 14$ is *not* the solution to the equation $x - 11 = 5$.

$$3 = 5$$

b) Substitute 5 in for d.

$$d + 3 = 3d - 7$$
$$5 + 3 = 3(5) - 7$$

Use order of operations to simplify both sides of the equation.

$$8 = 15 - 7$$

The left hand side equals the right hand side, so $d = -5$ is the solution to the equation $5d + 3 = 3d - 7$.

$$8 = 8$$

STOP Exercise Set - Introduction to Equations

Identify whether each is an expression or an equation.

15. $5x + 3$ 16. $2x - 3y = 6$ 17. $a + 10 = 15$ 18. $4a^2 - 5a + 7$

In each case, indicate whether the equation is true or false by simplifying the expressions on each side.

19. $16 \div 2 = 13 - 5$ 20. $10 \div 5 \cdot 2 = 11 - 7$ 21. $2(6 + 5) - 6 = 3^2 \cdot 2$ 22. $\frac{30}{5} = 10 - 4$

Determine whether the given number is the solution to the equation.

23. $x + 6 = 10$; $x = 4$
24. $z - 11 = 11$; $z = 11$
25. $\frac{n}{5} = 2$; $n = 10$
26. $2x + 4 = 12$; $x = 3$

Succeed in Math!

SETTING GOALS is a great way to MOTIVATE yourself.
Maybe you could...
- Set a goal to attend class every day!
- Set a goal to study math everyday!
- Then set a goal to pass your next exam!

TWO IMPORTANT POINTS ABOUT GOAL SETTING:
- As you begin make sure to set goals you KNOW you can succeed with!
- As you set a goal make to also set a reward for yourself if you do succeed!

1.7 Exericse Set - Putting It ALL Together

Vocabulary Check: Fill in each blank with a word from our Vocabulary Checklist to the right. Each word is used exactly once.

Vocabulary Checklist:
variable
expression
evaluate an expression
equation
solution to an equation

27. The way to tell between an expression and an equation is that an _____ always contains an equals sign " = " while an _____ does not.

28. A _____ is a letter or symbol that represents a number.

29. To _____ we substitute a given number in for the variable.

30. The _____ is the variable value that makes the equation true.

Evaluate the following expressions.

31. $b+9$ for $b=5$
32. $k-6$ for $k=12$
33. $\dfrac{x}{4}$ for $x=24$
34. $5 \cdot y$ for $y=3$
35. $3x+15$ for $x=3$
36. $2n+7$ for $n=2$
37. $120-15m$ for $m=8$
38. $375-25m$ for $m=15$
39. d^2+d for $d=9$
40. r^3+5 for $r=3$
41. x^2+3x+4 for $x=2$
42. y^2-y+6 for $y=5$

43. RT for $R=9,\ T=12$
44. bh for $b=6, h=4$
45. $P+T$ for $P=762, T=145$
46. $q \cdot r$ for $q=478, w=1721$
47. $\dfrac{b}{2a}$ for $b=18,\ a=3$
48. $2300t+127,000$ for $t=10$
49. $1,500t+45,000$ for $t=20$
50. x^2+y^2 for $x=7,\ y=3$
51. r^2-x^2 for $r=6,\ x=5$
52. $mx+b$ for $m=2, x=3, b=13$

Fill in the tables.

53.

x	$4x+5$
0	
3	
7	

55.

x	x^2-3x
3	
5	
7	

54.

x	$2x+7$
0	
1	
6	
13	

56.

x	x^2+4x
0	
1	
2	
3	

In each case, indicate whether the equation is true or false by simplifying the expressions on each side.

57. $5+9=2\cdot 6$

58. $16-4=3\cdot 4$

59. $4\cdot 5-9=4\cdot 2+3$

60. $6^2 \div 4 = 3^2$

61. $4(6-3)=2(7-2)$

62. $8-3(1+1)=15\div 5-1$

63. $[7+3]^2 = 5\cdot 5\cdot 2\cdot 2$

64. $2\cdot 3\cdot 7 = 20+2(13-2)$

65. $9+3[10-(3+4)]=5(6-4)+13$

66. $6+3(4+6)=4[15-3(9-7)]$

67. $\dfrac{3}{14}+\dfrac{5}{14}=\dfrac{4}{21}\cdot 3$

68. $\dfrac{2}{5}\div\dfrac{6}{11}=\dfrac{13}{15}-\dfrac{2}{15}$

Determine whether the given number is the solution to the equation.

69. $x+9=15$, $x=6$

70. $6=y-3$, $y=10$

71. $5x=15$, $x=5$

72. $6a=18$, $a=3$

73. $4g+7=14$, $g=2$

74. $9-3k=5$, $k=2$

75. $2=3g-7$, $g=4$

76. $12=3t+5$, $t=2$

77. $x=2x-6$, $x=6$

78. $3x=5x-2$, $x=1$

79. $x+10=3x+2$, $x=5$

80. $5t-3=2t+8$, $t=7$

81. $4(y-5)=2y$, $y=10$

82. $5b=3(b+2)$, $b=3$

83. $7(v-9)=5(v-7)$, $v=14$

84. $4(w+3)=9(w-2)$, $w=5$

85. $2(d-6)=3d-18$, $d=6$

86. $6(t-7)-12=3t-27$, $t=9$

87. $n+\dfrac{3}{8}=\dfrac{1}{2}$, $n=\dfrac{1}{8}$

88. $\dfrac{2}{3}=\dfrac{1}{9}+k$, $k=\dfrac{7}{9}$

89. $\dfrac{3}{4}y=\dfrac{1}{5}$, $y=\dfrac{2}{5}$

90. $\dfrac{3}{10}=\dfrac{1}{2}b$, $b=\dfrac{9}{15}$

91. If an object is dropped from a height of 250 feet, the expression $250-16t^2$ will give its height after t seconds. Evaluate $250-16t^2$ for $t=2$.

92. If a house is purchased for \$185,000 and the value goes up by \$4500 per year, the expression $185000+4500y$ will give the value after y years. Evaluate the expression $185000+4500y$ for $y=6$.

93. Write any two expressions that contain the variable h and the numbers 3 and 7.

94. Write any equation that contains the variable h and the numbers 3 and 7.

95. A computer repair service charges $50 plus $24 per hour. If the total bill for a customer is $194, the solution to the equation $50 + 24x = 194$ will give the number of hours the job took. Suppose a customer guesses that the job took 4 hours. Is she right? That is, is $x = 4$ the solution to the equation $50 + 24x = 194$?

96. A smart phone audio book club charges $35 for the app and $10 per book. If the total charge for a certain customer is $115, then the equation $35 + 10x = 115$ will give the number of books purchased. Were 8 books purchased? That is, is $x = 8$ a solution to the equation $35 + 10x = 115$?

Exercise Set - Chapter 1 Review

97. Find the prime factorization of 35.

98. Add and reduce if possible. $\dfrac{3}{7} + \dfrac{3}{7}$

99. Estimate the product $49(71)$ by rounding to the nearest ten.

100. Graph the numbers 430, 15, 780, and 350 on a number line using a scale of 100.

101. Find the area and perimeter of the parallelogram. [PN: base=8in, sides=5in, height=3in]

 **1.7 QUIZ YOURSELF:**

To make sure you are ready for the EXAM, try these problems without any help. Give yourself about 20 minutes and don't check the answers until you have completely finished.

1. Determine if the following an expression or equation. $7x - 19$
2. Evaluate $mx + b$ for $m = 3, x = 2, b = 5$

3. Evaluate $x^2 + 3x$ for $x = 5$
4. Determine if the equation is true or false. $7 \cdot 3 = 3(4 + 5) - 6$
5. Is $y = 5$ a solution to the equation $3y - 6 = 2y - 1$?

Answers to this Quiz Yourself are on page 639.

Chapter 1 Summary and Review

Section 1. 1 Whole Number Basics

Processes and Important Notes	Examples
Place Value and Naming Number: • Whole Numbers: 0,1,2,3,4,5,6,7,8,9,10,11,12,... • The place in a number that a digit occupies is called its **place value**. • **To read a whole number:** • Begin at the left, read each number in each period followed by the period name.	**Write the following whole numbers in words.** 1. 387,201 2. 5,003,515 **Solution:** 1. three hundred eighty-seven thousand, two hundred one 2. five million, three thousand, five hundred fifteen
Estimating: **To Round a Number to a Given Place Value:** • Look at the place value just to the right of the place value where we want to round: ○ If that digit is 5 or higher round up by adding 1 to the given place value. ○ If that digit is less than 5 round down by leaving the number in the place value. In both cases replace the digits to the right of the rounding place value with zeros.	**Round each number to the place value given.** 1. 7,256; hundreds 2. 55,615; ten-thousands **Solution:** 1. 7,300 2. 60,000
Number Lines: • A number line begins at zero and extends forever to the right. • The **scale** on the number line is the distance between each tic mark.	**Graph the following whole numbers on a number line. Use the scale indicated.** 1. 3, 5, 9, 1, 15; scale of 1 2. 15, 25, 30, 45; scale of 5 **Solution:** 1. 2.
Reading Tables and Graphs: • Tables • Bar Graph • Line Graph	**Example:**

1. Write the number 3,607 in words.
2. Round 149,752 to the nearest thousand.

Graph the following sets of numbers of a number line.
3. {2, 6, 8, 11, 9}
4. {25, 40, 80, 105, 95}, using a scale of 10.

5.   The following chart shows student enrollment for several different courses at a community college. How many students are enrolled in Trigonometry?

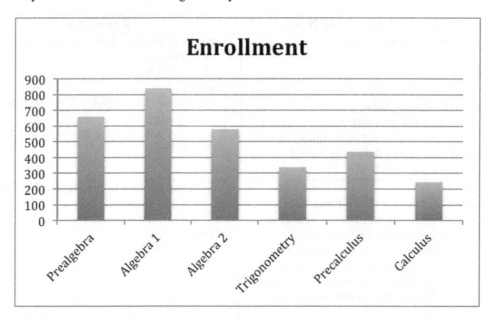

Section 1. 2 Adding and Subtracting Whole Numbers

Processes and Important Notes	Examples
Adding Whole Numbers: The process of finding a sum is called **addition**. Two or more numbers being added are called **addends** and the result is called the **sum** (or **total**). **To add two or more whole numbers:** • Stack the numbers, lining up their place values. • Starting with the ones place, add the digits in each place value. If the result for any place value is more than 9, *carry* the excess digit to the top in the next place value.	**Add.** 1. $903 + 349$ 2. $4,581 + 75$ 3. $\begin{array}{r} 127,924 \\ +92,575 \\ \hline \end{array}$ **Solution:** 1. $\begin{array}{r} 903 \\ +349 \\ \hline 1,252 \end{array}$ 2. $\begin{array}{r} 4,581 \\ +\ 75 \\ \hline 4,656 \end{array}$ 3. $\begin{array}{r} 127,924 \\ +92,575 \\ \hline 220,499 \end{array}$
Geometry: Finding Perimeter: The **perimeter** of an object is the distance around the object.	**Find the perimeter.** 1. A triangle with sides 78cm, 69cm, and 63cm 2. A polygon with sides 17m, 23m, 18m, 9m, 25m, and 31m. **Solution:** 1. $\begin{aligned} P &= 78 + 69 + 63 \\ &= 210cm. \end{aligned}$ 2. $\begin{aligned} P &= 17 + 23 + 18 + 9 + 25 + 31 \\ &= 123m. \end{aligned}$
Subtracting Whole Numbers: **Subtraction** is the process of finding the difference between two numbers. The first number in the difference is called the **minuend,** the second is	**Subtract.** 1. $431 - 99$

called the **subtrahend**. The result of a subtraction is called the **difference**. **To subtract two whole numbers:** • Stack the number, lining up their place values. For subtraction the larger number must always be on top. • Starting with the ones place, find the difference between the digits in each place value. • If the top digit is smaller, borrow from the next highest place value.	2. $\begin{array}{r} 472{,}909 \\ -45{,}011 \\ \hline \end{array}$ **Solution:** 1. $\begin{array}{r} 431 \\ -99 \\ \hline 332 \end{array}$ 2. $\begin{array}{r} 472{,}909 \\ -45{,}011 \\ \hline 427{,}898 \end{array}$
Properties of Addition and Subtraction: With addition, changing the order of addends does not change the sum. This is called **the commutative property of addition**. Three numbers being added can be regrouped with the same result. This is called **the associative property of addition**. If zero is added or subtracted to a number the result is the original number. This property of is called the **identity property of zero**.	**Tell which property is being used in the following example.** 1. $7+(8+15)=7+(15+8)$ 2. $67+0=67$ 3. $(34+75)+15=34+(75+15)$ **Solution:** 1. commutative property 2. identity property of zero 3. associative property

6. $37+89$	11. $5{,}673 + 33{,}901$
7. $45{,}982 - 599$	12. $23{,}798 - 23{,}798$
8. $875 - 109$	13. $918 - 0$
9. $1{,}267 - 867$	14. $6{,}089 + 99{,}999$
10. $0 + 467$	15. $67{,}001 - 13{,}889$

Estimate the result of each operation by rounding to the place value given before doing the operation.
16. $316-81$; hundred   17. $394{,}008+915{,}725$; thousand

18. Kathy has $876 in her checking account and then deposits her paycheck of $1,248. She then pays her bills of $425, $128, $46, and $29. What is her new account balance?
19. Find the perimeter of a rectangle with width 54 m. and length 78 m.
20. Find the perimeter of a triangle with sides that measure 23cm, 30cm, and 26cm.
21. Find the perimeter of the following figure. [PN: quadrilateral with sides 31ft, 24ft, 17ft and 27ft.]

Section 1. 3 Multiplying and Dividing Whole Numbers

Processes and Important Notes	Examples
Multiplying Whole Numbers: • Numbers being multiplied are called **factors**. The result of a multiplication is called the **product**.	**Multiply.** 1. $45\cdot110$ 2. $\begin{array}{r} 3050 \\ \times612 \\ \hline \end{array}$ **Solution:** 1. $\begin{array}{r} 110 \\ \times45 \\ \hline 550 \\ 440 \\ \hline 4{,}950 \end{array}$ 2. $\begin{array}{r} 3050 \\ \times612 \\ \hline 6100 \\ 3050 \\ 18300 \\ \hline 1{,}866{,}600 \end{array}$
Geometry: Finding Area:	**Find the area.**

• The **area** of an object measures how much space it takes up. • **Area of a Rectangle:** Area = length · width • **Area of a Parallelogram:** Area = base · height	1. Find the area of a rectangle with width 8 ft and length 23 ft. 2. Find the area of a parallelogram with base 35m and height 7m. **Solution:** $A = l \cdot w \qquad A = b \cdot h$ 1. $\quad = 8 \cdot 23 \qquad$ 2. $\quad = 35 \cdot 7$ $\qquad = 184\,ft^2 \qquad\qquad = 245\,m^2$
Dividing Whole Numbers: • In a division the number being dividing is called the **dividend**, the number we are dividing by is called the **divisor**, and the result is called **quotient**.	**Divide.** $23\overline{)4583}$ **Solution:** $\quad 199\,R6$ $23\overline{)4583}$ $\quad \underline{23}\downarrow\downarrow$ $\quad 228$ $\quad \underline{207}\downarrow$ $\quad\; 213$ $\quad\; \underline{207}$ $\qquad 6$
Properties of Multiplication and Division: • With multiplication, changing the order of the factors does not change the product. This is called **the commutative property of multiplication**. • Three numbers being multiplied can be regrouped with the same result. This is called **the associative property of multiplication**. • If a number is multiplied or divided by 1 the result is just the original number. This property is called **the identity property of one**. • The product of zero and any number is zero. • Zero divided by any other number is zero. • Dividing by zero is undefined. That is, the answer does not exist.	In each case, indicate which of the following properties is being demonstrated. **The Commutative Property, The Associative Property, One as the Identity, Multiplying by Zero, Dividing Zero, or Dividing by Zero** 1. $(7 \cdot 4) \cdot 5 = 7 \cdot (4 \cdot 5)$ 2. $63 \cdot 877 = 877 \cdot 63$ 3. $59 \cdot 1 = 59$ **Solution:** 1. associative property of multiplication 2. commutative property of multiplication 3. identity property of one **Find the following.** 1. $16 \cdot 0$ 2. $\dfrac{88}{0}$ 3. $0 \div 97$ **Solution:** 1. 0 2. undefined 3. 0

Perform the indicated operation.

22.	$225 \div 25$
23.	$75 \cdot 19$
24.	$0 \div 923$
25.	$44 \div 0$
26.	$105 \div 15$

27.	$34 \cdot 107$
28.	$1206 \div 18$
29.	$957 \cdot 1$
30.	$72 \div 72$
31.	$9102 \div 1$

32.	$1 \cdot 817$
33.	0×607
34.	$2935 \cdot 218$
35.	$1173 \div 23$

Estimate the result of each operation by rounding to the place value given before doing the operation.

36. 23×17 ; ten
37. $10,908 \times 7,803$; ten-thousand

38. $2345 \div 23$; tens
39. $471 \overline{)673,812}$; hundreds

40. Martha bought 38 dresses on sale for $29 that she plans to resale on ebay. How much did she spend on the dresses?
41. A florist has 3,570 red roses. How many bouquets of a dozen roses can she make? How many roses will she have left over?

Section 1. 4 Exponents and Order of Operations

Processes and Important Notes	Examples

Introduction to Exponents:
• An **exponent** is a number written just above the right side of a number to indicate repeated multiplication of that number.
• The **base** of an exponent is the number being multiplied.
• The expression b^n is read "b to the nth power".
Remark: The commutative and associative properties of multiplication are what allow us to rearrange these factors.
	Write the expression in expanded form.
	  1. 3^4 2. $2^3 \cdot 7^4$
	Solution:
	  1. $3^4 = 3 \cdot 3 \cdot 3 \cdot 3$
	  2. $2^3 \cdot 7^4 = 2 \cdot 2 \cdot 2 \cdot 7 \cdot 7 \cdot 7 \cdot 7$
	
	Rewrite each multiplication in exponent form.
	  $2 \cdot 2 \cdot 3 \cdot 3 \cdot 5 \cdot 5 \cdot 5$
	Solution:
	  $2 \cdot 2 \cdot 3 \cdot 3 \cdot 5 \cdot 5 \cdot 5 = 2^2 \cdot 3^2 \cdot 5^3$

Introduction to The Order of Operations:
The Order of Operations
• Do operations inside **grouping symbols** like parentheses first.
• Perform any **exponents** and **square roots** in the expression.
• Do **multiplication** and **division** moving left to right.
• Do **addition** and **subtraction** from left to right.
	Find the following.
	  1. $45 \div 9 \cdot 5 + 1$
	  2. $3^2 + 17 \cdot (10 - 7)$
	
	Solution:
	1. $\begin{aligned}&\underline{45 \div 9} \cdot 5 + 1\\ =&\underline{5 \cdot 5} + 1\\ =&\underline{25 + 1}\\ =&26\end{aligned}$ 2. $\begin{aligned}&3^2 + 17 \cdot \underline{(10 - 7)}\\ =&\underline{3^2} + 17 \cdot 3\\ =&9 + \underline{17 \cdot 3}\\ =&\underline{9 + 51}\\ =&60\end{aligned}$

More About Grouping Symbols:
• While parentheses are the most common grouping symbols, all of the following symbols can be used as grouping symbols.
Parentheses ( )   Brackets [ ]
 	
Braces { }   Division Bar ——
	Find the following.
	  1. $15 + \{5 + 2[3(16 - 12) + 17]\}$
	  2. $\dfrac{132 \div 11 \cdot 3 \div 3^2}{4^2 - 2 \cdot 6}$
	Solution:
	1. $15 + \{5 + 2[3(16 - 12) + 17]\}$ 2.
	$\dfrac{132 \div 11 \cdot 3 \div 3^2}{4^2 - 2 \cdot 6}$

$$= 15 + \left\{ 5 + 2 \left[3(4) + 17 \right] \right\}$$

$$= 15 + \left\{ 5 + 2 \left[12 + 17 \right] \right\}$$

$$= 15 + \left\{ 5 + 2 \left[29 \right] \right\}$$

$$= 15 + \left\{ 5 + 58 \right\}$$

$$= 15 + \left\{ 63 \right\}$$

$$= 78$$

$$= \frac{132 \div 11 \cdot 3 \div 9}{16 - 2 \cdot 6}$$

$$= \frac{12 \cdot 3 \div 9}{16 - 12}$$

$$= \frac{36 \div 9}{4}$$

$$= \frac{4}{4}$$

$$= 1$$

Find the following.

42. 3^3

43. 2^5

44. 5^3

45. 9^2

46. $3 \cdot 18 \div 6$

47. $8^2 - 3(5 - 2)$

48. $8 \cdot 5 + 2^3$

49. $7 \cdot 6 - 42$

50. $56 - 7 \cdot 8$

51. $11 \cdot 12 + 3^2 - 15$

52. $81 \div 9 + 3(8 - 3)$

53. $5^2 + 49 \div 7 - 13$

54. $7(29 - 24) + 1^4$

55. $2^3 + 4(18 - 9) \div 6$

56. $\left\{ 17 - 5 \left[25 - 3(17 - 9) \right] \right\} + 7$

57. $14 + 5 \left\{ 26 - 2 \left[18 \div 3 \cdot 2 + 1 \right] + 3 \right\}$

Section 1. 5 Factoring

Processes and Important Notes	Examples
Tests For Divisibility: • A number is **divisible** by another if it can be divided without a remainder.	**Use the divisibility tests to determine if the number is divisible by 2, 3, 4, 5, 6, 8, 9,or/and 10.** 7,812

Tests for Divisibility

Divisible by:	If...
2	...it is an even number.
3	...the sum of the digits is divisible by 3.
4	...the last 2 digits are divisible by 4.
5	...the last digit is 0 or 5.
6	...the number is divisible by both 2 and 3.
8	...the last three digits are divisible by 8.
9	...the sum of the digits is

Solution:
Divisible by:
2 : since it ends in 2
3: since the digits $7 + 8 + 1 + 2 = 18$ are divisible by 3
4: since 12(last 2 digits) is divisible by 4
5: NO
6: since divisible by 2 and 3
8: NO
9: since digits sum, 18 is divisible by 9
10: NO

	divisible by 9.
10	...the number ends in 0
12	...the number is divisible by both 3 *and* 4

Factorization Of a Number: • To **factor** a number means to write it as the product of two or more numbers. • The numbers in a product are called **factors**. • A factored form is called a **factorization**.	**Show two factorizations for 56.** **Solution:** $56 = 7 \cdot 8$ $56 = 2 \cdot 28$

Prime and Composite Numbers:
• A **composite number** is a number that can be factored into the product of two smaller numbers.
• A **prime number** is a number that can only be factored as the product of itself and 1.
• The numbers 0 and 1 are considered neither prime nor composite.
• To check if a number is composite- test the number using divisibility tests.
	Identify each number as prime or composite. If it is composite, show one factorization for the number that shows it is composite.
	  1. 34 2. 71 3. 891
	
	Solution:
	  1. Composite: $2 \cdot 17$
	  2. Prime
	  3. Composite: $3 \cdot 297$

Prime Factorizations: • The **prime factorization** of a number is the factorization that involves only prime numbers.	**Find the prime factorization of the number: 92** **Solution:** $92 = 2 \cdot 46$ $ = 2 \cdot 2 \cdot 23$ $92 = 2^2 \cdot 23$

Multiples:
The **multiples** of a number are the values we get from multiplying the number by the natural (counting) numbers.
	Find the following.
	  1. List the first 5 multiples for 3.
	  2. Is $2 \cdot 3 \cdot 7 \cdot 11$ a multiple of 77?
	Solution:
	  1. $3, 6, 9, 12, 15$
	  2. Yes, since $2 \cdot 3 \cdot 7 \cdot 11 = (2 \cdot 3) \cdot 77$.

Use the divisibility tests to determine if each number is divisible by 2, 3, 4, 5, 6, 8, 9 or 10.
  58. 128   59. 5,160   60. 72,313   61. 98,145

Find the prime factorization for the following whole numbers.
  62. 27   63. 56   64. 42   65. 72

  66. Find a factorization of 15 so that the sum of the factors is 8.
  67. Find a factorization of 36 so that the sum of the factors is 13.
  68. Find a factorization of 27 so that the sum of the factors is 28.
  69. Find a factorization of 99 so that the sum of the factors is 20.
  70. What is the 12th multiple of 15?
  71. What is the 55th multiple of 37?
  72. Is $2 \cdot 2 \cdot 2 \cdot 3 \cdot 5 \cdot 5 \cdot 11$ a multiple of 66?
  73. Is $2 \cdot 5 \cdot 7 \cdot 7 \cdot 23$ a multiple of 70?

Section 1. 6 Review of Basic Fractions

Processes and Important Notes	Examples
Understanding Fractions: • The bottom number in a fraction is called the **denominator**. It represents how many parts make a whole. • The top number in a fraction is called the **numerator**. It represents how many parts make up the fraction.	**Identify the numerator and denominator in the fraction and draw a picture to represent the fraction:** $\dfrac{3}{5}$ Solution: Numerator: 3 Denominator: 5 [PN: box with 5 parts, 3 shaded]
Building and Simplifying Fractions: • **The Fundamental Principle of Fractions:** $\dfrac{a \cdot c}{b \cdot c} = \dfrac{a}{b}$ and $\dfrac{a \div c}{b \div c} = \dfrac{a}{b}$ • Two or more fractions are called **equivalent fractions** if they represent the same amount. That is, if they reduce to the same fraction. • Removing a common from the numerator and denominator of a fraction is called **reducing** a fraction. • A fraction in **lowest terms** has no common factors in the numerator and denominator. **To reduce a fraction to lowest terms:** 1. Prime factor the numerator and denominator. 2. Remove any common factors. 3. Multiply the remaining factors in the numerator and denominator.	**Rewrite given fraction with new denominator.** $\dfrac{3}{7}$ with a denominator of 28. Solution: $\dfrac{3}{7} \cdot \dfrac{4}{4} = \dfrac{12}{28}$ **Reduce each fraction to lowest terms.** 1. $\dfrac{6}{9}$ 2. $\dfrac{20}{48}$ Solution: 1. $\dfrac{6}{9} = \dfrac{2 \cdot 3}{3 \cdot 3} = \dfrac{2}{3}$ 2. $\dfrac{20}{48} = \dfrac{2 \cdot 2 \cdot 5}{2 \cdot 2 \cdot 2 \cdot 2 \cdot 3} = \dfrac{5}{12}$
Multiplying and Dividing Fractions: • The fractions $\dfrac{a}{b}$ and $\dfrac{b}{a}$ are called **reciprocals**.	**Multiply or divide and reduce the final answer to lowest terms, if possible.** 1. $\dfrac{4}{9} \cdot \dfrac{5}{8}$ 2. $\dfrac{6}{11} \div \dfrac{9}{10}$ Solution: 1. $\dfrac{4}{9} \cdot \dfrac{5}{8} = \dfrac{\cancel{4}}{9} \cdot \dfrac{5}{2 \cdot \cancel{4}} = \dfrac{5}{18}$ 2. $\dfrac{6}{11} \div \dfrac{9}{10} = \dfrac{6}{11} \cdot \dfrac{10}{9} = \dfrac{2 \cdot \cancel{3}}{11} \cdot \dfrac{10}{3 \cdot \cancel{3}} = \dfrac{20}{33}$
Adding and Subtracting Fractions: • **To add or subtract fractions with like denominators, simply add or subtract the numerator and keep the denominator the same.** • **Reduce the fraction if possible, ALWAYS!**	**Add or subtract.** 1. $\dfrac{9}{19} + \dfrac{5}{19}$ 2. $\dfrac{11}{20} - \dfrac{3}{20}$ Solution: 1. $\dfrac{9}{19} + \dfrac{5}{19} = \dfrac{14}{19}$ 2. $\dfrac{11}{20} - \dfrac{3}{20} = \dfrac{8}{20} = \dfrac{2 \cdot \cancel{4}}{\cancel{4} \cdot 5} = \dfrac{2}{5}$

Draw a picture of the following fraction and label the numerator and denominator.

74. $\dfrac{1}{3}$ 75. $\dfrac{5}{8}$ 76. $\dfrac{10}{13}$ 77. $\dfrac{5}{12}$

Simplify the fraction.

78. $\dfrac{12}{20}$ 79. $\dfrac{77}{99}$ 80. $\dfrac{45}{81}$ 81. $\dfrac{10}{130}$

Perform the indicated operation.

82. $\dfrac{2}{7} \cdot \dfrac{3}{10}$ 85. $\dfrac{1}{7} \cdot \dfrac{4}{9}$ 88. $\dfrac{4}{9} \cdot \dfrac{3}{7}$ 91. $\dfrac{4}{15} \cdot \dfrac{5}{8}$

83. $\dfrac{6}{11} + \dfrac{2}{11}$ 86. $\dfrac{15}{26} - \dfrac{2}{26}$ 89. $\dfrac{1}{7} \div \dfrac{2}{49}$

84. $\dfrac{15}{23} - \dfrac{8}{23}$ 87. $\dfrac{15}{38} + \dfrac{4}{38}$ 90. $\dfrac{2}{11} \div \dfrac{3}{5}$

Section 1.7 Variable, Expressions and Equations

Processes and Important Notes	Examples
Introduction to Variables: • A **variable** is a letter that represents a number that is either unknown or that changes.	For each scenario, pick a variable to represent the unknown or changing value. The number of students in a class. **Solution:** Let **s** bet the number of students.
Introduction to Expressions: • An **expression** is a series of operations, numbers, and/or variables. • To **evaluate an expression** means to substitute a value for the variable(s) and perform the operations involved to get a number.	Evaluate each expression for the variable value(s) given. $b^2 - 4ac$; $a = 1, b = 6, c = 2$ **Solution:** $b^2 - 4ac = (6)^2 - 4(1)(2)$ $\qquad = 36 - 4(1)(2)$ $\qquad = 36 - 8$ $\qquad = 28$
Introduction to Equations: • An **equation** is a statement that two expressions are equal. • The **solution to an equation** is the value of the variable that makes the equation true. • **To check a solution to an equation:** • Substitute that number into the equation then use the order of operations to simplify each side to see if the equation is true.	Determine whether the given number is the solution to the equation. $3x + 8 = 2(x - 3);\ x = 4$ **Solution:** Replace x with 4. $3(4) + 8 = 2((4) - 3)$ $12 + 8 = 2(1)$ $20 = 2$ Since 20 is not 2, $x = 4$ is NOT a solution.

Label the following as an expression or an equation.

92. $6x - 45 = 1$ 94. $2x + 16 = 33$

93. $78 + y$ 95. $17 = 3(x - 1)$

Evaluate the following expressions.

96. $x + 15;\ x = 34$ 98. $x^2 + 3x;\ x = 4$

97. $3x - 14;\ x = 8$

99. $y^2 + 15$; $y = 5$

100. $mx + b$; $b = 3, m = 6, x = 8$

101. $b^2 - 4ac$; $a = 2, b = 5, c = 1$

Determine whether the given number is the solution to the equation.

102. $x + 23 = 45$; $x = 22$

103. $x - 9 = 33$; $x = 24$

104. $2x + 6 = 18$; $x = 5$

105. $3x - 1 = 8$; $x = 3$

Chapter 1 Test Yourself

You should give yourself about 90 minutes to complete these problems. DO NOT use notes, your book or any outside source of help, ONLY YOURSELF. Put question marks by the problems you are unsure about, but TRY all of the problems. Once your time is up, check your answers on page #.

1. Write the number in words: It is 5,680 miles from San Diego, Ca to Paris, France.
2. Use the divisibility tests: Is 125,680 divisible by 2, 3, 4, 5, 6, 8, 9, or 10?
3. Find the prime factorization of 98.
4. Is 201 prime or composite?
5. Find the 17th multiple of 11.
6. Draw a number line with a scale of 5 and graph the numbers 15, 20, 5, 75, 60.
7. Which property is being used: $(18 + 21) + 67 = (21 + 18) + 67$

Perform the indicated operations.

8. $238 - 176$
9. $(214)(67)$
10. $\dfrac{5}{18} + \dfrac{7}{18}$

11. $\dfrac{36}{77} \div \dfrac{16}{33}$
12. $3 \cdot 24 + 4 \cdot 6 - 13$
13. $72 \div 4 \cdot 3^2$
14. $\left[5 + 7(18 - 2^3)\right] + 17 \cdot 2$

15. **Evaluate:** $mx + b$; $m = 4, x = 5, b = 7$

16. **Evaluate:** πr^2 ; $\pi = \dfrac{22}{7}, r = 14$

Determine whether the given number is the solution to the equation.

17. $x + 15 = 38$; $x = 22$

18. $x \cdot 9 = 72$; $x = 8$

Estimate the answer by rounding to the nearest tens.

19. Josie is moving into her first apartment and needs to buy some furniture. She finds a table and chairs set for $78, a sofa for $98, a coffee table for $24, a bed for $129 and a dresser for $59. How much did she spend on furnishing her first apartment?

20. Scott and Jane are painting their living room that measures 11ft by 18ft and has 10 feet ceilings. How many square feet of paint do they need to buy?

Solve.

21. Alfonso and Jorge are making a cross-country road trip which is a total of 2,625 miles. They have already driven 1,371 miles of the trip. How many more miles do they still need to travel?

22. A local community college has a total of 13 classrooms, which have 42 desks in each classroom. How many students can the school accommodate at any given time?

23. Miranda took a total of 8 tests in her biology class this semester. She scored a 78 on 2 exams, 89, 93, 74 on three exams, and an 80. Find the average of her exam grades.

24. Bridgett is putting up a fence in her rectangular backyard that is 50 feet long by 48 feet wide. How many feet of fence will she need if her house will take up 30 feet on one side?

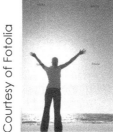

Chapter 2 : Integers

This Chapter is all about Positives and Negatives.

What's Inside?!

But WHY?

A negative times a negative is a positive

Courtesy of Fotolia

Courtesy of Fotolia

Succeed in Math!
Get tips on how to stay motivated for math class and college!

$-6 + 8 = 2$

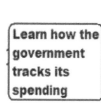

Learn how the government tracks its spending

Year	Spending above or below budget (in billions)
1996	-107
1998	126
2000	236
2002	-158
2004	+413
2006	-260

www.sbc.gov

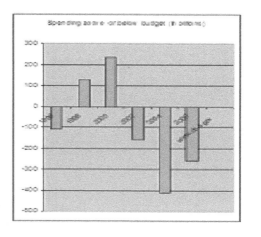

Spending above or below budget (in billions)

2.1 Introduction To Integers

Topics:
- Understanding Integers
- Comparing Integers
- Opposites
- Absolute Value

Are You Ready?!
To see if you are ready to understand this section, do the following short quiz.
1. What are 'whole numbers'?
2. Use a scale of 10 on a number line to graph the following numbers: 15, 70, 43
3. Fill the blank in with < or > to make the statement true: 15__23

Answers to Are You Ready?

(1) 0,1,2,3,4,...   *(2)*    *(3)* $15 < 23$

Understanding Integers

In Chapter 1 we looked at *whole numbers*: 0,1,2,3,4,5,6,.... . Negative numbers are also a part of exploring and applying math.

A **negative number** is a number that is less than zero.

Negative numbers are indicated by a dash in the front. For example, -7 is read "negative seven". Negative numbers are common in real-world applications:

Temperatures above freezing are positive and temperatures below freezing are negative.

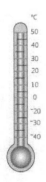

In business a profit or deposit is represented by a positive number and a loss or withdrawal is represented by a negative number.

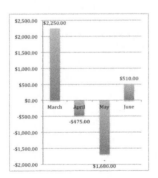

In football, a gain is represented by a positive number and a loss is represented by a negative number.

1st Down	-8 yards
2nd Down	3 yards
3rd Down	13 yards
4th Down	-2 yards

Example 1: Where in the World?
What integer should be used to represent the information given?
a) In January, the average temperature in northern Alaska is about 30 degrees below freezing.
b) The elevation of Mount Everest is 29,035 feet above sea level.
c) Amanda's bank account balance is overdrawn by $150.

Solution:
a) Since the temperature is below freezing, we would use -30 degrees to represent it.
b) Since the elevation is above sea level, we use the integer 29,035 feet to represent it.
c) An overdrawn account means the balance is below zero, so we would use the integer $-\$150$ to represent the balance.

The whole numbers along with their corresponding negatives are referred to as the *integers*.

The **integers** are whole numbers and their corresponding negatives
(or *opposites*). The integers can be listed as follows:
$...,-5,-4-3,-2,-1,0,1,2,3,4,5,...$

In Chapter 1 we used number lines to visualize whole numbers. Here is a number line that includes negative numbers along with positive numbers.

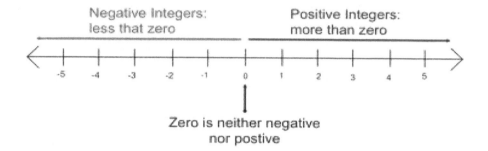

Recall that to graph a number, we put a point at its location on the number line.

Example 2: Graph the following list of numbers: -3,5,0,-4,3

Solution: We put a bold point at the location of each number in the list.

We have also worked with scaling a number line to include large numbers. Now we can use the same technique to include negative values.

Example 3: Where in the World?

The average yearly temperature for several different planets is given in the table below. Plot the temperatures on a number line. Use the first letter of the planet to label the point.   Use a scale of 100. That is, let each tic mark represent 100 degrees.

Planets	Average Temp (degrees)
Mercury	157
Uranus	-230
Earth	28
Venus	455
Jupiter	-170

Solution: Each tic mark will represents 100 degrees and we approximate where each value should be graphed. For reference we have included the first letter of the planet above its graphed temperature.

```
     U   J           E     M              V
 |--|--●--●--|--|--●--|--●--|--|--|--|--●--|--|
   -300  -200  -100    0   100  200  300  400  500
```

Being able to visualize information like this is important for seeing differences and patterns. Notice how much hotter Venus is than the other planets!

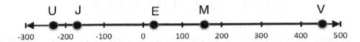

STOP Exercise Set - Understanding Integers

Use a positive or negative number to represent the information given.
1. An elevation of 25 feet *below* sea level.
2. A temperature of 52 degrees *above* freezing.
3. The Baltimore Ravens *gain* 14 yards on a pass play.
4. The Dallas Cowboys *lose* 8 yards from a sack.

Graph each list of numbers given on a number line.
5. -2, 5, 1
6. -3, 1, 7, -4
7. -53, 7, -13, 45, -30 (Use a scale of 10 units)
8. 150, -73, 0, 30, -190 (Use a scale of 25 units)

9. The following table shows some typical high and low temperatures in Moscow, Russia. Use the first letter of each month to label the temperature. (Hint: Use a scale of 5.)

Month	Average Temp (degrees Celsius)
February	-10
March	-4
July	19
August	17

10. The following table shows some typical average temperatures in Berlin, Germany. Use the first letter of each month to label the temperature. (Hint: Use a scale of 5.)

Month	Average Temp (degrees Celsius)
January	-13
February	3
May	15
July	18

Comparing Integers

Which is a greater profit: a profit of −$15 or a profit of $7? A profit of $7 is more than a profit of −$15 since −$15 would actually represent a loss! We use inequality symbols to compare integers.

The symbol < means 'is less than'.

The symbol > means 'is greater than'.

The symbol ≤ means 'is less than or equal to'.

The symbol ≥ means 'is greater than or equal to'.

Notice that on a number line, numbers to the right are greater than numbers to the left.

The number 7 is to the right of -10 so 7 is greater than -10. Using a number line (or a simple idea like profit and loss) makes sense out of statements that might otherwise seem confusing.

Example 4:
Fill in each blank with < or > to make the statement true using a number line as a reference.

a) −17 ___ 6   b) −23 ___ −15   c) 15 ___ −3

Solution:
a) −17 < 6 since -17 is to the left of 6 on a number line.
b) −23 < −15 since -23 is to the left of -15 on a number line.
c) 15 > −3 since 15 is to the right of -3 on a number line.

In Section 1.7, we introduced evaluating algebraic expression. We can now expand that idea to include ordering expressions with variables when given the variable value.

Example 5: Given $x = -8$, $y = -15$, and $z = 8$ fill the blank with a $<$ or $>$ to make each statement true.

a) $z \_\_\_ x$ b) $y \_\_\_ x$

Solution: We can just substitute in our variable values to make these statements simpler.

a) $z \_\_\_ x$ means $8 \_\_\_ -8$, since $8 > -8$, then $z > x$.

b) $y \_\_\_ x$ means $-15 \_\_\_ -8$, since $-15 < -8$, then $y < x$.

Example 6: Where in the World?
The following table gives record temperatures in degrees Fahrenheit for Fairbanks, Alaska by month.

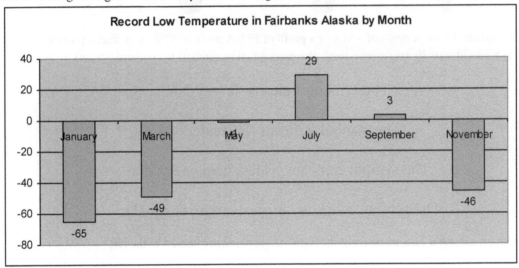

Answer the following questions.
a) What is the record temperature for the month of September?
b) Which month shown has had the highest record temperature?
c) Which month shown has had the lowest record temperature?
d) Use an inequality symbol to compare the record temperatures for the months of March and November.

Solution:
a) The month of September has a record temperature of 3 degrees.
b) The month with the highest record temperature is July at 29 degrees.
c) The month with the lowest record temperature would be the month that goes the furthest below zero. This would be January with a record temperature of -65 degrees.
d) The record for March is -49 while the record for November is -46. Using an inequality symbol to compare them gives $-46 > -49$. Note that -46 is actually the higher temperature and is therefore greater. Meaning November temperature $>$ March temperature.

STOP Exercise Set - Comparing Integers

For each statement, fill in an appropriate inequality symbol.

11. 17 ___ 23

12. 5 ___ − 5

13. −12 ___ 13

14. 18 ___ − 67

15. −7 ___ 3

16. −35 ___ − 32

17. −16 ___ − 13

18. −14 ___ 13

Given $a = 6$, $b = -20$, **and** $c = -18$, **fill in each blank with < or > to make the statement true.**

19. a ___ c

20. b ___ a

The following chart shows the low temperature over a typical week in Asheville, North Carolina.

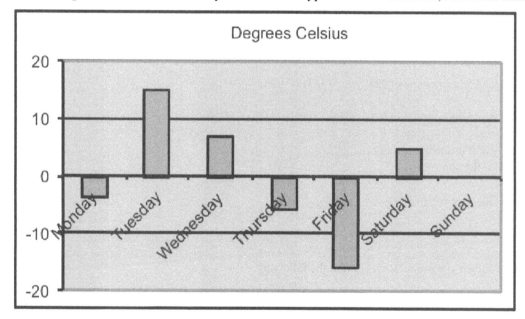

21. Which day had the lowest temperature?

22. Which day had the highest temperature?

23. Use an inequality to compare the low temperatures for Monday and Thursday.

24. Use an inequality to compare the low temperatures for Thursday and Sunday.

Opposites

Every number has an opposite…

- The numbers 5 and -5 are opposites.
- The numbers -347 and 347 are opposites.
- The numbers 4,100,000 and -4,100,000 are opposites.
- The number 0 is its own opposite.

We use a number line to define exactly what opposite means:

Opposite numbers are the same distance from zero on a number line.

So, for example, 5 and -5 are opposites because they are both 5 units away from zero.

5 and -5 are both five units away from zero on a number line.

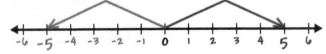

Working with opposites means having to interpret what the dash " – " means in different situations. For example, when a dash is in front of parentheses, it means to take the opposite of the number inside. The expression $-(7)$ means 'take the opposite of seven", so we have $-(7) = -7$. The expression $-(-13)$ means "take the opposite of -13", so we have $-(-13) = 13$.

Example 7: Simplify.

a) $-(923)$ b) $-(-3)$ c) $-\left[-(-8)\right]$

Solution:

a) $-(923)$ is read "the opposite of 923", so $-(923) = -923$.

b) $-(-3)$ is read "the opposite of -3", so $-(-3) = 3$

c) The expression inside the braces $-\left[-(-8)\right]$
$-(-8)$ means "the opposite of -8",
so $-(-8) = 8$.
This means "the opposite of 8". $= -[8]$
                                          $= -8$

Example 8: Given $a = 5$ and $b = -11$, find the following.

a) $-a$ b) $-b$ c) $-(-b)$

Solution: We substitute a with 5 and b with -11. To avoid confusion we put the substituted value in parentheses.

a) $-a = -(5) = -5$
b) $-b = -(-11) = 11$
c) $-(-b) = -(-(-11)) = -11$

STOP Exercise Set - Opposites

Give the opposite of each number.

25. 9

26. 4

27. −13

28. −8

Simplify.

29. −(4)

30. −(7)

31. −(−17)

32. −(−5)

33. −[−(−1)]

34. −[−(−3)]

Given that $u = 3$ **and** $v = -14$, **find the following.**

35. −u

36. −v

37. −(−v)

38. −(−u)

Absolute Value

Another concept related to integers and number lines is *absolute value*.

The **absolute value** of a number is the distance on a number line between that number and zero.

The absolute value of the number 4 is 4 since it is four units away from zero on a number line. The absolute value of −4 is also 4 because it is also four units away from zero. Remember, distance is always positive.

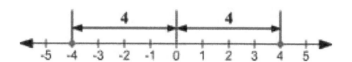

The symbol used to represent the absolute value of a number is $|\ |$. So $|-9|$ is read "the absolute value of negative nine" and $|-9| = 9$. On the other hand, the expression $-|9|$ means "the opposite of the absolute value of 9", so $-|9| = -9$.

Example 9: Simplify each expression.

a) $|45|$ b) $|-673|$ c) $-|3|$ d) $-|-13|$

Solution:

a) $|45| = 45$ since the number 45 is 45 units away from 0.

b) $|-673| = 673$ since the number -673 is 673 units away from 0.

c) $-|3|$ is read "the opposite of the absolute value of 3", so $-|3| = -3$.

d) $-|-13|$ is read "the opposite of the absolute value of negative 13", so $-|-13| = -(13) = -13$.

In regards to the order of operations the absolute value bars are considered grouping symbols.

An operation inside an absolute value should be done before taking the absolute value.

$$|7+5| = |12| = 12$$

An operation between absolute values should be done after the absolute value.

$$|-8| + |5| = 8 + 5 = 13$$

Example 10: Simplify each expression.

a) $|5+7|$ b) $|-3| + |-5|$ c) $\dfrac{|16|}{|-4|}$

Solution:

a) Do addition then find the absolute value since the operation is inside the absolute value bars.

$$|5+7| = |12| = 12$$

b) Take the absolute values then add since the addition is outside the absolute value bars.

$$|-3| + |-5| = 3 + 5 = 8$$

c) Take the absolute values then divide.

$$\frac{|16|}{|-4|} = \frac{16}{4} = 4$$

There is more to come on absolute value as grouping symbols when we take another look at the order of operations in Section 2.5.

Simplify.

39. $|13|$

40. $|-25|$

41. $-|-14|$

42. $-|8|$

43. $-(-|6|)$

44. $-(-|-23|)$

Perform the following operation.

45. $|7| \cdot |-4|$

46. $|-5| \cdot |9|$

47. $|-7| + |9|$

48. $|15 + 73|$

49. $|7 + 9|$

50. $\dfrac{|36|}{|-9|}$

2.1 Exercise Set - Putting it ALL Together

Use the terms from the Vocabulary Checklist on the right to fill the correct vocabulary word into its definition.

Vocabulary Checklist:
negative number
integer
opposite
absolute value

51. The word _____ refers to any positive or negative number that does not involve a decimal or fraction.

52. _____ numbers are the same distance from zero on a number line.

53. The _____ of a number is the distance on a number line between that number and zero.

54. A _____ is a number less than zero, indicated by a dash, like −9 .

Use a positive or negative number to represent the information given.
55.   Death Valley California is 282 feet below sea level.
56.   A drum track is 4 decibels below normal volume.
57.   A lead guitar amplifier is 10 decibels above normal volume.
58.   At 90 degrees (F) below zero your breath will freeze in midair and fall to the ground.

The following chart gives the monthly profit for a startup small business.

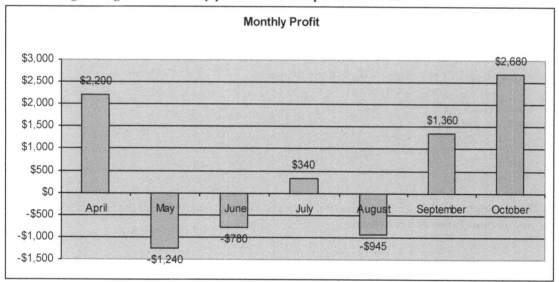

59. What was the profit for the month of September?
60. What was the profit for the month of August?
61. In which months did the small business loss money?
62. In which month did the small business have the highest profit? What was the highest profit?
63. Use an inequality symbol to compare the profits for the months of June and August.
64. Use an inequality symbol to compare the profits for the months of May and July.

Translate each statement to an expression then simplify.
65. the opposite of seventeen
66. the opposite of eighty
67. the opposite of negative twelve
68. the opposite of negative twenty-five

69. the absolute value of fifteen
70. the absolute value of negative seven
71. the opposite of the absolute value of thirty-two
72. the opposite of the absolute value of negative five

Simplify:

73. $-(-9)$

74. $-|-45|$

75. $|-38|$

76. $-[-(-8)]$

77. $-(6)$

78. $-|81|$

79. $-(-|96|)$

80. $-(-|-45|)$

Compare using inequality symbols: <, >, or =

81. $-(-24)\_\_|-24|$

82. $-(-45)\_\_-17$

83. $18\_\_-54$

84. $0\_\_-5$

85. $15\_\_0$

86. $-|-67|\_\_|67|$

87. $|-15|\_\_|9|$

88. $-24\_\_24$

89. $-34\_\_-23$

90. $-|89|\_\_|-16|$

91. $|-8|\_\_-(-9)$

Always True/ Never True/Sometimes True

92.   A positive number is greater than a negative number.
93.   The absolute value of a negative number is a positive number.
94.   A positive number is greater than the absolute value of a negative number.
95.   The absolute value of a positive number is a negative number.
96.   The opposite of a negative number is a positive number.

Given that $a=-7$, $b=4$, and $c=0$, find the following.

97. $|a|$
98. $-b$
99. $|b+c|$
100. $|a|+|b|$
101. $-(-c)$
102. $-(-a)$

Looking Ahead: The following exercises will help you connect with material in the next section. Use the number line below as a reference.

103.   On a number line, what integer is 5 units to the left of 2?
104.   On a number line, what integer is 9 units to the left of 6?
105.   On a number line, what integer is 6 units to the right of -3?
106.   On a number line, what integer is 8 units to the right of 0?
107.   On a number line, what integer is 2 units to the left of -7?
108.   On a number line, what integer is 7 units to the right of -3?

Exercise Set - Cumulative Review

109.   Evaluate $5x + 3$ for $x = 7$
110.   Reduce. $\dfrac{15}{25}$
111.   Write "ten thousand four hundred seven" as a whole number.
112.   Multiply. $5000(12)$
113.   Find the prime factorization of 700.

 # 2.1 QUIZ YOURSELF:

To make sure you are ready for the EXAM, try these problems without any help. Give yourself about 20 minutes and don't check the answers until you have completely finished.

1.   Graph the following numbers on a number line: $-3, 5, 1, -1, 2$
2.   Simplify. $-(-46)$
3.   Simplify. $-|-56|$
4.   Compare. -67 ___ -56
5.   Compare. $|-13|$ ___ $-(-14)$
6.   Translate and simplify: the opposite of negative fifteen
7.   Use an integer to represent the scenario: Scuba diving 105 feet below sea level off the coast of the Galapagos Islands.
8.   Given $x = -3, y = -5$, find $|x| + |x + y|$
9.   **True/False.** The opposite of the absolute value of a negative number is positive.

Answers to this Quiz Yourself are on page 649.

Succeed in Math!

Education Rules!!
A college degree equips you to help deal with big time economic, social, and environmental issues facing our world...oh...and...ah...

you'll also make about $23,000 a year more...

Are YOU up for the challenge?!

Courtesy of Fotolia

Succeed in Math!   Motivation

Motivation is what drives you to stay in math class and stay college. Motivation is what makes you study. Motivation is the WHY behind all your habits, good and bad.

College takes a lot of work. You have to spend hours every week in class learning and even more hours at home processing what you have learned. What motivates a person to spend so much time and money on higher education?

- **Learning** - Some students love to learn.
- **Career** – Some students are in college because they know exactly what they want to do for their lifelong career and they know that
- **Opportunity** – Some students are not exactly sure what they want to do when they leave college but know that whatever they decide to do they will have much more opportunity if they have a college degree.
- **Money** – Some students are in college because they know that whatever they decide to they will make more money doing it if they have a college degree. There is nothing wrong with this.

Let's take some time to figure what motivates YOU! And in case you are not very motivated to pass your college math class, we'll look at ideas and information that might help you get motivated.

Exercise #1: What Do YOU Want?
What motivates you to be in college? What do you want out of college? To learn? To be a well rounded person? Money? A career? Anything else? Fill in the space below with your answer. Don't just give a one word answers. Think and reflect.

_____

_____

_____

Exercise #2: The Bottom Line
Using your answers from Exercise #1, summarize your motivation and drive to succeed in college into one line. It can be as short as you want.

_____

Forcing yourself to think about what truly motivates you can be a powerful exercise. It can help you see that college is what you really want and/or need.

Ways to get motivated for college:
- Make friends with other people in your class who want to succeed.
- Make it a point to think about your future.
- Meet your professor and let them know what your goals are for the class.
- Visit a college counselor.

2.2 Adding Integers

Topics:

- Using A Number Line To Add
- Adding Integers With Like Signs
- Adding Integers With Different Signs
- Using Both Techniques

Are You Ready?!

To see if you are ready to understand this section, do the following short quiz.

1) What are integers?
2) Plot the following integers on a number line: 7, -3, 0, -5, 3
3) Add. $563 + 640$
4) Subtract. $67 - 39$

Answers to Are You Ready?

(1) ...,−4,−3,−2,−1,−,,1,2,3,4,...   *(2)* 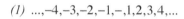   *(3) 1203*   *(4) 28*

Using A Number Line To Add

In football, if a team *gains* 7 yards on one play but then *losses* 9 yards on the next play, the overall result is a *loss* of 2 yards. This illustrates how positives and negatives are added. This is reflected in the following operation…

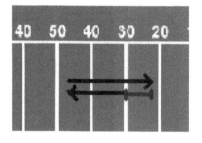

$$\underbrace{7}_{\substack{7 \text{ yard} \\ \text{gain}}} + \underbrace{(-9)}_{\substack{9 \text{ yard} \\ \text{loss}}} = \underbrace{-2}_{\substack{2 \text{ yard} \\ \text{loss}}}$$

The operation $7 + (-9) = -2$ shows that adding positives and negatives isn't always done by straight-forward addition. Fortunately there is a way to make the process easy: use a number line.

To illustrate using a number line, consider $2 + 7$.

Starting at 2 and moving 7 to the *right* gives the answer 9.

$$2 + 7 = 9$$

Now consider the integer sum $2+(-7)$.

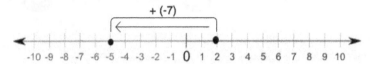

Starting at 2 and moving 7 to the *left* gives the answer -5

$$2+(-7)=-5$$

Addition of any integers can be carried out this way.

Good Question: When you added a positive, as in $2+7$, you moved 7 to the *right*. When you added a negative, as in $2+(-7)$, you moved 7 to the *left*. Why right for positive and left for negative?

Answer: Addition of a positive number increases your overall value. On a number line, numbers increase to the right. Addition of a negative number decreases your overall value. On a number line, numbers decrease to the left.

These examples suggest the following procedure for adding integers on a number line.

To add integers using a number line:
1. Start at the first number in the sum.
2. Adding a positive number moves your answer to the right.
3. Adding a negative number moves your answer to the left.

Example 1: Draw a number line to illustrate how to find each sum and give the result.

a) $-9+2$ b) $-3+(-6)$

Solution: When you are first getting started using a number line to add, feel free to count the spaces out. You will begin to get an understanding of how positives and negatives are added.

a) $-9+2=-7$

b) $-3+(-6)=-9$

You can even use this technique to add several numbers in the same problem. Start at the first number in the sum and move left or right for each number that follows.

Example 2: Draw a number line to illustrate how to find each sum and give the result

a) $-4+5+8$ b) $-6+9+(-5)$

Solution:

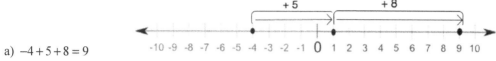

a) $-4+5+8=9$

b) $-6+9+(-5)=-2$

STOP Exercise Set - Using a Number Line to Add

1.   What is the overall result for a stock that losses 4 points one day and gains 1 the next day?
a) a loss of 5 points   b) a gain of 3 points   c) a loss of 3 points

2.   What is the overall result for a politician who gains 5 points in the polls one week and losses 7 points the next week?
a) a loss of 2 points   b) a gain of 12 points   c) a gain of 2 points

Draw a number line to illustrate how to find each sum and give the result.

3. $2+3$

4. $4+5$

5. $9+(-2)$

6. $-7+3$

7. $-7+(-3)$

8. $-12+(-6)$

9. $7+(-5)+(-2)$

10. $-4+(-10)+(-6)$

Adding Integers With Like Signs

In football, if a team has a loss of 10 yards on the first play and loses another 5 yards in the next play then they have a total loss of 15 yards. In this situation, we are actually adding negative numbers:

a loss of 10 yards plus a loss of 5 yards results in a loss of 15 yards
[PN: arrows pointing to the translation]
$$-10+(-5)=-15$$

Using number lines can be an important first step in adding integers to help visualize the process. When adding two integers that are both negative, you move in the same direction and the result is a negative number.

positive + positive = positive

negative + negative = negative

To add two negative numbers:
- Add their absolute values.
- The result is negative.

$$-3+(-7)=-10 \quad -2+(-3)=-5$$
$$-4+(-2)=-6 \quad\quad -7+(-9)=-16$$

Adding two negatives is just like adding two positives, except that the result is negative.

Example 3: Add.
a) $34 + 16$ b) $(-192)+(-270)$

Solution: In each case, we add the absolute values and keep the same sign as the two numbers.

a) This is just adding whole numbers: $34 + 16 = 50$

$$\begin{array}{r} 192 \\ +270 \\ \hline 462 \end{array}$$

b) First we add the absolute values:

Since the two numbers are both negative, the result is negative, so $(-192) + (-270) = -462$.

Good Question: You are saying that $-3+(-5)=-8$, but don't two negatives make a positive?

Answer: Two negatives make a positive when you are *multiplying* or *dividing*. In this section we are *adding*. With adding:

$$positive + positive = positive$$

According to the order of operations, if we have more than one sum in an expression we move from left to right performing each sum.

Example 4: Add
a) $-2+(-3)+(-5)+(-7)$ b) $(-57)+(-32)+(-12)$

Solution:
Working from left to right we find each sum.

a) $-2+(-3)+(-5)+(-7)$
$=-5+(-5)+(-7)$
$=-5+(-5)+(-7)$
$=-10+-7$
$=-17$

b) $(-57)+(-32)+(-12)$
$=-89+(-12)$
$=-101$

Example 5: Where in the World?

The following table gives the scores for players on the PGA tour after four rounds of golf. Each player's overall total score is found by adding the results from the four rounds. Add up the scores in each row to get the players' overall scores.

PGA SCORECARD

	ROUND 1	ROUND 2	ROUND 3	ROUND 4	OVERALL
TIGER	-4	-3	0	-2	
PHIL	-1	-3	-2	-3	
ARNOLD	0	-1	-2	-4	
DEEJAY	-3	-5	-4	-2	

Solution: Here is the table with the rows added to get the overall score (in blue).

	ROUND 1	ROUND 2	ROUND 3	ROUND 4	OVERALL
TIGER	-4	-3	0	-2	-9
PHIL	-1	-3	-2	-3	-9
ARNOLD	0	-1	-2	-4	-7
DEEJAY	-3	-5	-4	-2	-14

 STOP # Exercise Set - Adding Integers With Like Signs

Add.

11. 4 + 5

12. 21 + 17

13. (-5) + (-6)

14. -17 + (-7)

15. (-15) + (-48)

16. 143 + 178

17. 5230 + 4560

18. (-351) + (-238)

19. -24 + (-9) + (-13)

20. -9 + (-3) + (-45)

21. The following chart shows the weekly change in a stock over several weeks. The positive values represent an increase while the negative values represent a decrease. What is the combined result of week 2, week 3, and week 5?

Week	1	2	3	4	5
Change	6	-8	-3	4	-2

22. The table below shows the United States' debt over a period of several years. Add the column to find an integer that represents the countries over debt for this period. Source: www.cbo.gov

Year	Debt (in billions)
1977	-$54
1978	-$59
1979	-$41
1980	-$74
Total	?

Adding Integers With Different Signs

Suppose your checking account has a balance of –$70. This means you have overdrawn your account by $70. You immediately deposit your paycheck of $100 and find your new balance is $30.

This illustrates the operation $-70+100 = 30$. Even though we are adding, it appears that we are actually *subtracting*.

Now consider the addition $5+(-3)$. Using a number line for a visual reference of how addition works we see that adding 5 and -3 actually involves the *difference* between their absolute values:

To add a negative and positive:
- Subtract their absolute values.
- The result has the same sign as the number with the larger absolute value.

$$5+(-3) = 2$$

$$-9+2 = -7$$

The sum $5+(-3)$ comes out positive because 5 has a higher absolute value than -3. The sum $-9+2$ comes out negative because -9 has a higher absolute value than 2.

Example 6: Add without using a number line.

a) $-7+4$ 　　　　b) $(-37)+76$ 　　　　c) $135+(-160)$

Solution: In each case, we subtract the absolute values and decide if the result should be positive or negative.

a) 7 – 4 = 3, the answer is negative since -7 has a higher absolute value than 3. So -7 + 4 = -3.

b) 76 – 37 = 39, the answer is positive since 76 has a higher absolute value than -37. So 76 + (-37) = 39.

c) 160 – 135 = 25, the answer is negative since -160 has a higher absolute value than 135. So 160 + (-135) = 25.

Example 7: Where in the World? A submarine is cruising at a depth of -575 feet. The captain gives a command to move up 235 feet. What will the new depth be?

Solution: Starting at 575 feet below sea level and going up 235 feet is reflected in the sum -575 + 235.

To find the result we subtract the absolute values:
$$\begin{array}{r} 575 \\ -\underline{235} \\ 340 \end{array}$$

Since -575 has the higher absolute value, the result is negative and the result is -340 feet, which means 340 ft below sea level.

STOP Exercise Set - Adding Integers With Different Signs

Add.

23. -13 + 9
24. 7 + (-18)
25. 15 + (-2)
26. 3 + (-23)
27. 8 + (-8)
28. -7 + 7

29. $-34 + 78$
30. -45 + 14
31. $659 + (-724)$
32. $-1098 + 850$

33. Duane's bank account is overdrawn by \$153. If he makes a \$90 deposit, what integer represents the new balance?

34. A scuba diver is 42 feet below sea level. If she swims up 18 feet what integer represents her new depth?

Using Both Techniques

We have learned two techniques for adding integers. The challenge with adding several integers is that you may have to use one technique in the first step and the other technique in the second step.

$$(-3) + (-6) + 7$$

The first two numbers are both negative, so we add their absolute values. The result is negative.

$$(-3) + (-6) + 7$$
$$(-9) + 7$$

These two numbers have opposite signs, so we take the difference in their absolute value. The result is negative.

$$(-9) + 7$$
$$-2$$

Adding several integers means deciding in each step which technique we should use based on whether the integers we are adding have the same sign.

Example 8: Add.

a) $(-6) + (-3) + 7$ b) $12 + (-9) + 5$ c) $(-45) + 72 + (-100)$

Solution:

a) $(-6)+(-3)+7$
$= -9+7$
$= -2$

b) $12+(-9)+5$
$= 3+5$
$= 8$

c) $(-45)+72+(-100)$
$= 27+(-100)$
$= -73$

Example 9: Where in the World?
The Gallup Organization runs polls (surveys) and presents the results. The following chart shows Barak Obama's standing in the 2008 presidential race.

What was the overall result of the changes from March to September?

Changes in Obama's 2008 Standing	
Month	**Change in Standing**
March	-3 points
May	4 points
July	6 points
September	-5 points
www.nytimes.com	

Solution:
To get the overall result of the ups and downs, we simply add the results for each month:

$(-3)+4+6+(-5)$ So the over all result for the months is a 2 point increase.
$= 1+6+(-5)$
$= 7+(-5)$
$= 2$

STOP Exercise Set - Using Both Techniques

Add.
35. $6 + (-13) + (-8)$
36. $-21 + 34 + (-1)$
37. $8 + (-9) + 22$
38. $-16 + 5 + (-14)$
39. $23 + 78 + (-102)$
40. $56 + 92 + 14$

41. $153 + (-121) + (-67)$
42. $(-900) + (-600) + 500$
43. $-24 + (-98) + 45 + 15$
44. $-54 + 78 + (-16) + 22$

45. Check out the following activity list for Glenn's account. What will the result be from the activity?

Overdrawn Balance - Yikes!	-$105
paid emergency car repair	$120
paid fee from bank for being overdrawn	$25
deposited weekly check!	$300
celebrated end of overdrawn balance!	$80

46. The Gallup Organization runs polls (surveys) and presents the results. The following chart shows Barak Obama's standing in the 2008 presidential race. What was the overall result of the changes from April to October?

| Changes in Obama's 2008 Standing ||
Month	Change in Standing
April	5 points
June	-3 points
August	-6 points
October	3 points
www.nytimes.com	

Exercise Set - Putting it ALL Together

Add.

47. 9 + (-4)
48. 2 + (-8)
49. $314 + (-237)$
50. $-458 + 239$
51. -23+(-45)
52. -15 + (-36)
53. -15 + (-56) + 34
54. $23 + 18$
55. $25 + 37$
56. 39 + (-47) + (-82)
57. 17 + (-5)
58. -19 + 4
59. -72 + (-87)
60. $38 + 19$

61. $319 + 457$
62. $-151 + (-674)$
63. $3759 + (-1683)$
64. $-23 + 7$
65. -15 + 7 + (-12)
66. 8 + (-91) + 12
67. -90 + (-31) + 19 + (-23)
68. -10 + (-34) + 12 + 17
69. -3 + (-5) + 13 + (-34)
70. -87 + 45 + (-23) + (-12)
71. (-7) + 13 + (-14) + (-13) + 20
72. 8 + (-19) + (-10) + (-5) + (-34)

73. **Bank Account.** Yacoub discovers that he made a mistake balancing his checkbook and he has a balance of -$87. On top of that, the bank notifies him of an overdraft fee of $27 that will be taken from the account. He quickly makes a deposit of $212. What is his new balance?

74. **Bank Account.** Rachel discovers that she made a mistake balancing his checkbook and he has a balance of -$107. On top of that, the bank charges her an overdraft fee of $27. She quickly makes a deposit of $356. What is her new balance?

75. **Diving Expedition.** On a diving trip off the coast of Hawaii, Tejae dives down 40 ft and then she dives down another 25 ft. Represent her distance below sea level as an integer.

76. **Diving Expedition.** On a diving trip off the coast of Maui, Juan dives down 45 ft and then he dives down another 33 ft. Represent his distance below sea level as an integer.

77. The Dow Jones Industrial Average is gives the results of the stock market as a whole. The following chart shows changes in the Dow Jones Average over the course of one week. What was the overall result of the changes for the week?

Changes in Dow for Sept 8-12, 2008	
Day	**Change in Dow**
Monday	286 points
Tuesday	-284 points
Wednesday	35 points
Thursday	-170 points
Friday	-7 points
www. finance.yahoo.com	

78. The Dow Jones Industrial Average is gives the results of the stock market as a whole. The following chart shows changes in the Dow Jones Average over the course of one week. What was the overall result of the changes from Monday to Thursday?

Changes in Dow for Sept 8-12, 2008	
Day	**Change in Dow**
Monday	191 points
Tuesday	-40 points
Wednesday	-122 points
Thursday	7 points
www. finance.yahoo.com	

Always True, Never True, or Sometimes True?
79. The sum of two negative numbers is positive.
80. The sum of two positive numbers is positive.
81. The sum of a positive and a negative is negative.
82. The sum of a positive and a negative is positive.

Given that $w = -8$, $x = -5$, $y = 8$, **and** $z = -2$, **find the following sums.**
83. $w + x$
84. $w + y$
85. $x + y$
86. $x + y + z$
87. $x + x + z$
88. $w + x + y + z$

89. For the following two rows of numbers, create a third row by adding the stacked pairs. This is an important process for Intermediate Algebra.

$$\begin{array}{cccc} 3 & 5 & 7 & -2 \\ -3 & 0 & -9 & -6 \end{array}$$

90. For the following two rows of numbers, create a third row by adding the stacked pairs. This is an important process for Intermediate Algebra.

$$\begin{array}{cccc} -4 & -10 & -6 & 8 \\ 4 & 3 & -7 & 3 \end{array}$$

Exercise Set - Chapter 2 Review

91. Simplify. $-(-5)$
92. Simplify $|-9|+|-4|$
93. Fill in the blank with $<$ or $>$. -19 ___ -18
94. Graph the numbers -5, 3, 0, and -3 on a number line.
95. Without simplifying, translate "the opposite of the absolute value of negative nine" into an expression.

Exercise Set - Cumulative Review

96. Evaluate $\frac{1}{2}x+5$ for $x=4$.

97. Find the area.

98. Simplify. $7+3\cdot5^2$

99. Subtract and simplify if possible. $\frac{7}{15}-\frac{4}{15}$

100. Divide, if possible. $\frac{15}{0}$

2.2 QUIZ YOURSELF:

To make sure you are ready for the EXAM, try these problems without any help. Give yourself about 20 minutes and don't check the answers until you have completely finished.

1.   -98 + (-23)
2.   -45 + 17 + (-15)
3.   On Monday the Dow (stock market) was up 97 points. On Tuesday it was down 128 points. Represent the net gain or loss as an integer.
4.   A submarine dives below sea level 98 ft. An hour later, it dives down another 65 ft. Represent the total feet below sea level the submarine is.
5.   -104 + 67
6.   On a diving trip off the coast of Costa Rico, Laura dives down 37 ft and then she dives down another 12 ft. Represent her distance below sea level as an integer.
7.   -34 + (-56) + (-99) + 15
8.   True/ False. A negative number added to another negative number is always negative.

Answers to this Quiz Yourself are on page 649.

2.3 Subtracting Integers

Topics:
- Interpreting The Dash
- Subtracting Integers
- Addition And Subtraction Together

Are You Ready?
To see if you are ready to understand this section, do the following short quiz.
1) Subtract $5{,}023 - 1{,}365$ 2) Add $(-19) + 13$ 3) Add $6 + (-8) + (-4)$

Answers to this Are You Ready:
(1) 3,658   *(2) -6*   *(3)-6*

Interpreting The Dash

In this section, we will learn about subtracting with positives and negatives. Before we start doing the operation,, let's make sure we understand how to interpret the dash. The symbol " $-$ ", what we normally call a 'minus sign' has three distinct uses in math.

$7 - 3$ In this expression the dash represents subtraction.

-3 In this expression the dash indicates that a number is negative.

$-(5)$ In this expression the dash means "the opposite of".

Your ability to perform operations will depend on you being able to interpret what the dash means, especially since you will see the dash used several times in one problem. In this expression, the dash is used three times, each with a different meaning:

$$\underbrace{-(4)}_{\substack{\text{"take the} \\ \text{opposite"}}} + \underbrace{(5-8)}_{\text{subtraction}} + \underbrace{(-7)}_{\text{negative 7}}$$

Example 1: Without performing any of the operations, indicate what each dash in the expression means: 'the opposite of', subtraction, or a negative number.

a) $-19 - 13$ b) $-(-3) - (-8)$

Solution:

a) $-19 - 13$
The first dash represents a negative number. The second dash represents subtraction.

b) $-(-3) - (-8)$
The first dash means 'the opposite of', the second a negative number, the third a subtraction, and the fourth a negative number.

STOP Exercise Set - Interpreting The Dash

Without performing any of the operations or trying to simplify, indicate what the dash in each expression means: 'take the opposite of', subtraction, or a negative number.

1. $7-5$
2. $-(13)$

3. $7+(-3)$
4. $8-5$

Without performing any of the operations or trying to simplify, indicate what each dash in the expression means: 'the opposite of', subtraction, or a negative number.

5. $-19-7$

6. $-(-16)-13$

Subtracting Integers

The most common way of dealing with subtraction of integers is to rewrite the subtraction as an addition. Note that the following sums and differences give the same result:

$$9-5=4 \text{ and } 9+(-5)=4$$

$$150-60=90 \text{ and } 150+(-60)=90$$

This pattern suggests the following rule:

To rewrite a subtraction as an addition:
1. Leave the first number unchanged.
2. Change the subtraction to addition.
3. Write the *opposite* of the second number.

$$a-b=a+(-b)$$

This relationship is true for all positive or negative numbers. We can change any subtraction problem to an addition problem and use the techniques from Section 2.2 to find our answer.

$3 + ^-5 = ^-2$ $3 + ^-5 = ^-2$

$3 + ^-5 = ^-2$ $3 + ^-5 =$

$^-3 + ^-5 = ^-8$

Example 2: Change each subtraction problem to an addition problem, do not find the result.

a) $-7 - 3$ b) $8 - (-5)$

Solution:

a)   b)

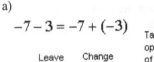

$$-7 - 3 = -7 + (-3)$$

Leave the first nunber alone | Change the - to a + | Take the opposite of the second number

$$8 - (-5) = 8 + 5$$

Leave the first nunber alone | Change the - to a + | Take the opposite of the second number

Part b) in the previous example represents the most interesting case in operating with integers:

subtracting a *negative* is equivalent to *adding* a *positive*
$$5 - (-3) = 5 + 3$$

This can be expressed symbolically as follows...

$$a - (-b) = a + b$$

Funny that the case that looks most confusing turns out to be the simplest. The subtraction $5 - (-3)$ is equivalent to the sum $5 + 3$, because you change the subtraction to addition and then take the opposite of -3. So $5 - (-3) = 5 + 3 = 8$.

Good Question: Subtracting a negative is the same as adding a positive? That just doesn't seem right.

Answer: Many students think that $5 - (-3) = 5 + 3$ goes against how we think of numbers. One way to justify this is to consider a number line.

Subtracting a positive moves you to the left. What else can subtracting a negative do but move you in the opposite direction; to the right?

$5 - 3 = 2$ $5 - (-3) = 8$

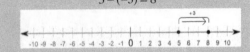

Example 3: Subtract.

a) $4 - 9$ b) $-3 - 7$

c) $9 - (-4)$ d) $-7 - (-15)$

$9 + +4$

Solution:
In each case we change the operation to addition and change the sign of the second number in the subtraction.

a) $4-9=4+(-9)=-5$

b) $-3-7=-3+(-7)=-10$

c) $9-(-4)=9+4=13$

d) $-7-(-15)=-7+15=8$

Example 4: Where in the World?
The highest elevation on Earth is Mount Everest at 29,035 feet. The lowest elevation is the Marianas Trench in the Pacific Ocean at -36,160 feet. Express the difference between these two elevations as a subtraction of integers and find the result.

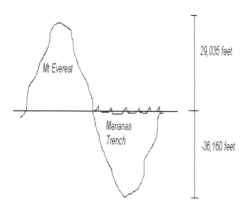

Solution: The word difference already suggests subtraction. The difference between 29,035 and $-36,160$ would be written as
$29,035 - (-36,160)$:

$$29,035 - (-36,160)$$
$$= 29,035 + 36,160$$
$$= 65,195$$

The distance between Earth's highest point and its lowest point is 65,195 feet.

If asked the previous example for themselves many students would just intuitively add the numbers 29,035 and 36,160 to get 65,160. And that's the point: subtracting a negative gives the same result as adding a positive.

$$3-|7+5\cdot 8|+(^-7)^2 \div 7^2$$
$$3-|7+40|+49 \div 49$$
$$3+(+33)^1 + 1$$
$$36 + 1^\wedge$$
$$= 37$$

$7-4$
$+^+33$

$3 + + 33$

STOP Exercise Set - Rewriting Subtraction as Addition

Rewrite the subtraction problem as addition and then add.

7. $15 - (-7)$

8. $23 - (-12)$

9. $15 - 90$

10. $35 - 129$

11. $-13 - 30$

12. $-76 - 35$

13. $-123 - (-67)$

14. $-257 - (-57)$

15. The highest elevation in California is at Mt. Whitney, which has an elevation of 14,494 feet. Death Valley has the lowest elevation, which is 282 feet below sea level. Express the difference between these two elevations as a subtraction of integers and find the result.

16. The highest elevation in Louisiana is at Driskill Mountain, which has an elevation of 535 feet. New Orleans has the lowest elevation, which is 8 feet below sea level. Express the difference between these two elevations as a subtraction of integers and find the result.

Addition and Subtraction Together

Here is a summary of all the rules for adding and subtracting integers.

Summary of Adding and Subtracting Integers:

Adding Two Integers:

- same sign – add their absolute value and keep the same sign
- different signs – subtract their absolute values and keep the sign of the "larger" number in absolute value

Subtracting Two Integers:

- rewrite the subtraction as addition using the rule $a - b = a + (-b)$

You may have to use any combination of these techniques in a problem that involves several operations. Remember that according to the order of operations, addition and subtraction are performed at the same time moving from left to right.

Example 5: Simplify.

a) $(-3) + 7 - 9$ b) $3 - (-5) + (-11) - 8$

Solution:

a)
$$(-3) + 7 - 9 = 4 - 9$$
$$= 4 + (-9)$$
$$= -5$$

b)
$$3 - (-5) + (-11) - 8 = 3 + 5 + (-11) - 8$$
$$= 8 + (-11) - 8$$
$$= -3 - 8$$
$$= -3 + (-8)$$
$$= -11$$

Example 6: Given $w = -5, x = 9, y = -13, z = -7$, find the following.

a) $w - y$ b) $w - x + y - z$

Solution:

a) Substitute in -5 for w and -13 for y. Be careful! The operation for $w - y$ is subtraction. On top of that y is a negative number. So we are subtracting a negative.

$$w - y = -5 - (-13)$$

Change the operation to addition.

$$= -5 + 13$$
$$= 8$$

b) Substitute in -5 for w, 9 for x, -13 for y, and -7 for z.

$$w - x + y - z = -5 - 9 + (-13) - (-7)$$

Perform the operations moving from left to right.

$$= -14 + (-13) - (-7)$$
$$= -27 - (-7)$$
$$= -27 + 7$$
$$= -20$$

Example 7: Eduardo keeps a note pad in his pocket and records every time he spends money to see where it's going. The following is 3 days worth of records on his debit card. What will be the final balance in the debit account?

Balance as of Monday	$220
Purchased new guitar amp	$145
Dinner and movie	$110
Deposit into account	$100
Unexpected car repair	$180

Solution: Starting with Monday's balance, subtract each purchase and add the deposit. This results in the expression $230 - 145 - 110 + 100 - 180$.

$$220 - 145 - 110 + 100 - 180 = 75 - 110 + 100 - 180$$
$$= -35 + 100 - 180$$
$$= 65 - 180$$
$$= -115$$

So the account balance will be -$115, which means it is overdrawn.

STOP Exercise Set - Addition and Subtraction Together

Perform the following operations.

17. $-34 - 15 + (-9)$
18. $90 + 15 - (-3)$
19. $56 - (-14) + 89$
20. $-13 + 45 - 75$
21. $-21 + 34 - 45$

22. $-3 + (-9) + 7 - 5$
23. $5 + (-8) - 3 + 1$
24. $-13 + 23 + 78 - 89$
25. $123 + (-201) - (-5)$
26. $345 + (-321) - (-1)$

Given $w = -2, x = 3, y = -1, z = -3$, **find the following.**

27. $w - y$
28. $x + y - z$
29. $w + z - x$

Given $a = -1, b = -5, c = 4, d = -7$, **find the following.**

30. $c - b$
31. $a - d$
32. $a - b + c$

Exercise Set - Putting it ALL Together

Subtract

33.	9 – 29		39.	9 - 9
34.	34 – 8		40.	12 - 12
35.	15 – (-4)		41.	-7 - (-5)
36.	4 – (-8)		42.	-14 - (-17)
37.	0 - 8		43.	437 - 512
38.	0 - 16		44.	-670 - 350

Perform the following operations.

45.	-3 + (-9)		51.	30 – 45
46.	-24 – (-34)		52.	-30 – 45
47.	-5 + (-8) – 16		53.	-25 – (-24)
48.	-12 – (-17) + 45		54.	-13 + (-28)
49.	$145 - (-145) + 15$		55.	-15 + (-34) – (-90)
50.	-145 – (-145) +12		56.	-7 + (-3) – (-12)

57. Min has $567 in her checking account. She spent $37 on gas, and then deposited her paycheck for $694. She then pays her bills which total $1494. What is her account balance?

58. Solama has $289 in his checking account. He spent $56 on groceries, and then deposited his paycheck for $874. He then pays his bills which total $1123. What is his account balance?

59. Louis currently his a balance of $165 in his checking account. He spends $36 on gas and $278 on bills, and deposits his paycheck for $194. What is his new account balance?

60. Carlos currently has a balance of $297 in his checking account. He spends $141 on groceries, and deposits his paycheck for $105. What is his new account balance?

61. Elevations in Colorado range from 3,350 feet on the Arkansas River near Holly in southeastern Colorado to 14,431 feet on Mt. Elbert in central Colorado. Express the difference between these two elevations as a subtraction of integers and find the result.

62. Elevations in the United States range from 20,320 feet on Mt. McKinley (Alaska) to 282 feet below sea level in Death Valley (California). Express the difference between these two elevations as a subtraction of integers and find the result.

The following table gives the recode high and low temperatures (in degrees Fahrenheit) for several states. Answer the questions that follow.

State	Record High	Record Low
Alaska	100°	-80°
California	134°	-45°
Florida	109°	-2°
Hawaii	100°	12°
Texas	120°	-23°

63. Which state has the coldest record low temperature?
64. What is the difference between California's highest and lowest temperature?
65. What is the difference between Alaska's highest and lowest temperature?
66. What is the difference between Hawaii's highest and lowest temperature?
67. What is the difference between Texas' record low and Alaska's record low?

68.   What is the difference between Hawaii's record low and Alaska's record low?

Businesses use the expression $R - C$ **to find out their profit where** R **represents revenue (the amount of money made) and** C **represents cost (the amount of money spent). Evaluate the expression** $R - C$ **for the values given below and interpret the result.**

69. $R = \$870$ and $C = \$250$ 71. $R = \$15,780$ and $C = \$20,720$
70. $R = \$1800$ and $C = \$1960$ 72. $R = \$37,900$ and $C = \$12,500$

Recall that operations inside absolute value bars | | should be done before taking the absolute value while operations outside absolute value bars should be done after taking the absolute value. In each exercise, simplify each expression.

73. $|5 - 7|$ and $|5| - |7|$ 76. $|-11 + (-5)|$ and $|-11| + |-5|$
74. $|-8| + |4|$ and $|-8 + 4|$ 77. $(-3) - |-15|$ and $|(-3) - (-15)|$
75. $|-3 - 9|$ and $|-3| - |9|$ 78. $-(-21) - |-8|$ and $|-(-21) - (-8)|$

Recall that a solution to an equation is a variable value that makes the equation true. For each equation, determine if the value given is a solution.

79. $x + 8 = 2, \ x = -6$ 82. $-8 = -9 + a, \ a = 1$
80. $-9 - y = 18, \ x = 9$ 83. $45 - k = 75, \ x = -30$
81. $6 + b = -2, \ x = 4$ 84. $-23 = -13 - t, \ t = -10$

Exercise Set - Chapter 2 Review

85.   Add. $-9 + 9$
86.   Fill in the blank with $<$ or $>$. -7 ___ 7
87.   Graph the numbers -90, 75, 10, and -35 on a number line using a scale of 25.
88.   Add. $25 + (-27)$
89.   Simplify. $|-14|$

Exercise Set - Cumulative Review

90.   Is $x = 5$ a solution to the equation $2x - 7 = 3$?
91.   Subtract and simplify if possible. $\dfrac{7}{15} - \dfrac{4}{15}$
92.   Simplify. $2[7 - (8 - 5)]$
93.   Evaluate $5x + 3y$ for $x = 2$ and $y = 6$.
94.   Write the number 415 in words.

2.3 QUIZ YOURSELF:

To make sure you are ready for the EXAM, try these problems without any help. Give yourself about 20 minutes and don't check the answers until you have completely finished.

Add or Subtract.

1. $-89 + 67$
2. $-20 + (-64)$
3. $34 - (-89)$
4. $-5 + (-12) - (-17)$
5. $-329 - (-62) + 78 + (-115)$

Given $w = -5, x = 8, y = -4, z = -12$, **find the following.**

6. $w + z$
7. $w - x + y - z$

8. Mike has \$345 in his checking account. He buys groceries for \$64 and gas for \$27. He then deposits his check for \$297. What is his new account balance?

9. Brian has an overdrawn balance of -\$97. He then gets a \$39 overdraft fee and quickly deposits his paycheck for \$389. Rent is due and he writes a check for \$310. What is his new account balance?

Answers to this Quiz Yourself are on page 649.

2.4 Multiplying and Dividing Integers

Topics:
- Multiplying Integers
- Dividing Integers

Are You Ready?
To see if you are ready to understand this section, do the following short quiz.
In each case, multiply or divide if possible.

1) $15(7)$ 2) $\dfrac{45}{9}$ 3) $14 \div 0$ 4) $245(14)$ 5) $228 \div 12$

Answers to this Are You Ready:
(1) 105   (2) 5   (3) undefined   (4) 3,430   (5) 19

Multiplying Integers

Recall that multiplication is shorthand for repeated addition. This gives a way to establish multiplication with negative numbers. Consider $4(-20)$ for example…

4 times -20 means to add -20 to itself four times…

$$4(-20) = \underbrace{(-20) + (-20) + (-20) + (-20)}_{\text{Add -20 to itself four times.}} = -80$$

This shows that when we multiply a negative number times a positive number: the result is negative. Recall that two numbers involved in a product are called *factors*.

Multiplying Integers with Different Signs:

If two factors have different signs, their product is negative.

$$(\text{positive}) \cdot (\text{negative}) = \text{negative} \qquad\qquad (\text{negative}) \cdot (\text{positive}) = \text{negative}$$
$$7(-5) = -35 \qquad\qquad\qquad\qquad (-7)(5) = -35$$

We already know that the product of two positive numbers is positive. For the rule that "two negatives make a positive", first let's do an example that will help you connect with this rule.

Example 1: Fill in the blanks to complete the pattern for each list of numbers.

$-25, -20, -15, -10, -5, \underline{}, \underline{}, \underline{}, \underline{}$

Solution:
This list of numbers is increasing by 5: $-25, -20, -15, -10, -5, 0, 5, 10, 15, 20$

So what does this have to do with multiplication? Below we have multiples of -5. Notice our missing products that involve two negative numbers.

$$3(-5) = -15$$
$$2(-5) = -10$$
$$1(-5) = -5$$
$$0(-5) = 0$$
$$-1(-5) = ?$$
$$-2(-5) = ?$$
$$-3(-5) = ?$$

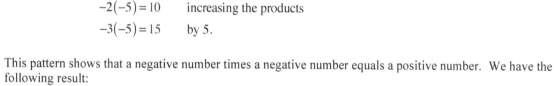

The only possible way to fill in the pattern is the same way we did in the example by adding 5 each time.

$$3(-5) = -15$$
$$2(-5) = -10$$
$$1(-5) = -5$$
$$0(-5) = 0$$
$$-1(-5) = 5 \qquad \text{The pattern continues by}$$
$$-2(-5) = 10 \qquad \text{increasing the products}$$
$$-3(-5) = 15 \qquad \text{by 5.}$$

This pattern shows that a negative number times a negative number equals a positive number. We have the following result:

Multiplying Integers with the Same Sign:
If two factors have the same sign, their product is positive.

$$\text{(positive)} \cdot \text{(positive)} = \text{positive} \qquad\qquad \text{(negative)} \cdot \text{(negative)} = \text{positive}$$
$$7 \cdot 5 = 35 \qquad\qquad\qquad\qquad (-7)(-5) = 35$$

Example 2: Multiply.

a) $-7(3)$ b) $(-5)(-9)$ c) $0(-6)$

Solution:

a) Since (negative)(positive) = negative, we have $-7(3) = -21$

b) Since (negative)(negative) = positive, we have $(-5)(-9) = 45$

c) Recall the property of zero: the product of zero and any number is zero. This applies to negative integers as well: $0(-6) = 0$

The "two negatives make a positive" rule should not be confused with addition.

Example 3: Multiply $(-4)(-5)$ and add $(-4)+(-5)$.

Solution: The product of two negatives is positive but the sum of two negatives is negative.

$$(-4)(-5) = 20 \text{ and } (-4)+(-5) = -9$$

Now let's take integer multiplication to the next level by multiplying several integers together.

Example 4: Multiply.

a) $(-5)(3)(-2)$ b) $(-3)(-3)(-3)(-3)$

Solution:

According to the order of operations, the multiplication should be done from left to right.

a) $(-5)(3)(-2) = (-15)(-2) = 30$

b) $(-3)(-3)(-3)(-3) = 9(-3)(-3) = -27(-3) = 81$

Example 5: Where in the World?

The Mesopelagic ocean layer goes to a depth of -3300 feet. The Bathypelagic layer is about 4 times as deep. How deep does the Bathypelagic layer go?

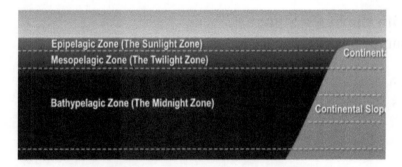

Solution: Since the Bathypelagic layer is 4 times as deep as the Mesopelagic, this problem is solved by the following multiplication $4(-3300) = -13,200$.

So the Bathypelagic layer goes to a depth of -13,200 feet.

STOP Exercise Set -Multiplying Integer

Fill in the blanks to complete the pattern for each list of numbers.

1. $-28, -21, -14, \underline{\quad}, \underline{\quad}, \underline{\quad}, \underline{\quad}$
2. $12, 9, 6, \underline{\quad}, \underline{\quad}, \underline{\quad}, \underline{\quad}$

Multiply.

3. $-5 \cdot 6$
4. $3(-8)$
5. $-12 \cdot -3$
6. $-4 \cdot -13$
7. $-98 \cdot -1$
8. $7 \cdot -6$

9. $-5 \cdot 0$
10. $-1(-3)(-5)$
11. $(-9)(10)(-4)$
12. $-7(-5)(-3)$

13. Find $(-7)(-9)$ and $(-7)+(-9)$.
14. Find $(-5)(-6)$ and $(-5)+(-6)$.
15. Find $(-10)(-4)$ and $(-10)+(-4)$.
16. Find $(-12)(-8)$ and $(-12)+(-8)$.

17. **Temperature Changes.** One cold January night in Asheville, NC the temperature dropped 2 degrees every hour for 5 hours. Represent the total temperature drop as an integer.

18. **Temperature Changes.** One cold February night in Boston, MA the temperature dropped 4 degrees every hour for 6 hours. Represent the total temperature drop as an integer.

Dividing Integers

The rules for dividing integers are the same as the rules for multiplying integers. Below are the rules with a quick example.

Dividing Integers:

The quotient of two numbers with the same sign is positive.

$$\frac{\text{positive}}{\text{positive}} = \text{positive} \qquad \frac{\text{negative}}{\text{negative}} = \text{positive}$$

$$\frac{36}{9} = 4 \qquad \frac{-36}{-9} = 4$$

The quotient of two numbers with different signs is negative.

$$\frac{\text{positive}}{\text{negative}} = \text{negative} \qquad\qquad \frac{\text{negative}}{\text{positive}} = \text{negative}$$

$$\frac{36}{-9} = -4 \qquad\qquad\qquad \frac{-36}{9} = -4$$

Why? Recall that every division problem can be written as multiplication using fractions.

$$15 \div 3 = 15 \div \frac{3}{1} = 15 \cdot \frac{1}{3}$$

Since division can always be rewritten as a product then it must follow the same rules as multiplication.

Example 6: Divide, if possible.

a) $\dfrac{-18}{-6}$ b) $-63 \div 7$ c) $\dfrac{625}{-5}$ d) $\dfrac{-9}{0}$

Solution:

a) $\dfrac{-18}{-6} = 3$

b) $-63 \div 7 = -9$

c) $\dfrac{625}{-5} = -25$

d) Recall the rules for division by zero: for any number a, $\dfrac{0}{a} = 0$ and $\dfrac{a}{0}$ is undefined. These rules apply to

integers as well. $\dfrac{-9}{0}$ represents division by zero, so it is undefined.

Example 7: Where in the World? Over the course of 8 months a start-up business has a loss of $19,200. What integer represents their monthly profit?

Solution: The company had a profit of -$19,200 over 8 months. To find the monthly profit we divide $(-19,200) \div 8 = 2,300$. So the monthly profit was -$2,300 which represents a loss of $2300.

STOP Exercise Set -Dividing Integers

Divide if possible.

19. $16 \div 4$

20. $25 \div 5$

21. $144 \div 12$

22. $132 \div 11$

23. $-100 \div 10$

24. $72 \div (-8)$

25. $-81 \div (-9)$

26. $-64 \div (-8)$

27. $\dfrac{-32}{-4}$

28. $\dfrac{16}{-8}$

29. $\dfrac{-5}{0}$

30. $\dfrac{0}{-14}$

31. $\dfrac{0}{-8}$

32. $\dfrac{-34}{0}$

33. **Price Depreciation.** Julia buys the new MAC AirBook for $1750. In 8 months, the price has decreased by $800. Represent the price decrease per month as an integer.

34. **Price Depreciation.** A new car sells for $16,500. In 2 months, the price has decreased by $2,700. Represent the price decrease per month as an integer.

Exercise Set - Putting it ALL Together

Divide.

35. $-24/6$

36. $-35 \div (-5)$

37. $\dfrac{28}{-4}$

38. $-63 \div (-7)$

39. $84/(-6)$

40. $\dfrac{95}{-5}$

41. $\dfrac{-54}{-3}$

42. $\dfrac{-143}{11}$

Perform the following operations, if possible.

43. $(-4)(7)$

44. $-67 \div 0$

45. $341 \div (-1)$

46. $(-14)(3)$

47. $0 \div (-8)$

48. $(7)(-23)$

49. $(5)(-31)$

50. $(-5)(0)(-1)$

51. $-128 \div (-4)$

52. $(-15)(-3)(0)$

53. $-36 \div (-3)$

54. $-128 \div (-4)$

55. $(-3)(-24)(-7)$

56. $792 \div (-6)$

57. $-132 \div 12$

58. $(-78)(-11)(-2)$

59. $(-15)(-34)$

60. $-5876 \div (-2)$

61. $-72 \div (-8) \cdot 3$

62. $(-6)(-6) \div (-9)$

63. $-12(4) \div (-8)(2)$

64. $-80 \div (-5) \div 2 \cdot (-3)$

65. **Submarine.** A submarine begins to dive below water at a rate of 21 feet per minute. What integer represents its elevation after 34 minutes?

66. **Submarine.** A submarine begins to dive below water at a rate of 45 feet per minute. What integer represents its elevation after 19 minutes?

67. **Business.** If Eloisa's Book Shop losses $120 during the first quarter, and this trend continues throughout the year. Represent her loss for the year as an integer. Hint: There are four quarters per year.

68. **Business.** If Andrew's Guitar Shop losses $230 during the first quarter, and this trend continues throughout the year. Represent his loss for the year. Hint: There are four quarters per year.

69. **Temperature Changes.** If the temperature in San Francisco, CA drops 12 degrees in 3 hours. What integer represents the average temperature drop per hour?

70. **Temperature Changes.** If the temperature in Ontario, CANADA drops 36 degrees in 4 hours. What integer represents the average temperature drop per hour?

71. **Credit Cards.** Over 4 months, Miguel charged $1620 on his credit card. How much did he charge each month on average?

72. **Credit Cards.** Over 5 months, Laura charged $1550 on her credit card. How much did she charge each month on average?

73. **Air Temperature.** As elevation increases, air pressure and temperature both decrease. Air temperature decreases about 2 degrees Celsius per 1000 feet of elevation increase. Represent the temperature decease as an integer is Jack climbs 5000 ft.

74. **Air Temperature.** As elevation increases, air pressure and temperature both decrease. Air temperature decreases about 2 degrees Celsius per 1000 feet of elevation increase. Represent the temperature decrease as an integer if Andrew climbs 12000 ft.

True/ False
75. A positive number multiplied by a negative number is always a positive number.
76. A positive number divided by a negative number is always positive number.
77. A negative number divided by a negative number is always a negative number.
78. A negative number divided by zero is zero.
79. A positive number divided by zero is undefined.

Exercise Set - Chapter 2 Review

80. Graph the numbers -5, -3, 1, and 3 on a number line.
81. Add. $-19+(-7)$
82. Add. $13+(-17)+(-10)$
83. Subtract $8-25$
84. Find $|-4-2|$ and $|-4|-|2|$.

Exercise Set - Cumulative Review

85. Find 5^3.
86. Find the prime factorization of 68.
87. Round 41,680 to the nearest hundred.
88. Add. $548+129+86$
89. List the first four multiples of 7.

2.4 QUIZ YOURSELF:

To make sure you are ready for the EXAM, try these problems without any help. Give yourself about 20 minutes and don't check the answers until you have completely finished.

Multiply or Divide.

1. $(-34)(-15)$

2. $(-342) \div (6)$

3. $-5 \div 0$

4. $(-12)(0)(-5)$

5. $0 \div (-45)$

6. If Lana's Bike Shop losses $370 during the first quarter, and this trend continues throughout the year. Represent her loss for the year as an integer.

7. If the temperature drops 24 degrees overnight (8 hours). What integer represents the average temperature drop per hour?

8. True/ False. A negative multiplied by a negative is a negative.

Answers for this Quiz Yourself are on page 649.

2.5 Exponents And Order Of Operations With Integers

Topics:
- Integers And Exponents
- Order Of Operations With Integers
- More About Grouping Symbols

Are You Ready?
To see if you are ready to understand this section, do the following short quiz.

1) $12 \div 2 \cdot 3$ 　　　　2) 6^2 　　　3) $(6-4)^3 + 3 \cdot 5$

Answers to this Are You Ready:
(1) 18 　　　　*(2) 36* 　　　*(3) 23*

Integers and Exponents

Recall from Section 1.2 that exponents are used to represent repeated multiplication. Of course, exponents can be used for negative integers as well.

$$\underset{\substack{\text{this is called}\\\text{exponential form}}}{(-5)^{\overset{\displaystyle exponent}{4}}} = \underbrace{(-5)(-5)(-5)(-5)}_{\substack{4 \ \ times\\ \text{this is called expanded form}}}$$

The exponential form $(-5)^4$ is read "negative five to the fourth power". When the base is a negative number, we always use parentheses around it.

Example 1: In each case identify the base and the exponent (or power) and write how the expression is read in English. (Hint: Recall that b^n is read as "b to the nth power".)

a) $(-3)^4$ 　　　b) $(-13)^9$ 　　　c) -5^3

Solution:
a) The base is -3. The exponent is 4. This is read "negative three to the fourth power".
b) The base is -13. The exponent is 9. This is read "negative thirteen to the ninth power".
c) The base is 5, since the negative is NOT inside the parentheses, it is not part of the base. The exponent is 3. This is read " the opposite of five to the third power".

Example 2: Rewrite each product using exponential form.

a) $(-8)(-8)(-8)$ b) $(-3)(-3)(-2)(-2)(-2)$

Solution:

a) $(-8)(-8)(-8)=(-8)^3$

b) $(-3)(-3)(-2)(-2)(-2)=(-3)^2(-2)^3$

Example 3: Without multiplying, rewrite each exponential expression in expanded form.

a) $(-15)^5$ b) $(-4)^2(-5)^3$

Solution:

a) $(-15)^5=(-15)(-15)(-15)(-15)(-15)$

c) $(-4)^2(-5)^3=(-4)(-4)(-5)(-5)(-5)$

Again, we always put a negative base in parentheses. This is very important. To raise a negative number to a power, it must be put in parentheses. If the negative sign is not inside the parentheses, it means to take the opposite.

$(-7)^2$ means $(-7)(-7)=49$ -7^2 means $-(7\cdot7)=-49$

$(-5)^3$ means $(-5)(-5)(-5)=-125$ -5^3 means $-(5\cdot5\cdot5)=-125$

Example 4: Simplify.

a) $(-9)^2$ b) -2^4 c) $(-4)^3$

Solution:

Remember we are only raising a negative number to a power if the negative number is in parentheses.

a) $(-9)^2=(-9)(-9)=81$

b) $-2^4=-(2\cdot2\cdot2\cdot2)=-16$

c) $(-4)^3=(-4)(-4)(-4)=-64$

STOP Exercise Set -Integers and Exponents

In each case identify the base and the exponent (or power) and write how the expression is read in English. (Hint: Recall that b^n is read as "b to the nth power".)

1. $(-3)^3$ 3. 5^2

2. 3^3 4. $(-2)^4$

Rewrite each product using exponential form.

5. $5\cdot5\cdot5\cdot5$ 8. $3\cdot3\cdot3(-5)(-5)(-5)(-5)$

6. $(-6)(-6)(-6)(-6)(-6)$

7. $(-2)(-2)(-2)(-2)(8)(8)$

Without multiplying, rewrite each exponential expression in expanded form.

9. $(-4)^3$

10. $(-5)^2$

11. $3^5 \cdot (-7)^3$

12. $(-4)^2 (-6)^3$

Simplify.

13. $(-2)^3$

14. $(-3)^2$

15. $(-5)^2$

16. -4^3

17. -3^2

18. $(-1)^5$

Order of Operations with Integers

The order of operations is the same for integers as for whole numbers:

Order of Operations
- Parentheses (grouping symbols)
- Exponents
- Multiplication and Division (from left to right)
- Addition and Subtraction (from left to right)

Example 5: Simplify.

a) $-5(3)^2 + (-7)$

b) $-3^2 + (-3)^2$

Solution:

a) Notice the parentheses are just there to indicate multiplication and to hold a negative number.

Since there is no operation *inside* the parentheses, we perform the exponent first.

$$-5(3)^2 + (-7)$$

Multiplication comes next.

$$= -5(9) + (-7)$$

The addition comes last.

$$= -45 + (-7)$$

$$= -52$$

b) The exponents are done first, keeping in mind the difference between -3^2 and $(-3)^2$.

$$-3^2 + (-3)^2$$

Now we add.

$$= -9 + 9$$

$$= 0$$

Here is an example that addresses some interesting cases and common mistakes students make with the order of operations.

Example 6: Simplify, if possible.

a) $10 - 2^2$ b) $7 - 3(2 - 5)$

Solution:

a) Remember that a negative number is not being raised to a power unless it is in parentheses.

$$10 - 2^2$$

Now we subtract.

$$= 10 - 4$$

$$= 6$$

> **CAUTION:** A subtraction symbol is never part of the base of an exponential expression:
> $10 - 2^2 = 10 + 4$ is WRONG!

b) The first step should be the subtraction in the parentheses.

$$7 - 3(2 - 5)$$

Next we multiply.

$$= 7 - 3(-3)$$

Finally, we subtract.

$$= 7 - (-9)$$

$$= 16$$

> **CAUTION:** It is tempting to subtract $7 - 3$ as the first step. But the 3 is being multiplied to the parentheses. We must resolve that multiplication before we subtract.
> $7 - 3(2 - 5) = 4(2 - 5)$ is WRONG!

Example 7: The expression $b^2 - 4ac$ is used in Intermediate Algebra to analyze graphs. Evaluate $b^2 - 4ac$ for $a = 2$, $b = -3$, and $c = 5$.

Solution: We substitute in the values given then we follow the order of operations.

$$(-3)^2 - 4(2)(5) = 9 - 4(2)(5)$$

$$= 9 - 40$$

$$= -31$$

> **Good Question:** I thought () were only used for order of operations, but I keep seeing them everywhere now. Why are they in the problem, if there is nothing to do inside the parenthesis?
>
> **Answer:** In chapter one, we only used parentheses to prioritize operations or to imply that we were multiplying. However, now that we have negatives, we use parentheses to include the negative with the number.

Example 8: Where in the World? A small company currently has $2,500 in its account to upgrade equipment. However they desperately need 6 new computers that each cost $675 each. If the company goes ahead with purchasing the 6 computers, what expression can be used to find the new balance in the account and what will that balance be?

Solution: There are two expressions that could be used to find the new account balance. Both give the same final result.

Approach #1:

$2,500 - 6(675)$

Start with $2,500 and take away $675 six times.

$2,500 - 6(675)$ multiply first

$= 2500 - 4050$ now subtract

$= -1550$

Approach #2:

$2,500 + 6(-675)$

Start with $2,500 and add $675 debt 6 times.

$2,500 + 6(-675)$ multiply first

$= 2500 + (-4050)$ now add

$= -1550$

Note that both approaches give the result that the account balance is $-\$1550$.

STOP Exercise Set -Order of Operations With Integers

Simplify using order of operations.

19. $2 \cdot (-8) \div 4 + (-3)$

20. $12 \div (-4) \cdot (-3) - 5$

21. $-4(9 - 13) + 8 \cdot (-3)$

22. $3(-7 + 11) - (-6) \cdot 7$

23. $-19 - (4 + 5)^2$

24. $-28 + (9 - 2)^2$

25. $3(2 - 8) + (-3)^2$

26. $-3(6 - 11) - 2^3$

Evaluate the expression $b^2 - 4ac$ **for the values given.**

27. $a = 5, b = -1, c = 3$

28. $a = -1, b = -4, c = 4$

29. $a = 3, b = 9, c = 0$

30. $a = -6, b = 0, c = 4$

More About Grouping Symbols

Because parentheses are used so often with integers, we incorporate other grouping symbols to avoid confusion. [Braces] and {Brackets} can also be used for grouping symbols.

Common Grouping Symbols

Parentheses	( )	
Braces	[ ]	Fraction Bar ———
Brackets	{ }	Absolute Value | |

Consider the following expression.

$$((5 + (-8)) + 7)^2$$

It's easy to get the parentheses mixed up. So, instead, we use braces and brackets as well.

$$\{[5 + (-8)] + 7\}^2$$

It's much easier to tell what parts are grouped and where to begin in this form.

Example 9: Simplify.

a) $[(-4)+8]^3$ b) $(-3)+\{4-[(-6)+8]\}$ c) $\dfrac{2\cdot[-5+(-2)]^2}{-20+6}$

Solution:

a) Add inside the brackets. $[(-4)+8]^3$

Now perform the exponent. $=[4]^3$

                                           $=64$

b) We begin with the inner most grouping symbol that has an operation.

As mentioned before, the parentheses do $(-3)+\{4-[(-6)+8]\}$
not have an operation inside, so we start
with the addition in the brackets.

Now we perform the subtraction in the $=(-3)+\{4-[2]\}$
braces.

Finally, we have addition. $=(-3)+\{2\}$

                                               $=-1$

c) Begin with the addition inside the $\dfrac{2\cdot[-5+(-2)]^2}{-20+6}$
brackets on top and add on bottom.

Next perform the exponent on top. $=\dfrac{2\cdot[-7]^2}{-14}$

Now the multiplication. $=\dfrac{2\cdot49}{-14}$

Divide last. $=\dfrac{98}{-14}$

                                               $=-7$

Remember that absolute value bars are treated like grouping symbols. So whatever is inside must be done first. Be careful not to confuse them for *just* grouping symbols like parentheses, braces, or brackets. The following example incorporates absolute value into order of operations problems.

Example 10: Simplify each expression.

a) $5\cdot(|-8|+3)$ b) $-|3\cdot4-2\cdot3|$

Solution:

a) While there is no operation in the $5\cdot(|-8|+3)$
absolute value, absolute value itself must
be done before any other operations.

Add inside the parenthesis.	$= 5 \cdot (8+3)$
Multiply.	$= 5 \cdot 11$
	$= 55$

b) This time we simplify all operations inside the absolute value before we perform it.

Multiply inside the absolute value bars.	$-\lvert 3 \cdot 4 - 2 \cdot 3 \rvert$
Subtract.	$= -\lvert 12 - 6 \rvert$
Take the absolute value.	$= -\lvert 6 \rvert$
	$= -6$

Example 11: Properties of Addition and Multiplication
Recall the commutative and associative properties covered in Chapter 1.

The Commutative Property
$$a + b = b + a$$
$$a \cdot b = b \cdot a$$

The Associative Property
$$(a + b) + c = a + (b + c)$$
$$(a \cdot b) \cdot c = a \cdot (b \cdot c)$$

These properties apply to integers as well. In each case, what property has been used to rewrite the expression.

a) $(-4) + 5 = 5 + (-4)$

b) $-3 \cdot (7 \cdot (-5)) = (-3 \cdot 7) \cdot (-5)$

c) $[(-5) + 2] + 3 = [2 + (-5)] + 3$

Solution:
a) Since the order of the addition was reversed, the commutative property has been used.

b) Since the two multiplications have been regrouped, the associative property has been used.

c) This is sort of a trick problem. While the form looks like something for the associative property, if look at what has been done we see that the order of the addition in the brackets has been reserved. So the commutative property has been used.

STOP **Exercise Set -More About Grouping Symbols**

Simplify each expression.

31. $[-9 + (12 - 5)]^2$

32. $\{5 - [25 + (-22)]\}^3$

33. $3[-12 + (5 - 19)] + 5$

34. $[6(-7) + (3 - 8)] + 2^2$

35. $\{-3 + [(9 - 12) - (-2)(4)]\}$

36. $\{5 - [(8 - 4) + (-99) \div (-3)]\}$

37. $-4|-5|+6\cdot 7$

38. $3|15|-3\cdot 2^3$

39. $-|34-56|-8(-6)$

40. $2|-8(-3)|+5$

41. $\dfrac{4(-6)-2\cdot(-9)}{5^2-3\cdot 8}$

42. $\dfrac{-3(-7)+13}{6^2-9\cdot 4}$

In each case, what property has been used to rewrite the expression.

43. $(-4)\cdot 5 = 5(-4)$

44. $-9+12 = 12+(-9)$

45. $18+(-7+21) = \{18+(-7)\}+21$

46. $-3(-7)(10) = -7(-3)(10)$

The EXAM is coming up!! What to do?!

- Visit your professor during office hours to get advice about preparing. They'll be glad to see you, I promise.
- Try the practice test on page ### to see if you're ready. No books or notes! Just you and a pencil, just like the test.
- Try the FREE resources from MyMathLab.com that came with your new book to access practice tests.

Courtesy of Fotolia

Whatever you do, do it NOW!
BRING IT! You CAN SUCCEED!

Exercise Set - Putting it ALL Together

Simplify.

47. 5^2

48. 7^2

49. -1^5

50. $(-1)^5$

51. $(-1)^2$

52. $(-1)^7$

53. $(-3)^4$

54. -7^2

55. $(-8)^2$

56. $(-10)^3$

57. $-4\cdot(-2)^3$

58. $3\cdot(-4)^2$

59. $4\cdot(-3)^3$

60. $-2(-9)^2$

61. $-2(15-7)+17$

62. $-5(8-14)-(-13)$

63. $(-3)^2$

64. -3^2

65. $(-25)\div(-5)(4)$

66. $(-49)\div(7)(-8)$

67. $8+(-5)(-3)$

68. $5^2+4(-6)-(-9)$

69. $2(-3)^3 - (-4) \div (-2)$

70. $(-2)^3 + (-5)(-6) - 7$

71. $3|3 - 9| + (-4)^2$

72. $-2|-18 - 2| - (-2)^3$

73. $\dfrac{(-3)^3 - (-5)}{-2^2 + (-2)(-3)}$

74. $\left\{ (15 - 12) - \left[-8 + (-4)(-1) \right] \right\}$

75. $\dfrac{(-4)^2 + 9}{(-3)(-6) - (-7)}$

76. $\dfrac{(-6)(-7) \div (-2) + 1^5}{-4^2 + 9}$

77. $\dfrac{(-8)(9) + 2}{-3^2 - (-1)^8}$

78. $\left\{ -3^2 - \left[9(-3) - (-5) \right] \right\}$

79. Simplify $(-9)^2$ and -9^2.

80. Simplify $(-5)^2$ and -5^2.

81. Simplify $(-2)^3$ and -2^3.

82. Simplify $(-4)^3$ and -4^3.

83. Lana's Bike Shop needs to buy 4 bikes at $150 each and 6 helmets at $12 each. How much will the bikes and helmets cost?

84. Glenn's Outfitter Store has $7640 in an account to buy new merchandise. He buys 5 tents at $65 each, 2 cooking stoves at $13 each, and 4 kayaks at $235 each. How much is left in the account?

85. Evaluate the expression $Ax + By$ for $A = 2$, $B = 1$, $x = -3$, and $y = 3$.

86. Evaluate the expression $Ax + By$ for $A = -1$, $B = 5$, $x = 2$, and $y = -3$.

87. Evaluate the expression $mx + b$ for $m = -3$, $x = 2$, and $b = 6$.

88. Evaluate the expression $mx + b$ for $m = 2$, $x = 4$, and $b = -5$.

89. **Average Temperature**
Recall that to calculate the *average* of a set of numbers we add the numbers and divide by the total number of numbers. The following table gives the high temperature over a five day period in October in Boston, MA. Find the average temperature for the five day period.

Day	Temperature (in degrees Celsius)
Monday	-13
Tuesday	-13
Wednesday	3
Thursday	8
Friday	-10

90. **Average Temperature**
Recall that to calculate the *average* of a set of numbers we add the numbers and divide by the total number of numbers. The following table gives the high temperature over a four day period in July in Anchorage, AK. Find the average temperature for the four day period.

Day	Temperature (in degrees Celsius)
Monday	14
Tuesday	-6
Wednesday	5
Thursday	11

Exercise Set - Chapter 2 Review

91. Divide. $36 \div (-9)$
92. Simplify. $-|-15|$
93. Subtract. $768 - (-5387)$
94. Simplify $-x$ given $x = -5$.
95. Multiply. $(-7)(-5)$

Exercise Set - Cumulative Review

96. Subtract and simplify if possible. $\dfrac{23}{45} - \dfrac{13}{45}$
97. Evaluate $b + 7$ given $b = 4$.
98. Estimate the difference $871 - 366$ by rounding to the nearest hundred.
99. Write "fourteen thousand twenty five" as a whole number.
100. Determine if the number 57 is prime or composite.

2.5 QUIZ YOURSELF:

To make sure you are ready for the EXAM, try these problems without any help. Give yourself about 20 minutes and don't check the answers until you have completely finished.

Simplify the following expressions.

1. -7^2

2. $-3(-2)^3$

3. $-36 \div (-4) \cdot 9$

4. $49 \div (-7) \cdot 2 - (-6)$

5. $\dfrac{-2^3 + 4(-3)}{(-5)^2 + (6)(-4)}$

6. $-3|21 - 45| + 5$

7. $\{(6-8) - [9 - (-5)(-11)]\}$

8. **Average Temperature:** The following table gives the high temperature over a four day period in January in Winterville, Maine.

Day	Temperature (in degrees Celsius)
Monday	-38
Tuesday	-15
Wednesday	-8
Thursday	5

Find the average temperature for the four day period.

9. According to order of operations, what should you do first in the following example?

$(-12) \div 6(-5)$

Answers to this Quiz Yourself are on page 649.

2.6 Signed Fractions

Topics:
- Simplifying Signed Fractions
- Multiplying and Dividing Signed Fractions
- Adding and Subtracting Signed Like Fractions

Are You Ready?

To see if you are ready to understand this section, do the following short quiz.

1) Simplify. $\dfrac{8}{12}$ 2) Multiply. $\dfrac{2}{3} \cdot \dfrac{9}{16}$ 3) Add. $\dfrac{3}{8} + \dfrac{1}{8}$

Answers to this Are You Ready:

(1) $\dfrac{2}{3}$ *(2)* $\dfrac{3}{8}$ *(3)* $\dfrac{1}{2}$

Simplifying Signed Fractions

In Section 1.6 we reviewed some basics of fractions. In this section, we will build on that foundation by looking at *signed fractions*.

The phrase **signed fractions** refers to fractions that are either positive or negative.

To represent a negative fraction we can put the negative sign in three places. These all represent the same fraction…

$$-\frac{a}{b} \qquad \frac{-a}{b} \qquad \frac{a}{-b}$$

Whether the negative sign is out front, with the numerator, or with the denominator, it just means that the fraction is negative.

Example 1: Express each negative fraction two other ways by moving the negative sign.

a) $-\dfrac{1}{2}$ b) $\dfrac{-5}{7}$

Solution:

a) The same fraction could be expressed as $\dfrac{-1}{2}$ or $\dfrac{1}{-2}$.

b) The same fraction could be expressed as $\dfrac{5}{-7}$ or $-\dfrac{5}{7}$.

Recall that to simplify a fraction we factor the numerator and denominator into prime factors and remove any common factors. The process is the same for fractions that involve negatives.

$$\frac{b \cdot a}{c \cdot a} = \frac{b \cdot \cancel{a}}{c \cdot \cancel{a}} = \frac{b}{c}$$

Example 2: Simplify each fraction.

a) $\dfrac{14}{-35}$

b) $-\dfrac{5}{15}$

c) $\dfrac{-12}{18}$

Solution: In each case we rely on prime factorizations the fundamental principle $\dfrac{b \cdot a}{c \cdot a} = \dfrac{b \cdot \cancel{a}}{c \cdot \cancel{a}} = \dfrac{b}{c}$.

a) When simplifying a negative fraction it is generally preferred to bring the negative out front of the fraction.

$$\frac{14}{-35} = -\frac{14}{35} = -\frac{\cancel{7} \cdot 2}{5 \cdot \cancel{7}} = -\frac{2}{5}$$

b) Remember that if all factors reduce in the numerator, there is still a factor of 1.

$$-\frac{5}{15} = -\frac{1 \cdot \cancel{5}}{3 \cdot \cancel{5}} = -\frac{1}{3}$$

c) Some fraction problems will have several prime factors, but the process is the same.

$$\frac{-12}{18} = -\frac{2 \cdot 2 \cdot 3}{2 \cdot 3 \cdot 3} = -\frac{\cancel{2} \cdot 2 \cdot \cancel{3}}{\cancel{2} \cdot \cancel{3} \cdot 3} = -\frac{2}{3}$$

Good Question: You keep going to prime factorizations to simplify fractions, but I do it this way...

$$\frac{-12}{18} = \frac{-12 \div 2}{18 \div 2} = \frac{-6}{9} = \frac{-6 \div 3}{9 \div 3} = \frac{-2}{3} = -\frac{2}{3}$$

I can simplify fractions this way, right?

Answer: Yes, you can, for now. But a time is coming in Prealgebra and particularly Beginning Algebra when you will *have* to rely on prime factorizations in just about every fraction exercise. So you may want to get used to using primes now.

STOP Exercise Set - Simplifying Signed Fractions

Express each fraction two other ways by moving the negative sign?

1. $-\dfrac{3}{5}$

2. $\dfrac{-4}{7}$

Simplify each fraction.

3. $-\dfrac{6}{9}$

4. $\dfrac{2}{-8}$

5. $\dfrac{-6}{18}$

6. $\dfrac{-16}{18}$

7. $-\dfrac{4}{8}$

8. $\dfrac{14}{-21}$

9. $\dfrac{-15}{20}$

10. $\dfrac{42}{-49}$

11. $\dfrac{-22}{33}$

12. $\dfrac{12}{-16}$

Multiplying and Dividing Signed Fractions

Below is a summary of the rules for multiplying and dividing fractions. Again, we will discuss why these rules work in great detail in Chapter 4.

Multiplying Fractions: Multiply the numerators and denominators separately.

$$\frac{a}{b} \cdot \frac{c}{d} = \frac{a \cdot c}{b \cdot d}$$

Dividing Fractions: Reciprocate the second fraction and multiply.

$$\frac{a}{b} \div \frac{c}{d} = \frac{a}{b} \cdot \frac{d}{c} = \frac{a \cdot d}{b \cdot c}$$

To multiply and divide signed fractions, we use the rules for multiplying and dividing positives and negatives: The product or quotient of two numbers with like signs is positive while the product or quotient of two numbers with different signs is negative. Also keep in mind that the final answer needs to be simplified to lowest terms, always.

Example 3: Multiply or divide.

a) $\left(-\dfrac{1}{2}\right)\left(\dfrac{-5}{7}\right)$

b) $-\dfrac{3}{7} \cdot \dfrac{2}{3}$

c) $-\dfrac{2}{15} \div \left(\dfrac{-6}{5}\right)$

Solution:
a) Since (negative)(negative) = positive, we drop the negative signs.

$$\left(-\frac{1}{2}\right)\left(\frac{-5}{7}\right) = \frac{1}{2} \cdot \frac{5}{7}$$

Rewrite the product as a single fraction. Since there are no common factors in the numerator and denominator there is nothing to do to simplify.

$$= \frac{1 \cdot 5}{2 \cdot 7}$$

Multiply the factors.

$$= \frac{5}{14}$$

b) Since (negative)(positive) = negative, we leave the negative sign in front of the fraction. As our first step we express the product as a single fraction.

$$-\frac{3}{7} \cdot \frac{2}{3} = -\frac{3 \cdot 2}{7 \cdot 3}$$

To simplify, remove the common factor of 3.

$$= -\frac{\cancel{3}\cdot 2}{7\cdot \cancel{3}}$$

Write the remaining factors.

$$= -\frac{2}{7}$$

c) First, we reciprocate the second fraction and change the operation to multiplication.

$$-\frac{2}{15}\div\left(\frac{-6}{5}\right)=-\frac{2}{15}\cdot\left(\frac{5}{-6}\right)$$

The answer will be positive since (negative) ÷ (negative) = positive, so we drop the negative signs. Express the product as a single fraction.

$$= \frac{2\cdot 5}{15\cdot 6}$$

To reduce, factor 15 and 6.

$$= \frac{2\cdot 5}{5\cdot 3\cdot 2\cdot 3}$$

Remove the common factors 2 and 5.

$$= \frac{\cancel{2}\cdot \cancel{5}}{\cancel{5}\cdot 3\cdot \cancel{2}\cdot 3}$$

Multiply the remaining factors. Remember there is still a factor of 1 in the numerator.

$$= \frac{1}{9}$$

 # Exercise Set - Multiplying and Dividing Signed Fractions

Multiply or divide and then simplify if possible.

13. $\dfrac{-1}{6}\cdot\dfrac{-2}{5}$

14. $\dfrac{-1}{3}\cdot\dfrac{-6}{7}$

15. $\left(\dfrac{18}{19}\right)\left(\dfrac{-3}{9}\right)$

16. $\left(-\dfrac{8}{15}\right)\left(-\dfrac{25}{17}\right)$

17. $\left(\dfrac{1}{4}\right)\div\left(\dfrac{-6}{5}\right)$

18. $\dfrac{1}{-5}\div\dfrac{-4}{15}$

19. $\left(\dfrac{1}{2}\right)\div\left(\dfrac{-4}{5}\right)$

20. $\left(-\dfrac{18}{22}\right)\div\left(-\dfrac{15}{11}\right)$

21. $\left(-\dfrac{21}{33}\right)\left(-\dfrac{11}{14}\right)$

22. $\left(\dfrac{-7}{12}\right)\left(\dfrac{6}{11}\right)$

Adding and Subtracting Signed Fractions

To add or subtract positive and negative fractions, we leave the denominator the same and add or subtract the numerators using the techniques for integers discussed in Sections 2.2 and 2.3.

Adding Fractions: Add the numerators and keep the common denominator.

$$\frac{a}{b} + \frac{c}{b} = \frac{a+c}{b}$$

Subtracting Fractions: Subtract the numerators and keep the common denominator.

$$\frac{a}{b} - \frac{c}{b} = \frac{a-c}{b}$$

As always, the final answer must be simplified to lowest terms.

Example 4: Add or subtract.

a) $\left(-\dfrac{1}{8}\right) + \left(-\dfrac{5}{8}\right)$

b) $\dfrac{4}{9} - \dfrac{7}{9}$

c) $\dfrac{7}{12} - \left(-\dfrac{5}{12}\right)$

Solution: When adding and subtracting with negative fractions, the negative sign of a negative fraction should be placed in the numerator.

a) First we rewrite the problem with the negatives in the numerators.

$$\left(-\frac{1}{8}\right) + \left(-\frac{5}{8}\right) = \left(\frac{-1}{8}\right) + \left(\frac{-5}{8}\right)$$

Now we can add the numerators.

$$= \frac{(-1)+(-5)}{8}$$

$$= \frac{-6}{8}$$

Finally, we move the negative sign to the front of the fraction and factor to simplify.

$$= -\frac{2 \cdot 3}{2 \cdot 4}$$

$$= -\frac{\cancel{2} \cdot 3}{\cancel{2} \cdot 4}$$

$$= -\frac{3}{4}$$

b) We subtract the numerators and keep the common denominator.

$$\frac{4}{9} - \frac{7}{9} = \frac{4-7}{9}$$

$$= \frac{-3}{9}$$

Now we factor to simplify the final answer.

$$= -\frac{3}{3 \cdot 3}$$

$$= -\frac{\cancel{3}}{3 \cdot \cancel{3}}$$

$$= -\frac{1}{3}$$

c) Recall that subtracting a negative is the same as adding a positive.

$$\frac{7}{12} - \left(-\frac{5}{12}\right) = \frac{7}{12} + \frac{5}{12}$$

Now we add the numerators.

$$= \frac{7+5}{12}$$

$$= \frac{12}{12}$$

Since $\frac{12}{12}$ is a whole, our result is:

$$= 1$$

STOP Exercise Set - Adding and Subtracting Signed Fractions

Add or subtract the following fractions.

23. $\dfrac{-2}{5} + \dfrac{1}{5}$

24. $\dfrac{-3}{7} + \dfrac{2}{7}$

25. $\dfrac{3}{8} + \dfrac{-2}{8}$

26. $\dfrac{-5}{7} - \dfrac{2}{7}$

27. $\dfrac{-8}{13} - \dfrac{3}{13}$

28. $\dfrac{11}{12} + \dfrac{-4}{12}$

29. $\dfrac{-2}{15} - \dfrac{-7}{15}$

30. $\dfrac{-7}{8} - \left(\dfrac{-1}{8}\right)$

31. $\dfrac{5}{9} - \left(-\dfrac{2}{9}\right)$

32. $\dfrac{3}{24} - \left(-\dfrac{7}{24}\right)$

Exercise set - Putting it ALL Together

Simplify the following fractions:

33. $\dfrac{-15}{-35}$

34. $\dfrac{-18}{-21}$

35. $\dfrac{-35}{49}$

36. $-\dfrac{24}{36}$

37. $-\dfrac{18}{24}$

38. $\dfrac{66}{-121}$

Perform the following operations:

39. $-\dfrac{1}{9}+\left(-\dfrac{2}{9}\right)$

40. $-\dfrac{3}{11}+\left(-\dfrac{5}{11}\right)$

41. $-\dfrac{15}{45}+\dfrac{6}{45}$

42. $\dfrac{17}{54}+\left(-\dfrac{7}{54}\right)$

43. $-\dfrac{4}{9}-\dfrac{1}{9}$

44. $-\dfrac{8}{13}-\dfrac{3}{13}$

45. $\dfrac{15}{24}+\left(\dfrac{-7}{24}\right)$

46. $\dfrac{47}{63}-\dfrac{2}{63}$

47. $\dfrac{-3}{4}\cdot\dfrac{8}{11}$

48. $\left(\dfrac{-7}{9}\right)\cdot\left(\dfrac{6}{13}\right)$

49. $\dfrac{15}{36}\cdot\left(-\dfrac{24}{25}\right)$

50. $\dfrac{-15}{21}\cdot\dfrac{9}{-65}$

51. $\left(-\dfrac{2}{3}\right)\div\left(\dfrac{-6}{7}\right)$

52. $\dfrac{2}{5}\div\left(\dfrac{-7}{15}\right)$

53. $\dfrac{-16}{27}\div\left(\dfrac{-8}{15}\right)$

54. $\dfrac{24}{27}\div\left(-\dfrac{8}{9}\right)$

55. $-\dfrac{25}{36}-\left(-\dfrac{13}{36}\right)$

56. $\left(-\dfrac{3}{42}\right)\cdot\left(\dfrac{14}{12}\right)$

True/False

57. The fraction $-\dfrac{3}{7}$ is equivalent to the fraction $\dfrac{-3}{-7}$.

58. The fractions $-\dfrac{1}{4}$, $\dfrac{-1}{4}$, and $\dfrac{1}{-4}$ are all equivalent.

59. Subtracting a negative fraction is the same as adding a positive fraction.

60. When simplifying fractions, if all factors of the numerator are removed, the result is an integer, as in $-\dfrac{2}{6}=-\dfrac{\cancel{2}}{\cancel{2}\cdot 3}=-3$.

Exercise Set - Chapter 2 Review

61. Find $-9+(-3)$ and $(-9)(-3)$.
62. Multiply. $(-3)(5)(-7)$
63. Subtract. $-16-(-13)$
64. Find $|x+y|$ given $x=-6$ and $y=-8$.
65. Add. $-5+(-7)+15+(-3)$

Exercise Set - Cumulative Review

66. Multiply. $67 \cdot 254$
67. Simplify to lowest terms. $\dfrac{14}{42}$
68. Divide, if possible. $\dfrac{0}{19}$
69. Find $4^2 \cdot 5^2$.
70. What is the 15th multiply of 4?

 # 2.6 QUIZ YOURSELF:

To make sure you are ready for the EXAM, try these problems without any help. Give yourself about 20 minutes and don't check the answers until you have completely finished.

Simplify the following fraction:

1. $\dfrac{-6}{18}$

2. $\dfrac{-12}{-144}$

Perform the following operations:

3. $\left(\dfrac{-16}{17}\right)\left(\dfrac{-1}{24}\right)$

4. $-\dfrac{5}{18}+\left(-\dfrac{7}{18}\right)$

5. $\left(\dfrac{-25}{32}\right)\div\left(\dfrac{5}{8}\right)$

6. $-\dfrac{5}{9}+\dfrac{2}{9}$

7. $\dfrac{-8}{9}-\left(\dfrac{-2}{9}\right)$

8. $\dfrac{-5}{12}-\dfrac{7}{12}$

9. $\left(\dfrac{22}{25}\right)\left(\dfrac{-5}{11}\right)$

10. $\left(-\dfrac{10}{11}\right)\div\left(-\dfrac{4}{5}\right)$

Answers to this Quiz Yourself are on page 649.

Chapter 2 Vocabulary

Write an "in your own" words definition for each vocabulary word that appeared in Chapter 2. If you need some help, the page number for the term is given.

1) Integer   3) Absolute Value
2) Opposite   4) Negative Number

Chapter 2 Summary

Section 2. 1 INTRODUCTION TO INTEGERS

Processes and Important Notes	Examples
Understanding Integers: A **negative number** is a number that is less than zero. The word **integer** refers to any positive or negative number that does not involve a decimal or fraction.	Of the following sets of numbers, list the integers in each set. $\left\{\dfrac{-3}{4}, 0, -5, 3\dfrac{1}{9}, \dfrac{8}{4}\right\}$ Solution: $0, -5, \dfrac{8}{4} = 2$
Number Lines: Note that positive numbers are to the right of zero, and negative numbers are to the left. Recall that to graph a number, we put a point at its location on the number line.	For the set given, represent the set on a number line, using a scale of 10. $\{-34, 42, 14, -50, -21\}$ Solution: (number line with scaling of 10 and points plotted accordingly.)
Ordering Integers: On a number line, numbers to the right are greater than numbers to the left.	Fill in an appropriate inequality symbol. (a) -34 _____ 17 (b) -12 _____ -17 Solution: (a) $-34 < 17$, since a negative is always less than a positive number. (b) $-12 > -17$, since -12 is to the right of -17 on a number line.

Opposites:
Opposite numbers are the same distance from zero on a number line.
	Simplify.
	(a) -(-6) (b) -(-(-19))
	
	Solution:
	   (a) -(-6) = 6
	   (b) -(-(-19)) = -(19) = -19

Absolute Value: The **absolute value** of a number is the distance on a number line between that number and zero.	Simplify. (a) $\|-6\|$ (b) $\|-4\| + \|-23\|$ Solution:

	(a) $|-6| = 6$
	(b) $|-4| + |-23| = 4 + 23 = 27$

Section 2. 2 ADDING INTEGERS

Processes and Important Notes	Examples
Using a Number Line to Add: To add integers using a number line: 1. Start at the first number in the sum. 2. Adding a positive number moves your answer to the right. 3. Adding a negative number moves your answer to the left. When you are first getting started using a number line to add, feel free to count the spaces out. You will begin to get an understanding of how positives and negatives are added.	Draw a number line to illustrate how to find each sum and give the result. $(-14) + 9$ **Solution:** (number line starting at -14 with arrow pointing to -5, which is 9 units away.) So, $(-14) + 9 = -5$
Adding Integers With Like Signs: To add two negative numbers: • Add their absolute values. • The result is negative. Adding two negatives is very similar to adding two positives.	**Add.** $(-23) + (-16)$ **Solution:** $(-23) + (-16) = -39$
Adding Integers with Different Signs: To add a negative and positive: • Subtract their absolute values. • The result has the same sign as the number with the larger absolute value.	**Add.** $51 + (-79)$ **Solution:** $51 + (-79) = -28$
Using Both Techniques: Adding several integers means deciding in each step which technique we should use based on the signs of the numbers involved.	**Add.** $34 + (-28) + (-31) + 15$ **Solution:** $34 + (-28) + (-31) + 15$ $= 6 + (-31) + 15$ $= -25 + 15$ $= -10$

Section 2. 3 SUBTRACTING INTEGERS

Processes and Important Notes	Examples
Interpreting the Dash: The dash has three distinct uses in math: • subtract • negative • take the opposite	In each expression, interpret the dash. • 6 - 9 represents subtraction • -13 represents a negative number • -(12) means "take the opposite of"
Rewriting Subtraction as Addition: To rewrite a subtraction as an addition: 1. Leave the first number alone. 2. Change the subtraction sign to an addition sign. 3. Write the *opposite* of the second number.	Rewrite the subtraction problem as addition and then add. (a) $-13 - 18$ (b) $31 - (-42)$ **Solution:**

subtracting a *negative* is equivalent to *adding* a *positive*	**(a)** $-13-18=-13+(-18)=-31$ **(b)** $31-(-42)=31+42=73$

Addition and Subtraction Together:
 Adding and Subtracting Integers
 • Adding Two Integers:
  ○ same sign – add their absolute value and keep the same sign
  ○ different signs – subtract their absolute values and keep the sign of the "larger" number
 • Subtracting Two Integers:
  ○ rewrite the subtraction as a sum using the rule $a-b=a+(-b)$
	(a) Simplify. $-16+(-21)-17-(-8)$
	 (b) Given $x=-3, y=-15, z=7$, **find** $x-y-(-z)$.
	
	 Solution:
	 (a) $-16+(-21)-17-(-8)$
	 $\quad =-37-17-(-8)$
	 $\quad =-54-(-8)$
	 $\quad =-54+8$
	 $\quad =-46$
	 (b) $x-y-(-z)=-3-(-15)-(-7)$
	 $\quad =-3+15+7$
	 $\quad =12+7$
	 $\quad =19$

Section 2. 4 MULTIPLYING AND DIVIDING INTEGERS

Processes and Important Notes	Examples

Multiplying Integers:
 To Multiply Integers:
 Multiply their absolute values. The sign of the result is as follows.
  (positive)(positive)=positive
  (negative)(negative)=positive
  (negative)(positive)=negative
  (positive)(negative)=negative
	Multiply.
	 (a) $(-12)\cdot(-5)$ **(b)** $(5)(-13)(0)$
	
	 Solution:
	 (a) $(-12)\cdot(-5)=60$
	 (b) $(5)(-13)(0)=0$

Dividing Integers: To Divide Integers: Divide their absolute values. The sign of the result is as follows. $\dfrac{positive}{positive}=positive$ $\dfrac{negative}{negative}=positive$ $\dfrac{positive}{negative}=negative$ $\dfrac{negative}{positive}=negative$	**Divide.** **(a)** $(-35)\div(-7)$ **(b)** $\dfrac{-28}{0}$ **Solution:** **(a)** $(-35)\div(-7)=5$ **(b)** $\dfrac{-28}{0}$ is undefined.

Section 2. 5 EXPONENTS AND ORDER OF OPERATIONS

Processes and Important Notes	Examples
Integers and Exponents: We ALWAYS put a negative base in parentheses. $(-7)^2$ means "negative seven squared". $(-7)^2 = (-7)(-7) = 49$ -7^2 means "the opposite of seven squared". $-7^2 = -(7 \cdot 7)$ $= -(49) = -49$	**Simplify.** **(a)** $(-3)^4$ **(b)** -4^2 **Solution:** **(a)** $(-3)^4 = (-3)(-3)(-3)(-3)$ $= 9(-3)(-3)$ $= -27(-3)$ $= 81$ **(b)** $-4^2 = -(4 \cdot 4) = -16$
Order of Operations With Integers: The order of operations is the same for integers as for whole numbers: • Work inside grouping symbols such parentheses first. • Perform any exponents in the expression. • Do multiplication and division moving left to right. • Do addition and subtraction from left to right.	**Simplify using order of operations.** **(a)** $8 \div (-2) \cdot (2) + 5$ **(b)** $\dfrac{-5^2 + 18 \div (-2)}{-7 + (-6)(4) - 3}$ **Solution:** **(a)** $8 \div (-2) \cdot (2) + 5 = -4 \cdot (2) + 5$ $= -8 + 5 = -3$ **(b)** $\dfrac{-5^2 + 18 \div (-2)}{-7 + (-6)(4) - 3} = \dfrac{-25 + 18 \div (-2)}{-7 + (-24) - 3}$ $= \dfrac{-25 + (-9)}{(-31) - 3} = \dfrac{-34}{-34} = 1$
More About Grouping Symbols: **Common Grouping Symbols** Parentheses ( ) Braces [ ] Brackets { } Fraction Bar ———	**Simplify the expression.** $\left\{ 16 - \left[5 + \left(-4^2 - (-10) \right) \right]^3 \right\} + 8$ **Solution:** $\left\{ 16 - \left[5 + \left(-4^2 - (-10) \right) \right]^3 \right\} + 8$ $= \left\{ 16 - \left[5 + \left(-16 - (-10) \right) \right]^3 \right\} + 8$ $= \left\{ 16 - \left[5 + \left(-16 + 10 \right) \right]^3 \right\} + 8$ $= \left\{ 16 - \left[5 + (-6) \right]^3 \right\} + 8$ $= \left\{ 16 - [-1]^3 \right\} + 8 = \left\{ 16 - (-1) \right\} + 8$ $= \{ 16 + 1 \} + 8 = 17 + 8 = 25$

Section 2. 6 FRACTIONS THAT INVOLVE INTEGERS

Processes and Important Notes	Examples
Simplifying Fractions: • Common factors in the numerator and denominator can be reduced • Multiply fractions by multiplying their numerators and denominators • Divide fractions by reciprocating the second	**Simplify.** **(a)** $\dfrac{-30}{75}$ **(b)** $\dfrac{-36}{-124}$ **Solution:**

fraction and multiplying • Add and Subtract fractions with a common denominator by adding or subtracting the numerators and keeping the same denominator	(a) $\dfrac{-30}{75} = -\dfrac{2 \cdot \cancel{3} \cdot \cancel{5}}{\cancel{3} \cdot \cancel{5} \cdot 5} = \dfrac{2}{5}$ (b) $\dfrac{-36}{-124} = \dfrac{\cancel{2} \cdot \cancel{2} \cdot 3 \cdot 3}{\cancel{2} \cdot \cancel{2} \cdot 31} = \dfrac{9}{31}$
Multiplying and Dividing Fractions: When multiplying and dividing negative fractions, just judge whether the final answer will be negative or positive then ignore the negative signs. **Multiplying Fractions:** $\dfrac{a}{b} \cdot \dfrac{c}{d} = \dfrac{a \cdot c}{b \cdot d}$ **Dividing Fractions:** $\dfrac{a}{b} \div \dfrac{c}{d} = \dfrac{a}{b} \cdot \dfrac{d}{c} = \dfrac{a \cdot d}{b \cdot c}$	**Multiply or Divide.** (a) $\dfrac{21}{50} \cdot \left(\dfrac{-15}{49}\right)$ (b) $\dfrac{-18}{55} \div \dfrac{9}{22}$ **Solution:** (a) $\dfrac{21}{50} \cdot \left(\dfrac{-15}{49}\right) = -\dfrac{3 \cdot \cancel{7}}{2 \cdot \cancel{5} \cdot 5} \cdot \dfrac{3 \cdot \cancel{5}}{\cancel{7} \cdot 7} = -\dfrac{9}{70}$
Adding and Subtracting Fractions: • When adding and subtracting, it is best to have the negative sign in the *numerator*: • But when you write your final answer, put the negative sign in *front* to impress your professor. This will show that you understand it can be in either position. $\dfrac{-a}{b} = -\dfrac{a}{b}$ **Adding Fractions:** $\dfrac{a}{b} + \dfrac{c}{b} = \dfrac{a+c}{b}$ **Subtracting Fractions:** $\dfrac{a}{b} - \dfrac{c}{b} = \dfrac{a-c}{b}$	**Add or Subtract.** (a) $\dfrac{-5}{8} + \dfrac{3}{8}$ (b) $\dfrac{15}{36} - \left(-\dfrac{5}{36}\right)$ **Solution:** (a) $\dfrac{-5}{8} + \dfrac{3}{8} = \dfrac{-2}{8} = -\dfrac{\cancel{2} \cdot 1}{\cancel{2} \cdot 2 \cdot 2} = -\dfrac{1}{4}$

Chapter 2 Review

Section 2. 1 Introduction to Integers

Write an integer to represent the number in each situation.
1. The highest point in Europe is at Mount Elbrus, Russia, where the elevation is 5,642 meters above sea level.
2. The lowest point in Africa is at Lake Assal, Djbouti, which is 512 feet below sea level.

Plot the points on a number line.
3. {2, -6, -8, 11, 9}
4. {25, -40, 80, 105, -95}, using a scale of 10.

Simplify.
5. $-(-51)$
6. $-(3)$
7. $-(-(-91))$
8. $|-14|$

9. $|345|$
10. $-|-671|$
11. $|-13+18|$
12. $|-29| + |-73|$

Compare the following using < or >.
13. $-31 \underline{\quad} -35$

14. $-25 \underline{\quad} |-45|$

16. $-|-10|$ ___ $-|-14|$

15. $-(-13)$ ___ $-|-15|$

Section 2. 2 Adding Integers

Add.

17. $17+98$

18. $-73+95$

19. $-45+(-23)$

20. $-18+(-7)$

21. $15+(-21)$

22. $-35+67$

23. $-617+892$

24. $-1209+(-582)$

25. $48+(-34)+(-81)+17$

26. $-52+(-40)+79+(-103)$

27.   **Stocks:** What is the overall result for this stock over this two-day period:
Wednesday: a *loss* of 5 points
Thursday: a *gain* of 2 points

28.   **Diving:** A driver is lifted down to 97 feet below the surface and then he swims down another 30 feet. What is her current depth as an integer?

29.   **Checking:** Sandra checks her checking account to find she has made a mistake and over drafted her account. The current balance is -$318. She immediately goes and makes a deposit of $783. What is her new account balance?

Section 2. 3 Subtracting Integers

Rewrite as addition.

30. $18-24$

31. $-36-(-15)$

32. $-83-41$

33. $13-(-59)$

Subtract or Add.

34. $81-(-19)$

35. $-123-(-5)$

36. $-50-81$

37. $-73-78$

38. $-41-37$

39. $15-(-83)$

40. $-98-(-41)+78$

41. $24+(-54)-(38)+71$

42.   **Checking:** Mark's checking account has a balance of $345 currently. He makes a deposit of $256 and then writes a check for $512. What is his new account balance?

43.   **Checking:** Chelsea has overdrawn her account and has -$189 as a current balance. She has two additional checks outstanding for $129 and $39. She hurries to the bank and makes a deposit of $312. Is her account still overdrawn after the checks clear and how much does she have as a current balance?

44.   **Elevation:** The Dead Sea Ultra Marathon starts at 900m above sea level and ends at 400m below sea level. Find the difference in the elevations to find the total meters of descent on this marathon.

Section 2. 4 Multiplying And Dividing Integers

Multiply or Divide.

45. $-4\cdot12$

46. $0(-17)$

47. $(-21)(-16)$

48. $(-27)\cdot5$

49. $(-34)(-21)$

50. $6(0)(-23)$

51. $(-6)(19)(-10)$

52. $25(-16)(-20)$

53. $102\div(-6)$

54. $-432\div(-12)$

55. $315\div(-45)$

56. $\dfrac{0}{-43}$

57. $-980 \div (-20)$

58. $-3042 \div 18$

59. $-\dfrac{91}{0}$

60. $2088 \div (-72)$

61. Brooke has a rental house that she rents for \$825 a month. If she does not have a rented for 8 months, represent the amount of money she lost over the 8 month period as an integer.

62. A submarine off the coast of Brazil is diving at a rate of 80 feet per minute. Represent the depth of the submarine after 14 minutes as an integer.

Section 2. 5 Exponents And Order Of Operations With Integers

Rewrite each product using exponential form.

63. $(-5)(-5)(-5)$

64. $(-7)(-7)(-3)(-3)(-3)(-3)$

Without multiplying, rewrite each exponential expression in expanded form.

65. $(-9)^4$

66. $(-4)^2(-5)^4$

Simplify.

67. $(-3)^4$

68. -3^4

Simplify.

69. $\dfrac{5-(-4)}{-12+(-26)}$

70. $(-3)^3 + 4(-3)^2 - 5(-3) + 1$

71. $(-9)^2$

72. $(-5)^3$

73. $-4^2 \cdot 3$

74. $-36 \div 2 \cdot (-3)$

75. $-3^2 - 9 + 18 \div 6$

76. $\dfrac{5(-9)+12}{-2^3-3}$

77. $-4\left(4^3 + (-3)^2 - 14\right) + (8-9)^5$

78. $8 - 3 \cdot \left[8 - 2\left(9 - 2^2\right) + (-13)\right] + 22$

79. **Evaluate** $b^2 - 4ac$ for $a = -3, b = 8, c = -1$.

80. **Evaluate** $b^2 - 4ac$ for $a = -9, b = -5, c = 11$

81. **Evaluate** $mx + b$ for $m = 2, b = -14, x = -3$

82. **Evaluate** $mx + b$ for $m = 7, b = 25, x = -9$

83. **Find the average:** -15, 32, -43, -49, 30

84. **Find the average:** -87, 95, 75, -103

Section 2. 6 Fractions That Involve Integers

Simplify.

85. $-\dfrac{15}{25}$

86. $\dfrac{8}{-16}$

87. $\dfrac{-45}{81}$

88. $\dfrac{21}{77}$

Perform the indicated operation.

89. $\dfrac{7}{15} + \dfrac{4}{15}$

90. $\dfrac{7}{18} + \dfrac{5}{18}$

91. $\left(\dfrac{-2}{9}\right)\left(\dfrac{-1}{3}\right)$

92. $\dfrac{-7}{8} \div \left(\dfrac{-4}{7}\right)$

93. $\dfrac{18}{35} - \dfrac{-3}{35}$

94. $\dfrac{15}{16} \cdot \left(\dfrac{-8}{27}\right)$

95. $-\dfrac{5}{24} \div \dfrac{10}{21}$

96. $-\dfrac{11}{18} - \dfrac{5}{18}$

97. $\dfrac{17}{42} - \left(-\dfrac{5}{42}\right)$

98. $\left(\dfrac{-21}{55}\right) \cdot \left(\dfrac{22}{35}\right)$

99. $\left(\dfrac{-1}{7}\right) \div \left(\dfrac{-3}{5}\right)$

100. $\dfrac{-9}{26} + \dfrac{-11}{26}$

Chapter 2 Test Yourself

You should give yourself about 90 minutes to complete these problems. DO NOT use notes, your book or any outside source of help, ONLY YOURSELF. Put question marks by the problems you are unsure about, but TRY all of the problems. Once your time is up, check your answers on page #.

1. Graph on a number line: -7, 0, 3
2. List all the even integers between -10 and 5.
3. $|-17|$
4. $-(-23)$
5. $21 - 5$
6. $-125 + (-16)$
7. $21 - (-56)$
8. $-187 + 78$
9. $-91 - (-37)$
10. $1023 + (-2304)$
11. $-542 - (-267)$
12. $-10345 + (-34907)$
13. $0(28)$
14. $(-9)(4)(-3)$
15. $\dfrac{-48}{-6}$

16. $(-5)^3$
17. -4^2
18. $(-3)^4$
19. $\dfrac{68}{0}$
20. $-14 \div 7(-2) \div 4(0)$
21. $9 + 2(5-8)^3$
22. $(-24) \div 3 \cdot (-2)$
23. $3^2 - 5\left\{\left[15 \div (-5) \cdot 2^3\right] - 23\right\}$
24. $\dfrac{12 + 4(-5)}{5^2 - 3 \cdot 7}$

25. Evaluate $mx + b$ for m = 3, x = -2 and b = 17

26. $\dfrac{7}{12} + \left(-\dfrac{1}{12}\right)$
27. $-\dfrac{29}{63} - \left(\dfrac{-47}{63}\right)$
28. $\dfrac{7}{18} \cdot \left(-\dfrac{9}{14}\right)$

29. $\dfrac{-15}{54} \div \left(-\dfrac{4}{45}\right)$
30. $\dfrac{14}{15} \cdot \dfrac{5}{8} \div \left(\dfrac{-4}{9}\right)$

31. Cari has a loan for $1948. She gets paid $278 and applies all of it toward the loan. Represent the balance on the loan as an integer.
32. Gretchen has $1,278 in her checking account. She pays $132 on her credit card bill, $325 on utilities and $675 on rent. She then deposits $451 into her account. What is her new balance?
33. Kevin charges $6240 on his credit card over six months. How much did he charge each month on average?
34. Tarah buys a new Trek bike and gets a loan for 12 months same as cash. She puts down $79 and plans to make monthly payments of $115 to pay the bike off in a year before any interest is added. How much was the purchase price of the bike?
35. Raul is the manager of Running is Fun sports store. Last year his salary was $47,359. This year, his salary increased to $53,985. By how much did his salary increase?
36. Hoggard High School is taking all 875 freshman civic students to Washington DC as a field trip for 3 nights. If each hotel room can accommodate 4 students, how many rooms need to booked for the trip?

Chapter 2 Cumulative Review

Find the prime factorization.

1. 72

2. 156

3. What factors of 18 have a sum of 11?
4. What factors of 56 have a sum of 15?
5. Place the following numbers on a number line: -2, 0, 5, -17, 9
6. Place the following numbers on a number line using a scale of 5:
   -40, 35, 25, -20, -15, 60

7. Which of the following numbers are integers? $-15, \dfrac{-2}{3}, 19, 0, \dfrac{12}{3}, 87$

Order the numbers using < or >.

8. $-34 \underline{\quad} -43$

9. $-98 \underline{\quad} 5$

Round to the specified place.

10. 71,289; hundreds

11. 319, 002; hundred thousands

Reduce the fraction:

12. $\dfrac{-121}{132}$

13. $\dfrac{570}{1920}$

Perform the indicated operation.

14. $68+114+37$
15. $295-117$
16. $372 \cdot 83$
17. $823 \cdot 0$
18. -5^2
19. $95 \div 0$
20. $1524 \div 12$
21. $-34-(-91)$
22. $0 \div (-523)$
23. $\dfrac{4}{9}-\dfrac{1}{9}$
24. $\dfrac{48}{65} \cdot \left(-\dfrac{39}{56}\right)$

25. $\dfrac{-81}{0}$

26. $\dfrac{16}{49}+\dfrac{5}{49}$

27. $-\dfrac{17}{25}-\left(-\dfrac{12}{25}\right)$

28. $\dfrac{13}{18} \cdot \dfrac{12}{17}$

29. $\dfrac{25}{38} \div \left(-\dfrac{10}{19}\right)$

Simplify using order of operations.

30. $2 \cdot (-3)^2$
31. $|-10|-|-21|$
32. $-(-14)+|34|$
33. $36 \div 3 \cdot 2$
34. $16+7(-5)$

35. $(-16)(0)(-5)+14$
36. $-5(7+4)+2^3$
37. $5+2\left(17-3^2\right)-15 \div 3$
38. $\dfrac{5 \cdot 7-3(25-24)^5}{8(15-9) \div 3}$

Evaluate the expression using the value given.

39. $12+x$, $x=25$
40. $2x-13$, $x=-4$
41. $3x-y+z$, $x=5, y=-2, z=-9$
42. $a-b$, $a=\dfrac{-3}{16}, b=\dfrac{7}{16}$

43. $mx + b$, $m = -4, x = -1, b = 8$

44. $b^2 - 4ac$, $a = 3, b = -2, c = -5$

45. Maribel's ipod currently has 314 songs on it. She downloads some new music and adds 78 songs to her play list. How many songs are now on her ipod?

46. It takes Summer 9 minutes to run a mile. On Monday, she ran 13 miles. How long did it take her in minutes?

47. Lydia buys 650 shares of Target stock at $23 per share. How much did she invest in Target?

48. Roland has 3500 shares of a stock that went down $7 per share on Friday. How much did he lose in his stocks on Friday?

49. There are 47 desks in the 13 classrooms in the Math department at a local community college. How many students can the classrooms accommodate at any given time?

50. Find the average of the daily temperatures over a 4 day period in New York City:
    $-15°, -6°, -5°, 10°$.

This Chapter is about simplifying expressions and solving equations.

Solve the equation.

$$-6x + 8 = 2x$$

Simplify the expression.

$$3(x + 5) - 7x$$

What's Inside?!
3.1 More About Algebraic Expressions
Succeed in Math!
3.2 Algebraic Equations and Their Solutions
3.3 Basic Properties of Equality
3.4 More About Solving Equations
3.5 Problem Solving
3.6 Introduction to Algebraic Fractions
Chapter Summary
Chapter Review
Test Yourself

Courtesy of
Fotolia

Succeed in Math!

In this Chapter we'll give you some tips on Time Management. Time Management means making time to study and sticking to it.

Find out how businesses use variables, expressions, and equations!

Nintendo Wii! On SALE Now!
Just $199 plus $39 per controller and $49 per game!

$$199 + 39c + 49g$$

Courtesy of Fotolia

Plus: Distributing negatives…

$$-3(2x - 8) = -3(2x) - (-3)(8) = -6x + 24$$

3.1 More About Algebraic Expressions

Topics:

- Terminology
- Combining Like Terms
- The Distributive Property
- A General Strategy For Simplifying Expressions

Are You Ready?

To see if you are ready to understand this section, do the following short quiz.

1. $4+(-2)$
2. $5-7+13$
3. $3(4+9)$

Answers to Are You Ready?

(1) 2   (2) 11   (3) 39

Terminology

Recall from Chapter 1 that an **expression** is a combination of operations, numbers and variables.

Numeric expressions contain only operations and numbers.

$$4(3-5) \qquad\qquad 3^2+5(3)-7$$

Algebraic expressions contain operations, number, and variables.

$$2b-7 \qquad\qquad x^2-2x+9$$

Let's learn the terminology involved with studying algebraic expressions.

The parts of an expression separated by addition are called the **terms** of an expression. Terms preceded by subtraction are considered negative.

A term will involve multiplication, division, and/or exponents of numbers and/or variables. If a term is preceded by subtraction, it is considered a negative term.

Example 1: How many terms are in each expression? List the terms.

a) $2x-3$ b) $2y^2-6y+3y-9$ c) $2wh+2wl+2hl$

Solution: Remember that the terms are the parts separated by addition or subtraction and that a term is considered negative if it is preceded by subtraction.

a) This expression has two terms: $2x$ and -3

b) This expression has four terms: $2y^2$, $-6y$, $3y$, -9

c) This expression has three terms: $2wh$, $2wl$, and $2hl$

Next...

The **coefficient** of a term is the numeric factor for that term.

Let's look at the coefficients in an expression with several terms.

$$5a^4 - 7a^3 + a^2 - a - 8$$

The coefficient of this term is 5	The coefficient of this term is -7, not 3. The coefficient is the number being *multiplied*, not the power.	The coefficient of this term is 1 since $a^2 = 1 \cdot a^2$	The coefficient of this term is -1 since $-a$ $= (-1)a$	A term with no variable is called a **constant term**. The coefficient of this term is -8.

Every term in an expression has a coefficient, even if we use 1 or -1 and even if the term and coefficient are the same, as with the constant term -8 above.

Example 2: List the coefficients in the following expression: $-8x + 3x^2y - x^3 + 10$

Solution: Remember that coefficients are the numeric factor, not the power. The coefficients are -8, 3, -1, and 10.

STOP Exercise Set - Terminology

Fill in the blanks with the correct vocabulary word.
1. The pieces of an expression separated by addition or subtraction are called the _____ of the expression.
2. The _____ of a term is the number being multiplied to that term.
3. A term with no variable is called a _____.

List the terms in each expression.
4. $3a + 6b - 7a - 9$
5. $-x^2 + 4x - 3$

In each expression give the number of terms, list the coefficients, and identify the constant term if there is one.

6. $5v + (-4w)$

7. $8x^2 - 5x + 12$

8. $x^2 - 9y^2$

9. $-xy^3$

10. $-9y^2 + 3y - 17$

11. $5a^3 + 7a^2 - a + 16$

Succeed in Math!   Time Management

Succeeding in math and college means balancing work and play.

In this chapter we will give you some tips on managing your time to make passing math and succeeding in college a priority.

Well, first of all, how many hours a week should I be studying?

How ever many hours it takes! But to get an idea, how hours a week does your class meet?

If your class meets 3 hours a week, you should study between 6 and 9 hours a week outside class.

If your class meets 4 hours a week, you should study between 8 and 12 hours a week outside class.

If your class meets 3 hours a week, you should study between 10 and 15 hours a week outside class.

Combining Like Terms

Have you ever heard the phrase "you can't add apples and oranges"?

4 apples + 3 apples = 7 apples   4 oranges + 7 oranges = 11 oranges

3 apples + 5 oranges cannot be added

This simple idea is actually very important in Algebra. Often expressions can be simplified by combining their terms, but we can only combine terms that are *like*.

Like terms are terms that have the exact same variable(s) raised to the exact same power(s).

Examples of Like Terms

$5y$, $-7y$, $8y$ These terms are *like terms* since they all have the same variable y raised to the same power, 1.

b^3, $-5b^3$ These are *like terms* since they have the same variables raised to the same powers.

16, -5, -8, 10   All constant terms are *like terms*.

Examples of Terms That Are NOT Like

$5x$, $-7y$ These are not like terms because they do not have the same variable.

$2b$, $7b^2$ These are not like terms because, while they have the same variable, the powers are different.

$3a^2b$, $5a^2$ These terms use both use a^2, so they look similar. But the second term does not have the variable b, so they are not like terms.

Example 3: In each case, determine if all the terms given are like terms.

a) $4t^2, 7t^2$ b) $3wr^2, -4wr^2$ c) $-5y, 7y^2$

Solution: Remember, like terms have the same variable(s) raised to the same power(s).

a) $4t^2, 7t^2$ are like terms.

b) $3wr^2, -4wr^2$ are like terms.

c) $-5y, 7y^2$ are not like terms.

Work in Algebra involves recognizing when terms are like terms. Two or more like terms can be combined into a single term. For example, the two terms in the expression $3x + 4x$ can be combined into the single term $7x$. Why? Recall that multiplication represents repeated addition:

$$3x + 4x = \overbrace{x+x+x}^{3x} + \overbrace{x+x+x+x}^{4x}$$

There seven x's total
which we
represent as $7x$.

This illustrates our next procedure:

To Combine Two or More Like Terms: Add or subtract the coefficients of the like terms without changing the variable(s).

Example 4: Each of the following expressions consists of two or more like terms. Combine into a single term.

a) $4x^2 + 7x^2$ b) $6ab + 7ab - 2ab$

Solution: In each case we combine the like terms by adding or subtraction the coefficients

a) $4x^2 + 7x^2 = (4+7)x^2 = 11x^2$

b) $6ab + 7ab - 2ab = (6+7-2)ab = 11ab$

Combining like terms is one way to *simplify* an algebraic expression. Consider the expression

$$8x + 5y + 3x + 7 + y + 11 + 2x$$

This expression has seven terms, and several of them are like terms. Let's rearrange the expression to group the like terms together. We can do this since addition is commutative: $a + b = b + a$.

$$\underbrace{8x + 3x + 2x}_{\text{like terms}} + \underbrace{5y + y}_{\text{like terms}} + \underbrace{7 + 11}_{\text{like terms}}$$

Now we combine the like terms by adding their coefficients

$$\underbrace{8x + 3x + 2x}_{} + \underbrace{5y + y}_{} + \underbrace{7 + 11}_{}$$

$$13x \quad + \quad 6y \quad + \quad 18$$

This is considered simplified form or the simplified expression.

Example 5: Simplify each expression by combining like terms.

a) $3a + 11 - 5a + 2$ b) $3x + 7y + 2 - 9y + 4$ c) $6x^2 + 3x - 16x - 8$

Solution:

a) Rearrange the algebraic expression with the like terms grouped together.

$3a + 11 - 5a + 2$
$= 3a - 5a + 11 + 2$

Combine like terms and the final answer is:

$= -2a + 13$

b) Rewrite the algebraic expression with the like terms grouped together.

$3x + 7y + 2 - 9y + 4$
$= 3x + 7y - 9y + 2 + 4$

Combine like terms and the final answer is:

$= 3x - 2y + 6$

c) Combine like terms. Remember that we add the coefficients and not the exponents.

$6x^2 + 3x - 16x - 8$

$= 6x^2 - 13x - 8$

Example 6: Suppose that a fellow student shows you the following work.

$$5x + 3x - 7 + 10$$
$$8x^2 - 17$$

There are two mistakes in the work. What are they?

Solution:
Mistake #1: $\qquad 5x + 3x = 8x$, not $8x^2$

Mistake #2: $\qquad -7 + 10 = 3$, not -17

The correct simplification would be $\quad \begin{array}{l} 5x + 3x - 7 + 10 \\ \qquad 8x + 3 \end{array}$

Example 7: Where in the World?
Bruce makes wooden basinets to sell. To make each basinet it costs $45 for wood, $13 for brackets, and $28 for trim. If the variable b represents the number of basinets he makes, then the expression $45b + 13b + 28b$ gives the total cost. Simplify the expression by combing like terms.

Solution: $\quad 45b + 13b + 28b = 86b$

In each case, determine if the terms given are like terms.

12. $6n, -13n$

13. $7x^2, -2x$

14. $15y^3x, \ -3yx^3$

15. $8b^2, -13b^2$

Simplify each expression by combining like terms.

16. $3x + 5x$

17. $6d - 9d$

18. $-5a + 8b + 7a$

19. $-12x + 16y + 9y$

20. $-3x + 6y + 8x + 10y$

21. $-6x^2 + 18x^2$

22. A company makes two types of tables: outdoor and indoor. To make an outdoor table costs $15 in labor and $8 in parts. To make an indoor table costs $24 in labor and $13 in parts. If the variable x represents the number of outdoor tables made and the variable y represents the number of indoor tables made then the expression $15x + 8x + 24y + 13y$ gives the total cost. Simplify the expression by combining like terms.

23. Every textbook made by a publisher costs $14 for materials, $10 for royalties, $32 for printing service, and $18 for supplementary materials. If c represents the total number of textbooks produced then the total is given by the expression $14c + 10c + 32c + 18c$. Simplify the expression by combining like terms.

The Distributive Property

Consider the expression $3(x + 5)$. According to the order of operations, we should perform the addition inside the parentheses first, then multiply the result by 3. But, since x represents an unknown value we cannot add first. We can, however, simplify the expression using a technique called *distribution*.

The Distributive Property:
A sum or difference multiplied by a number can be simplified by multiplying each term of the sum or difference by the number.

$$a(b + c) = a \cdot b + a \cdot c$$

$$a(b - c) = a \cdot b - a \cdot c$$

Going back to our expression, $3(x + 5)$, we see that it can be simplified using distribution as follows:

$$3(x + 5)$$
$$= 3 \cdot x + 3 \cdot 5$$
$$= 3x + 15$$

Example 8: Use the distributive property to simplify each expression.
a) $4(2x - 7)$ b) $-5(3 + 2x)$ c) $-2(7x - 15)$

Solution: In each case we multiply the number outside the parentheses to each term inside.
a) $4(2x - 7)$

Distribute the 4. $4(2x - 7) = 4 \cdot 2x - 4 \cdot 7$

Multiply and simplify. $= 8x - 28$

b) $-5(3 + 2x)$

When a negative number is distributed, be careful about dealing with the resulting positive/negative and addition/subtraction signs.

Distribute the -5. $-5(3 + 2x) = (-5) \cdot 3 + (-5) \cdot 2x$

Multiply. $= -15 + (-10x)$

Simplify. $= -15 - 10x$

c) $-2(7x-15)$

Distribute the -2.	$-2(7x-15)=(-2)\cdot 7x-(-2)\cdot 15$
Multiply.	$=-14x-(-30)$
Simplify.	$=-14x+30$

The form $-15-10x$ is considered a simpler form than $-15+(-10x)$ and $-14x+30$ is considered a simpler form than $-14x-(-30)$, so that is how we tend to write final answers.

Sometimes we may just see a negative sign front of parentheses, as in $-(4a-7)$. This is shorthand for multiplication by -1.

$$-(4a-7)=-1\cdot(4a-7)$$
$$=(-1)4a-(-1)7$$
$$=-4a-(-7)$$
$$=-4a+7$$

Most professors call this "distributing a negative sign" or "taking the opposite of an expression"..

Example 9: Simply each expression.
a) $-(-3+5y)$ b) $-(-9d-10)$

Solution: In each case we distribute the negative sign as a -1.

a) Rewrite the negative in front of the parenthesis as a -1.
$$-(-3+5y)=-1(-3+5y)$$
Distribute the -1.
$$=(-1)(-3)+(-1)\cdot 5y$$
Simplify and change addition of adding a negative to subtraction.
$$=3+(-5y)$$
The final answer is:
$$=3-5y$$

b) Rewrite the negative in front of the parenthesis as a -1.
$$-(-9d-10)=-1\cdot(-9d-10)$$
Distribute the -1.
$$=(-1)\cdot(-9d)-(-1)\cdot 10$$
Simplify and change subtraction of a negative to addition.
$$=9d-(-10)$$
The final answer is:
$$=9d+10$$

Using distribution is a technique for which many students do not need to show many steps. In fact, most students go from the original expression straight to the final answer in one step. Look at these simplified expressions and see if you understand without seeing the extra steps.

Using Distribution

[PN: Can we make this look like hand-writing with arrows?]

$4(5x-3)$	$-3(4+2h)$	$-(6x-8)$
$=20x-12$	$=-12-6h$	$=-6x+8$

All of our examples so far have had two terms in the parentheses. But distribution works the same no matter how many terms are inside the parentheses.

Example 10: Use distribution to simplify each expression.

a) $5(-2a+4b-9)$ b) $-(4h^3+3h^2-5h+9)$

Solution: In each case we multiply the number on the outside to each term in the parentheses.

a) $5(-2a+4b-9)$

Distribute the 5. $5(-2a+4b-9)=5\cdot(-2a)+5\cdot4b-5\cdot9$

Simplify. $=-10a+20b-45$

b) $-(4h^3+3h^2-5h+9)$

Rewrite, recall that a negative sign is $-(4h^3+3h^2-5h+9)=-1(4h^3+3h^2-5h+9)$
distributed as a -1.

Distribute the -1.

$=(-1)\cdot4h^3+(-1)\cdot3h^2-(-1)\cdot5h+(-1)\cdot9$

Simplify. $=-4h^3-3h^2-(-5h)+(-9)$

The final answer is: $=4h^3-3h^2+5h-9$

It is okay if you do not need the middle steps. Just be careful! Look at
these simplified expressions and see if you understand without seeing the extra steps.

Using Distribution

[PN: Can we make this look like hand-writing and show the distribution arcs?]

$3(2a-7b+5)$ $-2(x^2-11x+9)$ $-(4g^3-9g^2+8g-1)$

$=6a-21b+15$ $=-2x^2+22x-18$ $=-4g^3+9g^2-8g+1$

Example 11: Where in the World?
A promotion for 7 Hour Energy Drink is selling vendors the drink for \$3 each and the first 25 are free.
This means the total charge will be $3(x-25)$. Use distribution to simplify the expression $3(x-25)$.

Solution: $3(x-25)=3x-75$

Use the distributive property to simplify each expression.

24. $5(3x+1)$
25. $2(5x-7)$
26. $-4(m-6)$
27. $-5(x+9)$
28. $-7(2y+6)$

29. $-2(3g-6)$
30. $-(4t+1)$
31. $-(-5t+3)$
32. $-(9x^2-13x+6)$
33. $-(-3x^2+4x-15)$

34. $-5\left(3h^3-6h^2+11h+1\right)$

35. $4\left(-2g^3+4g^2-g+8\right)$

36. A train leaves two hours behind schedule and travels at a rate of 75 miles per hour. If t represents the amount of time since the scheduled departure then the expression $75(t-2)$ gives the total distance traveled. Use distribution to simplify the expression $75(t-2)$.

37. A book printer charges \$7 to print each book after the first 150. This means the total cost of printing b books is given by $7(b-150)$. Use distribution to simplify the expression $7(b-150)$.

A General Strategy For Simplifying Expressions

Combining like terms and the distributive property are two of the most important techniques through all of Algebra. Simplifying most expressions will require both distribution and combining like terms. Here are guidelines that show how to proceed.

To Simplify an Algebraic Expression:
1. Use the distributive property to remove any parentheses.
2. Combine like terms.

This is one of the most common procedures in all of Algebra: distribute *then* combine like terms.

Example 12: Simplify each expression.

a) $3(2w+4)+4(5+w)$ b) $4+3(2x+1-5y)-6x$

Solution: We will perform the distribution in one step.

a) Distribute the 3 and the 4. $3(2w+4)+4(5+w)=6w+12+20+4w$

Combine like terms and simplify. $=10w+32$

b) It is tempting to add $4+3$ at the beginning of the expression, but the 3 is being multiplied to the parentheses, so we must resolve that first. In general, always distribute to remove parentheses before you combine any like terms.

Distribute the 3. $4+3(2x+1-5y)-6x=4+6x+3-15y-6x$

Combine like terms and simplify. $=-5y+7$
Note that $6x-6x=0$.

$5-2(x+7)=5+(-2)(x+7)$

$\quad =5+(-2)\cdot x+(-2)\cdot 7$

$\quad =5+(-2x)+(-14)$

$\quad =5-2x-14$

If parentheses have subtraction as the operation in front of them, then the negative sign is distributed into the parentheses, whether there is a number included or not. This creates a sort of dual role for the minus sign. In the expression $5-2(x+7)$ the minus sign represents subtraction, but we distribute as if it were the number -2.

Example 13: Simplify each expression.

a) $4x - 2(x + 3)$ b) $-5(2d + 7) - 4(3 - d)$

Solution: Remember that a subtraction in front of parentheses results in distributing a negative.

a) $4x - 2(x + 3)$
Distribute the -2. $4x - 2(x + 3) = 4x - 2x - 6$

Combine like terms and simplify. $= 2x - 6$

b) $-5(2d + 7) - 4(3 - d)$
Distribute the -5 and the -4. $-5(2d + 7) - 4(3 - d) = -10d - 35 - 12 + 4d$

Combine like terms and simplify. $= -6d - 47$

Example 14: Where in the World?
A printing company charges a flat fee of $1500 plus $3 per book for printing and $2 per book for shipping. However, the first 100 books can be shipped for free. The total cost of producing x books is given by the expression $1500 + 3x + 2(x - 100)$. Simplify the expression.

Solution: We are just asked to simplify the expression $1500 + 3x + 2(x - 100)$.
Distribute the 2. $1500 + 3x + 2(x - 100) = 1500 + 3x + 2(x) - 2(100)$

Mulitply. $= 1500 + 3x + 2x - 200$

Combine like terms and simplify. $= 1300 + 5x$

Exercise Set - A General Strategy For Simplifying Expressions

Simplify each expression.

38. $5(2x + 1) + 8$

39. $4(3x - 5) + 9x$

40. $2t + 3(7t - 2)$

41. $-8(3y + 5) - 9$

42. $-3(k + 5) + 2(4k - 8)$

43. $7(2d - 4) - 4(3d + 1)$

44. $5(-3x + 4) - (7x - 12)$

45. $-2(p + 5) + 3(5p - 2)$

46. $-5 + 4(x + 1) + 7x$

47. $12 - 3(2x - 9) + 5x$

Exercise Set - Putting It ALL Together

48. What is the difference between a term and a coefficient?

49. Give an example of an expression that contains three like terms.

50. What is the difference between and term and a factor? (Hint: You can find the definition of *factor* in Section 1.4.)

51. What two procedures are discussed in this section for simplifying algebraic expressions? Which of these two procedures should always be done first?

Simplify each numeric expression two ways: using the order of operations and again using distribution.

52. $9(7+2)$

53. $5(12-3)$

54. $11(6-13)$

55. $2(1-19)$

Simplify the following expressions if possible.

56. $-4k+9k$

57. $-7h^3+8h^3$

58. $2x+9y$

59. $3x^2-3x$

60. $7p-0$

61. $0-7p$

62. $5g-5g$

63. $7(2x+3)$

64. $17x^2+3x^2-5$

65. $-3x+5y+8x+4x$

66. $6-12a+6a+18a$

67. $6(y-7)+23$

68. $9(4-n)-3$

69. $3m+24m-25m$

70. $7(g+2)-2(3g+1)$

71. $19-4(2b+5)$

72. $-12+7(4t+3)$

73. $-4(3a+1)-(-5a+7)$

74. $8(9-7x)$

75. $32-(7x+2)-14$

76. $12+6(8-3x)+15x$

77. Quicksilver is a clothing company that is considering a new line of shirts. It will cost $2500 for equipment plus $3 per shirt for material and $2 per shirt for shipping. The total cost of producing x shirts is given by the expression $2500+3x+2x$. Simplify the expression.

78. A toy company is making a new product. The cost of making the new toy will be $10,750 up front for equipment plus $5 per toy for materials and $4 per toy for labor. The total cost of producing t toys is given by the expression $10750+5t+4t$. Simplify the expression.

79. A moving company charges a flat fee of $750 plus $25 per hour. However, the first 3 hours are free. The total cost of having the moving company for h is given by the expression $750+25(h-3)$. Simplify the expression.

80. Be Well Fitness gym orders its recovery drinks online from a supplier. The drinks are $3 each but the supplier is having a special for large orders where the first 20 are free. If shipping costs $150 then the cost of buying d drinks is given by the expression $150+3(d-20)$. Simplify the expression.

81. Suppose that a fellow student shows you the following work:

$$-3g+g+13+(-10)$$
$$-3g-130$$

There are two mistakes in the work. What are they?

82. Suppose that a fellow student shows you the following work:

$$-2(4x+3)-7-10$$
$$-8x+6-3$$

There are two mistakes in the work. What are they?

83. Simplify $x\cdot x$ and $x+x$.

84. Simplify $b \cdot b \cdot b$ and $b+b+b+b$.
85. Simplify $(y)(y)(y)(y)$ and $y+y+y+y$.
86. Simplify $a \cdot a \cdot b \cdot b \cdot b \cdot b$ and $a+a+b+b+b+b$.
87. Simplify $x \cdot y \cdot x \cdot x \cdot y$ and $x+y+x+x+y$.
88. Simplify $9+5x$ and $(9)5x$.
89. Simplify $4 \cdot 5x \cdot 2$ and $4+5x+2$.

90. Consider the expression $-5+2(x+7)$
    a)   Evaluate the expression for $x=3$.
    b)   Simplify the expression.
    c)   Evaluate the simplified form for $x=3$.
    d)   What is your observation?

91. Consider the expression $-3(b+5)+7$
    a)   Evaluate the expression for $b=-2$.
    b)   Simplify the expression.
    c)   Evaluate the simplified form for $b=-2$.
    d)   What is your observation?

Exercise Set - Cumulative Review

92. Add and reduce, if possible. $\left(-\dfrac{6}{7}\right)+\left(\dfrac{3}{7}\right)$

93. Fill in the blank with < or >. $48\_\_\_-25$
94. Find the perimeter. [PN: triangle with sides 6ft, 9ft, and 12ft]
95. Is $3x+8=17$ an equation or an expression?
96.   Use long division to determine if 1564 is divisible by 4.

3.1 QUIZ YOURSELF:

To make sure you are ready for the EXAM, try these problems without any help. Give yourself about 20 minutes and don't check the answers until you have completely finished.

1. Consider the expression $-3x^2+5x-21$.
    a.   List the terms in the expression.
    b.   List the coefficients in the expression.
    c.   Does the expression have a constant term? If so, what is it?

Simplify.
2. $15x + 3y - 7x$
3. $3(2x - 5) + 8$
4. $19 + 3(y - 4)$
5. $2(3x - 7) + 3(5x - 11)$
6. $-(8 - x)$
7. $-3\left(7h^2 - 4h + 12\right)$
8. $16x + 6(4 - 3x) + 17$

Answers to this Quiz Yourself are on page 656.

Succeed in Math!   Managing Your Time

"A fruit never tasted so sweet as the one you walked furthest to pick."
AUTHOR UNKNOWN

Simply put...Succeeding in Math and College takes long hard work. But it sure is worth it!

THE COLLEGE RULE

To realize your potential in College you should study for 2 to 4 hours outside class for every hour you spend in class

This is why taking 12 credit hours makes you a "full-time" student! This is how college's decide how material should be in a course.

EXERCISE #1   Course Time Commitment Evaluation

Think about all your classes and make a quick judgment about whether you think their difficulty level is Easy, Medium, or Hard. Try this quick survey to get an idea of how much time you should be spending studying every week.

_____credit hours from easy classes × 2 = _____ hours

_____credit hours from medium classes × 3 = _____ hours

_____credit hours from hard classes × 4 = _____ hours

Total study hours per week = _____ hours

If you are not already studying this much, try it and see what happens! A lot of students think math is unmanageable are just not aware of college's demanding expectations on their time.

TIME MANAGEMENT STRATEGIES

*   **Prioritize your activities**. Make college one of your top priorities!
*   **Set realistic goals.** Set a goal to pass the next test or to do math everyday!

EXERCISE #2   Setting Goals

Write down three goals for your math class. Make sure that the goals are attainable, but also make sure they will test your abilities. It may not be in your best interest to make one of your goals "Make an A on the next test." How about, "Pass the next test," or "Have my homework complete three days before the test," or "Study for an hour and a half every day."

Goal 1: _____

Goal 2: _____

Goal 3: _____

- **Feeling listless? Make a list!** Making "To Do" lists is a wonderful tool for beginning to develop time management skills. Make a "To Do" list daily or weekly or both.
- **Just say "No".** Your social life is important but it needs to take a backseat to being successful in college.
- **Don't forget to reward yourself!** Discipline IS NOT the art of *avoiding* the fun stuff. Discipline is the art of *delaying* the fun stuff.
- **Use a day planner!**   People who start using day planners quickly wonder how they ever lived without it.

EXERCISE   #3   Trying a Day Planner

In the following day planner, fill out your commitments for a week: classes, work, sports practice, stuff like that. This will help you see how much time you have for studying and think about when you should schedule your study time. Don't forget the College Rule!

Sample Day Planner

Time	Monday	Tuesday	Wednesday	Thursday	Friday	Saturday	Sunday
7:00							
7:30							
8:00							
8:30							
9:00							
9:30							
10:00							
10:30							
11:00							
11:30							
12:00							
12:30							
1:00							
1:30							
2:00							
2:30							
3:00							
3:30							
4:00							
4:30							
5:00							
5:30							
6:00							
6:30							
7:00							
7:30							
8:00							
8:30							
9:00							
9:30							
10:00							
10:30							
11:00							

"If you don't know where you are going, you might wind up someplace else."
YOGI BERRA, *Baseball Hall of Famer*

3.2 Algebraic Equations And Solutions

Topics:
- Expressions Versus Equations
- Identifying Solutions to Equations
- Introduction To Solving Equations

Are You Ready?
1. $16 \div 2 \cdot 4$
2. $32 - 6 \cdot 7$
3. $(-2)^2 + 5 \cdot 3 - 12$

Answers to Are You Ready?
(1) 32   *(2) -10*   *(3) 7*

Expressions Versus Equations

We have devoted a lot of this book to expressions, and with good reason. Every math class you take from here on out will involve lots of algebraic expressions. But generally, the main focus in Algebra is on *equations*.

An **equation** is a statement that two expressions are equal.

For example, the statement $10 + 14 = 4(1 + 5)$ is an equation. Just like expressions, an equation can be numeric or algebraic.

A *numeric equation* has two numeric expressions set equal to each other:

$$4 + 7 = 11 \qquad\qquad -4(1 - 5) = 3^2 - 5^2$$

An *algebraic equation* has two algebraic expressions set equal to each other:

$$y + 9 = -13 \qquad\qquad 5x - 6 = 3(x - 4)$$

It will be important that you can distinguish between an expression and an equation. Just remember that an expression *does not* have an equals sign " = " and an equation *does*.

Examples of Expressions	Examples of Equations
$3(5) + (-4)^2$	$3 + 19 = 2 \cdot 11$
$4x + 5$	$5y - 3 = 2y + 5$
$3a^2 - 2a - 5$	$x^2 - 8x - 20 = 0$
$ad - bc$	$D = ad - bc$

Example 1: Identify whether each is an expression or an equation.

a) $3-4\left[8-(3+2)\right]$ b) $3+(-1)=40\div(3+17)$

c) $3(2a-1)=4a-7$ d) b^2-4ac

Solution: Since an equation is a statement about equality, it must have an equals sign (=).

a) $3-4\left[8-(3+2)\right]$ is an expression since it does not have an equals sign.
b) $3+(-1)=40\div(3+17)$ is an equation since it does have an equals sign.
c) $3(2a-1)=4a-7$ is an equation.
d) b^2-4ac is an expression.

Notice that every equation is made up of two separate expressions; one on the left side of the equals sign and one on the right side of the equals sign.

Example 2: What expression makes up the left side of the equation $4t-2(t+1)=3(t-5)$?

Solution: The expression on the left side is $4t-2(t+1)$.

Equations can be true or false. To decide if a numeric equation is true, use the order of operations to simplify the expression on each side. If the simplified values are equal, then the equation is true. If not, the equation is false.

This equation is true.	This equation is false.
$18\div3=10+(-4)$	$(-3)(5)=(-7)+(-3)$
$6=6$ True	$-15=-10$ False

Example 3: In each case, indicate whether the equation is true or false by simplifying the expressions on each side.

a) $3\cdot(5-8)=(2)(-5)$ b) $\dfrac{-7+3}{2}=-5-(-3)$

c) $7-3(2-4)=4+(-3)+12$

Solution: At each step we can work towards simplifying each side, but it is important to remember to do them separately.
a)
LEFT SIDE: Subtract inside the parenthesis. $3\cdot(5-8)=(2)(-5)$
RIGHT SIDE: Multiply.
LEFT SIDE: Multiply. $3\cdot(-3)=-10$
The left hand side does not equal the right hand $-9=-10$
side, so the equation is false.

b)
LEFT SIDE: Add the numerator. $\dfrac{-7+3}{2}=-5-(-3)$
RIGHT SIDE: Rewrite the subtraction as
addition.
LEFT SIDE: Divide. $\dfrac{-4}{2}=-5+3$
RIGHT SIDE: Add.

The left hand side equals the right hand side, so $-2 = -2$
the equation is true.

c)
LEFT SIDE: Subtract inside the parenthesis. $7 - 3(2-4) = 4 + (-3) + 12$
RIGHT SIDE: Add.
LEFT SIDE: Multiply. $7 - 3(-2) = 1 + 12$
RIGHT SIDE: Add.
LEFT SIDE: Rewrite the subtraction as $7 - (-6) = 13$
addition and add. $7 + 6 = 13$
The left hand side equals the right hand side, so $13 = 13$
the equation is true.

STOP Exercise Set - Expressions versus Equations

Identify whether each is an expression or an equation.

1. $5x - 17$
2. $34y + 5x$
3. $3x + 5 = 14$
4. $4x^2 - 5x + 7$

5. $3x^2 = 27$
6. $-2y^3 - 1 = 8$

In each case, indicate whether the equation is true or false by simplifying the expressions on each side.

7. $16 \div 2 = 13 - 5$
8. $10 \div 5 \cdot 2 = 9 - 5$

9. $2(3 + 5) - 4 = 3^2 \cdot 2$
10. $\dfrac{-30}{-5} = 3 \cdot 2$

Succeed in Math!

SETTING GOALS is a great way to MOTIVATE yourself.

Maybe you could...
- Set a goal to attend class every day!
- Set a goal to study math everyday!
- Then set a goal to pass your next exam!

TWO IMPORTANT POINTS ABOUT GOAL SETTING:
- As you begin make sure to set goals you KNOW you can succeed with!
- As you set a goal make to also set a reward for yourself if you do succeed!

Identifying Solutions to Equations

We now turn our attention to algebraic equations. Whether an algebraic equation is true or false depends on the value of the variable.

The equation $x + 4 = 9$ is TRUE if $x = 5$ because $5 + 4 = 9$ is TRUE.

The equation $x + 4 = 9$ is FALSE if $x = 3$ because $3 + 4 = 9$ is FALSE.

This brings us to our next definition.

The **solution to an equation** is the value of the variable that makes the equation true.

So $x = 5$ is the solution to the equation $x + 4 = 9$. The solution to an equation is not always obvious. For example, $x = 3$ is the solution to the equation $2x + 5 = 14 - x$. Why? Because when we substitute 3 in for x we get a true equation:

$$2x + 5 = 14 - x$$
$$2(3) + 5 = 14 - 3$$
$$6 + 5 = 11 \quad \text{True}$$

To determine if a given number is a solution to an equation:

- Substitute the number given into the equation.
- Use the order of operations to simplify each side to see if the equation is true.

We call this process "checking a solution".

Example 4: Determine whether the given value is the solution to the equation.

a) $2k - 8 = k + 5, \quad k = 10$

b) $5d + 3 = 3d - 7, \quad d = -5$

Solution: In each case we substitute in the variable value given and check to see if the resulting equation is true.

a) Substitute 10 in for k.

$$2k - 8 = k + 5$$
$$2(10) - 8 = 10 + 5$$

Use order of operations to simplify both sides of the equation.

$$20 - 8 = 15$$

The left hand side does not equal the right hand side, so $k = 10$ is not the solution to the equation $2k - 8 = k + 5$.

$$12 = 15$$

b) Substitute -5 in for d.

$$5d + 3 = 3d - 7$$
$$5(-5) + 3 = 3(-5) - 7$$

Use order of operations to simplify both sides of the equation.

$$-25 + 3 = -15 - 7$$

The left hand side equals the right hand side, so $d = -5$ is the solution to the equation $5d + 3 = 3d - 7$.

$$-22 = -22$$

STOP Exercise Set - Identifying Solutions to Equations

Determine whether the given value is the solution to the equation.

11. $x + 6 = 10$; $x = -4$

12. $z - 13 = 11$; $z = 11$

13. $-3x = 15$; $x = -5$

14. $\dfrac{n}{5} = -2$; $n = -10$

15. $2x + 4 = 12$; $x = 3$

16. $-3a + 5 = 2$; $a = -1$

17. $2b + 3 = -3b - 17$; $b = -4$

18. $3t - 9 = t + 2$; $t = 3$

19. $3(y - 2) = 2y + 5$; $y = 2$

20. $-4(a + 3) = 3(5 - a)$; $a = -27$

Introduction to Solving Equations

Now we understand how to identify an equation and decide if a given value is a solution. The main goal in Algebra is to find the solution on your own, which you are now ready to do. The next two sections are devoted to the process of solving equations. As an introduction we will look at solving equations for which the solution is clear if you know your multiplication table.

Example 5: Find the missing value to make the equation true.

a) $[\ ] + 6 = 8$

b) $\dfrac{18}{[\ ]} = 6$

c) $5 + [\ ] = 3^2$

Solution: In each case we use our knowledge of the four basic operations to find the missing value.

a) Since $2 + 6 = 8$, 2 is the missing value: $[2] + 6 = 8$

b) Since $\dfrac{18}{3} = 6$, 3 is the missing value: $\dfrac{18}{[3]} = 6$.

c) This one is easier if we take a step to simplify the right side:

$5 + [\ ] = 3^2$
$5 + [\ ] = 9$ Since 5+4=9, 4 is the missing value: $5 + [4] = 3^2$.

Now let's do the same kind of examples but use variables to express the missing value.

Example 6: Give the solution to each equation.

a) $a - 3 = 7$

b) $\dfrac{x}{2} = -3$

c) $d + 5 = 4 \cdot 2$

Solution: This is exactly like the fill in the blank exercise. Now, however, we are giving the value of a variable.

a) Since $10-3=7$, the solution to the equation $a-3=7$ is $a=10$.

b) Since $\dfrac{-6}{2}=-3$, the solution to the equation $\dfrac{x}{2}=-3$ is $x=-6$.

c) Simplifying the right side we get $d+5=8$. Since $3+5=8$, the solution to the equation $d+5=4\cdot2$ is $d=3$.

These examples are just an introduction to solving equations. In the next section we will look at techniques that will allow us to find the solutions to complicated equations like $5x+9=4(x+3)$.

STOP Exercise Set - Introduction to Solving Equations

Find the missing value to make the equation true.

21. $\square\cdot7=35$

22. $\square+5=18$

23. $\square-2=11$

24. $6+\square=12+3$

25. $\dfrac{\square}{-6}=-3$

26. $\dfrac{\square}{2}=5-8$

Give the solution to each equation.

27. $a+8=10$

28. $d-3=7$

29. $5x=35$

30. $6f=-42$

31. $\dfrac{d}{-4}=-9$

32. $3\cdot d=10-1$

Exercise Set - Putting It ALL Together

33. What does it mean for a number to be the solution to an equation?
34. What is the difference between a numeric equation and an algebraic equation?
35. What is the difference between an expression and an equation?
36. How can you tell if a given value is the solution to an equation?

Check to determine if the given value is a solution to the given equation.

37. $3x-10=-4$; $x=2$
38. $12=5x-3$; $x=4$
39. $8-x=2x-1$; $x=3$
40. $3h+8=h-2$; $h=-5$
41. $b-5=3(b+1)$; $b=7$
42. $y=4y+10$; $y=-4$

Find the missing value to make the equation true.

43. $4+\square=30$

44. $3+\square=56$

45. $3\cdot\square=8+7$

46. $12\cdot\square=-19-5$

47. $20 - \square = 12 - 6$

50. $\dfrac{\square}{4} = -11$

48. $\dfrac{\square}{3} = 7 + 4$

49. $\dfrac{\square}{-5} = -7$

Give the solution to each equation.

51. $5a = 15$

52. $7y = -42$

58. $\dfrac{x}{-3} = -7$

53. $16 - x = 3$

54. $y + 8 = 30$

59. $\dfrac{x}{4} = -6$

55. $x - 6 = 11$

56. $5h = 45$

60. $\dfrac{x}{-2} = -5$

57. $\dfrac{x}{6} = 18$

61.   An electrician needs to cut a 90 inch wire into three pieces so that the second piece is 6 inches longer than the first piece and the third piece is twice as long as the first. To find out how long to make the piece, he should solve the equation $x + (x + 6) + 2x = 90$. He guesses that the solution to the equation is $x = 18$. Is he correct? That is, is $x = 18$ the solution to the equation $x + (x + 6) + 2x = 90$?

62.   A manufacturer needs to find how many items can be produced for $1500. The cost is $525 plus $13 per item. To find out how many items can be made for $1500, they should solve the equation $525 + 13x = 1500$. The manufacturer guesses they can make 85 items. Are they correct? That is, is $x = 85$ a solution to the equation $525 + 13x = 1500$?

One way to find a solution to an equation is to just guess at the solution. In each of the following exercises you are given an equation and several variable values. Which of the variable values is the solution to the equation? If none of the given values is a solution, state this.

63. $5y = y - 8$; $y = -3, y = -2, y = -1, y = 0$

64. $2x + 5 = 9$; $x = -1, x = 0, x = 1, x = 2$

65. $3x + 8 = 5(x + 2)$; $x = -2, x = -1, x = 0, x = 0, x = 1, x = 2$

66. $c - 9 = -5c + 7$; $c = 0, c = 1, c = 2, c = 3$

Exercise Set - Chapter 3 Review

67.   Simplify $x + x + x$ and $x \cdot x \cdot x$.

68.   Simplify. $-8t + (-5t) + 7t$

69.   Distribute. $-7(-3g + 5)$

70.   Simplify. $3(x - 5) + 2x$

71.   Simplify. $-5b - 4(2b - 1)$

Exercise Set - Cumulative Review

72.   Simplify. $17 - 3[8 - (2 + 4)]$

73.   Subtract. $4582 - 0$

74.   Add and reduce, if possible. $\dfrac{7}{16} + \dfrac{9}{16}$

75.   Find -9^2 and $(-9)^2$.

76.   Add. $(-45) + (-21)$

 # 3.2 QUIZ YOURSELF:

To make sure you are ready for the EXAM, try these problems without any help. Give yourself about 20 minutes and don't check the answers until you have completely finished.

1.   Is $4(x - 6)$ an example or an equation or an expression?

2.   Simplify each side to see if the equation $7 + 3(4) = (-5)^2 + 15$ is true or false.

3.   Is $x = 5$ a solution to $6x - 5 = -35$?

4.   Is $y = -2$ a solution to $4(y - 1) = 2(-4 + y)$?

Give the solution to each equation.

5. $h - 4 = 8$

6. $8n = -56$

7. $\dfrac{x}{3} = 8$

Answers to this Quiz Yourself are on page 656.

3.3 Basic Properties of Equality

Topics:

- The Addition and Subtraction Property
- The Multiplication and Division Property
- Simplifying Equations

Are You Ready?

To see if you are ready to understand this section, do the following short quiz.

1. What is the additive inverse of 5?
2. What is the multiplicative inverse of -6?
3. Simplify. $2 + 3(x - 4)$

Answers to Are You Ready?

(1) -5 *(2)* $-\dfrac{1}{6}$ *(3)* $3x - 10$

The Addition and Subtraction Property

In the last section we solved equations like $x + 3 = 7$ using our knowledge of basic operations. However, in Algebra, we must be able to solve more complicated equations.

- To see how many comic books a bookstore we can print and stay in budget they may have to solve an equation like $5(b - 300) + 4,500 = 35,000$.

- Predicting how many years before a house is worth $150,000 may involve solving an equation like $2300t + 120,000 = 150,000$.

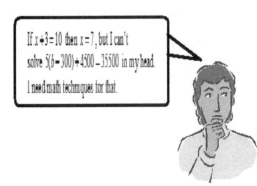

If $x + 3 = 10$ then $x = 7$, but I can't solve $5(b-300) + 4500 = 35500$ in my head. I need math techniques for that.

The process of finding the value that makes an equation true is called **solving the equation.**

To solve equations we operate on both sides, creating simpler *equivalent equations* until the final equation has the form $x = \text{number}$. One way to visualize how this process works, is to consider a set of scales. An equation is like a set of scales that are in balance.

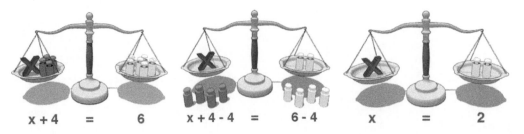

| x + 4 | = | 6 | x + 4 - 4 | = | 6 - 4 | x | = | 2 |

As long as we add or subtract the *same amount* to both sides, the scales (equation) will still be in balance.

Using scales this way demonstrates the first property of equality: *the addition property*.

The Addition/Subtraction Property of Equality

If $a = b$, then $a + c = b + c$ and $a - c = b - c$ for any real number c.
That is, any number can be added to or subtracted from both sides of an equation.

We add or subtract to both sides of an equation to undo the operation with the variable. This leaves the equation in the form $x = number$, which gives us the solution.

Example 1: In each case, add or subtract both sides of the equation to solve the equation.

a) $t + 35 = 143$ b) $5 = x - 4$

Solution:

a) To isolate the variable we subtract 3 from both sides of the equation.

$$t + 35 = 143$$
$$-35 \quad -35$$

Subtract. The solution to the equation is $t = 108$.

$$t = 108$$

b) To isolate the variable we add 4 to both sides of the equation.

$$5 = x - 4$$
$$+4 \quad +4$$

Add. Equations are reflective. That means $9 = x$ is equivalent to $x = 9$. So the solution to the equation is $x = 9$.

$$9 = x$$
$$x = 9$$

For the equation $5 = x - 4$, adding 4 to both sides to get the solution $x = 9$ may just seem like a clever trick since that solution may already be obvious. But consider the equation $c - 9 = -4$. The solution to this equation is not as obvious. But we can isolate the variable if we add 9 to both sides. Why add 9? We add 9 because that will have the effect of undoing the -9 on the left side.

Note that we can check to make sure that our solution is correct by substituting the value back into the equation and making sure we get a true equation.

Example 2: Use the addition and subtraction property of equality to solve each equation. Check your solution by substituting the variable back into the original equation.

a) $c - 9 = -4$ b) $-65 = f + 183$

Solution: In each case we add or subtract to both sides in order to isolate the variable on one side.

a) To isolate the variable we add 9 to both sides of the equation.

$$c - 9 = -4$$
$$+9 \quad +9$$
$$c = 5$$

To check the solution we let $c = 5$ in the equation $c - 9 = -4$:

$$5 - 9 = -4$$
$$-4 = -4$$ is true, so the solution is correct.

b) To isolate the variable, we subtract 183 from both sides of the equation.

$$-65 = f + 183$$
$$\underline{-183 \quad -183}$$
$$-248 = f$$
$$f = -248$$

To check the solution we let $f = -248$ in the equation $-65 = f + 183$:

$$-65 = -248 + 183$$
$$-65 = -65$$ is true, so the solution is correct.

Now let's consider a real-world application using this type of equation.

Example 3: A plane is flying a 3350 mile trip. So far, it has traveled 453 miles. To find the distance left to travel, the plane's computer must solve the equation $453 + d = 3350$, where d represents the remaining distance. What is the remaining distance?

Solution: We need to solve the equation $453 + d = 3350$.

To isolate the variable we subtract 453 from both sides of the equation.

$$453 + d = 3350$$
$$\underline{-453 \qquad -453}$$

Subtract.

$$d = 2897$$

The plane has 2897 miles left to fly.

STOP Exercise Set - The Addition and Subtraction Property

Use the addition and subtraction property of equality to solve each equation.

1. $x + 8 = 17$
2. $x - 12 = -5$
3. $n - 5 = -8$
4. $m + 17 = -25$

5. $-4 = k - 9$
6. $-3 + b = 6$
7. $m - 6 = -23$
8. $-41 = n - 12$

9. A health care center has a goal of raising \$3500 for medical research. So far they have raised \$1365. To find how much they have left to raise they can solve the equation $x + 1365 = 3500$ where x represents the amount left to raise. How much do they have left to raise?

10. According to Forbes website, NBA player Kobe Bryant earned \$43 million in 2010. This was \$22 million less than professional boxer Floyd Mayweather earned in the same year. To find out how much Floyd made we could solve the equation $43 = m - 22$ where m represents Mayweather's earnings. How much did Mayweather earn in 2010?

Succeed in Math!

To help organize and plan your classes, study time, and play time use a day planner. Students who start using a day planner quickly start wonder how they ever lived without one!

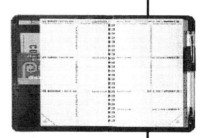

The Multiplication and Division Property

Notice that subtracting from both sides does not help solve an equation like $3x = 18$ since the operation on the variable is multiplication. This equation requires another property of equality that involves multiplication and division.

The Multiplication/Division Property of Equality

If $a = b$, then $a \cdot c = b \cdot c$ and $\dfrac{a}{c} = \dfrac{b}{c}$ for any real number c except $c = 0$.

That is, any number can be multiplied or divided to both sides of an equation, except zero.

Example 4: Use the multiplication and division property of equality to solve each equation. Check your solution by substituting the variable back into the original equation.

a) $3x = 18$

b) $\dfrac{a}{4} = 5$

Solution:

a) The variable is being multiplied by 3. To undo that and isolate the variable we divide both sides by 3.

$$\frac{3x}{3} = \frac{18}{3}$$
$$x = 6$$

To check the solution we let $x = 6$ in the equation $3x = 18$:

$$3(6) = 18 \text{ is true so the solution is correct.}$$

b) To isolate the variable we multiply both sides by 4.

$$4 \cdot \frac{a}{4} = 5 \cdot 4$$
$$a = 20$$

To check the solution we let $a = 20$ in the equation $\dfrac{a}{4} = 5$:

$$\frac{20}{4} = 5 \text{ is true so the solution is correct.}$$

As with addition and subtraction, if multiplying or dividing is done correctly then we will see the solution to the equation even when the solution is not obvious. Careful with those negatives numbers!

Example 5: Use the multiplication and division property of equality to solve each equation.

a) $-78 = -13b$ b) $-\dfrac{t}{7} = 4$

Solution:

a) To isolate the variable we divide both sides by -13.

$$-78 = -13b$$

$$\frac{-78}{-13} = \frac{-13b}{-13}$$

$$6 = 1b$$

$$6 = b$$

The solution is $b = -6$. $b = 6$

Check: $-78 = -13(6)$

$\quad\quad -78 = -78$ is true, so the solution is correct.

b) To isolate the variable we multiply both sides by 7.

$$-\frac{t}{7} = 4$$

$$7 \cdot -\frac{t}{7} = 4 \cdot 7$$

So the variable is not completely isolated. Now multiply by -1.

$$-t = 28$$

$$(-1)\cdot -t = 28 \cdot (-1)$$

The solution is $t = -28$. $t = -28$

Check: $-\dfrac{-28}{7} = 4$

$4 = 4$ is true, so the solution is correct.

Remark: You could also multiply by -7 as your first step to solve this equation:

$$-\frac{t}{7} = 4$$

$$-7\left(-\frac{t}{7}\right) = -7 \cdot 4$$

$$t = -28$$

Again let's look at how these kinds of equations come up in the real-world.

Example 6: Where in the World? Infinity's End is an art gallery in North Carolina. They sell custom art pieces for $350. Their revenue from last month's sales is $7,800. To find out how many art pieces were sold, they must solve the equation $350x = 7800$, where x represents the number of pieces sold. How many art pieces were sold last month?

Solution: We need to solve the equation $350x = 7800$.

Divide both sides by 350, since

x is multiplied by 350.

$$\frac{350x}{350} = \frac{7800}{350}$$

$$x = 68$$

So the company sold 68 pieces of art.

It is important that you can decide whether you should add, subtract, multiply, or divide to both sides when solving an equation. In this next example we have to decide which of the four operations should be done to solve the equation.

Example 7: Solve each equation.

a) $x + 7 = 3$ b) $6x = -72$ c) $-9 = x - 3$ d) $-\dfrac{x}{5} = 2$

Solution: Each equation requires a different requires a different operation to isolate the variable.

a) To isolate the variable we subtract 7 from both sides.

The solution is $x = -4$.

$$x + 7 = 3$$
$$\underline{-7 \quad -7}$$
$$x = -4$$

b) To isolate the variable we divide both sides by 6.

The solution is $x = -12$.

$$\frac{6x}{6} = \frac{-72}{6}$$
$$x = -12$$

c) To isolate the variable we add 3 to both sides.

The solution is $x = -6$

$$-9 = x - 3$$
$$\underline{+3 \quad +3}$$
$$-6 = x$$

d) To isolate the variable we multiply both sides by -5.

The solution is $x = -10$.

$$-5 \cdot -\frac{x}{5} = 2 \cdot -5$$
$$x = -10$$

 # Exercise Set - The Multiplication and Division Property

Use the multiplication and division property of equality to solve each equation.

11. $6a = 42$ 15. $-3h = -171$

12. $21 = 7b$ 16. $23b = -69$

13. $\dfrac{x}{3} = 8$ 17. $\dfrac{y}{17} = -7$

14. $4 = \dfrac{y}{2}$ 18. $-18 = \dfrac{k}{10}$

19.   A construction-size dump truck costs $45 per day to rent. To see how many days the truck can be rented for $585 we can solve the equation $45d = 585$ where d represents days. How many days can the truck be rented?

20.   If the length of a rectangle is 15 inches and the area is 360 square inches we can find the width of the rectangle by solving the equation $15w = 360$ where w represents the width. What is the width of the rectangle?

Simplifying Equations

We now know the basic principles of equality. They involve adding, subtracting, multiplying, and dividing on both sides of an equation to find the solution. Now we can look at equations that need to be simplified on each side before we can solve.

$$-13 + 5x + 8 - 4x = 9 + (-5)$$
$$-5 + x = 4$$

Consider the equation $-13 + 5x + 8 - 4x = 9 + (-5)$.

Before we operate on both sides we should combine like terms on each side of this equation. When we do this it is important to simplify each side *separately*.

$$-5 + x = 4$$
$$\underline{+5 \quad +5}$$
$$x = 9$$

Now that the equation is simplified we solve by adding 5 to both sides.

Simplifying an equation as the first part of solving may also involve distribution.

Example 8: Simplify each side of the equation, then solve using the properties of equality.

a) $5 + (-14) = 4x - 8 - 7x + 8$ b) $3a - 2(a + 4) = 7 - 10$

Solution: We simplify each side of each equation being careful to keep them separate.

a) Simplify the right and left sides of the equations separately by using order of operations.

$$5 + (-14) = 4x - 8 - 7x + 8$$
$$-9 = -3x$$

Isolate the variable by dividing both sides by -3.

$$\frac{-9}{-3} = \frac{-3x}{-3}$$

$$3 = x$$
$$x = 3$$

b) On the left hand side, distribute the -2.
On the right hand side, subtract.

$$3a - 2(a + 4) = 7 - 10$$
$$3a - 2a - 8 = -3$$

Simplify the left hand side of the equation.

$$a - 8 = -3$$

Isolate the variable by adding 8 to both sides.

$$a - 8 = -3$$
$$\underline{+8 \quad +8}$$

$$a = 5$$

Example 9: Where in the World?

Starved Rock Bike Shop has the following discount package: $12 for cleaning, $14 for gear alignment, $5 for new tire tubes. If, on a certain day they make $341 in discount packages and need to know how many were sold they could solve the equation $12x + 14x + 5x = 341$, where x represents the number of packages sold. In this case, how many discount packages were sold?

Solution: We just need to solve the equation $12x + 14x + 5x = 341$.

Combine like terms on the left side.

$$12x + 14x + 5x = 341$$
$$31x = 341$$

Now divide both sides by 31.

$$\frac{31x}{31} = \frac{341}{31}$$
$$1x = 11$$
$$x = 11$$

So 11 discount packages were sold.

STOP Exercise Set - Simplifying Equations

Simplify each side of the equation, then solve.

21. $19x - 18x = -10$ 25. $17x - 16x + 25 = -34$
22. $5x - 4x = 9$ 26. $12h + 2 - 11h = 15$
23. $8x + 3 - 7x = 6$ 27. $5a - 2(2a + 1) = 15 + 9$
24. $-5x + 6x + 17 = -28$ 28. $7 + 3(2d + 3) - 5d = 12 - 8$

29.   A manufacturer makes clock radios. To supply each unit costs $13 in labor, $5 in parts, and $2 for shipping. To find out how many radios can be supplied for $1500 we could solve the equation $13p + 5p + 2p = 1500$. How many radios can be supplied for $1500?

30.   Three cyclist are traveling at 15, 11, and 14 miles per hour. To find the amount of time it will take for them to travel a combined total of 920 miles we could solve the equation $15t + 11t + 14t = 920$ where t represents time. How long will it take?

Exercise Set - Putting It ALL Together

31.   In the equation $b - 8 = 9$, what operation is the variable involved in? What operation will we have to perform to isolate the variable?

32.   In the equation $45 = 9k$, what operation is the variable involved in? What operation will we have to perform to isolate the variable?

33.   In the equation $8 = \dfrac{t}{6}$, what operation is the variable involved in? What operation will we have to perform to isolate the variable?

34.   In the equation $7 + x = 6$, what operation is the variable involved in? What operation will we have to perform to isolate the variable?

Solve.

35. $n + 5 = 23$

36. $m - 13 = 78$

37. $7n = 56$

38. $-18m = 36$

39. $-88 = -2x$

40. $-105 = 3x$

41. $\dfrac{x}{12} = -2$

42. $-45 = \dfrac{x}{-2}$

43. $-8 = y - 5$

44. $k + 9 = -14$

45. $11 = \dfrac{m}{5}$

46. $\dfrac{h}{17} = -13$

47. $29x + 16 - 28x = -8$

48. $78 - (3 - y) = 15$

49. $-11y + 34 + 12y = 67 - 23$

50. $17a - 15a = 23 + 11$

51. $-8b + 11b = 18 + 12$

52. $5x - 2(2x + 5) = 23$

53. $12 - (x - 4) = 16 - 3$

54. $7x + 3(-2x + 1) + 12 = 8$

55. $6(x - 9) - 5x = 14$

56. $21t + 8 - 20t = 19$

57. $8x + 11x - 13x = -17 + 24 - 13$

58. $-7p + 9p + 2p = 11 - 21 - 2$

59.   John is on a 45-mile hiking trip. So far, he has hiked 17 miles. To find the distance left to hike, he can solve the equation $17 + d = 45$, where d represents the remaining distance. What is the remaining distance he has to hike?

60.   A bus is traveling up the east coast from Miami to New York City, a total distance of 1,290 miles. So far it has traveled 769 miles. To find the distance left to travel, the bus driver must solve the equation $769 + d = 1290$, where d represents the remaining distance. What is the remaining distance?

61.   A plane is flying a 750 mile trip. The plane is traveling at a rate of 250mph. To find the time to travel in hours, the plane's computer must solve the equation $750 = 250t$, where t represents the time of hours. How many hours does it take the plane to fly 750 miles?

62.   DJ, Jamie and their kids are driving to the beach, a 476 mile trip. They are traveling at a rate of 68mph. To find the time to travel in hours, they must solve the equation $476 = 68t$, where t represents the time of hours. How many hours does it take them to drive 476 miles?

63.   A landscaping company has a package that includes $25 for mowing, $16 for trimming, and $10 for clearing. Suppose $1275 is made in one month selling these packages. The equation $25x + 16x + 10x = 1275$ can be used to find the number of packages sold where x represents the number of packages sold. In this case, how many packages were sold?

64.   A custom bike takes 4 hours to manufacture and 2 hours to assemble. To find out how many custom bikes can be made in 204 hours we can solve the equation $4b + 2b = 204$ where b represents the numbers of bikes. How many bikes can be made?

65.   What is wrong with the following argument?

Consider the equation $3 + 7 = 3 \cdot 5$. Multiply both sides by zero: $0 \cdot (3 + 7) = (3 \cdot 5) \cdot 0$

$$0 \cdot (3 + 7) = (3 \cdot 5) \cdot 0$$

Now simplify using the order of operations: $0 \cdot 10 = 15 \cdot 0$

$$0 = 0$$

Since $0 = 0$ is true, the original equation $3 + 7 = 3 \cdot 5$ is true.

66.   What is wrong with the following argument?

For the equation $v - 9 = 3 + 4$ we add 9 to the left side to undo subtraction by 9: $v - 9 + 9 = 3 + 4$
                                                                                              $v = 7$

This gives the solution $v = 7$.

For the following exercises use the formula $A = l \cdot w$ to find the missing side of the rectangle.
67.

A=45ft^2 w=?

5 ft

68.

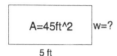

A=56in^2 w=?

7in

69.

A=36cm^2

11cm

l=?

70.

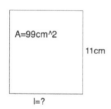

A=99cm^2

11cm

l=?

71.   Find the value of x given that the perimeter of the figure below is 63.

3x   2x

4x

72.   Find the value of x given that the perimeter of the figure below is 48.

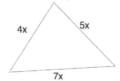

4x   5x

7x

Exercise Set - Chapter 3 Review

73.   Simplify. $3(d - 7) - 2(5d + 6)$
74.   Indicate whether the equation $4 \cdot 5 = 14 - (2 - 8)$ is true or false.
75.   Simplify $p + p + p + p + p$ and $p \cdot p \cdot p \cdot p \cdot p$.
76.   Is $8(w + 6)$ an equation or an expression?

77.　　Is $d = -3$ a solution to the equation $2d + 7 = d - 2$?

Exercise Set - Cumulative Review

78.　　Find the average of the numbers 7, 4, 15, and 2.
79.　　Write the number 5,200 in words.
80.　　List all the even integers between and including -2 and 6.
81.　　Translate "the absolute value of negative three" into an expression and simplify.
82.　　Evaluate the expression $mx + b$ for $m = -2$, $x = 5$, and $b = 7$.

 # 3.3 QUIZ YOURSELF:

To make sure you are ready for the EXAM, try these problems without any help. Give yourself about 20 minutes and don't check the answers until you have completely finished.

Solve.
1.　m + (-3) = -17
2.　26 = x + 13
3.　-12y = -132
4.　18 – 2 = 13x -12x
5.　8x – 7x = 23
6.　67 + 14 = x
7.　3h = -27
8.　$\dfrac{8x}{9} = -32$
9.　12 – 3(n + 2) + 4n = 29
10.　26 - (g + 5) = 45 + 11

Answers to this Quiz Yourself are on page 656.

3.4 More About Solving Equations

Topics:
- Using Both Properties Of Equality
- Equations With The Variable On Each Side
- An Overall Strategy For Solving

Are You Ready?

To see if you are ready to understand this section, do the following short quiz.

1. Simplify. -3x -7(2x + 9)
2. Solve. x + 3 = 8
3. Solve. $\dfrac{x}{-5} = 6$

Answers to Are You Ready?

(1) $-17x - 63$ *(2)* $x = 5$ *(3)* $x = -30$

Using Both Properties of Equality

In Section 3.3 we learned the basic properties of equality, but the equations we solved only used one property per equation. For the equations in this section, we may have to use both of the properties of equality discussed in the last section. Consider the equation $3x + 7 = 22$. Solving this equation requires two steps.

As our first step we subtract 7 from both sides to get the variable term alone on the left side.

$$3x + 7 = 22$$
$$\underline{-7 \quad -7}$$
$$3x = 15$$

As our second step we divide both sides by 3.

$$\frac{3x}{3} = \frac{15}{3}$$
$$x = 5$$

Here are examples that show slight variations on the same idea.

Example 1: Solve each equation.

a) $4x - 5 = 15$ b) $-47 = -7x + 51$

Solution:

a) Add 5 to both sides.

$$4x - 5 = 15$$
$$\underline{+5 \quad +5}$$
$$4x = 20$$

Divide both sides by 4

$$\frac{4x = 20}{4 \quad \quad 4}$$
$$x = 5$$

b) Subtract 51 from both
sides and simplify.

$$-47 = -7x + 51$$
$$\underline{-51 \qquad -51}$$
$$-98 = -7x$$

Divide both sides by -7.

$$\frac{-98 = -7x}{-7 \quad -7}$$
$$14 = x$$
$$x = 14$$

Remember, if necessary you will have to simplify each side of an equation before you apply the properties of equality to both sides, as in these next examples.

Example 2: Solve each equation.

a) $15 = -3(x-2)$

b) $4x + 5 - 8 = 2x - (x-5) - x$

Solution:

a) Distribute the -3 on the right side.

$$15 = -3(x-2)$$
$$15 = -3x + 6$$

Subtract 6 from both sides.

$$15 = -3x + 6$$
$$\underline{-6 \qquad -6}$$
$$9 = -3x$$

Divide both sides by -3.

$$\frac{9 = -3x}{-3 \quad -3}$$
$$-3 = x$$
$$x = -3$$

b) This equation involves distribution and combining like terms, so which should we do first? Distribution!

Simplify both sides of the equation.
- Distribute the negative on the right side
- Combine like terms on each side separately

Notice that the variable cancels out completely on the right side.

$$4x + 5 - 8 = 2x - (x-5) - x$$
$$4x - 3 = 2x - x + 5 - x$$
$$4x - 3 = 5$$

Add 3 to both sides.

$$4x - 3 = 5$$
$$\underline{\quad +3 \ +3}$$
$$4x = 8$$

Divide both sides by 4.

$$\frac{4x = 8}{4 \quad 4}$$

The solution is:

$$x = 2$$

Example 3: Alien Workshop manufactures skateboards. Their monthly production budget is $45,000. They pay $6,000 per month for maintenance, and each skateboard costs $13 to make. The solution to the equation $45,000 = 6000 + 13b$ will tell them how many skateboards they can manufacture and stay within their monthly budget where b represents the number of boards. How many boards can they make?

Solution: The answer is the solution to the equation $45,000 = 6000 + 13b$, so let's solve it.

First we subtract 6,000 from both sides.

$$45,000 = 6000 + 13b$$
$$\underline{-6000 \quad -6000}$$
$$19000 = 13b$$

Now divide both sides by 13

$$\underline{19000 = 13b}$$
$$\quad 13 \quad \quad 13$$

The solution is:

$$950 = b$$

So Alien Workshop will be able to make 950 boards per month.

 STOP Exercise Set - Using Both Properties of Equality

Solve each equation.

1. $2x + 3 = 11$
2. $4x - 5 = 15$
3. $30 = 17m - 4$
4. $-4 = 16x + 12$
5. $-5b + 2 = -18$
6. $-3y - 8 = -17$
7. $2(x + 5) = 16$
8. $7(t - 5) = 14$
9. $6 = -3(p - 4)$
10. $-5(2x + 1) = 15$

Equations With The Variable On Each Side

If an equation has the variable on both sides, you will need to subtract and/or add on both sides to eliminate the variable term on one side. From here on out, many of our equations will require that we add or subtract from both sides more than once.

Example 4: Solve each equation.

a) $5x - 9 = 3x + 7$

b) $2x + 8 = 3x + 5(x - 2)$

Solution:

a) Subtract $3x$ from both sides.

$$5x - 9 = 3x + 7$$
$$\underline{-3x \quad\quad -3x}$$
$$2x - 9 = 7$$

Add 9 to both sides.

$$2x - 9 = 7$$
$$\underline{\quad +9 \ +9}$$
$$2x = 16$$

Divide both sides by 2.

$$\frac{2x}{2} = \frac{16}{2}$$

The solution is:

$$x = 8$$

b)
Distribute the 5 on the right side.

$$2x + 8 = 3x + 5(x - 2)$$
$$2x + 8 = 3x + 5x - 10$$

Combine like terms on the right side.

$$2x + 8 = 8x - 10$$

Subtract $8x$ from both sides.

$$2x + 8 = 8x - 10$$
$$\underline{-8x \quad\quad -8x}$$
$$-6x + 8 = -10$$

Subtract 8 from both sides.

$$-6x + 8 = -10$$
$$\underline{\quad\quad -8 \quad -8}$$
$$-6x = -18$$

Divide both sides by -6.

$$\frac{-6x}{-6} = \frac{-18}{-6}$$

The solution is:

$$x = 3$$

These types of equations also come up in application problems.

Example 5: Vince is a freelance artist who has to choose between two job offers. The first pays $35 per hour but requires that he buy $85 worth of new material himself. The second offer only pays $28 per hour but includes a bonus of $580. In order to figure out how many hours of work would make the two jobs pay the same, he can solve the equation $35h - 85 = 28h + 580$ where h is the number of hours worked. How many hours of work make the offers pay the same?

Solution: To answer the question we need to solve the equation $35h - 85 = 28h + 580$.

Subtract $28h$ to both sides.

$$35h - 85 = 28h + 580$$
$$\underline{-28h \qquad -28h}$$
$$7h - 85 = 580$$

Add 85 to both sides.

$$7h - 85 = 580$$
$$\underline{+85 \quad +85}$$
$$7h = 665$$

Divide both sides by 7.

$$\frac{7h}{7} = \frac{665}{7}$$

The solution is:

$$h = 95$$

Vince would have to work 95 hours for the two offers to pay the same.

Good Question: Do I always have to get the variable on the left hand side?

Answer: Absolutely not. Some people like to get the variable on the left hand side, so the result reads x = answer. However, it is exactly the same to have answer = x. You should proceed with what feels natural.

 # Exercise Set - Equations With The Variable On Each Side

Solve each equation.

11. $6y - 8 = 4y$

12. $-2x + 21 = 5x$
13. $-13x + 14 = x$
14. $11g = 9 + 8g$

15. $5k - 6 = 4k + 8$
16. $-3t + 7 = -4t + 15$
17. $9x - 6 = 5x - 2$
18. $16x - 32 = 2x + 24$
19. $-8u + 13 = 3u + 2$
20. $2d - 14 = 17d + 31$

An Overall Strategy for Solving Equations

We have looked at many different situations and techniques for solving equations. It might seem tough to keep it all straight, so let's look at a brief set of steps that can be used to solve any equation.

To Solve an Equation:

1. Simplify each side separately by distributing then combining like terms.
2. Add and/or subtract to both sides of the equation so that the variable terms are on the same side and constant terms are on the other side.
3. Multiply and/or divide both sides of the equation by the coefficient of the variable term.

If you can follow those steps in that order, any equation can be solved even if it looks very complicated.

Example 6: Solve each equation.
a) $-2(x+3)=-5x+13+2x$ b) $3[2(x-7)+5]=7x-8$

Solution: As we work through these examples we will reinforce the steps shown above.

a) **Step 1: Simplify each side separately by distributing then combining like terms.**

$$-2(x+3)=-5x+13+2x$$

Distribute the -2 on the left side and combine like terms on the right side.

$$-2x-6=-3x+13$$

Step 2: Add or Subtract to both sides of the equations so that the variable terms are on the same side and terms with no variable are on the other side.

$$\begin{array}{r} -2x-6=-3x+13 \\ +3x \quad\quad +3x \\ \hline x-6=13 \end{array}$$

Add $3x$ to both sides.

Add 6 to both sides.

$$\begin{array}{r} x-6=13 \\ +6 \;\; +6 \\ \hline x=19 \end{array}$$

There is no division or multiplication to be done for this equation.

b) **Step 1: Simplify each side separately by distributing then combining like terms.**

$$3[2(x-7)+5]=7x-8$$

Distribute the 2 inside the brackets on the left side.
Combine like terms inside the brackets.

$$3[2x-14+5]=7x-8$$

$$3[2x-9]=7x-8$$

Distribute the 3 on the left hand side.

$$6x-27=7x-8$$

Step 2: Add or Subtract to both sides of the equations so that the variable terms are on the same side and terms with no variable are on the other side.
Subtract $7x$ from both sides.

$$\begin{array}{r} 6x-27=7x-8 \\ -7x \quad\quad -7x \\ \hline -x-27=-8 \end{array}$$

Add 27 to both sides.

$$\begin{array}{r} -x-27=-8 \\ +27 \;\; +27 \\ \hline -x=19 \end{array}$$

Step 3: Multiply or Divide both sides of the equation by the variable's coefficient.
Divide both sides by -1.

$$-x = 19$$
$$\frac{-x}{-1} = \frac{19}{-1}$$
$$x = -19$$

Exercise Set - An Overall Strategy for Solving Equations

Solve each equation.

21. $8(3x - 5) + 2 = 5(8 - x)$
22. $-3(4x + 3) - 1 = 9(5 - 2x)$
23. $3(2x - 1) + 4x = -4(x + 5)$
24. $2(5x - 3) - 4x = 6(3 - x)$
25. $2(x + 1) - (4x - 11) = 7x + 11 - x$
26. $-2(x - 2) + (3x + 5) = 6x - (1 - x)$
27. $4[3(x - 1) + 9] = 6x - 1$
28. $5(x + 3) - 1 = -3x - 2$
29. $2x + 7 - 9 = 6x - 2(3x + 5)$
30. $4x - 5 - 8x = 7x - 3(3x + 5) + 2x$

Exercise Set - Putting It ALL Together

TRUE or FALSE

31. When solving an equation, it doesn't matter whether you add/subtract first or multiply/divide first.
32. In the equation $3(x - 6) = 5x - 7$ our first step would be to divide both sides by 3.
33. Equations with a variable on each side of the equals sign cannot be solved at all.
34. You should make sure to simplify each side of an equation separately.

Solve each equation.

35. $7x + 5 = 12$
36. $19x - 6 = 18x$
37. $-9 - 3x = 6x$
38. $-8x + 3 = 43$
39. $35n + 3 = 16n + 22$
40. $12w - 8 = 8w + 24$
41. $-2(y + 1) = 3y - 1$
42. $3(-2x - 5) = 5x + 7$
43. $6p - 22 = 8p$
44. $-7e + 24 = -5e$

45. $6(4 - 5x) - 13 = 2(4x + 1)$
46. $7x = -2(-3x + 1) + 23$
47. $25 = 3(5 - 2x) + 10$
48. $8 - (3a + 7) = 3(2a - 5) + 21$
49. $4(x + 9) - (4x - 2) = 3x + 8$
50. $2(5x - 1) + (8x - 3) = 9 - 2x$
51. $-3[2(x + 4) + 8] = 5x - 2$
52. $17x - 3 + 12x = 4(7x - 1) + 2x - 8$
53. $-12 + 13g - 18 = 5g - 3(2g - 5) + 2x$
54. $-7[5 - 3(x + 1) + 2] = -x + 12$

55. The cost for cable TV is $35 a month plus the cost of any on demand movies you order. On demand movies cost $5 each. If Jay's cable bill is $80, we can find how many movies he ordered by solving the equation, $80 = 35 + 5m$, where m represents the number of movies Jay ordered. Find how many movies Jay ordered for the month.

56. Joquin bought a used car is that cost $1200 down, plus $160 per month. The total amount paid for the car is $6960. We can find how many months Jim paid on the car by solving the equation, $6960 = 1200 + 160m$, where m represents the number of months Jim paid on the car. Find how many months Jim paid on the car.

57.   The cost to produce bikes is $400 plus $125 per bike for the materials. To find out how many bikes we could produce with $900, we can solve the equation $900 = 400 + 125b$, where b represents the number of bikes. Find the number of bikes we can produce.

58.   The cost to produce running shoes is $50 plus $35 per wetsuit for the materials. To find out how many pair of shoes we could produce with $750, we can solve the equation, $750 = 200 + 35b$, where b represents the number of bikes. Find the number of bikes we can produce.

59.   A dump truck driver rental charges $45 plus $3 for each mile after 50 miles. To find out how far the driver will go for $270, we can solve the equation $45 + 3(x - 50) = 270$ where x represents the number of miles driven. How many miles will driver go for $270?

60.   A caterer recommends having 15 drinks on hand plus 2 more for each guest after the 10th guest. If Lisa has 62 drinks available, she can find out how many guests she can serve by solving the equation $15 + 2(x - 10) = 62$. How guests can Lisa serve?

61.   The length of a rectangle is 5 feet longer than the width. If the perimeter is 62 feet, the width can be found by solving the equation $2(w + 5) + 2w = 62$. What where is the width of the rectangle?

62.   The length of a rectangle is 3 inches less than the width. If the perimeter is 54 inches, the width can be found by solving the equation $2(w - 3) + 2w = 54$. What is the width of the rectangle?

Exercise Set - Chapter 3 Review

63.   Determine if the equation $7 + (-3) + (-9) = -2(4) + 3$.
64.   Simplify $6(5x)(2)$ and $6 + 5x + 2$.
65.   Are $5y$ and $5y^2$ like terms?
66.   Solve. $\dfrac{r}{3} = -6$
67.   Is $4m + 7(m - 8)$ an expression or an equation?

Exercise Set - Cumulative Review

68.   Multiply. $16(-35)$
69.   Find $4^3 \cdot 2^3$.
70.   Find $a + b + c$ given $a = -8$, $b = 6$, and $c = 12$.
71.   Graph the numbers 80, 250, 125, and 160 on a number line using a scale of 25.\
72.   Fill in the blank with $<$, $>$, or $=$. $-|14|$ ___ $-(-14)$

3.4 QUIZ YOURSELF:

To make sure you are ready for the EXAM, try these problems without any help. Give yourself about 20 minutes and don't check the answers until you have completely finished.

1. $3x - 5 = 10$
2. $28 = 7(2x + 8)$
3. $-4(x + 3) = -12$
4. $8x + 21 = -3x + 10$
5. $-2(7 - 8x) - 11 = 5(3x + 1)$
6. $-2x = 4(7x + 2) + 22$
7. $-[6 + 2(2x + 7) + 5] = x - 15$
8. Ricardo bought a used car is that cost $2500 down, plus $210 per month. The total amount paid for the car is $10,060. We can find how many months Jim paid on the car by solving the equation, $10,060 = 2500 + 210m$, where m represents the number of months Ricardo paid on the car. Find how many months Ricardo paid on the car.

Answers to this Quiz Yourself are on page 656.

3.5 Problem Solving

Topics:

- Translating English into Math
- Introduction to Problem Solving
- More About Solving Applications
- Applications Involving Geometry

Are You Ready?

To see if you are ready to understand this section, do the following short quiz.

1. Distribute. $-4(2x-5)$

2. $2 \cdot 5^2 \div 10 - 27 \cdot 2$

3. $\dfrac{7 \cdot 3 + 5}{6 \cdot 2 + 1}$

4. Solve. $7x + 3 = 17$

Answers to Are You Ready?

(1) $-8x + 20$ *(2)* -49 *(3)* 2 *(4)* $x = 2$

Translating English into Math

Now that we can solve equations, we consider situations where applied math requires creating equations. The most important part of solving applications is the ability to translate English into math symbols. There are certain key words to identify when creating expressions and equations.

Operation or Symbol	Common Key Words and Phrases
Addition +	plus, added to, more than, total, increased by, sum
Subtraction −	minus, taken away from, less, less than, decreased by, subtract, subtracted from, difference
Multiplication •	of, times, per, multiplied by, product, twice, half
Division ÷	divided by, divided up, quotient, per
Equal Sign =	is, was, is equal to, is the same as, result is, yields
Variable x	what number, what value, a number, some number, an unknown value

Let's look at creating expressions that involve variables.

Example 1: For each phrase, create an expression that involves a variable.
a) "the bonus B divided up into nine parts"
b) "three minus the current rate k"
c) "four less than ten times the width w"
d) "seventeen added to twice an unknown value"

Solution: In each exercise we rewrite the statements with arrows pointing out how the words are written as symbols.
[PN: Arrows pointing words to symbols/number]
a) "the bonus B dividing up into nine parts"

$$B \div 9$$

This can also be written as $\dfrac{B}{9}$, which is more common in Algebra.

b) "three minus the current rate k"

$$3 - k$$

c) When the phrase "less than" is used to indicate subtraction the number mentioned first comes after the number mentioned second.

"four less than ten times the width w"

$$10w - 4$$

d) We will use the variable x to represent "some unknown value".

"seventeen added to twice some unknown value"

$$2x + 17$$

The next example involves creating equations.

Example 2: Translate each sentence into an algebraic equation. Do not solve the equation.
a) Five times what value equals 175?
b) If you double a number and add 7 the result is 59.
c) 4 less than some value is equal to the same number times 5.
d) 2 times the sum of a number and 8 is the same as the product of the number and 10.

Solution: Again, many students always use the variable x when they create equations. We will use a different variable for each example just to make the point that you can use any variable you like.
[PN: Arrows pointing words to symbols/number]
a) Five times what value equals 175?
$$5 \cdot x = 175$$

b) If you double a number and add 7 the result is 59
$$2n + 7 = 59$$

c) 4 less than some value is equal to the same number times 5.
$$k - 4 = 5k$$

d) 2 times the sum of a number and 8 is the same as the product of the number and 10.
$$2(t + 8) = 10t$$

Let's look at a real-world example of creating an expression.

Example 3: Where in the World? The Nintendo Wii discount package we bought involved buying the Wii system for $299 plus $25 per controller purchased and $40 per game purchased. Assign variables to the scenario and create an expression for the total charge of the package.

Solution: We let c = number of controllers purchased and g = number of games purchased. We translate the phrase "$299 plus $25 per control purchased and $40 per game". Remember that the word "per" in this context translates into multiplication.

$$\text{\$299 plus \$25 per control purchased and \$40 per game}$$

$$299 + 25 \cdot c + 40 \cdot g$$

$$299 + 25c + 40g$$

Translate the following English expressions into algebraic expressions:
1. a number minus six
2. a number plus eight
3. three times the sum of a number and five
4. twice a number minus seven
5. five less than four times some number
6. sixteen added to twice a number

Translate the following sentences into algebraic equations. Do not solve.
7. Five minus a number is twenty eight.
8. Twenty one plus a number is twelve.
9. A number plus twelve is equal to eight times the same number.
10. A number minus six is equal to fourteen plus three times the number.
11. Twice the sum of number and three is thirteen.
12. Four times the sum of a number and two is fifteen.

For each real-world phrase, first assign a variable. Then create an expression to represent the statement.
13. eleven times the number of movie tickets sold
14. five added to the cost of dinner
15. 456 miles divided by the speed at which you are driving
16. the price of a airline ticket minus a $45 discount

Succeed in Math!

College Graduates...
- ...make about $20,000 a year more.
- ...have more hobbies.
- ...make better consumer decisions.
- ...have more opportunities.
- ...have a healthier outlook.

Courtesy of Fotolia

Introduction to Problem Solving

We are learning Algebra so we can solve aplications in the real world. There are some key ideas to being successful at problem-solving in math:

1. **READ THE PROBLEM**
It is common for students to read an application just one time and stop there. You should read an application problem through at least three times before you go to the next step.

2. **ASSIGN A VARIABLE**
Ask yourself the question "What am I being asked to find?" and assign a variable to that value. This is an important step in moving towards an equation.

3. **SUMMARIZE THE INFORMATION**
Rewrite the parts of the problem that you know involve algebra. If the problem involves a geometric figure, like a triangle or a rectangle, draw a picture to help organize the information.

4. **DO THE MATH**
This means to translate your summarized information into an equation and solve it. Do not use the original problem to create your equation, use your summary instead.

5. **ANSWER THE QUESTION**
Give your answer. Always make sure to include units ("$", "feet", "inches, etc.) Check that your answer makes sense? Is the answer too big to make sense? Too small?

The KEY to getting good at application problems is to take a careful approach. Follow these steps and you WILL get better:
1) **READ THE PROBLEM**
2) **ASSIGN A VARIABLE**
3) **SUMMARIZE THE INFORMATION**
4) **DO THE MATH**
5) **ANSWER THE QUESTION**

In the next two examples we are not solving the application problems. Instead, we are looking at the parts to set up an algebraic equation to solve the problem. This is generally the most difficult part of the whole process of solving.

Example 4: For the following application, we will walk through the first few steps for solving the application. Fill in the blanks in each step.

A game designer is helping to create Zombie Squad 8. He wants to start at a level with 14 zombies and add 6 per minute. How many minutes of game play will it take for the total number of zombies to equal 50?

[PN: Can we make this look like it was 'torn' from the homework?]

ASSIGN A VARIABLE

m = _____

SUMMARIZE THE INFORMATION   14 zombies and add _____ per minute

total number of zombies = _____

DO THE MATH   14 zombies add _____ per minute equals _____

_____ + _____ = _____

Solution: Not all parts of solving this application are included in this example. We need to practice setting up the problem by creating an equation.

ASSIGN A VARIABLE	We are being asked to find how many *minutes* it will take to get to 50 zombies. m = the number of minutes
SUMMARIZE THE INFORMATION	14 zombies and increase by __6___ per minute until he reaches __50___
DO THE MATH	14 zombies and increase by __6__ per minute until he reaches __50__ ___14___ + ___6m___ = ___50___

In the next example, when we ASSIGN A VARIABLE we use one variable to describe two unknown values in the problem.

Example 5: For the following application, we will walk through some of the steps for solving word problems. Fill in the blanks in each step.

Lana has ordered brackets and bolts for her boat trailer store. The invoice says there are 152 parts total. She knows there are three times as many bolts as brackets. How many bolts and how many brackets are in the order?

[PN: Can we make look like it was 'torn' from the homework?]

ASSIGN A VARIABLE	x = _____ 3x = _____
SUMMARIZE THE INFORMATION	total of _____ parts, so brackets plus bolts = _____

DO THE MATH	brackets plus bolts = _____
	_____ + _____ = _____

Solution: Once again, not all parts of solving an application are included in this outline, only the first three steps to clarify how to create the equation.

[PN: Can we make it look like the blanks were filled in by hand?]

ASSIGN A VARIABLE	The problems states "there are three times as many bolts as brackets" so…
	x = _number of brackets_____
	$3x$ = _number of bolts_____
SUMMARIZE THE INFORMATION	total of ___152____ parts, so
	brackets plus bolts = _152_____
DO THE MATH	brackets plus bolts = _152_____
	__x___ + ___3x____ = __152_____

STOP Exercise Set - Introduction to Problem Solving

For the following application, some of the steps for solving word problems are outlined. Fill in the blanks in each step.

17. Jorge is training for a marathon. His first long run was 4 miles. He is increasing his long run by 2 miles each week. How many weeks does he need to train to reach a 26 mile run?

ASSIGN A VARIABLE	w = _____
SUMMARIZE THE INFORMATION	4 and add _____ per week
	wants to reach mileage = _____
DO THE MATH	Staring mileage plus _____miles per week = _____
	_____ + _____ = _____

18. DeWayne started a saving account with $300. Each month he contributes $75. How many months will it take for the account to reach $2175?

ASSIGN A VARIABLE	m = _____
SUMMARIZE THE INFORMATION	start with _____ and add _____ per month total amount = _____
DO THE MATH	$300 and add _____ per month equals _____ _____ + _____ = _____

19. Donna has ordered tires and chains for her bike shop. The invoice says there are 214 items total. She knows there are twice as many tires as chains. How many tires and how many chains are in the order?

ASSIGN A VARIABLE	x = _____ 2x = _____
SUMMARIZE THE INFORMATION	total of _____ items tires plus chains = _____
DO THE MATH	_____ + _____ = _____

20. Lucas ordered kick boards and pull buoys for the municipal pool. The invoice says there are 98 items total. He knows there are fifteen more kick boards as pull buoys. How many kick boards and pull buoys are in the order?

ASSIGN A VARIABLE	x = _____ x + 15 = _____
SUMMARIZE THE INFORMATION	total of _____ items kick boards plus pull buoys = _____
DO THE MATH	_____ + _____ = _____

More About Solving Applications

Okay, now that we have practiced the harder steps in solving applications, let's go all the way through the process and get a final answer for some applications.

Example 6: Create an equation that corresponds to the following application and solve.

Rather than count all the money in the tip jar for the day, Edile just took the total pile of money and divided it up into 6 stacks of the same amount, one stack for each employee. If the result was $18 for each employee, what was the total amount in the tip jar for the day?

Solution: Let's use the problem solving steps included at the beginning of the section. Start by reading the problem thoroughly.

ASSIGN A VARIABLE	$T =$ the money in the tip jar.
SUMMARIZE THE INFORMATION	total amount divided into 6 stacks result was $18 for each employee
DO THE MATH	total amount divided into 6 piles, result was 18 [PN: arrows pointing out translation] $\dfrac{T}{6} = 18$ So the equation $\dfrac{T}{6} = 18$ can be used to solve this application.
Solve: • Multiply both sides by 6:	$6 \cdot \dfrac{T}{6} = 18 \cdot 6$ $T = 108$
ANSWER THE QUESTION	The tip jar had a total of $108 in it.

Note that this answer makes sense in light of the application.

GOOD QUESTION: As soon as I read that last word problem, I knew I could get the correct answer by multiplying $6 \cdot 18 = 108$. Why go through the rest of that stuff?

ANSWER: You're missing the point of the exercise. We are not practicing simple arithmetic; we are practicing *using Algebra to solve problems*. Soon you will not be able to solve the applications with clever tricks. You will *have* to use variables and equations. So practice now, while the problems are easier.

The next example is one that involves two unknown quantities. We use one variable to describe both quantities.

Example 7: Create an equation that corresponds to the following application and solve.

A warehouse manager has received an overstock shipment of washers and dryers. He knows there are 274 units total, but he does not know how many washers and how many dryers. However, the washers and dryers are paired together and there are 18 washers left over, so there are 18 more washers than there are dryers. How many washers and how dryers are in the shipment?

Solution:

ASSIGN A VARIABLE	We are being asked to find the number of washers and the number of dryers. We are total there are 18 more dryers than washers, so we have: x = number of washers $x + 18$ = number of dryers
SUMMARIZE THE INFORMATION	274 units total means number of washers + number of dryers = 274
DO THE MATH	number of washers + number of dryers = 274 $x + x + 18 = 274$
Solve: • Combine like terms. • Subtract 18 from both sides. • Divide both sides by 2.	$x + x + 18 = 274$ $2x + 18 = 274$ $2x = 256$ $x = 128$
ANSWER THE QUESTION	Since x represents the number of washers, there are 128 washers. There are 18 more dryers than that: 128+18=146. There are 128 washers and 146 dryers.

STOP Exercise Set - More About Solving Applications

Solve the following application problems by using the 5-step method.

21. A number plus five is the same as three times the number plus nine. Find the number.

22. Three times the sum of a number and seven is thirty. What is the number?

23. Summer and Shane go out to dinner and a movie on a date. The cost of dinner was $45. They bought two movies tickets and spent a total of $67 on the evening. How much did each movie ticket cost?

24. Two friends go out for a run. One of the friends runs 4 miles more than the other, and they ran a total of 28 miles. How many miles did they each run?

25. A guitar shop manager has received an overstock shipment of acoustic guitars and cases for them. He knows there are 78 units total, but he does not know how many guitars and how many cases there are. However, all of the guitars are in cases and there are 12 cases left over, so there are 12 more cases than there are guitars. How many guitars and how many cases are in the shipment?

26. The owner of a local golf shop set aside some petty cash, but forgot how much was there. Out of the money, she paid $430 for a delivery, took out $40 to pay for lunch for the shop pro. She put $210 back in the petty cash draw and counted the money. She had a total of $950 now. How much did she have originally in the petty cash drawer?

Applications Involving Geometry

Geometry formulas are often used in application problems. Here is a short review of some geometry formulas you need to know when applying math.

[PN: please include picture with formulas]

Squares, Rectangles, and Triangles

Area of a Square: $A = s^2$

Perimeter of a Square: $P = 4s$

Area of a Rectangle: $A = L \cdot W$

Perimeter of a Rectangle: $P = 2L + 2W$

Area of a Triangle: $A = \dfrac{1}{2}bh$

Angles

Supplementary Angles: $A + B = 180^o$

Complementary Angles: $A + B = 90^o$

Sum of Angles in Triangle: $A + B + C = 180^o$

It may be helpful to keep in mind that if an application mentions any kind of geometric object (square, rectangle, triangle, etc) the problem usually involves a geometry formula that you will need to know.

For some applications, the geometry information will be summarized in a picture for you, as in this next example. If not, it is always a good idea to draw a picture that represents the information given.

Example 8: An artist is creating a triangular design. One angle of the triangle will be 42 degrees. For the other two angles she wants for one of the angle to be twice as big as the other. What will be the measure of each of the other angles?

Solution: We will go through the steps for solving applications even though the drawing to the right already gives us variables and summarizes most of what we need.

ASSIGN A VARIABLE	x = measure of the first angle 2x = measure of the second angle
SUMMARIZE THE INFORMATION	We redraw the triangle without all that artsy stuff in it. The only other thing we need to include is the formula for the angles in a triangle. for any triangle: A + B + C = 180

DO THE MATH	$A + B + C = 180$ [PN: arrows for translation] $42 + x + 2x = 180$
Solve • Combine like terms. • Subtract 42 from both sides. • Divide both sides by 3.	$42 + x + 2x = 180$ $42 + 3x = 180$ $3x = 138$ $x = 46$
ANSWER THE QUESTION	The first angle will be 46 degrees. The second angle is twice that measure: $2 \cdot 46 = 92$. The first angle will be 46 degrees and the second will be 92 degrees.

For the next example, we will draw and label a picture for ourselves.

Example 9: The Garganchu-Brain 3000 is a think pad that can do almost anything. To perform all its functions, the rectangular design must have an area of 96 square inches. For convenience, it should be 12 inches long. What should the width be?

Solution:

ASSIGN A VARIABLE	Since we are asked to find the width of the think pad, we have w = width of the pad
SUMMARIZE THE INFORMATION	The problem involves a rectangle. The length of the rectangle is given as 12 inches. We are also told the total area is 96 square inches. **w = ?** **12 inches** total area is 96 square inches area formula for a rectangle $A = l \cdot w$
DO THE MATH	$A = l \cdot w$ $96 = 12 \cdot w$
Solve: • Divide both sides by 12.	$96 = 12w$ $8 = w$
ANSWER THE QUESTION	The width of the think pad will be 8 inches. This answer makes sense in light of the problem.

Create an equation that corresponds to each application and solve.

27. Two angles are complementary. One angle measures 32° more than the other one. Find the measure of each angle. [PN: Picture with angles labeled]

28. The 1st angle in a triangle measures 84°. The 3rd angle is three times as big as 2nd angle. Find the measure of each angle. [PN: Picture with angles labeled]

29. The area of a rectangular window is 115 ft^2. If the length is 23 ft. What is the width?

30. The perimeter of a rectangular garden is 75 ft. The width is 10 ft. less than the length. Find the dimensions of the garden.

Exercise Set - Putting It ALL Together

Translate each phrase into an algebraic equation or expression. If it is an algebraic equation, solve.

31. Six subtract a number
32. Nine subtract twice a number
33. Forty subtracted from a number
34. Fifteen subtracted from thrice a number
35. A number plus seven
36. Sixteen subtract a number is three.
37. Twice a number subtract a number is seven.
38. Three times a number is twelve.
39. A number plus twenty five is 45.
40. Five subtracted from a number is eight.
41. Six subtracted from a number is twenty seven.
42. Five divided by the sum of a number and two
43. Four divided by the difference a number and three
44. Twice the sum of a number and three plus six
45. Seven minus three times the sum of a number and two
46. Five plus the difference of a number and three divided by twice the number

47. Antwon bought an ipod for $85 plus $1 per song on itunes purchased and $10 per album purchased on itunes. If the variable s represents the number of songs purchased and a represents the number of albums purchased, create an expressions for the total charge of the setting up his new ipod.

48. Alan is setting up his music studio and wants to buy a Schecter Hellraiser Electric guitar for $749, guitar cords for $21 each, and new microphones for $50 each. If the variable c represents the number of cords purchased and m represents the number of microphones purchased, create an expressions for the total charge for new equipment.

49. A travel agent is working on packages for a Vegas vacation. The airfare costs $244 (total), the hotel costs $157 per night and it costs $175 per show they go to see. If the variable h represents the number of nights they stay in a hotel and s represents the number of shows they went and saw, create an expression for the total charge of their vacation to Vegas.

Translate each sentence into an algebraic equation and solve the equation.

50. A number minus twelve is equal to five.
51. A number plus ten is equal to twenty.
52. Twice a number plus four is three.
53. Five times the difference of a number and three yields twelve.
54. Sixteen subtracted from a number results in twelve.

55. Twenty-three minus a number is the same as ten.

Solve.

56. One number is fifteen more than another number. The sum of the two numbers is 93. Find the two numbers.

57. One number is three times another number. The difference of the two numbers is 78. Find the two numbers.

58. One number is six more than the other. The sum of the numbers is 54. Find the numbers.

59. One number is seven less than the other. The sum of the numbers is 31. Find the numbers.

60. Two angles are supplementary. The 2nd angle is twenty more than the 1st. Find the measure of the two angles. [PN: Picture with angles labeled]

61. Two angles are complementary. The 1st is $31°$ less than the second angle. Find the measure of the angles. [PN: Picture with angles labeled]

62. In a right triangle, the smaller angle is $23°$ degrees less than the other angle. Find the measure of the angles in the triangle. [PN: Picture with angles labeled]

63. In a right triangle, the middle angle is $18°$ degrees more than the smaller angle. Find the measure of the angles in the triangle. [PN: Picture with angles labeled]

64. The perimeter of a rectangular garden is 105 m. The length is twice as long as the width. Find the dimensions of the garden. [PN: Picture with angles labeled]

65. The perimeter of a rectangle is 26 centimeters. The length is 3 centimeters longer than the width. What are the dimensions of the rectangle?

66. Two angles are supplementary. One angle measures $28°$ more than the other one. Find the measure of each angle. [PN: Picture with angles labeled]

67. Two angles are complementary. One angle measures $18°$ more than the other one. Find the measure of each angle. [PN: Picture with angles labeled]

68. The 1st angle in a triangle is twice as big as the 2nd. The 3rd angle is twenty more than the 2nd. Find the measure of each angle.

69. The area of the face of Ellie's ipod is $66\ cm^2$. If the width is 6 cm, what is the length?

70. You are using 170 feet of fencing to create a rectangular pen. If the need the width to be 34 feet, what will be the length?

71. You have 240 feet of fencing to create a rectangular area. If you want the length of the area to be 85 feet, what will be the width?

72. Lance Armstrong bikes the tour de France. During the last 2 days of the tour, he rides a total of 280 kilometers. On the last day, he rides three times the distance than on the second to last. How many kilometers did he ride each day of last two days of the tour?

73. Enrique bikes down the coast of California from San Francisco to Santa Barbara, a total of 320 miles. He bikes twice as many miles the second day as he does the first. How many miles did he bike each day?

Exercise Set - Chapter 3 Review

74. Fill in the blank to complete the equation. $4 \cdot \boxed{} = -12$
75. Solve. $-5w = 75$
76. Solve. $7h - 11h = 8 - 24$
77. Solve. $3(x - 4) - 5x = 6$
78. Simplify. $-7a + 6b + 9a - 5b$

Exercise Set - Cumulative Review

79. Multiply. $(7)(6)(0)(5)$
80. Reduce. $\dfrac{12}{51}$
81. Find $|6 - 9|$ and $|6| - |9|$.
82. Divide. $(-54) \div (6)$
83. Add. $583 + 98$

 # 3.5 QUIZ YOURSELF:

To make sure you are ready for the EXAM, try these problems without any help. Give yourself about 20 minutes and don't check the answers until you have completely finished.

Write as an algebraic expression or equation.

1. Six added to a number is equal to twelve
2. Twice the sum of a number and five
3. Five times the difference of number and two is the same as four
4. The quotient of a number and seven is negative one
5. A number subtracted from thirty-two
6. One number is four times another number. The sum of the numbers is 35. Find the numbers.

7. The perimeter of a triangle is 97 meters. The 1st side is twice the 2nd side and the 3rd side is 13 meters more than the 2nd side. Find the length of each side of the triangle.

8. Angel started a savings account with $750. Every month she deposits $60 into the account. How many months will it take her to have in $1650 her savings account?

9. Two angles are complementary. One angle is $25°$ less than the other one. Find the measure of the angles.

10. A furniture store in a shipment of couches and loveseats of 145 pieces of furniture. The store usually sells these as a set. However, when the manager sets them up, he finds that there is an abundance of loveseats. He has an extra 19 loveseats. Find how many couches and how many loveseats were in the shipment.

Answers to this Quiz Yourself are on page 656.

3.6 Introduction to Algebraic Fractions

Topics:
- Algebraic Fractions
- Simplifying Algebraic Fractions
- Multiplying and Dividing Algebraic Fractions
- Adding and Subtracting Like Algebraic Fractions

Are You Ready?
To see if you are ready to understand this section, do the following short quiz.

1. Simplify. $\dfrac{15}{42}$

2. Multiply. $\dfrac{24}{25} \cdot \dfrac{35}{48}$

3. Subtract. $\dfrac{5}{18} - \left(-\dfrac{5}{18}\right)$

Answers to Are You Ready?

(1) $\dfrac{5}{14}$ *(2)* $\dfrac{7}{10}$ *(3)* $\dfrac{5}{9}$

Algebraic Fractions

We now explore fractions that involve one or more variables, like $\dfrac{7x^2}{15y}$.

An **algebraic fraction** or **rational expression** is a fraction that involves one or more variables.

We will give algebraic fractions the same treatment we did fractions in Sections 1.6 and 2.6: simplifying, multiplying, dividing then addition and subtraction of fractions with the same denominator.

First we evaluate algebraic fractions like we did with other expressions.

Example 1: Evaluate each algebraic fraction using the variable values given.

a) $\dfrac{-b}{2a}$, $a = 5$ and $b = 4$ b) $\dfrac{a+b+c}{3}$, $a = 5$, $b = 8$, and $c = -4$

Solution: In each case we substitute in the variable values given.

a) Substitute $a = 5$ and $b = 4$. $\dfrac{-b}{2a} = \dfrac{-(4)}{2(5)}$

Simplify. $= \dfrac{-4}{10}$

Factor to simplify.

$$= -\frac{2\cdot 2}{5\cdot 2} = -\frac{2\cdot \cancel{2}}{5\cdot \cancel{2}}$$

$$= -\frac{2}{5}$$

b) Substitute $a = 5$, $b = 8$, and $c = -4$.

$$\frac{a+b+c}{3} = \frac{5+8+(-4)}{3}$$

Next we add in the numerator.

$$= \frac{9}{3}$$

Factor to simplify.

$$= \frac{3\cdot 3}{3} = \frac{\cancel{3}\cdot 3}{\cancel{3}} = \frac{3}{1}$$

$$= 3$$

Example 2: Where in the World? The algebraic fraction $\dfrac{M\cdot m}{d^2}$ is used by astronomers to find the gravitational pull between planets or stars. Evaluate this algebraic fraction for $M = 3$, $m = 8$, and $d = 6$.

Solution:
Substitute $M = 3$, $m = 8$, and $d = 6$.

$$\frac{M\cdot m}{d^2} = \frac{3\cdot 8}{6^2}$$

Rather than multiply and then factor, we can factor from here.

$$= \frac{3\cdot 8}{6\cdot 6} = \frac{3\cdot 2\cdot 2\cdot 2}{3\cdot 2\cdot 3\cdot 2}$$

Remove the common factors.

$$= \frac{\cancel{3}\cdot \cancel{2}\cdot \cancel{2}\cdot 2}{\cancel{3}\cdot \cancel{2}\cdot 3\cdot \cancel{2}}$$

$$= \frac{2}{3}$$

STOP Exercise Set -Algebraic Fractions

1. Evaluate $\dfrac{2A}{h}$ for A = 36 and h=18

2. Evaluate $\dfrac{3A}{b}$ for A = 54 and b =9

3. Evaluate $\dfrac{x+y}{24}$ for $x = 12$ and $y = -2$

4. Evaluate $\dfrac{w-3}{p}$ for $w = 11$ and 13

5. Evaluate $\dfrac{ab^3}{c}$ for a = -1, b = 2 and c = -4

6. Evaluate $\dfrac{-2xy^2}{3z}$ for x = -6, y = 5 and z = 10

7. Evaluate $\dfrac{-b}{2a}$ for $a = -6$, $b = 9$

8. Evaluate $\dfrac{-b}{2a}$ for $a = 5$, $b = -15$

Simplifying Algebraic Fractions

Algebraic fractions can be simplified the same way that numeric fractions are; factor and reduce factors common to the numerator and denominator. Including variables makes it necessary to work with exponents. Recall the following about exponents and variables.

$$\underbrace{x^4}_{\substack{\text{This is}\\\text{called}\\\text{exponential}\\\text{form}}} = \underbrace{x\cdot x\cdot x\cdot x}_{\substack{\text{This is called}\\\text{expanded form.}}}$$

To simplify an algebraic fraction:
- Simplify the numeric part as normal (factor and reduce)
- Write variables with exponents in expanded form to see what variables the numerator and denominator have in common.
- Use exponential form to express the final answer.

Example 3: Simplify each algebraic fraction.

a) $\dfrac{5a^3}{15a}$

b) $\dfrac{21dg}{28dg^2}$

Solution: For each fraction we rewrite the numbers using prime factorizations and rewrite the exponential forms in expanded form then remove common factors.

a) Factor the coefficients and write exponents in expanded form.

$$\frac{5a^3}{15a} = \frac{5\cdot a\cdot a\cdot a}{3\cdot 5\cdot a}$$

Remove common factors in the numerator and denominator. Notice that the variable a is a common factor and is removed the same way a number would be.

$$= \frac{\cancel{5}\cdot \cancel{a}\cdot a\cdot a}{3\cdot \cancel{5}\cdot \cancel{a}}$$

Write the variable multiplication in exponent form for the final answer.

$$= \frac{a^2}{3}$$

b) This fraction contains two variables, but the process is still the same.

$$\frac{21dg}{28dg^2}$$

Factor the coefficients and write exponents in expanded form.

$$= \frac{3\cdot 7\cdot d\cdot g}{2\cdot 2\cdot 7\cdot d\cdot g\cdot g}$$

Remove common factors in the numerator and denominator.

$$= \frac{3\cdot \cancel{7}\cdot \cancel{d}\cdot \cancel{g}}{4\cdot \cancel{7}\cdot \cancel{d}\cdot \cancel{g}\cdot g}$$

Write the fraction in exponential form.

$$= \frac{3d}{4g}$$

STOP Exercise Set -Simplifying Algebraic Fractions

Simplify each algebraic fraction.

9. $\dfrac{18}{39a}$

10. $\dfrac{2x}{3x}$

11. $\dfrac{14b}{21b}$

12. $\dfrac{15x^2}{60x^3}$

13. $\dfrac{-44y^4}{55y}$

14. $\dfrac{-81x^3}{27x^2}$

15. $\dfrac{-45h^4}{18h}$

16. $\dfrac{-27b^4}{-30b^2}$

17. $\dfrac{54d^4e}{-45e}$

18. $\dfrac{64ab^3}{24a^2b}$

Multiplying and Dividing Algebraic Fractions

Once again here are the rules for fraction multiplication and division, as we saw in section 1.6.

Multiplying Fractions

$$\frac{a}{b} \cdot \frac{c}{d} = \frac{a \cdot c}{b \cdot d}$$

Dividing Fractions

$$\frac{a}{b} \div \frac{c}{d} = \frac{a}{b} \cdot \frac{d}{c} = \frac{a \cdot d}{b \cdot c}$$

To work with algebraic fractions we need to know the process for expanding and simplifying for variables with exponents as we have already learned in chapter 1.

Example 4: Multiply.

a) $\dfrac{t^2}{8} \cdot \dfrac{3}{h}$

b) $\dfrac{3a^2}{5} \cdot \dfrac{10}{a}$

Solution: The fact that these products involve variables does not change the general approach. We just need to be careful about reducing and dealing with exponents.

a) Write the product as a single fraction.

$$\frac{t^2}{8} \cdot \frac{3}{h} = \frac{t^2 \cdot 3}{8 \cdot h}$$

There are no common factors, so we just multiply.

$$= \frac{3t^2}{8h}$$

b) Write the product as a single fraction.

$$\frac{3a^2}{5} \cdot \frac{10}{a} = \frac{3a^2 \cdot 10}{5 \cdot a}$$

Now we look for common factors by factoring the numbers and rewriting the variables with exponents in expanded form.

$$= \frac{3 \cdot a \cdot a \cdot 2 \cdot 5}{5 \cdot a}$$

Remove the common factors of 5 and a, then multiply.

$$= \frac{3 \cdot a \cdot a \cdot 2 \cdot 5}{5 \cdot a} = \frac{6a}{1} = 6a$$

Recall that to divide fractions, we multiply by the reciprocal of the second fraction.

Example 5: Divide.

a) $\dfrac{-20x}{11} \div 16$

b) $\dfrac{19a}{27} \div \dfrac{5a}{9b}$

Solution:
a) Rewrite the whole number as a fraction.

$$\frac{-20x}{11} \div 16 = \frac{-20x}{11} \div \frac{16}{1}$$

Take the reciprocal of the second fraction and change the operation to multiplication.

$$= \frac{-20x}{11} \cdot \frac{1}{16}$$

Rewrite the product as a single fraction and prime factor the numerator and denominator.

$$= \frac{-20x \cdot 1}{11 \cdot 16} = -\frac{2 \cdot 2 \cdot 5 \cdot x}{11 \cdot 2 \cdot 2 \cdot 2 \cdot 2}$$

There are common factors of 2 and 2 in the numerator and denominator.

$$= -\frac{2 \cdot 2 \cdot 5 \cdot x}{11 \cdot 2 \cdot 2 \cdot 2 \cdot 2} = -\frac{5x}{44}$$

The final answer is $\dfrac{-5x}{44}$.

b) Take the reciprocal of the second fraction and change the operation to multiplication.

$$\frac{19a}{27} \div \frac{5a}{9b} = \frac{19a}{27} \cdot \frac{9b}{5a}$$

Rewrite the product as a single fraction and prime factor the numerator and denominator.

$$= \frac{19 \cdot a \cdot 3 \cdot 3 \cdot b}{3 \cdot 3 \cdot 3 \cdot 5 \cdot a}$$

There are common factors of a, 3, and 3 in the numerator and denominator.

$$= \frac{19 \cdot a \cdot 3 \cdot 3 \cdot b}{3 \cdot 3 \cdot 3 \cdot 5 \cdot a} = \frac{19b}{15}$$

The final answer is $\dfrac{19b}{15}$.

Exercise Set - Multiplying and Dividing Algebraic Fractions

19. $\dfrac{6x}{7} \cdot \dfrac{14}{15}$

20. $\dfrac{4a}{5} \cdot \dfrac{10a}{11}$

21. $6 \cdot \dfrac{x}{2}$

22. $6b\left(\dfrac{2b}{15}\right)$

23. $\left(\dfrac{10}{t}\right)\left(\dfrac{3}{15t}\right)$

24. $5x\left(\dfrac{1}{10}\right)$

25. $\dfrac{-2x}{5} \div \dfrac{4}{7}$

26. $\dfrac{8y}{9} \div \dfrac{4}{5}$

27. $\dfrac{2x^2}{7} \div \dfrac{4x}{21}$

28. $\dfrac{-3a^3}{8} \div \dfrac{-6a}{7}$

Adding and Subtracting Algebraic Fractions

As with Section 1.6 and 2.6, all the algebraic fractions that we add or subtract in this section will have a common denominator.

Adding Fractions

$$\dfrac{a}{b} + \dfrac{c}{b} = \dfrac{a+c}{b}$$

Subtracting Fractions

$$\dfrac{a}{b} - \dfrac{c}{b} = \dfrac{a-c}{b}$$

Often adding and subtracting algebraic fractions involves combing like terms, a technique we have been using this whole chapter.

Example 6: Add or subtract and simplify if possible.

a) $\dfrac{2a}{7} + \dfrac{3a}{7}$ b) $\dfrac{5x}{6y} - \dfrac{8x}{6y}$

Solution:

a)

$$\dfrac{2a}{7} + \dfrac{3a}{7}$$

To add like fractions we add the numerators and keep the common denominator.

$$= \dfrac{2a+3a}{7}$$

We can combine like terms in the numerator. Since the fraction will not simplify this is our final answer.

$$= \dfrac{5a}{7}$$

b)

$$\dfrac{5x}{6y} - \dfrac{8x}{6y}$$

To subtract like fractions we subtract the numerators and keep the common denominator.

$$= \frac{5x - 8x}{6y}$$

We can combine like terms in the numerator.

$$= \frac{-3x}{6y}$$

Factor to simplify.

$$= -\frac{3 \cdot x}{2 \cdot 3 \cdot y} = -\frac{\cancel{3} \cdot x}{2 \cdot \cancel{3} \cdot y}$$

$$= -\frac{x}{2y}$$

STOP Exercise Set - Adding and Subtracting Algebraic Fractions

29. $\dfrac{2x}{9} + \dfrac{5x}{9}$

30. $\dfrac{9a}{16} - \dfrac{5a}{16}$

31. $\dfrac{15ab}{16} - \dfrac{3ab}{16}$

32. $\dfrac{24x^2}{25x} + \dfrac{14x^2}{25x}$

33. $\dfrac{7}{45x} + \dfrac{8}{45x}$

34. $\dfrac{32}{33b^2} - \dfrac{10}{33b^2}$

Exercise Set - Putting it ALL Together

Evaluate each algebraic fraction using the variable values given. Simplify your answer if possible.

35. $\dfrac{-x}{3y}$ for x = 3 and y = -2

36. $\dfrac{-b}{2a}$ for a = 2 and b = 6

37. $\dfrac{-b}{2a}$ for a = 3 and b = -6

38. $\dfrac{8-x}{3-y}$ for x = 2 and y = 2

39. $\dfrac{d}{t}$ for d = 130 and t = 4

40. $\dfrac{P-2l}{2}$ for $P = 36$ and $l = 5$

Simplify each algebraic fraction.

41. $\dfrac{-18a^5}{9a^2}$

42. $\dfrac{24a^3}{4a}$

43. $\dfrac{16x^5y^2}{8xy^2}$

44. $\dfrac{-81x^3y^2}{27x^2y}$

45. $\dfrac{-21c^4d^3}{-3cd^5}$

46. $\dfrac{-36ab^3}{4a^2b}$

47. $\dfrac{-18a^5}{9a^2}$

48. $\dfrac{24a^3}{4a}$

Perform the indicated operation.

49. $\dfrac{6}{7y} \cdot \dfrac{14y^2}{15}$

50. $\dfrac{a}{2} \cdot \dfrac{5}{7}$

51. $\dfrac{3}{8} \cdot \dfrac{h}{4}$

52. $\dfrac{3}{x} \cdot \dfrac{5x^2}{2}$

53. $-\dfrac{2}{21yx^2}\left(-\dfrac{35xy}{36}\right)$

54. $\dfrac{16xy}{35} \cdot \dfrac{21y}{36x}$

55. $\dfrac{3b}{17} \cdot 5$

56. $\dfrac{x}{3} \cdot 3$

57. $-\dfrac{15ab}{51} \cdot \dfrac{17}{45b}$

58. $\left(\dfrac{7}{24y}\right)\left(\dfrac{8y}{77}\right)$

59. $\dfrac{8xy^3}{11x} \cdot \dfrac{33xy}{36x^3y^4}$

60. $\left(\dfrac{-7gh}{16h^2}\right) \div \left(\dfrac{-15h}{32g}\right)$

61. $\dfrac{2x^2y^3}{5x} \div \dfrac{4xy}{7}$

62. $\dfrac{-3x^3}{14y} \div \dfrac{4x^2y}{7y^2}$

63. $\dfrac{-15x^2}{16} \div \dfrac{-25xy}{26y^3}$

64. $\dfrac{14xy}{25} \div \dfrac{21y^2}{10x}$

65. $\dfrac{5a}{6} - \dfrac{3a}{6}$

66. $\dfrac{7m}{16} + \dfrac{5m}{16}$

67. $\dfrac{-15ab}{19c} + \dfrac{7ab}{19c}$

68. $\dfrac{-7x}{26y} + \left(\dfrac{-6x}{26y}\right)$

69. $\dfrac{16mn}{27} - \left(-\dfrac{5mn}{27}\right)$

70. $\dfrac{27x}{55} - \left(\dfrac{-13x}{55}\right)$

71. $\dfrac{-11a^2b}{80} - \dfrac{9a^2b}{80}$

72. $\dfrac{17x^3y}{25} + \left(\dfrac{-7x^3y}{25}\right)$

Exercise Set - Chapter 3 Review

73. Simplify $4(5+1)$ using the distributive property and then again using the order of operations. Comment on the results.

74. Are $6x^2y$ and $-x^2y$ like terms?

75. Fill in the blank to complete the equation. $9 + \square = 7 + 4$

76. Translate the phrase "five times a number plus seven is equal to twenty-two" into an equation. Do not solve.

77. Solve. $7 - 6h = 5$

Exercise Set - Cumulative Review

78. Add. $(-14) + 8 + (-7)$

79. Multiply. $(-6)(3)(5)$

80. Write $(-8)^4$ in expanded form.

81. Divide. $1548 \div (-6)$

82. Evaluate $5m^2$ for $m = -3$

3.6 QUIZ YOURSELF:

To make sure you are ready for the EXAM, try these problems without any help. Give yourself about 20 minutes and don't check the answers until you have completely finished.

Evaluate the following expression for given values.

1. $\dfrac{-b}{2a}$; for $a = -3$; $b = 18$

2. $\dfrac{5x^2}{yz}$; for $x = -2, y = -1, z = 4$

Simplify.

3. $\dfrac{21x}{28y}$

4. $\dfrac{16m^5}{64m}$

5. $\dfrac{-18a^3b^4}{42a^2b}$

Perform the indicated operations.

6. $\dfrac{12x}{15} \cdot \dfrac{9x}{14}$

7. $\dfrac{9a^2}{28} \div \dfrac{-5ab}{36b^3}$

8. $\dfrac{13x}{17} + \left(\dfrac{-6x}{17} \right)$

9. $\dfrac{-30s^3t}{49t} \cdot \dfrac{14t^2}{25s^4}$

10. $\dfrac{7a^2b}{24} - \left(\dfrac{-5a^2b}{24} \right)$

Answers to this Quiz Yourself are on page 656.

Chapter 3 Vocabulary

Write an "in your own" words definition for each vocabulary word that appeared in Chapter 3. If you need some help, the page number for the term is given.

1) numeric expression
2) algebraic expression
3) terms
4) coefficient
5) constant term

6) like terms
7) equation
8) numeric equation
9) algebraic equation
10) algebraic fraction

Chapter 3 Summary

Section 3.1: More About Algebraic Expressions

Processes and Important Notes	Examples

Terminology:
 	
Recall from Chapter 1 that a **numeric expression** involves operations and numbers and that an **algebraic expression** involves operations, numbers, and one or more variables
 	
The parts of an expression separated by addition (or subtraction) are called the **terms** of an expression.
 	
The **coefficient** of a term is the number being multiplied to that term.
 	
A term with no variable is called a **constant term**.
	List the terms, coefficients and whether the expression is numeric or algebraic.
	
	(a) $-5x^2 + 17xy$
	
	(b) $-15x^2 + 6xy - 5$
	
	Solution:
	
	(a) terms: $-5x^2, 17xy$
	
	   coefficients: $-5, 17$
	
	   algebraic expression
	(b) terms: $-15x, 6xy, -5$
	
	   coefficients: $-15, 6, -5$
	
	   algebraic expression

Combining Like Terms: **Like terms** are terms that have the same variable(s) raised to the same power(s). • Two or more like terms can be combined into a single term. **To combine like terms**, add or subtract the coefficients of those terms without changing the variable(s).	Combine like terms. (a) $19m - 6m$ (b) $-13x^2y + 12x + 37x^2y - 45x + 67$ Solution: (a) $19m - 6m = 13m$ (b) $-13x^2y + 12x + 37x^2y - 45x + 67$ $\quad = 24x^2y - 33x + 67$
The Distributive Property: A sum or difference multiplied by a number can be simplified by multiplying each part of the sum or difference by the number. **To simplify an algebraic expression:** 1. Use the distributive property to remove any parentheses. 2. Combine like terms.	Simplify. (a) $-3(7x - 8)$ (b) $13m - 8(-3m + 5) + 23$ Solution: (a) $-3(7x - 8) = -21x + 24$ (b) $13m - 8(-3m + 5) + 23$ $\quad = 13m + 24m - 40 + 23$ $\quad = 37m - 17$

Section 3.2: Equations and Their Solutions

Processes and Important Notes	Examples

Expression vs. Equation:
 	
An **equation** is a statement that two expressions are equal.
A **numeric equation** only contains operations and numbers.
An **algebraic equation** contains operations, numbers, and at least one variable.
A **numeric equation** involves two numeric expressions
An **algebraic equation** involves one or two algebraic expressions
	Identify whether each is an expression or an equation.
	
	(a) $17x+13=5$
	(b) $2x^2+9$
	
	Solution:
	   (a) equation
	   (b) expression

Identifying Solutions to Equations: The **solution to an equation** is the value of the variable that makes the equation true.	Determine whether the given number is the solution to the equation. $5x-6=19$, if $x=-5$ **Solution:** Substitute $x=-5$ to see if equation is true. $5x-6=19$ $\quad=5(-5)-6$ $\quad=-25-6$ $\quad-31\neq19$

Introduction to Solving Equations:	Give the solution to each equation.
	
	(a) $\dfrac{\square}{8}=12-14$ **(b)** $m+7=18$
	
	Solution:
	
	(a) $\dfrac{\square}{8}=12-14 \;\rightarrow\; \dfrac{\square}{8}=-2$
	    Since -16 divided by 8 is -2, then $\square=-16$
	(b) $m+7=18$
	    Since 11 + 7 = 19, then $m=11$

Section 3.3: Basic Principles of Equality

Processes and Important Notes	Examples

The Addition and Subtraction Property:
 	
You can add or subtract anything from both sides of an equation.
 	
If $a=b$, then $a+c=b+c$ and $a-c=b-c$ for any real number c.
 	
The process of operating on both sides of an
	Solve.
	(a) $m+8=14$ **(b)** $17=b-12$
	
	Solution:
	(a) $m+8=14$ **(b)** $17=b-12$
	   $\underline{-8\;-8}$ $\underline{+12\;\;+12}$
	     $m=6$ $29=b$

equation to rewrite it into the simple form *variable = number* is called **solving the equation** or **isolating the variable** or **solving for the variable**.	
The Multiplication and Division Property: You can multiply or divide both sides of an equation by anything except zero. • If $a = b$ and $c \neq 0$, then $a \cdot c = b \cdot c$ and $\dfrac{a}{c} = \dfrac{b}{c}$ for any real number c.	Solve. **(a)** $-11x = -99$ **(b)** $\dfrac{m}{-3} = -12$ Solution: **(a)** $\dfrac{-11x}{-11} = \dfrac{-99}{-11}$ **(b)** $-\cancel{3} \cdot \dfrac{m}{-\cancel{3}} = -12 \cdot -3$ $x = 9$ $m = 36$
Simplifying Equations: 1. Simplify both sides of the equation. 2. Solve using one of the properties.	Simplify Equation and Solve. $15 - 3(4x - 1) + 13x = -18 + 2$ Solution: $15 - 3(4x - 1) + 13x = -18 + 2$ $5 - 12x + 3 + 13x = -16$ $x + 18 = -16$ $\underline{\quad -18 \quad -18}$ $x = -34$

Section 3.4: More About Solving Equations

Processes and Important Notes	Examples

Using Both Principles of Equality:
 	
Always get the variable term alone on one side and then solve using the property of equality for multiplication or division.
 	
Make sure to only combine *like terms* when adding or subtracting to both sides.
	Solve.
	(a) $5x + 2 = -18$ **(b)** $-3(x + 2) = 15$
	
	Solution:
	(a) $5x + 2 = -18$ **(b)** $-3(x + 2) = 17$
	    $\underline{-2 \quad -2}$ $-3x - 6 = 17$
	      $5x = -20$ $\underline{+6 \quad +6}$
	                       $-3x = 33$
	    $\dfrac{5x}{5} = \dfrac{-20}{5}$ $\dfrac{-3x}{-3} = \dfrac{33}{-3}$
	       $x = -4$ $x = -11$

Equations With the Variable on Each Side:
 	
1. Get variable terms on one side and constant terms on the other side.
2. Solve using the properties of equality.
	Solve. $15m + 9 = 4m - 23$
	
	Solution: $15m + 9 = 4m - 23$
	         $\underline{-4m \quad\quad -4m}$
	        $11m + 9 = -23$
	        $11m + 9 = -13$
	           $\underline{-9 \quad -9}$
	           $11m = -22$

	$\dfrac{11m}{11} = \dfrac{-22}{11}$ $m = -2$
An Overall Strategy For Solving **Steps for solving an equation:** 1. Simplify each side separately by distributing and/or combining like terms 2. Add or Subtract to both sides of the equations so that terms with a variable are on the same side and terms with no variable are on the other side 3. Multiply or Divide both sides of the equation by the reciprocal of the variable's coefficient.	**Solve.** $-2(2c-1)+6c = -3c-(-2+c)$ **Solution:** $-2(2c-1)+6c = -3c-(-2+c)$ $-4c+2+6c = -3c+2-c$ $2c+2 = -4c+2$ $\underline{+4c \qquad +4c}$ $6c+2 = 2$ $6c+2 = 2$ $\underline{-2 \quad -2}$ $6c = 0$ $c = 0$

Section 3.5: Problem Solving

Processes and Important Notes	Examples
Translate English Into Math: **Key Words Chart** | Operation or Symbol	Common Key Words and Phrases
Addition **+**	plus, added to, more than, total, increased by
Subtraction **—**	minus, taken away from, less, less than, decreased by, subtract, subtracted from
Multiplication **•**	of, times, per
Division **÷**	divided by, divided up, quotient
Equal Sign **=**	is, was, is equal to, is the same as, result is
Variable x	what number, what value, a number, some number, an unknown value | When the phrase "less than", is used, the first number mentioned comes *after* the operation.	**For each phrase, create an expression or equation that involves a variable.** **(a)** the quotient of a number and negative five **(b)** ten minus three times some number yeilds six. **Solution:** **(a)** $\dfrac{x}{-5}$ **(b)** $10-3x = 6$
Problem Solving: The KEY to getting good at word problems is to take a careful approach. Carefully follow these steps and you WILL get better: **1) RE-RE-READ THE PROBLEM**	**Solve the following word problems by using the 5-step method.** In a right triangle, the second angle is twice the measure of the smaller angle. Find the measure of the angles in the triangle.

2)   **ASSIGN A VARIABLE**
3)   **SUMMARIZE THE INFORMATION**
4)   **DO THE MATH**
5)   **ANSWER THE QUESTION**

Important Formulas:
Area of a Rectangle: $A = l \cdot w$
Perimeter of a Rectangle: $P = 2l + 2w$
Supplementary Angles: $A + B = 90^o$
Complementary Angles: $A + B = 180^o$
Sum of Angles in Triangle: $A + B + C = 180^o$

Solution:

ASSIGN A VARIABLE:
x = measure of the first angle
2x = measure of the second angle

SUMMARIZE THE INFORMATION
for any triangle: A + B + C = 180

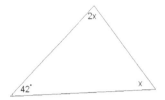

DO THE MATH
$90^\circ + 2x + x = 180^\circ$
$90^\circ + 3x = 180^\circ$
$3x = 90^\circ$
$x = 30^\circ$

ANSWER THE QUESTION
The measure of the angles are:
$x = 30^\circ$
$2x = 60^\circ$

Section 3.6: Introduction to Algebraic Fractions

Processes and Important Notes	Examples
Algebraic Fractions: An **algebraic fraction** or **rational expression** is a fraction that involves one or more variables.	Evaluate. $\dfrac{-2ab}{5c^2}$ for a = 10 , b = -3 and c = -2 Solution: $\dfrac{-2ab}{5c^2} = \dfrac{-2(10)(-3)}{5(-2)^2} = \dfrac{-2(2 \cdot 5)(-3)}{5(2)(2)}$ $= \dfrac{-2(2 \cdot 5)(-3)}{5(2)(2)} = 3$
Simplifying Algebraic Fractions: **To reduce an algebraic fraction:** • Reduce the numeric part as normal (by factoring and reducing) • Write variables with exponents in expanded form to see what variables will reduce. • Use exponential form to express the final answer.	Simplify each algebraic fraction. $\dfrac{5a^3}{15a^2}$ Solution: $\dfrac{5a^3}{15a^2} = \dfrac{5 \cdot a \cdot a \cdot a}{3 \cdot 5 \cdot a \cdot a} = \dfrac{5 \cdot a \cdot a \cdot a}{3 \cdot 5 \cdot a \cdot a} = \dfrac{a}{3}$
Multiplying and Dividing Algebraic Fractions:	Multiply. $\dfrac{6b}{7} \cdot \dfrac{2}{3}$

Rule for Multiplying Fractions:	**Solution:**
$\dfrac{a}{b} \cdot \dfrac{c}{d} = \dfrac{a \cdot c}{b \cdot d}$	$\dfrac{6b}{7} \cdot \dfrac{2}{3} = \dfrac{6b \cdot 2}{7 \cdot 3} = \dfrac{2 \cdot 3 \cdot b \cdot 2}{7 \cdot 3} = \dfrac{2 \cdot \cancel{3} \cdot b \cdot 2}{7 \cdot \cancel{3}} = \dfrac{4b}{7}$
Rule for Dividing Fractions:	**Divide.** $\dfrac{15}{y^2} \div \left(-\dfrac{10}{3y} \right)$
$\dfrac{a}{b} \div \dfrac{c}{d} = \dfrac{a}{b} \cdot \dfrac{d}{c} = \dfrac{a \cdot d}{b \cdot c}$	**Solution:**
	$\dfrac{15}{y^2} \div \left(-\dfrac{10}{3y} \right) = -\dfrac{15}{y^2} \cdot \dfrac{3y}{10} = -\dfrac{15 \cdot 3y}{y^2 \cdot 10} = -\dfrac{5 \cdot 3 \cdot 3y}{y \cdot y \cdot 2 \cdot 5}$
	$= -\dfrac{\cancel{5} \cdot 3 \cdot 3 \cdot \cancel{y}}{\cancel{y} \cdot y \cdot 2 \cdot \cancel{5}} = -\dfrac{9}{2y}$
Adding and Subtracting Like Algebraic Fractions:	**Add.** $\dfrac{15ab^2}{24} + \left(\dfrac{-3ab^2}{24} \right)$
Rule for Adding Fractions:	**Solution:**
$\dfrac{a}{b} + \dfrac{c}{b} = \dfrac{a+c}{b}$	$\dfrac{15ab^2}{24} + \left(\dfrac{-3ab^2}{24} \right) = \dfrac{15ab^2 - 3ab^2}{24} = \dfrac{12ab^2}{24}$
Rule for Subtracting Fractions:	$= \dfrac{12 \cdot 1 \cdot ab^2}{2 \cdot 12} = \dfrac{\cancel{12} \cdot 1 \cdot ab^2}{2 \cdot \cancel{12}} = \dfrac{1ab^2}{2}$
$\dfrac{a}{b} - \dfrac{c}{b} = \dfrac{a-c}{b}$	

Chapter 3 Review

Section 3.1 More About Algebraic Expressions

List the number of terms, the coefficients of the terms, and constant term if there is one.

1. $16x^3 - 3x^2 + 451$
2. $-3e^4 + 15e^3 - (-17e) + 1$

Two terms are given below. Fill in the blank so that the terms are like terms.

3. $91a^3b^2$ $-18\square^3 b^\square$

4. $-2g^5h$ $45\square^5 h^\square$

Simplify.

5. $4x + 18x$

6. $3m + 19m + (-3m)$

7. $-34x + 67y + (-27y) - 18x$

8. $-3a + 17a + 13 + 2a^2 + 1$

9. $14 - 4(8 - x)$

10. $5(4x + 1)$

11. $-(3x - 17)$

12. $-(9t^3 + 5t^2 - 18)$

13. $-5(7m + 2) - 23$

14. $3(2x - 5) - 5(6x + 1)$

15. $2n - 3(8 - 11n) - (-6)$

16. $-2[5(3 - b) + 2b] - 4(7b - 2)$

17. $18m + 35n - 2(m + 5) - 17n$

18. $8y - 2[4(3 - y) + 12] - 7y$

19. A moving company charges \$58 plus \$38 per hour but the first two hours are free. The total cost of using the company's service for t hours is given by the expression $58 + 38(t - 2)$. Simplify the expression.

20. A yoga studio offers classes at a rate of \$15 per class plus a sign up fee of \$49, but the first 3 classes are free. The total cost for taking y yoga classes is given by the expression $49 + 15(y - 3)$. Simplify the expression.

Section 3.2 Equations and Their Solutions

Decide if the following are expressions or equations.

21. $17x - 21 + 4x$
22. $-21 = 3h - 18$
23. $24 - 7(9n + 3) = 2(n + 1)$
24. $-6y^2 + 2(3y - 4) + 34$

25. Is $h = 2$ a solution to the equation $2h + 5 = 3h - (-3)$?

26. Is $y = -1$ a solution to the equation $7(2y - 3) = 35$?

27. Is $s = -5$ a solution to the equation $s + 11 = -2(s + 2)$?

28. Is $x = 10$ a solution to the equation $2x = -3x + 10$?

Fill in the blank to complete each equation.

29. $12 + \square = 28$

30. $-2 \cdot \square = -18$

31. $\square - 36 = 5$

32. $-8 = -18 + \square$

33. $\dfrac{\square}{-8} = -7$

34. $\dfrac{\square}{11} = -5$

Section 3.3 Basic Principles of Equality

Solve using the properties of equality.

35. $x + 17 = 23$

36. $x - 45 = 14$

37. $19 = m + 2$

38. $21k = -63$

39. $w + -5 = 55$

40. $21 - 34 = b - 12$

41. $-7y = -21$

42. $2t - (t + 6) = -14$

43. $\dfrac{a}{-8} = 16$

44. $\dfrac{h}{8} = -5$

45. $7x + 26 - 6x = 27 - 19$

46. $12 - 14 = 8g + 1 - 7g$

47. $-5x - 13 + 6x = 28 - 17$

48. $23x - 2(11x + 5) = -17$

49. A traveler is driving at 65 miles an hour. The trip is 780. To find out how long it will take the driver can solve the equation $65t = 780$ where t represents hours. How long will the trip take?

50. A factory machine makes 325 guitars strings per day. Today the machine has already made 147 strings. To find out how many more it will make we can solve the equation $s + 147 = 325$ where s represents the number of strings left to make. How many strings are left?

Section 3.4 More About Solving Equations

51. $5x - 1 = 16$

52. $4z + 3 = -13$

53. $32 - 5a = 18$

54. $-69 + 9 = -12(p + 2)$

55. $-7x + 5x + 8 = -10$

56. $5n + 9 = 3n - 11$

57. $16m + 2(-9m - 6) = -19 - (-27)$

58. $-5t - 105 = 5t$

59. $3x - 7x + 15 = 19$

60. $33m - 18 = 27m$

61. $-3(5h + 1) + 18h = 6h + 15$

62. $-23 - 4(5x - 1) = 29 - 36$

63. To rent a dump truck costs $45 plus $20 for every hour after 3 hours. A construction foreman gets a bill for $285. To find out how many the truck was used he can solve the equation $45 + 20(h - 3) = 285$ where h represents the number of hours. How long was the truck rented?

64. Wayne is writing a book and has two options for payment. He can either take $250 grant plus $3 per page or he can take a $450 grant plus $2 per page. To find out how many pages would make the two options give the same amount of money he can solve the equation $250 + 3p = 450 + 2p$ where p represents the number of pages he writes. How many pages will make the two options the same?

Section 3.5 Problem Solving

Translate each phrase into an expression or equation.

65. twelve subtract twice a number

66. four times the sum of a number and eight

67. twelve minus twice the difference of a number and four is eighteen

68. the quotient of a number and twenty yields the opposite of three.

For each scenario create a corresponding algebraic expression.

69. Ellie hires a screen artist to design t-shirts for her cycling group. The artist charges an upfront cost of $45 and then $12 per t-shirt plus $3 per color she wants used. Write an algebraic expression for

the total cost of the t-shirts. Let x = the number of t-shirts and p = the different colors of paint used.

70. Jessica hired a photographer to shoot her wedding. He charges a flat rate of $300 in addition to $55 for every hour he is at the wedding. Write an algebraic expression for the total cost of the photographer. Let h = the number of hours the photographer is at the wedding.

Solve.

71. One number is eight more than another number. The sum of the two numbers is fifty. Find the two numbers.

72. Two angles are supplementary. One angle measures $44°$ more than the other one. Find the measure of each angle. [PN: Picture with angles labeled]

73. In a right triangle, the larger angle is two more than three times the smaller angle. Find the angles in the triangle. [PN: Picture with angles labeled]

74. The perimeter of Wayne's garden is 154 ft. The length is 7 feet longer than the width. Find the dimensions of his garden.

Section 3.6 Introduction To Algebraic Fractions

Simplify.

75. $\dfrac{24xy}{36y}$

76. $\dfrac{44m^7}{77m^9}$

77. $\dfrac{15a^2b}{-20a}$

78. $\dfrac{-27g^3h^5}{45gh^2}$

Perform the indicated operation.

79. $\dfrac{4x}{25} \cdot \dfrac{3h}{16}$

80. $\dfrac{4e^3}{7} \div \dfrac{12e}{19}$

81. $\dfrac{36x^2y^3}{55} \div \dfrac{9x^3}{22y}$

82. $\dfrac{7b}{13} + \dfrac{2b}{13}$

83. $\dfrac{15}{21m} - \dfrac{-3}{21m}$

84. $\dfrac{25xy}{38} \div \dfrac{15y^3}{19x}$

85. $\dfrac{4a^3b^2}{7a} \cdot \dfrac{5b}{7a}$

86. $\dfrac{-22x^3}{13} + \left(\dfrac{-4x^3}{13}\right)$

87. $\dfrac{14s^2t^4}{15s} \cdot \dfrac{30t}{49t^3}$

88. $\dfrac{13h}{16} - \left(\dfrac{-2h}{16}\right)$

89. $\dfrac{16m^2n}{27n} + \left(\dfrac{-7m^2n}{27n}\right)$

90. $\dfrac{7b^2}{19} + \left(\dfrac{-7b^2}{19}\right)$

Chapter 3 Test Yourself

You should give yourself about 90 minutes to complete these problems. DO NOT use notes, your book or any outside source of help, ONLY YOURSELF. Put question marks by the problems you are unsure about, but TRY all of the problems. Once your time is up, check your answers on page #.

List the number of terms, the coefficients of the terms, and constant term if there is one:

1. $-x^3 + 17x - 143$

2. $15h^4 - 31h^2 + 16h - (-16)$

3. Two terms are given below. Fill in the blank so that the terms are like terms.

$$14a^2b^4 \qquad -9\square^2 b^\square$$

Simplify.

4. $3x + 5x + (-7x)$

5. $4m + 16 - 17m - 6m^2 + 1$

6. $6(x + 9) - 13$

7. $-4(2a - 9)$

8. $-(18e^3 - 12e^2 + 73)$

9. $-17 + 8(11 - 3x) + 5x$

10. A moving company charges $85 plus $30 per hour but the first two hours are free. The total cost of using the company's service for t hours is given by the expression $80 + 30(t - 2)$. Simplify the expression.

11. Is $b = -3$ the solution to the equation $4b + 5 = 2b - 1$?

Solve.

12. $x - 5 = -7$

13. $143 = b + 91$

14. $-12x = 48$

15. $\dfrac{-x}{8} = -7$

16. $4x + 18 - 3x = 19$

17. $2z + 5 = 27$

18. $42 - 7m = -16$

19. $18 + 7 = -5(y - 2)$

20. $35x - 2(17x - 6) = -18 - 31$

21. $7t - 28 = -7t$

22. A bike shop has $5100 to spend making custom bikes. The cost will be $550 plus $350 per bike. To find out how many bikes can be made they can solve the equation $550 + 350b = 5100$ where b represents the number of bikes made. How many bikes can the shop make?

Translate each phrase into an expression or equation.

23. five subtracted from a number is equal to three times the number

24. five times the sum a number and twelve

Solve.

25. One number is five more than another number. The sum of the two numbers is 23. Find the two numbers.

26. To rent a jack hammer, a rental company charges $35 plus $6 per hour. If the bill is for $83, how many hours was the jack hammer used?

27. Two angles are complementary. The first angle is nine more than twice the second. Find the two angles. [PN: Picture with angles labeled]

28. The perimeter of Vince's studio is 110 ft. The length is 17 feet longer than the width. Find the dimensions of his studio.

Chapters 1 – 3 Cumulative Review

1. What factors of 28 have a sum of -16?
2. Find the prime factorization of 96.

Reduce the expression.

3. $\dfrac{-88}{121}$

4. $\dfrac{65x^3y^8}{26xy^2}$

Simplify.

5. $17 + 38 - (-52) + (-29)$

6. $-5 - 2\left(14 - 2^2\right) + 27 \div (-3)$

7. $\dfrac{-4 \cdot 3 - 6\left(17 - 18\right)^4}{2\left(12 - (-3)\right) \div 5}$

8. $0 \div (-342)$

9. $913 \div (-1)$

10. $-|-45| - |-7|$

11. $15 \div 3 \cdot (-5)$

12. $(-2)^3 + 15 \cdot 3$

13. $\dfrac{22}{35} \cdot \dfrac{14}{33}$

14. $\dfrac{5}{21} - \left(\dfrac{-9}{21}\right)$

15. $\dfrac{17m}{19} + \dfrac{23m}{19}$

16. $\dfrac{17}{45} \div \dfrac{34}{81}$

17. $\dfrac{29k}{54} - \dfrac{9k}{54}$

18. $\dfrac{16n^3}{51n} + \dfrac{23n^3}{51n}$

19. $\dfrac{-13m^2e}{14} \div \dfrac{26e^3}{35m^4}$

20. $\dfrac{-100g^2h}{121} \cdot \left(\dfrac{-33gh}{40g^3h^2}\right)$

Combine like terms.

21. $15x - 8x + 19x$

22. $28m - 52m + 83$

23. $-7m + 12 - (-18m) - 9$

24. $14x^2 - 3(x - 7) + 5x + 2x^2 - 11$

Solve.

25. $x - 5 = 29$

26. $-7x = -49$

27. $2x + 1 = 37$

28. $\dfrac{c}{-3} = -15$

29. $\dfrac{k}{6} = -12$

30. $-5m - 3 = 27$

31. $9x = -54$

32. $-75 - (-3) = -8y$

33. $-8x = -62 + 6$

34. $18 - 4b = -9 + 5$

35. $-9 = 3x + 6$

36. $4x - 3(x - 11) = 16$

37. $7n + 13 - 2n = 3(n + 1)$

38. $7(m + 5) - 3(2m + 1) = 13m + 8$

Evaluate.

39. $mx + b$, for $m = 7, x = 0, b = -17$

40. $b^2 - 4ac$, for $a = 1, b = -5, c = 6$

41. $\dfrac{-b}{2a}$, for $a = -8, b = 32$

42. $\dfrac{x^3y^2}{3z}$, for $x = -3, y = 2, z = -4$

Translate the following into an expression or equation.

43. fifteen subtracted from twice a number
44. the product of a number and the opposite of twelve is the same as the sum of the opposite of thirty-five and nine.

Solve the problem.

45. Find Jack's exam average in his biology class if he scored a 92, 67, 93, and 90 on the first 4 exams in the class.
46. Liz bought books for the students in her literature class. Each book cost $7 and there is a total of 36 students. How much did Liz spend on the books?
47. Two angles are complementary. The second angle is four times as large as the first angle. Find the measure of each angle.
48. In a triangle, the first angle is twice the size of the second angle and the third angle is 36° more than the second angle. Find the measure of each angle in the triangle.
49. One number is 23 more than another number. The sum of the numbers is 67. Find the two numbers.
50. Terry and Paulette go out to a arts festival in San Jose, CA. Paulette spends $177 more on glass sculptures than Terry spends on artwork. If they spent a total of $419, how much did Paulette spend on glass?

Prealgebra

Chapter 4 : Fractions

Chapter 4 goes into more detail about fractions.

What's Inside?!

4.1 More Fraction Fundamentals
4.2 Multiplying Fractions
4.3 Dividing Fractions
4.4 LCM and LCD
4.5 Adding and Subtracting Fractions
4.6 Order of Operations with Fractions

Time to look at Mixed Numbers:

$$2\frac{1}{3}\cdot\frac{3}{4}=\frac{7}{3}\cdot\frac{3}{4}=\frac{7\cdot\cancel{3}}{\cancel{3}\cdot4}=\frac{7}{4}$$

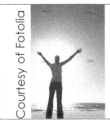

Courtesy of Fotolia

Different people learn math different ways. In this chapter we'll at how to take advantage of the three common learning styles: visual, auditory and kinesthetic

Plus!!

Learn how artists use fractions, geometry formulas, and the order of operations to frame amazing pieces!

[PN: art with dimensions $10\frac{3}{4}$ by $16\frac{5}{8}$ inches]

Since the perimeter of a rectangle is $P=2W+2L$ we have…

Courtesy of Fotolia

$$P=2\left(10\frac{3}{4}\right)+2\left(16\frac{5}{8}\right)=\frac{2}{1}\cdot\left(\frac{43}{4}\right)+\frac{2}{1}\cdot\left(\frac{133}{8}\right)=\frac{219}{4}=54\frac{3}{4}\text{ inches.}$$

4.1 More Fraction Fundamentals

Topics:

- Reviewing the Basics
- Proper Fraction, Improper Fractions, and Mixed Numbers
- Fraction that Involve 1 or 0
- Graphing Fractions and Mixed Numbers

Are You Ready?

To see if you are ready to understand this section, do the following short quiz.

1. Draw a picture to represent the fraction $\dfrac{3}{5}$.

2. Find $11 \cdot 3 + 4$.
3. Write the prime factorization of 63.
4. Rewrite $5 \cdot 5 \cdot b \cdot b \cdot b \cdot b$ using exponents.
5. Write $a^3 b^4$ in expanded form.

Answers to Are You Ready?

(1) [PN: pic]   *(2) 37*   *(3) $3^2 \cdot 7$*   *(4) $5^2 \cdot b^4$*   *(5) $a \cdot a \cdot a \cdot b \cdot b \cdot b \cdot b$*

Reviewing the Basics

You have been working with fractions since Chapter 1. You may look back in Section 1.6, Section 2.6 and Section 3.6 to refresh yourself on what we have learned so far. Here is one more look at how we simplify and operate with fractions.

Fraction Procedure	General Rule
Simplifying: To simplify a fraction to lowest terms, we use factoring and the Fundamental Principle of Fractions.	$\dfrac{a \cdot c}{b \cdot c} = \dfrac{a \cdot \not{c}}{b \cdot \not{c}} = \dfrac{a}{b}$
Multiplying: To multiply fractions, we multiply the numerators and denominators.	$\dfrac{a}{b} \cdot \dfrac{c}{d} = \dfrac{a \cdot c}{b \cdot d}$
Dividing: To divide fractions, we reciprocate the second fraction and multiply.	$\dfrac{a}{b} \div \dfrac{c}{d} = \dfrac{a}{b} \cdot \dfrac{d}{c} = \dfrac{a \cdot d}{b \cdot c}$
Adding: To add fractions with a common denominator, we add the numerators and keep the same denominator.	$\dfrac{a}{c} + \dfrac{b}{c} = \dfrac{a+b}{c}$
Subtracting: To subtract fractions with a common denominator, we subtract the numerators and keep the same denominator.	$\dfrac{a}{c} - \dfrac{b}{c} = \dfrac{a-b}{c}$
Don't forget that the final answer should always be simplified.	

Here is an example for each operation.

Example 1: Find the following. Reduce your answer, if possible.

a) $\dfrac{3}{5} \cdot \dfrac{10}{11}$
b) $\dfrac{4x}{9} - \dfrac{x}{9}$
c) $-\dfrac{3b}{4} \div \dfrac{5b}{14}$
d) $\dfrac{-13}{15} + \dfrac{8}{15}$

Solution:

a) First we rewrite the product as a single fraction.

$$\dfrac{3}{5} \cdot \dfrac{10}{11} = \dfrac{3 \cdot 10}{5 \cdot 11}$$

Now we factor to simplify. The numerator and denominator both have a common factor of 5. Multiply the remaining factors.

$$= \dfrac{3 \cdot 2 \cdot \cancel{5}}{\cancel{5} \cdot 11} = \dfrac{6}{11}$$

Heads Up!
This chapter is about advanced fraction work. It is very important that you take the time to review these fraction basics.
Set yourself up to succeed!

b) Note that both fractions have the same denominator, so we just subtract the numerators and keep the denominator 9.

$$\dfrac{4x}{9} - \dfrac{x}{9} = \dfrac{4x - x}{9} = \dfrac{3x}{9}$$

Now we simplify. The numerator and denominator have a common factor of 3.

$$= \dfrac{\cancel{3} \cdot x}{\cancel{3} \cdot 3} = \dfrac{x}{3}$$

c) Take the reciprocal of the second fraction and change the operation to multiplication.

$$-\dfrac{3b}{4} \div \dfrac{5b}{14} = -\dfrac{3b}{4} \cdot \dfrac{14}{5b}$$

Rewrite the product as a single fraction.

$$= -\dfrac{3b \cdot 14}{4 \cdot 5b}$$

Continue to factor to work towards a simplified answer.

$$= -\dfrac{3 \cdot b \cdot 2 \cdot 7}{2 \cdot 2 \cdot 5 \cdot b}$$

Remove the common factors of 2 and b. Multiply the remaining factors.

$$= -\dfrac{3 \cdot \cancel{b} \cdot \cancel{2} \cdot 7}{\cancel{2} \cdot 2 \cdot 5 \cdot \cancel{b}} = \dfrac{21}{10}$$

d) Since both fractions have the same denominator, we can just add the numerators and keep the denominator 15.

$$\dfrac{-13}{15} + \dfrac{11}{15} = \dfrac{-13 + 11}{15}$$

Since this fraction can not simplify, this is our final answer.

$$= \dfrac{-2}{15}$$

STOP Exercise Set - Reviewing Some Basics

1. Simplify. $\dfrac{-25}{35}$

2. Simplify. $\dfrac{44t}{55t^2}$

3. $\dfrac{4}{5} - \dfrac{2}{5}$

4. $\dfrac{6}{13} \div \dfrac{3}{26}$

5. $\dfrac{4p}{15} + \dfrac{p}{15}$

6. $\dfrac{6x}{25} \cdot \dfrac{15}{9x^2}$

7. $\dfrac{8b}{21} \div \dfrac{4}{21}$

8. $-\dfrac{5}{12} - \dfrac{7}{12}$

9. $\dfrac{10}{21} - \left(-\dfrac{4}{21}\right)$

10. $\dfrac{-5}{8} \cdot \dfrac{-4}{7}$

Succeed in Math   Learning Styles

A LOT of research has been about how people learn math. There are three primary LEARNING STYLES...

AUDITORY learners learn best by LISTENING.

VISUAL learners learn best by SEEING.

KINESTHETIC learners learn best by being ACTIVE.

Which type of learning are YOU?! In this chapter we'll you decide and give you some tips based on your learning style.

You can get more information by doing the exercises on page # and by looking our SUCCEED ads throughout the chapter.

Proper Fractions, Improper Fractions, and Mixed Numbers

We will spend the rest of this chapter studying deeper into fractions. To begin, let's look at some terms used in describing different types of fractions.

If the numerator of a fraction is less than the denominator then the fraction is called a **proper fraction**.

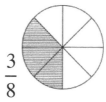

Proper fractions like $\frac{3}{8}$ represent part of a whole.

If the numerator of a fraction is larger than the denominator then the fraction is called an **improper fraction**.

$$\frac{9}{8}$$

Improper fractions like $\frac{9}{8}$ have enough parts to make at least one whole.

A **mixed number** involves a whole part and a proper fraction.

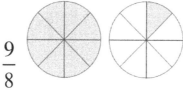

$2\frac{2}{5}$

Mixed numbers like $2\frac{2}{5}$ show how many wholes and how many parts. The mixed number $2\frac{3}{5}$ is read and interpreted as "two and three-fifths"

Fractions that include variables are called **algebraic fractions** or **rational expressions**.

Since the values in an algebraic fraction like $\frac{5x}{7y^2}$ are unknown we do not use shaded regions to represent them.

Example 2: Classify each number as a proper fraction, an improper fraction, a mixed number or an algebraic fraction.

a) $\dfrac{7}{5}$ b) $-\dfrac{11}{12}$ c) $-8\dfrac{2}{13}$ d) $\dfrac{15}{6}$ e) $\dfrac{4x}{19y}$

Solution:
a) This is an improper fraction since the numerator is larger than the denominator.
b) This is a proper fraction since the numerator is smaller than the denominator. Note that the negative sign does not affect whether a fraction is proper or improper.
c) This is a mixed number since it involves a whole number and a fraction.
d) This is an improper fraction.
e) This is an algebraic fraction since there are variables.

An improper fraction can always be rewritten as a mixed number and a mixed number can always be rewritten as an improper fraction.

$\dfrac{11}{4}$ can be rewritten as $2\dfrac{3}{4}$ $2\dfrac{1}{3}$ can be rewritten as $\dfrac{7}{3}$

[PN: fraction picture for each]   [PN: fraction picture for each]

To rewrite a mixed number as an improper fraction:

- Multiply the denominator by the whole part and add that value to the numerator.
- This new number is the numerator of the improper fraction. Keep the denominator the same.

$$2\dfrac{1}{3} = \dfrac{2 \cdot 3 + 1}{3} = \dfrac{7}{3}$$

To rewrite an improper fraction as a mixed number:

- Divide the numerator by the denominator.
- The quotient is the whole part and the remainder is the numerator of the fraction.
- Keep the denominator the same.

$$\dfrac{11}{4} \to 4\overline{)11}^{\,2R3} \to 2\dfrac{3}{4}$$

Example 3: Convert each improper fraction to a mixed number and each mixed number to an improper fraction.

a) $-\dfrac{17}{3}$ b) $6\dfrac{3}{4}$ c) $\dfrac{318}{9}$ d) $-12\dfrac{7}{8}$

Solution:

a) If an improper fraction is negative then the equivalent mixed number is negative. So we ignore the negative and divide 17 by 3.

$$\frac{17}{3} \rightarrow 3\overline{)17}^{\,5R2}$$

- The quotient is the whole part.
- The remainder is the numerator of the fraction.
- Keep the same denominator.

$5\frac{2}{3}$ [PN: can we get creative using arrows to point to the parts?]

Don't forget our original fraction was negative. Our final answer is:

$-5\frac{2}{3}$

b) We start by evaluating the expression $6 \cdot 4 + 3$.

$6 \cdot 4 + 3 = 24 + 3 = 27$

- The result 27 is the numerator of the improper fraction.
- Keep the denominator the same.

$6\frac{3}{4} = \frac{6 \cdot 4 + 3}{4} = \frac{27}{4}$

[PN: can we use arrows to point the parts?]

The improper fraction is:

$\frac{27}{4}$

c) This exercise demonstrates how reducing can come up with mixed numbers. To begin we divide 318 by 9.

$$\frac{318}{9} \rightarrow 9\overline{)318}^{\,35R3}$$

- The quotient is the whole part.
- The remainder is the numerator of the fraction.
- Keep the same denominator.

$35\frac{3}{9}$

Notice that the fraction part will reduce by 3. Make sure to reduce the fraction part of a mixed number when appropriate.

$\frac{3}{9} = \frac{1}{3}$

Our final answer is:

$35\frac{1}{3}$

d) If a mixed number is negative then the equivalent improper fraction is negative. So we ignore the negative and evaluate the expression.

$12 \cdot 8 + 7$

- The result of $12 \cdot 8 + 7$ is the numerator of the improper fraction.
- Keep the same denominator.

$12\frac{7}{8} = \frac{12 \cdot 8 + 7}{8} = \frac{103}{8}$

Don't forget our original mixed number was negative.

$-\frac{103}{8}$

Example 4: Where in the World? It takes 18 inches of trim for Bruce to build one custom cabinet. He currently has 81 inches of trim. The improper fraction $\frac{81}{18}$ represents the number of cabinets he can put trim on. Convert the improper fraction $\frac{81}{18}$ to a mixed number and interpret the results.

Solution:
First we convert to a mixed number.

$$\frac{81}{18} \rightarrow 18\overline{)81}^{\,4R9} \rightarrow 4\frac{9}{18} = 4\frac{1}{2}$$

So the mixed number equivalent to $\frac{81}{18}$ is $4\frac{1}{2}$. That 4 is the whole part and $\frac{1}{2}$ is the fraction part means that Bruce has enough trim to finish four custom cabinets and half of another.

One more note about mixed numbers. When working with variables, we never use mixed numbers. An algebraic fraction should never be written as a mixed number.

 Exercise Set - Proper Fractions, Improper Fractions, and Mixed Numbers

Classify each number as a proper fraction, improper fraction, mixed number or algebraic fraction.

11. $\frac{4}{9}$ 13. $-\frac{12m}{17}$ 15. $-\frac{101}{78}$

12. $\frac{21}{11}$ 14. $-6\frac{1}{12}$ 16. $\frac{51x^2}{19y}$

Convert each improper fraction to a mixed number if appropriate and each mixed number to an improper fraction. Remember if a fraction contains a variable it should not be written as a mixed number.

17. $6\frac{1}{5}$ 19. $\frac{21}{5}$ 21. $\frac{65}{4}$ 23. $\frac{17t}{6}$

18. $8\frac{2}{3}$ 20. $\frac{9}{4x}$ 22. $-3\frac{4}{5}$ 24. $-9\frac{2}{7}$

Fractions that Involve 1 or 0

There are a few different situations involved with having 1 or 0 as the numerator or denominator of a fraction and when the overall value of a fraction is 1 or 0. All these examples rely on interpreting the fraction bar as a division symbol. Let's explore these situations now.

Example 6: Simplify if possible.

a.) $\dfrac{0}{-8}$

b.) $\dfrac{-8}{0}$

Solution:

a.) Recall from Section 1.3 that $\dfrac{0}{8} = 0 \div 8 = 0$.

b.) $\dfrac{-8}{0} = -8 \div 0$. Recall that this division is undefined. That is, it cannot be done. This means that $\dfrac{-8}{0}$ is undefined.

Example 7: Simplify the following if possible.

a.) $\dfrac{5}{1}$

b.) $\dfrac{1}{5}$

c.) $\dfrac{-5}{-5}$

Solution: Again we get our results by interpreting the fraction bar as division.

a.) $\dfrac{5}{1} = 5 \div 1 = 5$

b.) $\dfrac{1}{5}$ cannot be reduced since the division $1 \div 5$ cannot be performed using whole numbers.

c.) $\dfrac{-5}{-5} = (-5) \div (-5) = 1$

We can state the results from these important examples in a general way as follows.

From any non-zero integer a:

$$\frac{0}{a} = 0 \qquad \frac{a}{0} \text{ is undefined} \qquad \frac{a}{1} = a \qquad \frac{a}{a} = 1$$

Example 8: Where in the World? The expression $\dfrac{d}{t}$ is used to find the speed of an object where d represents the distance traveled and t represents the time it takes to travel the distance. Which variable value would make the fraction $\dfrac{d}{t}$ undefined: $t = 0$ or $d = 0$?

Solution: Substituting $t = 0$ into the expression would give $\dfrac{d}{0}$, which is undefined. So the variable value $t = 0$ makes the expression $\dfrac{d}{t}$ undefined.

 # Exercise Set - Fraction That Involve 1 or 0

Simplify the following if possible or state that it is undefined.

25. $\dfrac{7}{7}$ 27. $\dfrac{1}{3}$ 29. $\dfrac{0}{75}$ 31. $\dfrac{-9}{1}$ 33. $\dfrac{26}{0}$

26. $\dfrac{-15}{0}$ 28. $\dfrac{3}{1}$ 30. $\dfrac{0}{6}$ 32. $\dfrac{1}{-14}$ 34. $\dfrac{-19}{-19}$

35. In the expression $\dfrac{C}{d}$, which variable value would cause the fraction to be undefined: $C = 0$ or $d = 0$?

36. In the expression $\dfrac{y}{x}$, which variable value would cause the fraction to be undefined: $x = 0$ or $y = 0$?

Graphing Fractions and Mixed Numbers

To graph fractions and mixed numbers on a number line we must understand how fractions represent part of a whole.

To Graph a Fraction or Mixed Number:
- Use the whole part to locate the number on the graph. If the whole part is 0, then the number is between 0 and 1 or between -1 and 0.
- Use the denominator to divide each whole up into equal parts. Use the numerator to plot the point.

The fraction $\dfrac{1}{5}$ represents a number that is bigger than zero but smaller than one. So $\dfrac{1}{5}$ would be graphed between 0 and 1 on a number line.

[PN: number line labeled for integers between -2 and 3 with $\frac{1}{5}$ graphed]

Notice that $\frac{1}{5}$ is closer to 0 than 1.

The mixed number $5\frac{1}{2}$ represents a number that is right in the middle of 5 and 6. So $5\frac{1}{2}$ would be graphing between 5 and 6 on a number line.

[PN: number line labeled for integers between 4 and 7 with $5\frac{1}{2}$ graphed]

Good Question: Okay, I get that fractions are graphed between integers. But how do I know where fractions should be placed in relation to each other? For example, how should $\frac{4}{7}$ and $\frac{5}{8}$ be placed if I graphed them both?

Answer: Graphing $\frac{4}{7}$ and $\frac{5}{8}$ together requires work with a least common denominator. Don't worry about that right now. For your exercises we won't give you issues like that. We just want you to develop an intuitive understanding of how fractions are generally graphed.

Example 8: Graph $-3, \frac{1}{4}, -1\frac{5}{6}, \frac{13}{5}$ and $\frac{0}{5}$ on a number line.

Solution: Graphing $-3, \frac{1}{4}$ and $-1\frac{5}{6}$ will be straight forward. But to see where $\frac{13}{5}$ falls, we should express it as a mixed number: $\frac{13}{5} = 2\frac{3}{5}$. Also, note that $\frac{0}{5} = 0$.

[PN: number line with all numbers graphed]

 Exercise Set - Graphing Fractions and Mixed Numbers

Graph each list of number on a number line.

37. $\frac{1}{2}, 1\frac{1}{2}, 2\frac{1}{2}, 3\frac{1}{2}, 4\frac{1}{2}$

39. $-\frac{4}{5}, 0, \frac{1}{3}, -2\frac{4}{7}$

38. $-1\frac{1}{3}, -\frac{1}{3}, \frac{2}{3}, 1\frac{2}{3}, 2\frac{2}{3}$

40. $\frac{1}{2}, \frac{6}{5}, \frac{8}{9}, -3\frac{1}{8}, 1\frac{2}{5}$

4.1 Exercise Set - Putting it ALL Together

Vocabulary Check. Fill in each blank with a word from our Vocabulary Checklist to the right. Each word is used exactly once.

41. A number that has a whole part and a fraction part is called a

_____.

42. A fraction with the numerator smaller than the denominator is called a

_____.

43. A mixed number call always be expressed as an _____.

> **Vocabulary Checklist:**
> proper fraction
> improper fraction
> mixed number

Represent each shaded region as a proper fraction or as both an improper fraction and a mixed number.

44. [PN: picture for $\frac{1}{5}$]

45. [PN: picture for $\frac{7}{3}$]

46. [PN: picture for $\frac{9}{2}$]

47. [PN: picture for $\frac{6}{7}$]

Draw and shade a diagram to represent each fraction or mixed number.

48. $\frac{1}{3}$

49. $2\frac{1}{4}$

50. $\frac{7}{3}$

51. $\frac{3}{7}$

Convert to an improper fraction:

52. $9\frac{2}{7}$

53. $-13\frac{3}{5}$

54. $-3\frac{14}{15}$

55. $2\frac{18}{29}$

What fraction or mixed number would be used to represent each scenario?

56. Cane needs to cut a board to exactly six and one-fourth feet.
57. A scientist brings a solution to a temperature of negative five and seven-tenths degrees.
58. A hydration system is to be buried four and three-eights inches below ground level.
59. The rain storm provided two and five-sixteenths inches of rain.

Simplify and convert to a mixed number if appropriate. If the fraction is undefined state this.

60. $\frac{14}{6}$

61. $\frac{42}{56}$

62. $\frac{15}{0}$

63. $\frac{10}{26}$

64. $\frac{26d}{4d}$

65. $\frac{1}{5}$

66. $\frac{5}{1}$

67. $\frac{-30}{27x}$

68. $\frac{13}{0}$

69. $\frac{77}{33}$

70. $\frac{35x}{50x}$

71. $\frac{0}{-19}$

Perform the indicated operation:

72. $\dfrac{5}{6} - \dfrac{1}{6}$

75. $\dfrac{13}{28b^2} \cdot \dfrac{21b}{25}$

78. $\dfrac{7}{15} \cdot \left(\dfrac{-9}{28}\right)$

81. $-\dfrac{4}{13} - \dfrac{9}{13}$

73. $\dfrac{15t}{24} + \dfrac{7t}{24}$

76. $\dfrac{13}{15} - \dfrac{3}{15}$

79. $\dfrac{36}{45} + \dfrac{-6}{45}$

82. $\dfrac{32}{121} \div \dfrac{21}{55}$

74. $\dfrac{6}{11} \div \dfrac{3}{22}$

77. $\dfrac{4}{7} \cdot \dfrac{14}{15}$

80. $\left(\dfrac{-34}{13}\right) \div \left(\dfrac{-17}{39}\right)$

83. $\dfrac{37}{68} - \dfrac{25}{68}$

If the fraction part of a mixed number can be reduced it should be. Reduce the fraction part of each mixed number.

84. $7\dfrac{2}{8}$

85. $-2\dfrac{3}{15}$

86. $14\dfrac{3}{27}$

87. $35\dfrac{5}{75}$

88. It takes four tires to make complete set. A storage room currently has 35 tires. Convert the improper fraction $\dfrac{35}{4}$ to a mixed number and interpret the results.

89. It take12 glasses to fill one order. A kitchen cabinet currently has 78 glasses. Convert the improper fraction $\dfrac{78}{12}$ to a mixed number and interpret the results.

90. One cell phone contains 3 microchips. An manufacturer has access to 65 microchips. Convert the fraction $\dfrac{65}{3}$ to a mixed number and interpret the results.

91. Four laps around a regulation track is equivalent to one miles. Lee runs 19 laps. Convert the fraction $\dfrac{19}{4}$ to a mixed number and interpret the results.

Graph the following fraction or list of fractions.

92. $-\dfrac{2}{3}$

93. $\dfrac{7}{9}$

94. $4\dfrac{3}{7}$

95. $5\dfrac{1}{4}$

96. $\dfrac{1}{3}, 3\dfrac{3}{5}, 4\dfrac{5}{6}, 1\dfrac{1}{2}$

97. $-3\dfrac{3}{4}, 1\dfrac{2}{5}, -\dfrac{7}{8}, \dfrac{1}{3}$

98. What fractions have been graphed on the following number line?
[PN: dot at $-\dfrac{2}{3}$, $\dfrac{1}{3}$ and $\dfrac{5}{3}$]

99. What fractions have been graphed on the following number line?
[PN: dot at $-\dfrac{1}{5}$, $\dfrac{4}{5}$ and $\dfrac{7}{5}$]

100. What mixed numbers have been graphed on the following number line?
[PN: dot at $\dfrac{1}{2}$, $1\dfrac{1}{2}$, $2\dfrac{1}{2}$ and $3\dfrac{1}{2}$]

101. What mixed numbers have been graphed on the following number line?

[PN: dot at $-1\frac{1}{3}$, $1\frac{2}{3}$ and $3\frac{1}{3}$]

102. The following table gives the height of several past and present major league basketball players. Graph the heights on a number line. *Source: google.com*

Player	Height (in feet)
Michael Jordan	$6\frac{1}{2}$
Lebron James	$6\frac{2}{3}$
Pau Gasol	7
Earl Boykins	$5\frac{5}{12}$

103. The following table gives the height of several major league baseball players. Graph the heights on a number line. *Source: google.com*

Player	Height (in feet)
Hank Aaron	6
Alexander Rodriguez	$6\frac{1}{4}$
Mickey Mantle	$5\frac{11}{12}$
Loek Van Mil	$7\frac{1}{6}$

TRUE or FALSE
104. Every proper fraction can be rewritten as a mixed number.
105. When converting a mixed to an improper fraction, the numerator does not change.
106. To multiply fractions we need for them to have a common denominator.
107. A fraction with numerator of zero is undefined.

108. What is the difference between a mixed number and a proper fraction?
109. What is the difference between proper fraction and an improper fraction?
110. What is the difference between a numeric fraction and an algebraic fraction?

Exercise Set - Cumulative Review

111. Solve. $x + 9 = 4$
112. Graph $-3, 4, 1, 0, -1$ on a number line.
113. Translate "some number minus eight is the same as two times the number" into math symbols.
114. Simplify. $8 - 3 \cdot 2$
115. Add. $-13 + 8 + (-3)$

4.1 QUIZ YOURSELF

To make sure you are ready for the EXAM, try these problems without any help. Give yourself about 20 minutes and don't check the answers until you have completely finished.

1. $\dfrac{4}{15} + \dfrac{1}{15}$

2. $\dfrac{7}{25} \cdot \dfrac{10}{21}$

3. $\dfrac{7}{12} \div \dfrac{3}{4}$

4. $\dfrac{16}{27} - \dfrac{-2}{27}$

5. Convert to an improper fraction. $-3\dfrac{4}{7}$

6. Simplify. $\dfrac{54}{63}$

7. Simplify. $\dfrac{-72x^2y}{98xy^2}$

8. Evaluate $\dfrac{b^2 - 4ac}{2a}$ for $a = 1$, $b = 6$ and $c = 5$.

Answers to this Quiz Yourself are on page 671.

Succeed in Math!   **Learning Styles**

Different students learn math in different ways. Let's identify your LEARNING STYLE and look at some suggestions for how you can take advantage

Exercise #1   Are You a Visual Learner?

Consider the following questions carefully and answer "YES" or "NO" to each.

_____ Do you rewrite a formula or concept to remember it?

_____ Do you find the boxes, graphs, and diagrams in your textbooks useful?

_____ Is it difficult for you to understand what your instructor is saying if it isn't written on the board?

_____ Do you imagine yourself doing the steps before you start the problem?

_____ When you study, do you rely heavily on the notes you take in math class?

_____ Do you try to visualize your notes in your head when you're taking a test?

_____ Do you prefer written instructions to oral instructions?

SUGGESTIONS

- Notes are very important for you, make them organized and thorough.
- Professors and textbooks often suggest that people draw boxes, pictures, or diagrams in order to help them solve word problems.
- Note cards are a good study tool for helping you remember concepts and formulas.
- Rewriting important information, such as your class notes will be very helpful.
- Modern textbooks make use of effective design and sharp illustrations. You may even want to consider getting a second textbook to reference.
- Write in your textbook. Underline things, write in the margins, and use a highlighter.

Exercise #2   Are You an Auditory Learner?

Consider the following questions carefully and answer "yes" or "no" to each.

_____ Do you prefer listening in class to taking notes?

_____ Do you have difficulty following written solutions on the blackboard unless the teacher also verbally explains all the steps?

_____ Do you remember more of what you hear than what you see?

_____ Do you find that your learning is most productive when you are discussing problems with an instructor or classmate?

_____ Do you prefer to have someone explain a problem than read it?

_____ Do you ever find yourself saying numbers and/or steps out loud when you are doing a math problem?

_____ Do you prefer oral instructions to written instructions?

SUGGESTIONS

- One way to really facilitate this is to bring a tape recorder to class. Ask your professor's permission first. **Listen to them again later as you look over your notes.**
- Consider using shorthand note-taking so you don't spend too much time writing.
- Sit near the front of the classroom so you can clearly hear your teacher.
- Ask questions in class! When professors answer questions they tend to talk more. Ask for clarification of steps when you get lost.
- Repeat things out loud to yourself when you study: formulas, concepts, how to solve certain problems, instructions for homework. Read your textbook out loud.
- Find a classmate who takes good notes and ask if you can photocopy his or her notes after class.
- Do not rely on photocopying other people's notes too often or you will get lazy.
- A study group will be good for you because they are heavy on mathematical conversation.
- Record formulas and concepts on a cassette or some audio device and listen to it a few times. You will be amazed at the results!

Exercise #3   Are You a Kinesthetic Learner?

Consider the following questions carefully and answer "yes" or "no" to each.

_____   Have you learned math best with hands-on activities involved?

_____   Do you ever pace or change position when you do your math homework?

_____   Do you have a hard time verbally explaining how to do a problem?

_____   Do you find that math ideas don't click for you until you do the problems?

_____   If you are having a good study session, does it involve a lot of small breaks?

_____   Do you enjoy figuring out math puzzles?

_____   Do you connect best with math ideas if they are real-life experiences?

_____   Do you have a tendency to doodle during math lectures?

SUGGESTIONS

- Get creative, dynamic, and active. Focus on doing problem after problem.
- Rewriting your class notes after class will be extremely beneficial for you.
- Use a stress ball in class; it may help when you're feeling restless or antsy.
- Try problems immediately after you are shown how.
- Move! When you study, stand up or even pace while you think about a problem. Move around. Take one-minute breaks to do push-ups or sit-ups.
- Use learning maps on big sheets of construction paper with markers.
- Be creative! Go outside and trace a formula in the sand or physically walk out the formula.
- Make a cheat sheet and tape it to the treadmill . Have the cheat sheet laminated and tape it to your surfboard.

"One hundred percent of the shots you don't make don't go in."
WAYNE GRETZKY, *Canadian hockey player*

Exercise #4   Your Results?

_____   Based on these exercises, what do you think is your primary learning style?

_____   What do you think is your secondary learning style?

_____   What do you think is your weakest learning style?

Look at the suggestions made for studying in your primary and perhaps secondary learning style and pick the four that you think would be most helpful for you. List them and explain why you think that suggestion is a good idea for you.

1. _____

_____

2. _____

_____

3. _____

_____

4. _____

_____

_____

When you do these exercises about LEARNING STYLES, keep in mind that we are NOT trying to run your study time for you. YOU do whatever works for YOU. We just think these suggestions might help you study more effectively.

4.2 Multiplying Fractions

Topics:
- Understanding Fraction Multiplication
- More About Multiplying Fractions
- Multiplying Mixed Numbers
- Solving Equations

Are You Ready?

To see if you are ready to understand this section, do the following short quiz.

1. Find $\dfrac{1}{2} \cdot \dfrac{3}{5}$.

2. Simplify the fraction $\dfrac{21}{35}$.

3. Give the prime factorization of 56.

4. Find the area of a rectangle with a length of 3 feet and a width of 7 feet.

5. Draw a picture to represent the fraction $\dfrac{4}{7}$.

Answers to Are You Ready?

(1) $\dfrac{3}{10}$ *(2)* $\dfrac{3}{5}$ *(3)* $2^3 \cdot 7$ *(4) 21 ft^2*   *(5) [PN: picture]*

Understanding Fraction Multiplication

You already know HOW to multiply fractions: $\dfrac{a}{b} \cdot \dfrac{c}{d} = \dfrac{a \cdot c}{b \cdot d}$. But now we explore WHY we multiply fractions that way.

Consider the product $\dfrac{2}{3} \cdot \dfrac{4}{7}$. One way to interpret the product $\dfrac{2}{3} \cdot \dfrac{4}{7}$ is finding "two-thirds of $\dfrac{4}{7}$".

To find two-thirds of $\dfrac{4}{7}$, begin by looking at a picture of $\dfrac{4}{7}$.   [PN: picture of $\dfrac{4}{7}$]

We divide each part of the 7 parts into 3 equal parts.   [PN: picture of $\dfrac{4}{7}$ being divided into three parts using dotted lines]

Now we highlight $\dfrac{2}{3}$ or "2 out of every 3" of the shaded pieces.   [PN: previous picture now has $\dfrac{2}{3}$ of the shaded pieces in a darker color.]

And here is the resulting picture. The resulting fraction is $\dfrac{8}{21}$.   [PN: Picture of $\dfrac{8}{21}$]

This process helps verify our rule for multiplying fractions: $\dfrac{2}{3} \cdot \dfrac{4}{7} = \dfrac{2 \cdot 4}{3 \cdot 7} = \dfrac{8}{21}$.

To Multiply Fractions Using Pictures:
- Draw a picture of the second fraction using a rectangle.
- Use denominator of the first fraction to draw horizontal lines and shade the numerator of fraction being multiplied to get product.

Example 1: Use pictures to perform each multiplication.

a) $\dfrac{1}{2} \cdot \dfrac{3}{4}$ b) $\dfrac{2}{3} \cdot \dfrac{4}{5}$

Solution:

a) We interpret this multiplication as " $\dfrac{1}{2}$ of $\dfrac{3}{4}$ "   [PN: 3/4]

and begin by drawing the fraction $\dfrac{3}{4}$.

Now we cut each of the pieces in half. For each   [PN: picture]
shaded piece, we reshade one of the two.

The resulting fraction is 3/8.

b) We interpret this multiplication as " $\dfrac{2}{3}$ of $\dfrac{4}{5}$ "   [PN: 4/5]

and begin by drawing the fraction $\dfrac{4}{5}$.

Now we divide each of the pieces into thirds. For   [PN: picture]
each shaded piece we reshade two of the three.

The resulting fraction is 8/15.

STOP Exericse Set - Understanding Fraction Multiplication

Translate each phrase into math symbols. You do not have to find the answer.

1. one-half of $\dfrac{3}{10}$

2. two-fifths of $\dfrac{6}{7}$

3. three-fourths of one-half

4. two-thirds of one-eleventh

Use pictures to perform each multiplication.

5. $\dfrac{1}{2} \cdot \dfrac{5}{6}$

7. $\dfrac{3}{4} \cdot \dfrac{4}{9}$

6. $\dfrac{1}{3} \cdot \dfrac{3}{4}$

8. $\dfrac{2}{3} \cdot \dfrac{3}{5}$

More About Multiplying Fractions

The next three examples show some more advanced fraction multiplications that involve working with larger numbers, more than one fraction, and having more variables in the multiplication. For all these situations, it is important to rewrite the product as a single fraction then factor to simplify without multiplying the numbers together.

Example 2: Working with Larger Numbers

Multiply.

a) $-\dfrac{14}{25} \cdot \dfrac{35}{21}$

b) $-\dfrac{39}{40} \cdot (-16)$

Solution:

a) First we write the product as a single fraction.

$$-\dfrac{14}{25} \cdot \dfrac{35}{21} = -\dfrac{14 \cdot 35}{25 \cdot 21}$$

For fractions with larger numbers it is easier to factor from this point than to multiply then factor.

$$= -\dfrac{7 \cdot 2 \cdot 5 \cdot 7}{5 \cdot 5 \cdot 3 \cdot 7}$$

Simplify by the common factors of 7 and 5 in the numerator and denominator, and multiply.

$$= -\dfrac{\cancel{7} \cdot 2 \cdot \cancel{5} \cdot 7}{\cancel{5} \cdot 5 \cdot 3 \cdot \cancel{7}} = \dfrac{14}{15}$$

b) Rewrite the -16 as a fraction.

$$-\dfrac{39}{40} \cdot (-16) = -\dfrac{39}{40} \cdot \left(-\dfrac{16}{1}\right)$$

Write the product as a single fraction. Note that we no longer need the negative signs since a negative times a negative equals a positive.

$$= \dfrac{39 \cdot 16}{40 \cdot 1}$$

Instead of relying completely on prime factorizations to simplify, we can try to recognize common factors. For example, there is a common factor of 8 in 16 and 40.

$$= \dfrac{39 \cdot \cancel{8} \cdot 2}{\cancel{8} \cdot 5 \cdot 1}$$

$$= \dfrac{39 \cdot 2}{5} = \dfrac{78}{5}$$

Example 3: Working with More than One Fraction

Multiply.

a) $\dfrac{1}{3} \cdot (-5) \cdot \dfrac{6}{11}$ b) $\dfrac{3}{4} \cdot \dfrac{8}{7} \cdot \dfrac{35}{39}$

Solution:

a) When more than one fraction is involved in a product we take the same basic approach. Write the product as a single fraction and multiply.

$$\frac{1}{3} \cdot \frac{-5}{1} \cdot \frac{6}{11} = \frac{1(-5)(6)}{3(1)(11)} = \frac{1(-5)(2 \cdot \cancel{3})}{\cancel{3}(1)(11)} = \frac{-10}{11}$$

b) We begin by writing the product as a single fraction.

$$\frac{3}{4} \cdot \frac{8}{7} \cdot \frac{35}{39} = \frac{3 \cdot 8 \cdot 35}{4 \cdot 7 \cdot 39}$$

It is not a good a idea to multiply at this point. Instead we factor to reveal common factors.

$$= \frac{3 \cdot 4 \cdot 2 \cdot 5 \cdot 7}{4 \cdot 7 \cdot 3 \cdot 13}$$

Simplify the common factors of 4, 3, and 7.

$$= \frac{\cancel{3} \cdot \cancel{4} \cdot 2 \cdot 5 \cdot \cancel{7}}{\cancel{4} \cdot \cancel{7} \cdot \cancel{3} \cdot 13}$$

Multiply the remaining factors to get the final answer.

$$= \frac{10}{13}$$

Good Question: My last teacher showed me a shortcut he called "Cross Canceling" where you simplify from the start. It looks like this... $-\dfrac{\overset{2}{\cancel{14}}}{\underset{5}{\cancel{25}}} \cdot \dfrac{\overset{7}{\cancel{35}}}{\underset{3}{\cancel{21}}} = \dfrac{14}{15}$. Can I use that approach?

Answer: As a professor, I used to love this approach. But I stopped teaching it because it almost always creates problems for the student later on. Personally, I would encourage you not to use it. But you are your own master and the technique can work. Ask your current professor what she thinks.

When algebraic fractions are involved, we use our knowledge of exponents to help in reducing.

Example 4: Working with More Variables

a) $\dfrac{5}{3a^6} \cdot \dfrac{a^4}{10}$ b) $\dfrac{-12xy}{21y^2} \cdot \dfrac{y^3}{6x^2}$

Solution: The fact that these products involve variables does not change the general approach. We just need to be careful about reducing and dealing with exponents.

a) Write the product as a single fraction.

$$\frac{5}{3a^6} \cdot \frac{a^4}{10} = \frac{5 \cdot a^4}{3a^6 \cdot 10}$$

Even though these fractions have higher powers does not

change our approach. We look for common factors by factoring the numbers and rewrite the variables with exponents in expanded form.

$$= \frac{5 \cdot a \cdot a \cdot a \cdot a}{3 \cdot a \cdot a \cdot a \cdot a \cdot a \cdot 2 \cdot 5}$$

Simplify by the common factors of 5 and a.

$$= \frac{\cancel{5} \cdot \cancel{a} \cdot \cancel{a} \cdot \cancel{a} \cdot \cancel{a}}{3 \cdot \cancel{a} \cdot \cancel{a} \cdot \cancel{a} \cdot \cancel{a} \cdot a \cdot a \cdot 2 \cdot \cancel{5}}$$

Multiply the remaining factors. Remember that there still a factor of 1 in the numerator.

$$= \frac{1}{6a^2}$$

b) Write the product as a single fraction.

$$\frac{-12xy}{21y^2} \cdot \frac{y^3}{6x^2} = \frac{-12xy \cdot y^3}{21y^2 \cdot 6x^2}$$

Now we look for common factors by factoring the numbers and rewrite the variables with exponents in expanded form.

$$= -\frac{3 \cdot 2 \cdot 2 \cdot x \cdot y \cdot y \cdot y \cdot y}{3 \cdot 7 \cdot y \cdot y \cdot 2 \cdot 3 \cdot x \cdot x}$$

There are common factors of 3, 2, x, y, and y.

$$= -\frac{\cancel{3} \cdot \cancel{2} \cdot 2 \cdot \cancel{x} \cdot \cancel{y} \cdot \cancel{y} \cdot y \cdot y}{\cancel{3} \cdot 7 \cdot \cancel{y} \cdot \cancel{y} \cdot \cancel{2} \cdot 3 \cdot \cancel{x} \cdot x}$$

Rewrite the leftover factors.

$$= -\frac{2 \cdot y \cdot y}{7 \cdot 3 \cdot x}$$

Multiply the remaining factors and use exponent notation.

$$= -\frac{2y^2}{21x}$$

Example 5: A fellow student has a problem about fraction multiplication written on a piece of paper but the second fraction is just a smudge.

$$\frac{3y}{4} \cdot \frac{?}{?} = \frac{15y}{8x}$$

[PN: can we make this look like a page with the second fraction smudged?]

What is the missing fraction?

Solution: To multiply fractions we just multiply the numerators and denominators, so we can look at them separate.

$$\frac{3y}{4} \cdot \frac{?}{?} = \frac{3y \cdot ?}{4 \cdot ?} = \frac{15y}{8x}$$

To get $15y$ in the numerator, we would need to multiply $3y$ by 5.

To get $8x$ in the denominator we would need to multiply 4 by $2x$.

Note that $\dfrac{3y}{4} \cdot \dfrac{5}{2x} = \dfrac{3y \cdot 5}{4 \cdot 2x} = \dfrac{15y}{8x}$, so the missing fraction must be $\dfrac{5}{2x}$.

Example 6: Where in the World? Andrew works for a biotech company. During a phone call his boss makes the following statement, "There is about $5,700 in grant money left and your department will get about two-thirds of that." As they are talking Andrew looks around but doesn't see a calculator. Quick! What is two-thirds of $5,700?!

Solution:

"Two-thirds of $5700" can be expressed as multiplication.

$$\frac{2}{3} \cdot 5700$$

Rewrite 5700 as $\frac{5700}{1}$.

$$= \frac{2}{3} \cdot \frac{5700}{1}$$

Rewrite as a single fraction.

$$= \frac{2 \cdot 5700}{3 \cdot 1}$$

Simplify the fraction.

$$= \frac{2}{3} \cdot 5700 = \frac{2}{3} \cdot \frac{5700}{1} = \frac{2 \cdot 5700}{3 \cdot 1} = \frac{2 \cdot 3 \cdot 1900}{3 \cdot 1} = 2 \cdot 1900 = 3800$$

The answer is:

$$= 2 \cdot 1900 = 3800$$

So Andrew's department will get about $3,800.

STOP Exercise Set - More About Multiplying Fractions

Multiply.

9. $\dfrac{30}{49} \cdot \dfrac{42}{90}$

13. $\dfrac{15}{27} \cdot (-81)$

17. $6 \cdot \dfrac{x}{2}$

10. $\dfrac{-12}{49} \cdot \dfrac{-14}{15}$

14. $\dfrac{24}{45} \cdot \dfrac{-18}{21} \cdot \dfrac{7}{8}$

18. $6b\left(\dfrac{2b}{15}\right)$

11. $(-22) \cdot \dfrac{-8}{121}$

15. $\dfrac{d}{12} \cdot \dfrac{4}{9d}$

19. $\left(\dfrac{10}{t}\right)\left(\dfrac{3}{15t}\right)$

12. $18 \cdot \dfrac{5}{27}$

16. $\dfrac{8c^2}{11} \cdot \dfrac{22}{25c}$

20. $-\dfrac{2}{21yx^2}\left(-\dfrac{35xy}{36}\right)$

21. The town of Leland, NC has a population of 43,800 people. A newspaper report says that about two-thirds of the population supports a new city proposition. How many people support the proposition?

22. It is very difficult to make micro chips for computers. In fact, about one-fifth of all microchips made are defective. If 4075 microchips are made, how many do you expect to be defective?

Multiplying Mixed Numbers

Recall that every mixed number can be written as an improper fraction, as in $2\frac{1}{5} = \frac{11}{5}$. This is an important idea when multiplying mixed numbers because mixed numbers must be turned to improper fractions to be multiplied.

To multiply mixed numbers we must change them to improper fractions first.

Example 7: Multiply. Express your final answer as a mixed number.

a) $3\frac{4}{5} \cdot \left(-7\frac{1}{2}\right)$ b) $\frac{-3}{4} \cdot 1\frac{2}{5} \cdot (-2)$

Solution:

a) Convert the mixed numbers to improper fractions.

$$3\frac{4}{5} \cdot \left(-7\frac{1}{2}\right) = \frac{19}{5} \cdot \left(\frac{-15}{2}\right)$$

Write the product as a single fraction. Also, since we know the product will be negative we bring a negative to the front of the fraction.

$$= -\frac{19 \cdot 15}{5 \cdot 2}$$

Factor in order to simplify. The numerator and denominator both have a common factor of 5.

$$= -\frac{19 \cdot \cancel{5} \cdot 3}{\cancel{5} \cdot 2}$$

Multiply the remaining factors.

$$= -\frac{57}{2}$$

Convert to a mixed number.

$$= -28\frac{1}{2}$$

b) Convert the mixed number to an improper fraction and rewrite the integer as a fraction.

$$\frac{-3}{4} \cdot 1\frac{2}{5} \cdot (-2) = \frac{-3}{4} \cdot \frac{7}{5} \cdot \frac{-2}{1}$$

Write the product as a single fraction. Notice that since two of the factors are negative the product will be positive.

$$= \frac{3 \cdot 7 \cdot 2}{4 \cdot 5 \cdot 1}$$

Simplify. The numerator and denominator both have a common factor of 2.

$$= \frac{3 \cdot 7 \cdot \cancel{2}}{\cancel{2} \cdot 2 \cdot 5 \cdot 1}$$

Multiply the remaining factors.

$$= \frac{21}{5}$$

Convert $\frac{21}{10}$ to a mixed number.

$$= 2\frac{1}{10}$$

Example 8: Where in the World? True Story. We have small plot beside our house we are thinking about walling in so Holly can have a bicycle workshop. Here are the dimensions according to my tape measure. How many square feet is the plot? Express the final answer as a mixed number.

[PN: length = $11\frac{3}{8}$', width = $6\frac{7}{16}$'. Is it possible to make it look like two sides are made up of house walls?]

Solution: Recall that the area of a rectangle can be found using the formula $A = l \cdot w$. The area is given by the multiplication $11\frac{3}{8} \cdot 6\frac{7}{16}$.

Express each number as an improper fraction.

$$11\frac{3}{8} \cdot 6\frac{7}{16} = \frac{95}{8} \cdot \frac{27}{4}$$

Rewrite the product as a single fraction. Notice the only factors in 8 and 16 is 2 since $8 = 2^3$ and $16 = 2^4$. Since neither number in the numerator is even, this fraction will not simplify.

$$= \frac{95 \cdot 27}{8 \cdot 16}$$

Multiply the factors.

$$= \frac{2565}{32}$$

Convert back to a mixed number.

$$= 80\frac{5}{32}$$

The plot has $80\frac{5}{32}$ square feet, or $80\frac{5}{32} ft^2$.

 Exercise Set - Multiplying Mixed Numbers

Multiply.

23. $1\frac{2}{3} \cdot 3\frac{3}{4}$

24. $2\frac{1}{4} \cdot 1\frac{1}{3}$

25. $1\frac{2}{13} \cdot 5\frac{1}{5}$

26. $3\frac{3}{7} \cdot 3\frac{1}{4}$

27. $8 \cdot 5\frac{5}{8}$

28. $7\frac{7}{12} \cdot (-6)$

29. $\left(-4\frac{10}{11}\right) \cdot \left(-2\frac{5}{6}\right)$

30. $3\frac{7}{9} \cdot \left(-1\frac{10}{17}\right)$

31. $-4\frac{1}{2} \cdot 4\frac{2}{3}$

32. $12\frac{2}{5} \cdot 2\frac{3}{31}$

33. Lisa has small plot beside her house that she wants to plant a vegetable garden. The dimensions are $12\frac{7}{8}$ ft by $8\frac{2}{3}$ ft. How many square feet is the plot? Express the final answer as a mixed number.

34. Tarah and Chad are building a playhouse for Maeve in the backyard. They have reserved a spot that is $4\frac{1}{2}$ ft wide by $5\frac{1}{3}$ ft long. How many square feet is the spot for Maeve's playhouse? Express the final answer as a mixed number.

Solving Equations

It is time to turn our attention back to solving equations that involve fractions. To start we look at handling a coefficient in front of the variable, as in an equation like $\frac{3}{5}x = \frac{1}{2}$.

In an equation like this, one way to isolate the variable is by multiplying both sides of the equation by the reciprocal of the fraction in front of the variable.

This is a very useful approach since $\frac{a}{b} \cdot \frac{b}{a} = \frac{ab}{ab} = 1$.

> Recall that the **reciprocal** of $\frac{a}{b}$ is $\frac{b}{a}$.
>
> Sometimes we can multiply both sides of an equation by a reciprocal to isolate a variable.

Example 9: Solve the following. Where appropriate, leave your answers as improper fractions.

a) $\frac{3}{5}x = \frac{1}{2}$ b) $-\frac{4}{5}k = 7$

Solutions:

a) Multiply each side by $\frac{5}{3}$, the reciprocal of $\frac{3}{5}$. $\frac{3}{5}x = \frac{1}{2}$

Note that $\frac{5}{3} \cdot \frac{3}{5}x = \frac{15}{15}x = 1x$.

$$\frac{5}{3} \cdot \frac{3}{5}x = \frac{5}{3} \cdot \frac{1}{2}$$

Multiply on each side.

$$x = \frac{5}{6}$$

b) Multiply each side by $-\frac{5}{4}$, the reciprocal of $-\frac{4}{5}k = 7$

$-\frac{4}{5}$. Note that $\frac{-5}{4} \cdot \frac{-4}{5}k = \frac{-20}{-20}k = 1k$.

$$\frac{-5}{4} \cdot \frac{-4}{5}k = \frac{-5}{4} \cdot 7$$

Multiply on each side.

$$k = \frac{-35}{4}$$

Example 10: Translate the following sentence into a math equation and solve.

"One-third of what number is six-thirteenths?"

Solution:
As in Chapter 3, we write the sentence and use arrows to show words are translated into symbols.

"One-third of what number is six-thirteenths?"

$$\frac{1}{3}x = \frac{6}{13}$$

Now to solve. Multiply each side by $\frac{3}{1}$, the

reciprocal of $\frac{1}{3}$.

$$\frac{3}{1} \cdot \frac{1}{3}x = \frac{3}{1} \cdot \frac{6}{13}$$

Multiply on each side.

$$x = \frac{18}{13} = 1\frac{5}{13}$$

STOP Exercise Set - Solving Equations

Solve the following.

35. $\frac{2}{7}x = \frac{6}{11}$

36. $\frac{5}{8}x = \frac{1}{4}$

37. $\frac{3}{5}x = \frac{-1}{6}$

38. $\frac{-8}{9}x = \frac{2}{3}$

39. $\frac{3}{7}x = -9$

40. $\frac{-7}{9}y = -21$

41. $-5a = \frac{15}{16}$

42. $\frac{-3}{4}g = \frac{-24}{27}$

Translate the following sentence into a math equation and solve.
43. One-half of what number is three fourths?
44. Five sixths of what number is eight ninths?
45. Eleven fifteens of what number is twenty-two?
46. Two and one-third of what number is six-sevenths?

4.2 Exercise Set - Putting it ALL Together

Multiply.

47. $\frac{15}{24} \cdot (-32)$

48. $\frac{13}{72} \cdot \frac{18}{29}$

49. $\frac{19}{54} \cdot \frac{18}{38}$

50. $\dfrac{-5}{88} \cdot \dfrac{-16}{25}$

51. $\dfrac{16xy}{35} \cdot \dfrac{21y}{36x}$

52. $\dfrac{8xy^3}{11x} \cdot \dfrac{33xy}{36x^3y^4}$

53. $\dfrac{6}{7y} \cdot \dfrac{14y^2}{15}$

54. $5\dfrac{5}{12} \cdot -3\dfrac{9}{15}$

55. $5\dfrac{2}{3} \cdot 1\dfrac{1}{17}$

56. $\left(\dfrac{7}{24y}\right)\left(\dfrac{8y}{77}\right)$

57. $-3\dfrac{1}{5} \cdot 7\dfrac{3}{4}$

58. $-2\dfrac{3}{8} \cdot (-4)$

59. $\dfrac{15}{78} \cdot 26$

60. $\dfrac{3}{8} \cdot \dfrac{h}{4}$

61. $\dfrac{5}{6} \cdot \dfrac{-3}{10} \cdot \dfrac{24}{25}$

62. $\dfrac{26}{45} \cdot \dfrac{6}{17} \cdot \dfrac{34}{39}$

63. $\dfrac{a}{2} \cdot \dfrac{5}{7}$

64. $\dfrac{3}{x} \cdot \dfrac{5x^2}{2}$

65. $5x\left(\dfrac{1}{10}\right)$

66. $\dfrac{3b}{17} \cdot 5$

67. $\dfrac{x}{3} \cdot 3$

68. $\dfrac{11}{14} \cdot \dfrac{2}{15} \cdot \dfrac{10}{33}$

69. $-\dfrac{15ab}{51} \cdot \dfrac{17}{45b}$

Solve.

70. $-\dfrac{2}{3}x = -8$

71. $\dfrac{8}{11}x = \dfrac{3}{22}$

72. $-5k = \dfrac{1}{2}$

73. $\dfrac{-5}{24}x = -\dfrac{5}{8}$

74. $\dfrac{-21}{25}x = \dfrac{-1}{10}$

75. $\dfrac{3}{7}x = -9$

76. Multiply each of the following:

$$6x \cdot \dfrac{1}{6x} \qquad 6 \cdot \dfrac{1}{6x} \qquad 6x \cdot \dfrac{1}{6}$$

77. Multiply each of the following:

$$14a \cdot \dfrac{1}{7a} \qquad 14 \cdot \dfrac{1}{7a} \qquad \dfrac{1}{7} \cdot 14a$$

78. Multiply each of the following:

$$25b \cdot \left(-\dfrac{1}{5b}\right) \qquad \left(-\dfrac{1}{5}\right) \cdot 25b \qquad 25 \cdot \left(-\dfrac{1}{5b}\right)$$

79. Multiply each of the following:

$$\left(-\dfrac{1}{12k}\right)(-24k) \qquad \left(-\dfrac{1}{12k}\right)(-24) \qquad \left(-\dfrac{1}{12}\right)(-24k)$$

80. Complete the following multiplication table of fractions.

×	$\frac{1}{2}$	$\frac{1}{3}$	$\frac{1}{4}$	$\frac{1}{5}$
$\frac{1}{2}$				
$\frac{1}{3}$				
$\frac{1}{4}$				
$\frac{1}{5}$				

81. A framed painting measures $8\frac{1}{4}$ in. by $12\frac{1}{2}$ in. How much area does it take up on the wall when hung?

82. Martha bought a rug for her living room. It measures $9\frac{3}{8}$ ft. by $11\frac{2}{5}$ ft. Find the area that the rug will cover.

83. Lana wants to plant a vegetable garden and has a rectangle plot that is $15\frac{3}{4}$ ft long and $6\frac{4}{7}$ ft. wide. How much area does she have to garden?

84. To determine the charge for printing flyers for an event, the printer must determine the area of the posters. What is the area of the poster to the right? [PN: $2\frac{3}{8}$ feet by $1\frac{1}{4}$ feet]

Courtesy of Fotolia

85. Mike wants to use stone blocks that measure $6\frac{3}{5}$ in. wide to border his vegetable garden. If it takes 20 blocks to accomplish this, what is the perimeter of his garden?

86. Carrie is making chocolate chips. The recipe calls for $2\frac{3}{4}$ c. of flour and makes 36 cookies. She is having a dinner party and only needs 27 cookies and doesn't want leftovers; she is going on a diet tomorrow. How much flour should she use? Hint: 27 is $\frac{3}{4}$ of 36.

87. Between the ages of 3 and 10 a typical child grows at a rate of about $\frac{5}{24}$ of an inch every month. At this rate, how many inches should a child grow in one year (twelve months)?

88. Katie and Carrie drive at 70mph for $7\frac{5}{8}$ hr. How far did they drive?

89. Lana rides her bike at 18mph for $2\frac{3}{5}$ hr. How far did she ride?

90. Glenn and Sharon go for a boat ride in the lake. The ride up the waterway at a rate of $18\frac{1}{2}$ mph for $\frac{2}{3}$ hr. How far did they go? If they turn around to go back, what is the total distance they went?

Rolling Stone Magazine took a survey of 1000 people to see which form of entertainment people enjoyed most between music, movies, video games, reading, and TV. The pie chart below gives the fraction of people that preferred each category. So, for example, in the survey $\frac{1}{50}$ of the people preferred movies most. Answer the questions that follow. *Source: Rolling Stone Magazine*

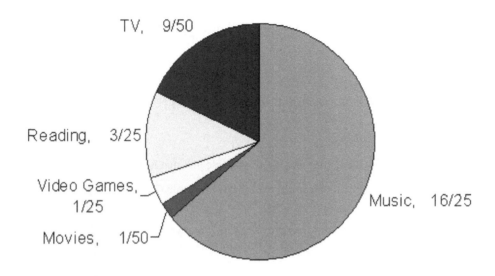

91. What fraction of the people preferred reading?
92. What fraction of the people preferred music?
93. Of the 1000 people surveyed, how many preferred movies?
94. Of the 1000 people surveyed, how many preferred music?
95. Of the 1000 people surveyed, how many preferred video games?
96. Of the 1000 people surveyed, how many preferred reading?

Exercise Set - Chapter 4 Review

97. Graph $4, \frac{1}{3}, -2\frac{1}{2}, \frac{5}{2}$ on a number line.

98. Add. $\frac{5}{17} + \frac{12}{17}$

99. Subtract. $\dfrac{5}{6} - \dfrac{(-4)}{6}$

100. Which fraction is undefined? $\dfrac{-6}{0}$ or $\dfrac{0}{-6}$

101. Rewrite $-9\dfrac{1}{2}$ as an improper fraction?

Exercise Set - Cumulative Review

102. Simplify. $-3a + 5y + 6a - 9y$
103. Simplify. $-3(2x + 5) + 15x$
104. Evaluate $t^2 + 3t$ for $t = 5$.
105. Multiply. $(3)(-7)(-2)$
106. Fill in the blank with $<$, $>$, or $=$. $-16\_\_\_-12$

 # 4.2 QUIZ YOURSELF

To make sure you are ready for the EXAM, try these problems without any help. Give yourself about 20 minutes and don't check the answers until you have completely finished.

1. $\dfrac{36}{49} \cdot \dfrac{14}{27}$ 2. $\dfrac{9}{16} \cdot (-24)$ 3. $\dfrac{14}{25} \cdot 3\dfrac{4}{7}$ 4. $7\dfrac{1}{2} \cdot \left(-6\dfrac{2}{5}\right)$ 5. $-10\dfrac{4}{5} \cdot 2\dfrac{5}{9}$

6. Solve. $\dfrac{-6}{11}k = \dfrac{6}{11}$

7. Solve. $\dfrac{-22}{35}n = \dfrac{-22}{35}$

8. A recipe for peanut butter cookies calls for $1\dfrac{1}{2}$ c. of peanut butter. How much peanut butter would you need to make $\dfrac{5}{6}$ of the recipe?

9. Belinda drove at 55mph for $4\dfrac{9}{22}$ hr. How far did she drive?

10. Betty's green house is $12\dfrac{7}{8}$ ft. wide by $25\dfrac{3}{5}$ ft. long. What is the area of the greenhouse floor?

Answers to this Quiz Yourself are on page 671.

4.3 Dividing Fractions

Topics:
- Understanding Fraction Division
- More About Dividing Fractions
- Dividing Mixed Numbers

Are You Ready?
To see if you are ready to understand this section, do the following short quiz.
1. What is the reciprocal of -6 ?

2. Multiply. $\dfrac{15}{49} \cdot \left(-\dfrac{21}{45}\right)$

3. Simplify the algebraic fraction $\dfrac{12p}{33p^3}$.

Answers to Are You Ready?

(1) $-\dfrac{1}{6}$ *(2)* $-\dfrac{1}{7}$ *(3)* $\dfrac{4}{11p^2}$

Understanding Fraction Division

In Section 4.2 we looked at why fraction multiplication works the way it does. Let's now explore fraction division in a similar way as multiplication: $\dfrac{a}{b} \div \dfrac{c}{d} = \dfrac{a}{b} \cdot \dfrac{d}{c} = \dfrac{a \cdot d}{b \cdot c}$. Frankly, fraction division is not as easy to illustrate as multiplication. But it can be done reasonably easy if we use simple fractions. Recall that a quotient like $15 \div 3$ can be interpreted as the question "How many 3s are there in 15?" There are five 3s in 15, so $15 \div 3 = 5$. So a fraction division like $\dfrac{2}{3} \div \dfrac{1}{6}$ can be interpreted as the question "How many $\dfrac{1}{6}$ s are in $\dfrac{2}{3}$?" Let's draw a picture to illustrate how to get the answer.

Begin with the fraction 2/3.   [PN: a picture of 2/3]

Now divide up the fraction so that 6 parts make a whole.   [PN: three dotted lines to make six parts]

How many $\dfrac{1}{6}$ s are in $\dfrac{2}{3}$? We see just by counting that   [PN: use previous picture and count shaded parts]

there are 4. So $\dfrac{2}{3} \div \dfrac{1}{6} = 4$.

This helps verify our "reciprocate and multiply rule for dividing fractions:

$$\frac{2}{3} \div \frac{1}{6} = \frac{2}{3} \cdot \frac{6}{1} = \frac{2 \cdot 6}{3 \cdot 1} = \frac{2 \cdot 2 \cdot \cancel{3}}{\cancel{3} \cdot 1} = \frac{4}{1} = 4$$

Example 1: Use pictures to illustrate and answer each fraction division problem.

a) $\dfrac{4}{5} \div \dfrac{1}{10}$ b) $3 \div \dfrac{1}{4}$

Solution:

a) $\dfrac{4}{5} \div \dfrac{1}{10}$

Begin with 4/5.   [PN: a picture of 4/5]

Divide the parts so that there are 10 parts total.   [PN: draw 2 dotted lines to make 10 parts.]

Count up the $\dfrac{1}{10}$ s.   [PN: count up parts]

There are 8 of the fraction $\dfrac{1}{10}$.   This means $\dfrac{4}{5} \div \dfrac{1}{10} = 8$.

b) $3 \div \dfrac{1}{4}$

Begin with 3.   [PN: a picture of 3]

Divide each whole into 4 parts.   [PN: draw 2 dotted lines in each whole to make 4 parts.]

Count up the 1/4.   [PN: count up parts]

There are 12 of the fraction $\dfrac{1}{4}$

There are 8   This means $3 \div \dfrac{1}{4} = 12$.

 Exercise Set - Understanding Fraction Division

Translate each statement into fraction division. Do not find the answer.

1. How many $\dfrac{1}{9}$ s are in $\dfrac{1}{3}$?   3. How many $\dfrac{1}{4}$ s are in 2?

2. How many $\dfrac{1}{8}$ s are in $\dfrac{3}{4}$?   4. How many $\dfrac{2}{3}$ s are in6?

Use pictures to perform each division.

5. $\dfrac{4}{5} \div \dfrac{1}{10}$ 7. $4 \div \dfrac{1}{2}$

6. $\dfrac{2}{3} \div \dfrac{1}{9}$ 8. $3 \div \dfrac{1}{4}$

More About Dividing Fractions

As with fraction multiplication, we now take the time to look at some fraction division problems that involve larger numbers, more than two fractions, and algebraic fractions.

Example 2: Divide, if possible. Reduce your final answer.

a) $-\dfrac{25}{42} \div \dfrac{30}{21}$

b) $\dfrac{45}{81} \div 18$

c) $0 \div \dfrac{-13}{14}$

Solution:

a) Take the reciprocal of the second fraction and change the operation to multiplication.

$$-\frac{25}{42} \div \frac{30}{21} = -\frac{25}{42} \cdot \frac{21}{30}$$

Rewrite the product as a single fraction and prime factor the numerator and denominator.

$$= -\frac{5 \cdot 5 \cdot 3 \cdot 7}{2 \cdot 3 \cdot 7 \cdot 2 \cdot 3 \cdot 5}$$

Simplify by the common factors of 5, 3, and 7 in the numerator and denominator.

$$= -\frac{\cancel{5} \cdot 5 \cdot \cancel{3} \cdot \cancel{7}}{2 \cdot 3 \cdot \cancel{7} \cdot 2 \cdot \cancel{3} \cdot \cancel{5}} = -\frac{5}{12}$$

b) Rewrite the whole number as a fraction.

$$\frac{45}{81} \div 18 = \frac{45}{81} \div \frac{18}{1}$$

Take the reciprocal of the second fraction and change the operation to multiplication.

$$= \frac{45}{81} \cdot \frac{1}{18}$$

Rewrite the product as a single fraction and prime factor the numerator and denominator.

$$= -\frac{3 \cdot 3 \cdot 5}{3 \cdot 3 \cdot 3 \cdot 3 \cdot 2 \cdot 3 \cdot 3}$$

Simplify by the common factors of 3, and 3 in the numerator and denominator.

$$= -\frac{\cancel{3} \cdot \cancel{3} \cdot 5}{\cancel{3} \cdot \cancel{3} \cdot 3 \cdot 3 \cdot 2 \cdot 3 \cdot 3} = \frac{5}{162}$$

c) Recall that $0 \div b = 0$ for any nonzero number b. This is true for fractions as well.

$$0 \div \frac{-13}{14} = 0$$

The next example involves algebraic fractions.

Example 3: Divide.

a) $\dfrac{-20x}{11} \div 16$

b) $\dfrac{-63y^2}{32x} \div \dfrac{7y}{8x}$

Solution:

a) Rewrite the whole number as a fraction.

$$\dfrac{-20x}{11} \div 16 = \dfrac{-20x}{11} \div \dfrac{16}{1}$$

Take the reciprocal of the second fraction and change the operation to multiplication.

$$= \dfrac{-20x}{11} \cdot \dfrac{1}{16}$$

Rewrite the product as a single fraction.

$$= \dfrac{-20x \cdot 1}{11 \cdot 16}$$

Rather than all the way to prime factors to reduce we may recognize the common factor of 4.

$$= -\dfrac{4 \cdot 5 \cdot x}{11 \cdot 4 \cdot 4}$$

Simplify by the common factor of 4.

$$= -\dfrac{\cancel{4} \cdot 5 \cdot x}{11 \cdot \cancel{4} \cdot 4}$$

Multiply the remaining factors.

$$= -\dfrac{5x}{44}$$

b) Take the reciprocal of the second fraction and change the operation to multiplication.

$$\dfrac{-63y}{32x} \div \dfrac{7y^2}{8x} = \dfrac{-63y}{32x} \cdot \dfrac{8x}{7y^2}$$

Rewrite the product as a single fraction and prime factor the numerator and denominator.

$$= -\dfrac{3 \cdot 3 \cdot 7 \cdot y \cdot 2 \cdot 2 \cdot 2 \cdot x}{2 \cdot 2 \cdot 2 \cdot 2 \cdot 2 \cdot x \cdot 7 \cdot y \cdot y}$$

Simplify by the common factors of 2, 2, 2, 7, x, and y in the numerator and denominator.

$$= -\dfrac{3 \cdot 3 \cdot \cancel{7} \cdot \cancel{y} \cdot \cancel{2} \cdot \cancel{2} \cdot \cancel{2} \cdot \cancel{x}}{\cancel{2} \cdot \cancel{2} \cdot \cancel{2} \cdot 2 \cdot 2 \cdot \cancel{x} \cdot \cancel{7} \cdot \cancel{y} \cdot y} = -\dfrac{9}{4y}$$

STOP Exercise Set - More About Dividing Fractions

Find the reciprocal of each rational number, if it exists.

9. $\dfrac{1}{3}$ 10. $-\dfrac{3}{4}$ 11. 6 12. 0

Divide.

13. $\dfrac{16}{25} \div \dfrac{4}{7}$ 18. $\dfrac{-8}{15} \div \dfrac{24}{35}$

14. $\dfrac{-5}{8} \div \dfrac{25}{32}$ 19. $\dfrac{-2x}{5} \div \dfrac{4}{7}$

15. $\dfrac{8}{27} \div \dfrac{3}{4}$ 20. $\dfrac{8y}{9} \div \dfrac{4}{5}$

16. $\dfrac{-15}{18} \div \dfrac{-5}{8}$ 21. $\dfrac{2x^2}{7} \div \dfrac{4x}{21}$

17. $\dfrac{9}{-10} \div \dfrac{12}{35}$ 22. $\dfrac{-3a^3}{8} \div \dfrac{-6a}{7}$

Dividing Mixed Numbers

As with fraction multiplication, mixed numbers must be converted to improper fractions before they are divided.

Example 4: Divide. Write your final answer as a mixed number if appropriate.

a) $-1\dfrac{3}{4} \div \left(-3\dfrac{1}{2}\right)$ b) $9 \div 7\dfrac{1}{5}$

Solution:

a) $-1\dfrac{3}{4} \div \left(-3\dfrac{1}{2}\right)$

Convert both mixed numbers to improper fractions.

$$-1\dfrac{3}{4} \div \left(-3\dfrac{1}{2}\right) = \dfrac{-7}{4} \div \dfrac{-7}{2}$$

Take the reciprocal of the second fraction and change the operation to multiplication.

$$= \dfrac{-7}{4} \cdot \dfrac{-2}{7}$$

Rewrite the product as a single fraction and prime factor the numerator and denominator. Notice that a negative times a negative is positive, so we can drop the negative signs.

$$= \dfrac{-7 \cdot (-2)}{4 \cdot 7} = \dfrac{7 \cdot 2}{2 \cdot 2 \cdot 7}$$

Simplify by the common factors of 2 and 7 in the numerator and denominator.

$$= \dfrac{7 \cdot 2}{2 \cdot 2 \cdot 7} = \dfrac{1}{2}$$

The final answer is $\dfrac{1}{2}$.

b) $9 \div 7\frac{1}{5}$

Rewrite the whole number as a fraction and rewrite the mixed number as an improper fraction.	$9 \div 7\frac{1}{5} = \frac{9}{1} \div \frac{36}{5}$

Take the reciprocal of the second fraction and change the operation to multiplication.

$$= \frac{9}{1} \cdot \frac{5}{36}$$

Rewrite the product as a single fraction and prime factor the numerator and denominator.

$$= \frac{9 \cdot 5}{1 \cdot 36} = \frac{3 \cdot 3 \cdot 5}{1 \cdot 2 \cdot 2 \cdot 3 \cdot 3}$$

Simplify by the common factors of 3 and 3 in the numerator and denominator.

$$= \frac{3 \cdot 3 \cdot 5}{1 \cdot 2 \cdot 2 \cdot 3 \cdot 3} = \frac{5}{4}$$

Rewrite the fraction 5/4 as a mixed number.

$$\frac{5}{4} = 1\frac{1}{4}$$

The final answer is $1\frac{1}{4}$.

Example 5: Where in the World? Willow wants a retaining wall for a section of her garden. Using a tape measure, she finds that the space set aside for the garden has a length of $13\frac{1}{8}$ feet. The border she wants to use comes in pieces that are each $1\frac{3}{4}$ feet. How many border pieces does she need to purchase?

Solution: Finding the number of pieces needed will require the fraction division $13\frac{1}{8} \div 1\frac{3}{4}$.

Convert both mixed numbers to improper fractions.

$$13\frac{1}{8} \div 1\frac{3}{4} = \frac{105}{8} \div \frac{7}{4}$$

Take the reciprocal of the second fraction and change the operation to multiplication.

$$= \frac{105}{8} \cdot \frac{4}{7}$$

Rewrite the product as a single fraction and prime factor the numerator and denominator.

$$= \frac{3 \cdot 5 \cdot 7 \cdot 2 \cdot 2}{2 \cdot 2 \cdot 2 \cdot 7}$$

Simplify by the common factors of 2 and 7 in the numerator and denominator.

$$= \frac{3 \cdot 5 \cdot \cancel{7} \cdot \cancel{2} \cdot \cancel{2}}{\cancel{2} \cdot \cancel{2} \cdot 2 \cdot \cancel{7}} = \frac{15}{2}$$

Rewrite the improper fraction 15/2 as a mixed number.

$$\frac{15}{2} = 7\frac{1}{2}$$

The final answer is $7\frac{1}{2}$.

Since she needs $7\frac{1}{2}$ pieces, she will need to buy 8 of them to section off the garden space.

STOP Exercise Set - Dividing Mixed Numbers

23. $\dfrac{7}{8} \div 3\dfrac{1}{5}$

24. $5\dfrac{1}{4} \div \dfrac{7}{11}$

25. $2\dfrac{2}{3} \div 1\dfrac{1}{4}$

26. $5\dfrac{1}{5} \div 1\dfrac{3}{4}$

27. $7\dfrac{1}{3} \div 7\dfrac{6}{7}$

28. $3\dfrac{1}{2} \div 2\dfrac{5}{8}$

29. $-13 \div 3\dfrac{5}{7}$

30. $3\dfrac{1}{6} \div (-38)$

31. $-1\dfrac{1}{7} \div -4\dfrac{2}{3}$

32. $-8\dfrac{2}{3} \div -3\dfrac{1}{6}$

Succeed in Math! Work hard and don't give up!

Courtesy of Fotolia

Albert Einstein failed as a teacher but revolutionized Physics.

Harrison Ford was told by Columbia Pictures that he would never make it as an actor but went on to play Han Solo in Star Wars!

Courtesy of Fotolia

Mario failed as a plumber but went on to defeat Bowser 9 times!

Walt Disney was fired from a newspaper for "lack of imagination" then invented Mickey Mouse and made millions!

4.3 Exercise Set - Putting it ALL Together

TRUE or FALSE

33. Every number has a reciprocal that can be used for division.
34. To divide fractions we reciprocate the second fraction and change the operation to multiplication.
35. The quotient of two negative fractions is positive.
36. To divide mixed numbers you can choose to leave or as mixed numbers or convert them to improper fractions.

Divide if possible.

37. $\dfrac{3}{7} \div 6$

38. $14 \div \dfrac{4}{5}$

39. $0 \div \dfrac{-12}{17}$

40. $\dfrac{13}{18} \div \dfrac{26}{27}$

41. $\dfrac{5}{16} \div 0$

42. $\dfrac{16}{25} \div 8$

43. $\dfrac{-5}{12} \div \dfrac{-25}{32}$

44. $\dfrac{27}{28} \div \dfrac{4}{21}$

45. $\dfrac{-19}{54} \div \left(-\dfrac{38}{81}\right)$

46. $\left(-\dfrac{8}{15}\right) \div \left(-\dfrac{12}{35}\right)$

47. $21 \div \left(-\dfrac{7}{8}\right)$

48. $6 \div \dfrac{1}{6}$

49. $\dfrac{1}{11} \div (-11)$

50. $30 \div \dfrac{10}{13}$

51. $-1\dfrac{3}{5} \div 6\dfrac{2}{3}$

52. $5\dfrac{1}{5} \div 1\dfrac{2}{15}$

53. $-7\dfrac{5}{9} \div 3\dfrac{2}{12}$

54. $\left(-12\dfrac{1}{2}\right) \div \left(-8\dfrac{1}{3}\right)$

55. $\dfrac{5}{14} \div \dfrac{10x}{7}$

56. $\dfrac{4}{33} \div \dfrac{6}{11y^2}$

57. $0 \div \dfrac{4}{5q}$

58. $\dfrac{-6x^2}{7y} \div \dfrac{3x}{7y}$

59. $\dfrac{a^2c}{8} \div \dfrac{5c^3}{6}$

60. $\dfrac{a^2}{b} \div \dfrac{a}{b^3}$

61. $\dfrac{x}{y} \div \dfrac{x^2}{y}$

62. $\dfrac{5q^2}{14} \div 0$

63. $5k \div \dfrac{15k^2}{7}$

64. $8t^2 \div \dfrac{16t}{9c}$

65. $\dfrac{2x^2y^3}{5x} \div \dfrac{4xy}{7}$

66. $\dfrac{-3x^3}{14y} \div \dfrac{4x^2y}{7y^2}$

67. $\dfrac{-15x^2}{16} \div \dfrac{-25xy}{26y^3}$

68. Complete the table.

Number	Opposite	Reciprocal
$\dfrac{3}{5}$		
$-\dfrac{1}{7}$		
8		

69. Complete the table.

Number	Opposite	Reciprocal
$-\dfrac{9}{11}$		
14		
$\dfrac{1}{2}$		

70. Multiply $\dfrac{4}{7}$ to its reciprocal. What is the result?

71. Multiply $-\dfrac{3}{5}$ to its reciprocal. What is the result?

72. Multiply 6 to its reciprocal. What is the result?

73. Multiply -15 to its reciprocal. What is the result?

74. A classroom is 23 ft. wide. If each student's desk needs $3\dfrac{1}{5}$ ft, how many desks can you fit in a row?

75. The area of Katie's blueberry garden is $11\dfrac{1}{4} \; m^2$. How many blueberry bushes can she plant if each bush should have $2\dfrac{2}{3} \; m^2$ of garden space?

76. An Italian restaurant baker is making breadsticks and has $25\dfrac{3}{8}$ lbs. of dough. If each breadstick requires $\dfrac{9}{16}$ lbs. of dough, how many breadsticks can he make?

77. Prisacilla wants to use stone blocks that are $9\dfrac{7}{8}$ in. wide to border her flower garden. If the perimeter of his garden is $87\dfrac{3}{4}$ in., how many blocks does she need?

78. Tarah runs a ½ marathon in $2\dfrac{1}{6}$ hrs. A ½ marathon is $13\dfrac{1}{10}$ miles. At what rate was Tarah running? Let r be the rate at which Tarah runs in mph.

79. Jose runs a ½ marathon in $1\dfrac{7}{8}$ hrs. A ½ marathon is $13\dfrac{1}{10}$ miles. At what rate was Jose running? Let r be the rate at which Alan runs in mph.

Exercise Set - Chapter 4 Review

80. Add. $\dfrac{-7}{15} + \dfrac{2}{15}$

81. Subtract. $\dfrac{3}{7} - \dfrac{5}{7}$

82. Simplify. $\dfrac{-9}{-9}$

83. Find the area of the rectangle. [PN: rectangle with sides $2\dfrac{1}{2}$ by $1\dfrac{1}{4}$]

84. Convert to a mixed number if appropriate. $\dfrac{7}{5y}$

Exercise Set - Cumulative Review

85. Translate the following phrase into math symbols.
    "five minus three times some number"

86. If the temperature is dropped at a rate of 6 degrees per hour, what integer represents the change in temperature after 7 hours?

87. Add. $-75 + (-14) + 53$

88. Use the order of operations to find the sums $(9 + 5) + 6$ and $9 + (5 + 6)$.

89. Renting a cotton candy machine costs a flat fee of $15 plus $4 per hour. Suppose the machine is rented for 8 hours. Find an expression that gives the total charge and find the total charge.

4.3 QUIZ YOURSELF

To make sure you are ready for the EXAM, try these problems without any help. Give yourself about 20 minutes and don't check the answers until you have completely finished.

1. Find the reciprocal: $\dfrac{-5}{17}$

2. Find the reciprocal: $9\dfrac{4}{5}$

3. Divide. $\dfrac{12}{13} \div \dfrac{24}{29}$

4. Divide. $2\dfrac{2}{3} \div 1\dfrac{1}{4}$

5. Divide. $-3\dfrac{1}{5} \div 2\dfrac{2}{15}$

6. Divide. $\dfrac{9a^2}{28} \div \dfrac{-5ab}{36b^3}$

7. Solve. $\dfrac{-72}{85}x = \dfrac{-9}{15}$

8. Solve. $\dfrac{8}{27}x = (-24)$

9. Rich runs a marathon in $3\dfrac{7}{12}$ hours. A marathon is $26\dfrac{1}{5}$ miles. At what rate was Rich running? Let r be the rate at which Rich runs in mph.

10. Carlos is planting a citrus orchard and has $860 \ yd^2$ of land. Each orange tree requires $5\dfrac{3}{4} \ yd^2$ of land. How many trees can he plant?

Answers for this Quiz Yourself are on page 671.

4.4 LCM And LCD

Topics:
- **LCM Of Integers And Algebraic Expressions**
- **Building Up Fractions**
- **LCD Of Two or More Fractions**
- **Ordering Fractions**

Are You Ready?
To see if you are ready to understand this section, do the following short quiz.
1. Find the prime factorization of 168.
2. List the first eight multiples of 7.
3. Simplify to determine if the fractions $\dfrac{3}{15}$ and $\dfrac{2}{10}$ are equivalent.
4. Compare -13 __ 12

Answers to Are You Ready?

(1) $2^3 \cdot 3 \cdot 7$ *(2) 7, 14, 21, 28, 35, 42, 49, 56*   *(3) yes*   *(4) <*

LCM Of Integers And Algebraic Expressions

Recall the following definition from Section 1.5.

> The **multiples** of a number are the values obtained by multiplying the number by the natural (counting) numbers: 1,2,3,4,5,…

Multiples of 5:
5,10,15,20,25,30,35,40,45,50,55,60,65,70...

Multiples of 13:
13,26,39,52,65,78,91,104,127,130,143…

Example 1: List the first three multiples that 2 and 3 have in common.

Solution: Begin by just listing the first few multiples of 2 and 3.

Multiples of 2:
2, 4, 6, 8, 10, 12, 14, 16, 18, 20, 22, 24,…

Multiples of 3:
3, 6, 9, 12, 15, 18, 21, 24, 27, 30, 33, 36,…
[PN: circle all the common multiples]

From these lists, we see that the first three multiples 2 and 3 have in common are 6, 12, and 18.

Advance work with fractions involves finding the smallest multiple two numbers have in common.

The **least common multiple (or LCM)** of two or more integers is the smallest multiple they have in common.

Similar to the last example, consider the multiples of 4 and 6 together and circle the ones they have in common.

Multiples of 4: 4, 8, 12, 16, 20, 24, 28, 32, 36...   [PN: Circle 12, 24 and 36 in both lists]
Multiples of 6: 6, 12, 18, 24, 30, 36, 42, 48...

4 and 6 have lots of multiples in common, but 12 is the *least common multiple* of 4 and 6 because it is the smallest multiple they both have in common.

Example 2: In each problem, use lists to find the least common multiple of the numbers given.

a) 8 and 12   b) 7, 3, and 6

Solution: In each exercise we start by listing several multiples of the first number. Then we list multiples of the second until we hit the LCM.

a) 8 and 12
Multiples of 8: 8, 16, 24, 32, 40, 48, 56, 64, 72,...
Multiples of 12: 12, 24, 36, 48,...

The least common multiple of 8 and 12 is 24.

b) 7, 3, and 6
For three numbers the process is the same, we just have three lists of multiples to consider.

Multiples of 7: 7, 14, 21, 28, 35, 42, 49, 56,...
Multiples of 3: 3, 6, 9, 12, 15, 18, 21, 24, 27, 30, 33, 36, 39, 42, 45,...
Multiples of 6: 6, 12, 18, 24, 30, 36, 42

The least common multiple of 7, 3, and 6 is 42.

Making lists of numbers is a good way to find the least common multiple of smaller numbers, but if the numbers are larger it may not be practical. For example, the least common multiple between 7, 45, and 13 is 4095. We would have to list the first 585 multiples of 7 to reach 4095! YIKES!

Fortunately there is another way to find the least common multiple of two or more numbers without having to make lists.

To Find the Least Common Multiple Using Prime Factorizations:
1. Write the prime factorization of each number.
2. Pick one of the prime factorizations and include it in the LCM.
3. Finish the LCM by including whatever prime numbers are not already included from the other numbers.

Example 3: For each set of numbers given, use prime factorizations to find the LCM.

a) 14 and 18   b) 54 and 30   c) 6, 8, and 11

Solution:
a) 14 and 18

Begin by writing the prime factorization for each number.

$14 = 2 \cdot 7$
$18 = 2 \cdot 3 \cdot 3$

Find the LCM:
- Pick one of the prime factorizations and include it in the LCM.
- Finish the LCM by including whatever prime numbers are not already included from the other numbers.

$LCM = \underbrace{2 \cdot 7}_{\substack{\text{begin with} \\ \text{the prime} \\ \text{factors of 14}}} \cdot \underbrace{3 \cdot 3}_{\substack{\text{For 18, the} \\ \text{prime factor} \\ \text{2 is already} \\ \text{included in} \\ \text{the LCM. These} \\ \text{are the prime} \\ \text{factors of} \\ \text{18 NOT already} \\ \text{included.}}} = 126$

The least common multiple for 14 and 18 is 126.

b) 54 and 30

Begin by writing the prime factorization for each number.

$54 = 2 \cdot 3 \cdot 3 \cdot 3$
$30 = 2 \cdot 3 \cdot 5$

Find the LCM:
- Pick one of the prime factorizations and include it in the LCM.
- Finish the LCM by including whatever prime numbers are not already included from the other numbers.

$LCM = \underbrace{2 \cdot 3 \cdot 3 \cdot 3}_{\substack{\text{Begin with the} \\ \text{prime factors} \\ \text{of 54}}} \cdot \underbrace{5}_{\substack{\text{5 is the} \\ \text{only prime} \\ \text{factor of 30} \\ \text{not already} \\ \text{included}}} = 210$

The least common multiple for 54 and 39 is 210.

c) 6, 8, and 11

Begin by writing the prime factorization for each number.

$6 = 2 \cdot 3$
$8 = 2 \cdot 2 \cdot 2$
$11 = 1 \cdot 11$

Find the LCM:
- Pick one of the prime factorizations and include it in the LCM.
- Finish the LCM by including whatever prime numbers are not already included from the other numbers.

$LCM = \underbrace{2 \cdot 3}_{\substack{\text{begin with} \\ \text{the prime} \\ \text{factors of 6}}} \cdot \underbrace{2 \cdot 2}_{\substack{\text{these are} \\ \text{the prime} \\ \text{factors of} \\ \text{8 not already} \\ \text{included}}} \cdot \underbrace{11}_{\substack{\text{11 must} \\ \text{be included} \\ \text{as well}}} = 264$

The Least Common Multiple for 6, 8 and 11 is 264.

We can use prime factorizations to find the least common multiple of expressions that contain a variable.

Example 4: Find the LCM for 15 and $6x$.

Solution: Let's use the same approach as in the last example.

Begin by writing the prime factorization for each number.

$$15 = 3 \cdot 5$$
$$6x = 2 \cdot 3 \cdot x$$

Find the LCM:
- Pick one of the prime factorizations and include it in the LCM.
- Finish the LCM by including whatever prime numbers are not already included from the other numbers.

$$LCM = \underbrace{3 \cdot 5}_{\substack{\text{Begin with} \\ \text{the prime} \\ \text{factorization} \\ \text{for 15}}} \cdot \underbrace{2 \cdot x}_{\substack{\text{2 and x} \\ \text{are the} \\ \text{factors of} \\ \text{6x not} \\ \text{already listed.}}} = 30x$$

The least common multiple for 15 and $6x$ is $30x$.

STOP **Exercise Set - LCM of Integers And Algebraic Expressions**

1.   List the first three multiples that 3 and 6 have in common.
2.   List the first three multiples that 4 and 6 have in common.
3.   List the first three multiples that 5 and 9 have in common.
4.   List the first three multiples that 4 and 8 have in common.

In each problem, use lists to find the least common multiple of the numbers given.

5.   6 and 18
6.   4 and 9

7.   12 and 15
8.   10 and 16

For each set of numbers given, use prime factorizations to find the LCM.

9.   12 and 18
10. 36 and 27

11. $3x^2y$ and $7xy$
12. $5a^3b$ and $15ab^2$

Building Up Fractions

Recall that we simplify fractions using the fundamental principle of fractions:

A factor common to the numerator and denominator of a fraction can be removed to give an equivalent fraction.

$$\frac{a \cdot c}{b \cdot c} = \frac{a}{b}$$

The same principle can be used to build up fractions, that is, to write them with a larger numerator and denominator.

A common factor can be multiplied into the numerator and denominator of a fraction to give an equivalent fraction.

$$\frac{a}{b} = \frac{a \cdot c}{b \cdot c}$$

For example, think of all the ways to express "one-half".

$$\frac{1}{2} \qquad \frac{1}{2} = \frac{1 \cdot 3}{2 \cdot 3} = \frac{3}{6} \qquad \frac{1}{2} = \frac{1 \cdot 5}{2 \cdot 5} = \frac{5}{10} \qquad \frac{1}{2} = \frac{1 \cdot 13}{2 \cdot 13} = \frac{13}{26}$$

[PN: can we have pictures to accompany each fraction: 1/2, 3/6, 5/10, 13/26]

The key is that to get an equivalent fraction we must multiply both the numerator and denominator by the same value. The justification for why this works is simple.

$$\frac{1}{2} = \frac{1}{2} \cdot 1 = \frac{1}{2} \cdot \frac{5}{5} = \frac{1 \cdot 5}{2 \cdot 5} = \frac{5}{10}$$

Multiplying the numerator and denominator of a fraction by the same number is equivalent to multiplying the fraction by the number 1, which does not change its value.

Example 5: Rewrite $\dfrac{5}{7}$ with a denominator of 21.

Solution: Remember, even though we want to change the denominator we must multiply the numerator as well to have an equivalent fraction.

To get a denominator of 21 we must multiply by 3 in the numerator and denominator.

$$\frac{5}{7} = \frac{5 \cdot 3}{7 \cdot 3} = \frac{15}{21}$$

Let's look at similar examples with larger numbers and a variable.

Example 6: Rewrite $-\dfrac{13}{17}$ with a denominator of 102.

Solution: Once again remember, even though we want to change the denominator we must multiply the numerator as well to have an equivalent fraction.

a) What should we multiply 17 by to get 102? Since 102/17=6, we should multiply by 6 in the numerator and denominator.

$$-\frac{13}{17} = -\frac{13 \cdot 6}{17 \cdot 6} = -\frac{78}{102}$$

Example 7: Rewrite $\dfrac{5}{6}$ with a denominator of $84x^2$.

What should we multiply 6 by to get 84? Since 84/6=14, we should multiply by 14 in the numerator and denominator. We also need to multiply in the numerator and denominator by the variable x twice to get x^2.

$$\frac{5}{6} = \frac{5 \cdot 14 \cdot x \cdot x}{6 \cdot 14 \cdot x \cdot x} == \frac{70x^2}{84x^2}$$

Good Question: What's the point in building up fractions? I thought the whole point was to simplify them.

Answer: We often have to build up fractions to add or subtract them. This process (presented in Section 4.5) is very challenging for many students. So we're using Section 4.4 to just look at the fundamentals involved. This next example is where things should really start to look familiar from work you have done in previous math classes.

Here is an example of building up two fractions so that they have the same denominator, which is what we will be a big focus in the rest of this section and the next section.

Example 8: Rewrite the fractions $\dfrac{7}{15}$ and $\dfrac{1}{9}$ so that they both have a common denominator of 45.

Solution:

To get a denominator of 45, we should multiply $\dfrac{7}{15}$ by $\dfrac{3}{3}$.

$$\frac{7}{15} = \frac{7 \cdot 3}{15 \cdot 3} = \frac{21}{45}$$

To get a denominator of 45, we should multiply $\dfrac{1}{9}$ by $\dfrac{5}{5}$.

$$\frac{1}{9} = \frac{1 \cdot 5}{9 \cdot 5} = \frac{5}{45}$$

STOP Exercise Set - Building Up Fractions

Rewrite each fraction as an equivalent fraction with the given denominator.

13. $\dfrac{1}{2}$, denominator 14

14. $\dfrac{2}{3}$, denominator 24

15. $\dfrac{4}{5}$, denominator 35

16. $\dfrac{1}{7}$, denominator 63

17. $\dfrac{7}{8}$, denominator 72

18. $\dfrac{3}{11}$, denominator 44

19. $\dfrac{12}{25x}$, denominator $50x^3$

20. $\dfrac{13a}{15b^2c}$, denominator $45b^3c$

21. Rewrite the fractions $\dfrac{5}{14}$ and $\dfrac{4}{21}$ so that they both have a common denominator of 42.

22. Rewrite the fractions $\dfrac{7}{12}$ and $\dfrac{21}{40}$ so that they both have a common denominator of 120.

LCD Of Two or More Fractions

As we have been exploring, to add or subtract two or more fractions they must have the same denominator. If the fractions have different (or unlike) denominators, we build them up so that the denominators are the same.

> The **least common denominator (LCD)** of two or more fractions is the least common multiple of their denominators.

Example 9: Find the least common denominator between $\dfrac{3}{14}$ and $\dfrac{10}{21}$. Then rewrite each fraction so that it has the LCD as the denominator.

Solution: The LCD for the fractions is just the LCM for the denominators. So we need to find the LCM between 14 and 21. We have two techniques to do this.

Using Lists of Multiples

Multiples of 14:
14, 28, 42, 54, ...
Multiples of 21:
21, 42, 63, 84, ...

The LCD is 42

Using Prime Factorizations:

$14 = 2*7$
$21 = 3*7$

$LCD = \underbrace{2 \cdot 7}_{\substack{\text{Here are} \\ \text{the factors} \\ \text{of 14.}}} \cdot \underbrace{3}_{\substack{\text{3 is the} \\ \text{only prime} \\ \text{factor of} \\ \text{21 missing.}}} = 42$

The least common denominator between $\dfrac{3}{14}$ and $\dfrac{10}{21}$ is 42.

Now we rewrite each fraction so that it has 42 as its denominator.

To get a denominator of 42, we should multiply $\dfrac{3}{14}$ by $\dfrac{3}{3}$.

$$\frac{3}{14} = \frac{3 \cdot 3}{14 \cdot 3} = \frac{9}{42}$$

To get a denominator of 42, we should multiply $\dfrac{10}{21}$ by $\dfrac{2}{2}$.

$$\frac{10}{21} = \frac{10 \cdot 2}{21 \cdot 2} = \frac{20}{42}$$

Example 10: Find the least denominator between $\dfrac{11}{25}$ and $\dfrac{8}{35b}$. Then rewrite each fraction so that it has the LCD as the denominator.

Solution: When a variable is included in the exercise, we should use prime factorizations to find the LCD.

Begin by writing the prime factorization for each number.

Find the LCM:
- Pick one of the prime factorizations and include it in the LCM.
- Finish the LCM by including whatever prime numbers are not already included from the other numbers.

$$LCD = \underbrace{5 \cdot 5}_{\substack{\text{Begin with} \\ \text{the prime} \\ \text{factors of 25}}} \cdot \underbrace{7 \cdot b}_{\substack{\text{These are} \\ \text{the factors} \\ \text{of 35b that} \\ \text{are not} \\ \text{already} \\ \text{included.}}} = 175b$$

The Least Common Denominator for $\dfrac{11}{25}$ and $\dfrac{8}{35b}$ is 175b.

Now we rewrite each fraction so that it has 175b as its denominator.

To get a denominator of 42, we should multiply $\dfrac{11}{25}$ by $\dfrac{7b}{7b}$.

$$\frac{11}{25} = \frac{11 \cdot 7b}{25 \cdot 7b} = \frac{77b}{175b}$$

To get a denominator of 42, we should multiply $\dfrac{8}{35b}$ by $\dfrac{5}{5}$.

$$\frac{8}{35b} = \frac{8 \cdot 5}{35b \cdot 5} = \frac{40}{175b}$$

Example 11: Find the least common denominator between $\dfrac{7}{9}$, $\dfrac{13}{24}$, and $\dfrac{1}{6}$. Then rewrite each fraction so that it has the LCD as the denominator. Let's find the LCD using prime factorization.

Solution:

Begin by writing the prime factorization for each number.

$$9 = 3 \cdot 3$$
$$24 = 2 \cdot 2 \cdot 2 \cdot 3$$
$$6 = 2 \cdot 3$$
$$LCD = \underbrace{3 \cdot 3} \cdot \underbrace{2 \cdot 2 \cdot 2} = 72$$

Find the LCM:

- Pick one of the prime factorizations and include it in the LCM.
- Finish the LCM by including whatever prime numbers are not already included from the other numbers.

Begin with the prime factors of 9

These are the prime factors of 24 not already included. Note that all the prime factors of 6 are already listed.

The LCD for $\dfrac{7}{9}$, $\dfrac{13}{24}$, and $\dfrac{1}{6}$ is 72.

Now we rewrite each fraction so that it has 72 as its denominator.

To get a denominator of 72, we should multiply $\dfrac{7}{9}$ by $\dfrac{8}{8}$.

$$\frac{7}{9} = \frac{7 \cdot 8}{9 \cdot 8} = \frac{56}{72}$$

To get a denominator of 72, we should multiply $\dfrac{13}{24}$ by $\dfrac{3}{3}$.

$$\frac{13}{24} = \frac{13 \cdot 3}{24 \cdot 3} = \frac{39}{72}$$

To get a denominator of 72, we should multiply $\dfrac{1}{6}$ by $\dfrac{12}{12}$.

$$\frac{1}{6} = \frac{1 \cdot 12}{6 \cdot 12} = \frac{12}{72}$$

STOP Exercise Set - LCD Of Two of More Fractions

Find the least common denominator between the given fractions. Then rewrite each fraction so that it has the LCD as the denominator.

23. $\dfrac{4}{15}$ and $\dfrac{1}{9}$

24. $\dfrac{13}{16}$ and $\dfrac{7}{24}$

25. $\dfrac{2}{5x}$ and $\dfrac{7}{15}$

26. $\dfrac{2}{3}$ and $\dfrac{7}{12y}$

27. $\dfrac{1}{3}$, $\dfrac{11}{12}$, and $\dfrac{13}{18}$

28. $\dfrac{5}{8}$, $\dfrac{15}{16}$, and $\dfrac{7}{20}$

Ordering Fractions

To use inequality symbols with fraction often requires rewriting them so they have a common denominator.

For example, it may not be obvious how the fractions $\dfrac{11}{14}$ and $\dfrac{7}{10}$ compare.

To compare two fractions with the inequality symbol like < or >:
- Build the fractions up to have a common denominator.
- Compare the numerators.

Example 12: Fill in the blank with the symbol <, >, or =.

$$\frac{11}{14} \underline{\quad} \frac{7}{10}$$

Solution: To compare fractions, rewrite them as fractions with the same denominator and compare the numerators.

Find the LCD for the fractions being compared. The LCM of 14 and 10 is 70, so the LCD for $\frac{11}{14}$ and $\frac{7}{10}$ is 70.

Rewrite each fraction with a denominator of 70.
- Multiply $\frac{11}{14}$ by $\frac{5}{5}$.

$$\frac{11}{14} = \frac{11 \cdot 5}{14 \cdot 5} = \frac{55}{70}$$

- Multiply $\frac{7}{10}$ by $\frac{7}{7}$

$$\frac{7}{10} = \frac{7 \cdot 7}{10 \cdot 7} = \frac{49}{70}$$

Now the fill in the blank can be rewritten this way:

$$\frac{11}{14} \underline{\quad} \frac{7}{10}$$
$$\downarrow \qquad \downarrow$$
$$\frac{55}{70} \underline{\quad} \frac{49}{70}$$

Now, compare the numerators. $\frac{55}{70}$ is greater than $\frac{49}{70}$.

$$\frac{55}{70} \underline{\quad} > \underline{\quad} \frac{49}{70}$$

The answer to the comparison is:

$$\frac{11}{14} \underline{\quad} > \underline{\quad} \frac{7}{10}$$

STOP Exercise Set - Ordering Fractions

In each case, fill in the blank with the symbol <, >, or =.

29. $\frac{5}{9} \underline{\quad} \frac{8}{21}$

30. $\frac{12}{15} \underline{\quad} \frac{19}{24}$

31. $\frac{5}{18} \underline{\quad} \frac{-17}{18}$

32. $\frac{-15}{26} \underline{\quad} \frac{7}{26}$

4.4 Exercise Set - Putting it ALL Together

Vocabulary Check: Fill in each blank with a word from our Vocabulary Checklist to the right. Each word is used exactly once.

Vocabulary Checklist:
multiple
least common multiple (LCM)
least common denominator (LCD)

33.   The _____ of two or more numbers is the smallest multiple the numbers have in common.

34.   If we multiply a number by all the natural numbers 1, 2, 3, 4, … then we are listing the _____ of that number.

35.   The smallest denominator that two or more fractions can have in common is called the _____ of the fractions.

36.   Find the least common multiple for 12 and 60.
37.   Find the least common multiple for 14 and 35.
38.   Find the least common multiple for 12 and 15.
39.   Find the least common multiple for 9 and 21.
40.   Find the least common multiple for 51 and $34x^2$.
41.   Find the least common multiple for $26a$ and $22b^2$.
42.   Find the least common multiple for 6, 7, and 8.
43.   Find the least common multiple for 12, 9, and 39.

Find the least common denominator between the given fractions. Then rewrite each fraction so that it has the LCD as the denominator.

44. $\dfrac{8}{11}$ and $\dfrac{3}{4}$

45. $\dfrac{3}{5}$ and $\dfrac{7}{12}$

46. $\dfrac{4}{7}$ and $\dfrac{8}{19}$

47. $\dfrac{11}{14}$ and $\dfrac{14}{15}$

48. $\dfrac{13}{36}$ and $\dfrac{29}{42}$

49. $\dfrac{33}{40}$ and $\dfrac{35}{56}$

50. $\dfrac{25}{42}$ and $\dfrac{37}{182}$

51. $\dfrac{12}{99}$ and $\dfrac{65}{121}$

52. $\dfrac{49}{306}$ and $\dfrac{27}{154}$

53. $\dfrac{15}{34}$ and $\dfrac{151}{306}$

54. $\dfrac{9}{16xy}$ and $\dfrac{35}{48x}$

55. $\dfrac{8}{11x}$ and $\dfrac{15}{33}$

56. $\dfrac{18}{19x}$ and $\dfrac{7}{8y}$

57. $\dfrac{101}{132a}$ and $\dfrac{31}{44y}$

58. $\dfrac{4}{5}, \dfrac{7}{12}$, and $\dfrac{17}{60}$

59. $\dfrac{1}{3}, \dfrac{7}{9}$, and $\dfrac{11}{18}$

60. $\dfrac{9}{14}, \dfrac{20}{77}$, and $\dfrac{79}{154}$

61. $\dfrac{1}{4}, \dfrac{30}{51}$, and $\dfrac{25}{68}$

62. $\dfrac{16}{35}, \dfrac{9}{22}$, and $\dfrac{67}{154}$

63. $\dfrac{15}{38}, \dfrac{34}{57}$, and $\dfrac{100}{133}$

Fill in each blank with <, > or = to make the statement true.

64. $\dfrac{5}{11}$ —— $\dfrac{2}{3}$

65. $\dfrac{2}{5}$ —— $\dfrac{14}{35}$

66. $\dfrac{1}{4}$ —— $\dfrac{1}{6}$

67. $\dfrac{7}{15}$ —— $\dfrac{11}{21}$

68. $\dfrac{13}{24}$ —— $\dfrac{27}{40}$

69.   In your own words, explain the difference between least common multiple (LCM) and least common denominator (LCD)

70.   In your own words, explain how to find the least common multiple of two or more numbers.

Exercise Set - Chapter 4 Review

71.   Divide if possible. $0 \div \dfrac{5x}{6}$

72.   Multiply. $5x \cdot \left(-\dfrac{1}{5x} \right)$

73.   Multiply. $\dfrac{33x}{14} \cdot \dfrac{7x}{22}$

74.   Which variable value would cause the expression $\dfrac{a}{b}$ to have an overall value of zero: $a = 0$ or $b = 0$?

75.   Add and simplify. $\dfrac{3}{14} + \dfrac{5}{14}$

Exercise Set - Cumulative Review

76.   Find the perimeter. [PN: rectangle with sides 15cm and 11cm]
77.   Is $x = 5$ a solution to the equation $3x - 7 = x + 3$?
78.   Fill in the blank with $<$ or $>$. $-14 \underline{} -8$
79.   Evaluate. $-32 \div (-8) \cdot 5$
80.   Evaluate $a - b$ for $a = -9$ and $b = -6$.

4.4 QUIZ YOURSELF

To make sure you are ready for the EXAM, try these problems without any help. Give yourself about 20 minutes and don't check the answers until you have completely finished.

1.   List the first three multiples that 18 and 15 have in common.
2.   Find the LCM of 78 and 52
3.   Find the LCM of $34x^4y^2$ and $6x^2y^2$

4.   Rewrite the fraction $\dfrac{14}{35}$ with 105 as the denominator.

Find the least common denominator between the given fractions. Then rewrite each fraction so that it has the LCD as the denominator.

5. $\dfrac{9}{65}$ and $\dfrac{15}{39}$ 8. $-\dfrac{19}{34} \underline{} -\dfrac{17}{38}$

6. $\dfrac{56}{77xy}$ and $\dfrac{25}{42y^2}$

7. $\dfrac{7}{8}, \dfrac{18}{25},$ and $\dfrac{27}{40}$

Answers to this Quiz Yourself are on page 671.

4.5 Adding And Subtracting Fractions

Topics:
- Adding and Subtracting Unlike Fractions
- Mixed Numbers
- Solving Equations

Are You Ready?
To see if you are ready to understand this section, do the following short quiz.

1. Subtract and simplify if possible. $\dfrac{13}{15} - \dfrac{2}{15}$

2. Add and simplify if possible. $\dfrac{11}{35} + \left(-\dfrac{16}{35}\right)$

3. Convert $-3\dfrac{2}{7}$ to an improper fraction.

4. Build up the fraction $\dfrac{3}{8}$ so that it has a denominator of 56.

Answers to Are You Ready?

(1) $\dfrac{4}{5}$ *(2)* $-\dfrac{1}{7}$ *(3)* $-\dfrac{23}{7}$ *(4)* $\dfrac{3}{8} = \dfrac{21}{56}$

Adding and Subtracting Unlike Fractions

We have already been working with adding and subtracting fractions.

Adding Fractions	Subtracting Fractions
$\dfrac{a}{b} + \dfrac{c}{b} = \dfrac{a+c}{b}$	$\dfrac{a}{b} - \dfrac{c}{b} = \dfrac{a-c}{b}$

We now turn to adding and subtracting fractions with different denominators.

Two or more fractions that have different denominators are called **unlike fractions**.

If two fractions have different denominators, one or both of the fractions must be built up so that the denominators are the same. We will explore to methods for this process. The first method relies on finding the LCD as side work.

Method #1 To Add or Subtract Fractions with Different Denominators: Finding the LCD

1. Identify the Least Common Denominator (LCD) of all the fractions involved.
2. Build up the fractions so that they all share the same denominator (the LCD).
3. Add as normal.
4. Simplify the final answer if possible.

Example 1: Subtract.

a) $\dfrac{11}{18} - \dfrac{5}{12}$

b) $\dfrac{13}{24} - \dfrac{15}{16}$

Solution: Let's take this first problem step by step.

a) $\dfrac{11}{18} - \dfrac{5}{12}$

1. Identify the Least Common Denominator (LCD) of all the fractions involved.	We can use either of the techniques from Section 4.4 the LCD for $\dfrac{11}{18}$ and $\dfrac{5}{12}$. Listing factors to find the LCD: 18, **36**, 54, 72, 80, … 12, 24, **36**, 48, 60, … Using Prime Factorizations to get the LCD: $18 = 3 \cdot 3 \cdot 2$ $12 = 2 \cdot 2 \cdot 3$ $LCD = 3 \cdot 3 \cdot 3 \cdot 2 = 36$ The LCD for $\dfrac{11}{18}$ and $\dfrac{5}{12}$ is 36.
2. Build up the fractions so that they all share the same denominator (the LCD)	$\dfrac{11}{18} - \dfrac{5}{12} = \dfrac{11 \cdot 2}{18 \cdot 2} - \dfrac{5 \cdot 3}{12 \cdot 3} = \dfrac{22}{36} - \dfrac{15}{36}$ Multiply the numerator and denominator by 2 to get the LCD 36 Multiply the numerator and denominator by 3 to get the LCD 36
3. Add as normal.	$\dfrac{22}{36} - \dfrac{15}{36} = \dfrac{22-15}{36} = \dfrac{7}{36}$
4. Simplify if possible.	$\dfrac{7}{36}$ is already in lowest terms.

b) $\dfrac{13}{24} - \dfrac{15}{16}$

1. Identify the Least Common Denominator (LCD) of all the fractions involved.	We can use either of the techniques from Section 4.4 the LCD for $\dfrac{13}{24}$ and $\dfrac{15}{16}$. Listing factors to find the LCD: 24, **48**, 72, 96, 120, … 16, 32, **48**, 64, 80, …

Using Prime Factorizations to get the LCD:

$24 = 2 \cdot 2 \cdot 2 \cdot 3$

$16 = 2 \cdot 2 \cdot 2 \cdot 2$

$LCD = 2 \cdot 2 \cdot 2 \cdot 3 \cdot 2 = 48$

The LCD for $\dfrac{13}{24}$ and $\dfrac{15}{16}$ is 48.

2. Build up the fractions so that they all share the same denominator (the LCD)

$$\dfrac{13}{24} - \dfrac{15}{16} = \dfrac{13 \cdot 2}{\underbrace{24 \cdot 2}} - \dfrac{15 \cdot 3}{\underbrace{16 \cdot 3}} = \dfrac{26}{48} - \dfrac{45}{48}$$

Multiply the numerator and denominator by 2 to get the LCD 48

Multiply the numerator and denominator by 3 to get the LCD 48

3. Add as normal.

$$\dfrac{26}{48} - \dfrac{45}{48} = \dfrac{26 - 45}{48} = \dfrac{-19}{48}$$

4. Simplify if possible.

$\dfrac{-19}{48}$ is already in lowest terms.

Here is an alternative approach to adding or subtracting unlike fractions. This method using prime factorizations to identify what extra factors each fraction's denominator needs.

Method #2 To Add or Subtract Fractions with Different Denominators: Using Prime Factorizations

1. Rewrite each denominator using its prime factorization.
2. Build up each fraction so that all the denominators have the same prime factorization.
3. Multiply the numerators and denominators back together.
4. Add or subtract as normal.
5. Simplify the final answer if possible.

Example 2: Add.

a) $\dfrac{4}{15} + \dfrac{10}{21}$ b) $\dfrac{5}{18} + \dfrac{9}{14}$

Solution: Let's take this example STEP by STEP.

a) $\dfrac{4}{15} + \dfrac{10}{21}$

1. Rewrite each denominator using its prime factorization.

$$\dfrac{4}{3 \cdot 5} + \dfrac{10}{7 \cdot 3}$$

2. Build up each fraction so that all the denominators have the same prime factorization.

For the denominators to be the same, the first denominator needs to be multiplied by 7. So we multiply it in the numerator AND denominator.

For the denominators to be the same, the second denominator needs to be multiplied by 5. So we multiply 5 in the numerator AND denominator.

$$\dfrac{7 \cdot 4}{7 \cdot 3 \cdot 5} + \dfrac{10 \cdot 5}{7 \cdot 3 \cdot 5}$$

3. Multiply the numerators and denominators back

$$\dfrac{7 \cdot 4}{7 \cdot 3 \cdot 5} + \dfrac{10 \cdot 5}{7 \cdot 3 \cdot 5} = \dfrac{28}{105} + \dfrac{50}{105}$$

together.

4. Add or Subtract as normal.

$$\frac{28}{105} + \frac{50}{105} = \frac{28+50}{105} = \frac{78}{105}$$

5. Simplify the final answer if possible.

Let's use prime factorizations to try and simplify: $\dfrac{78}{105} = \dfrac{2 \cdot \cancel{3} \cdot 13}{5 \cdot 7 \cdot \cancel{3}} = \dfrac{26}{35}$

Our final answer is $\dfrac{26}{35}$.

b) $\dfrac{5}{18} + \dfrac{9}{14}$

1. Rewrite each denominator using its prime factorization.

$$\frac{5}{2 \cdot 3 \cdot 3} + \frac{9}{2 \cdot 7}$$

2. Build up each fraction so that all the denominators have the same prime factorization.
    Multiply numerators and denominators of each fraction.

$$= \underbrace{\frac{5 \cdot 7}{2 \cdot 3 \cdot 3 \cdot 7}}_{\substack{\text{For the denominators to} \\ \text{be same, the first} \\ \text{denominator needs a} \\ \text{7, so we need to} \\ \text{multiply the numerator} \\ \text{and denominator by 7.}}} + \underbrace{\frac{9 \cdot 3 \cdot 3}{2 \cdot 7 \cdot 3 \cdot 3}}_{\substack{\text{For the denominators to} \\ \text{be same, the second} \\ \text{denominator needs a} \\ \text{3·3, so we need to} \\ \text{multiply the numerator} \\ \text{and denominator by 3·3.}}} = \frac{35}{126} + \frac{81}{126}$$

3. Add or Subtract as normal.

$$\frac{35}{126} + \frac{81}{126} = \frac{35+81}{126} = \frac{116}{126}$$

4. Simplify the final answer if possible.

Let's use prime factorizations to try and simplify:
$$\frac{116}{126} = \frac{\cancel{2} \cdot 2 \cdot 29}{\cancel{2} \cdot 7 \cdot 3 \cdot 3} = \frac{58}{63}$$

Our final answer is $\dfrac{58}{63}$.

Here is an example that shows the two methods side by side.

Example 3: Subtract $-\dfrac{11}{42}-\dfrac{15}{56}$.

Solution: The two different approaches are compared side by side. See which one you like best.

Method#1: Using the LCD

1. Identify the Least Common Denominator (LCD) of all the fractions involved.

The LCD for 42 and 56 is 168.

2. Build up the fractions so that they all share the same denominator (the LCD).

$$-\frac{11}{42}-\frac{15}{56}=-\frac{4\cdot 11}{4\cdot 42}-\frac{15\cdot 3}{56\cdot 3}$$

$$=-\frac{44}{168}-\frac{45}{168}$$

3. Add as normal.

$$-\frac{44}{168}-\frac{45}{168}=\frac{-44-45}{168}$$

$$=\frac{-99}{168}$$

$$=-\frac{99}{168}$$

4. Simplify the final answer if possible.

$$-\frac{99}{168}=\frac{-3\cdot\cancel{3}\cdot 11}{2\cdot 2\cdot 2\cdot\cancel{3}\cdot 7}=-\frac{33}{56}$$

Method #2: Using Prime Factorizations

1. Rewrite each denominator using its prime factorization.

$$-\frac{11}{42}-\frac{15}{56}=-\frac{11}{2\cdot 3\cdot 7}-\frac{15}{2\cdot 2\cdot 2\cdot 7}$$

2. Build up each fraction so that all the denominators have the same prime factorization.

$$=-\frac{2\cdot 2\cdot 11}{2\cdot 2\cdot 2\cdot 3\cdot 7}-\frac{3\cdot 15}{3\cdot 2\cdot 2\cdot 2\cdot 7}$$

3. Multiply the numerators and denominators back together.

$$=-\frac{44}{168}-\frac{45}{168}$$

4. Subtract as normal.

$$=\frac{-44-45}{168}=\frac{-99}{168}$$

5. Simplify the final answer if possible.

$$=\frac{-3\cdot\cancel{3}\cdot 11}{2\cdot 2\cdot 2\cdot\cancel{3}\cdot 7}=-\frac{33}{56}$$

Our final answer is $-\dfrac{33}{56}$.

Good Question: Looking at the example above Method #2 looks more complicated. Does it have any advantage?

Answer: With Method #2 you don't have to do any scratch work to find the LCD. Look at this series of steps...

$$-\frac{11}{42}-\frac{15}{56}=-\frac{11}{2\cdot 3\cdot 7}-\frac{15}{2\cdot 2\cdot 2\cdot 7}=-\frac{2\cdot 2\cdot 11}{2\cdot 2\cdot 2\cdot 3\cdot 7}-\frac{3\cdot 15}{3\cdot 2\cdot 2\cdot 2\cdot 7}$$

The method of using prime factorizations to find the LCD is built right into this step.

Good Question: So which method should I use?

Answer: Whichever one WORKS FOR YOU!

We can use the same techniques to add or subtract more than two fractions.

Example 4: Find $\dfrac{1}{3}+\dfrac{15}{22}-\dfrac{5}{6}$.

Solution:

Let's use Method #1: Using the LCD to go through this exercise.

1. Identify the Least Common Denominator (LCD) of all the fractions involved.

The LCD for $\dfrac{1}{3}$, $\dfrac{15}{22}$, and $\dfrac{5}{6}$ is 66.

2. Build up the fractions so that they all share the same denominator (the LCD).

$$\frac{1}{3}+\frac{15}{22}-\frac{5}{6}=\frac{22\cdot1}{22\cdot3}+\frac{3\cdot15}{3\cdot22}-\frac{11\cdot5}{11\cdot6}=\frac{22}{66}+\frac{45}{66}-\frac{55}{66}$$

3. Add as normal.

$$\frac{22}{66}+\frac{45}{66}-\frac{55}{66}==\frac{22+45-55}{66}=\frac{12}{66}$$

4. Simplify the final answer if possible.

$$\frac{12}{66}=\frac{\cancel{6}\cdot2}{\cancel{6}\cdot11}=\frac{2}{11}$$

The final answer is:

$$\frac{2}{11}$$

Example 5: Add $-\dfrac{11}{210}+\dfrac{45}{308}$.

Solution: For such large numbers, let's use Method #2: Using Prime Factorizations to go through this exercise.

1. Rewrite each denominator using its prime factorization.

$$-\frac{11}{210}+\frac{45}{154}=-\frac{11}{2\cdot3\cdot7\cdot5}+\frac{45}{2\cdot7\cdot11}$$

2. Build up each fraction so that all the denominators have the same prime factorization.

$$-\frac{11}{2\cdot3\cdot7\cdot5}+\frac{45}{2\cdot7\cdot11}=-\frac{11\cdot11}{11\cdot2\cdot3\cdot7\cdot5}+\frac{45\cdot3\cdot5}{2\cdot2\cdot7\cdot11\cdot3\cdot5}$$

3. Multiply the numerators and denominators back together.

$$-\frac{11\cdot11}{11\cdot2\cdot3\cdot7\cdot5}+\frac{45\cdot3\cdot5}{2\cdot2\cdot7\cdot11\cdot3\cdot5}=-\frac{121}{2310}+\frac{675}{2310}$$

4. Add or Subtract as normal.

$$-\frac{121}{2310}+\frac{675}{2310}=\frac{-121+675}{2310}=\frac{554}{2310}$$

5. Simplify the final answer if possible.

$$\frac{554}{2310}=\frac{\cancel{2}\cdot277}{\cancel{2}\cdot1155}=\frac{277}{1155}$$

Using tests for divisibility we see 277 is a prime number. Our final answer is:

$$\frac{277}{1155}$$

STOP Exercise Set - Adding and Subtracting Unlike Fractions

Add or Subtract. Simplify your answer if possible.

1. $\dfrac{1}{2}+\dfrac{2}{4}$

2. $\dfrac{7}{12}+\dfrac{2}{3}$

3. $\dfrac{5}{9}+\dfrac{2}{5}$

4. $\dfrac{15}{36}-\dfrac{2}{9}$

5. $\dfrac{-7}{18}-\dfrac{5}{24}$

6. $\dfrac{15}{21}-\dfrac{6}{14}$

7. $\dfrac{1}{2}+\dfrac{5}{34}-\dfrac{1}{4}$ 9. $-\dfrac{8}{117}+\dfrac{11}{45}$ 12. $\dfrac{5x}{12}+\dfrac{2x}{3}$

8. $\dfrac{3}{10}+\dfrac{5}{11}-\dfrac{7}{22}$ 10. $\dfrac{11}{44}-\dfrac{45}{77}$

11. $\dfrac{7a}{11}+\dfrac{3a}{4}$

Mixed Numbers

There are two ways to deal with adding and subtracting mixed numbers.

Method #1 To Add or Subtract Mixed Numbers: Convert the mixed numbers to improper fractions and add or subtract as normal.

Example 6: Add. Express your final answer as a mixed number.

a) $-3\dfrac{2}{7}+1\dfrac{3}{14}$ b) $5\dfrac{3}{4}+2\dfrac{7}{10}$

Solution:

a) $-3\dfrac{2}{7}+1\dfrac{3}{14}$

First, we convert each mixed number to an improper fraction.

$$-3\dfrac{2}{7}+1\dfrac{3}{14}=-\dfrac{23}{7}+\dfrac{17}{14}$$

Next we get a common denominator.

$$-\dfrac{23}{7}+\dfrac{17}{14}=-\dfrac{2\cdot 23}{2\cdot 7}+\dfrac{17}{14}=-\dfrac{46}{14}+\dfrac{17}{14}$$

Now we can add as normal.

$$-\dfrac{46}{14}+\dfrac{17}{14}=\dfrac{-46+17}{14}=\dfrac{-29}{14}$$

Simplify if possible.

$$-\dfrac{29}{14}\text{ is already in lowest terms.}$$

Finally, we convert our answer to a mixed number.

$$-\dfrac{29}{14}=-2\dfrac{1}{14}$$

b) $5\dfrac{3}{4}+2\dfrac{7}{10}$

First, we convert each mixed number to an improper fraction.

$$5\dfrac{3}{4}+2\dfrac{7}{10}=\dfrac{23}{4}+\dfrac{27}{10}$$

Next we get a common denominator.

$$\dfrac{23}{4}+\dfrac{27}{10}=-\dfrac{5\cdot 23}{5\cdot 4}+\dfrac{2\cdot 27}{2\cdot 10}=\dfrac{115}{20}+\dfrac{54}{20}$$

Now we can add as normal.

$$=\dfrac{115+54}{20}=\dfrac{169}{20}$$

Simplify if possible.

$$\dfrac{169}{20}\text{ is already in lowest terms.}$$

Finally, we convert our answer to a mixed number. $\dfrac{169}{20} = 8\dfrac{9}{20}$

Method #2 To Add or Subtract Mixed Numbers: Add or subtract the whole and fractional parts separately.

Example 7: Subtract.

a) $7\dfrac{4}{7} - 1\dfrac{4}{9}$ b) $-2\dfrac{5}{6} - 5\dfrac{7}{9}$

Solution: We can subtract the whole parts and fraction parts as long as we are careful.

a) $7\dfrac{4}{7} - 1\dfrac{4}{9}$

Whole Part:
$7 - 1$

$= 6$

Fraction Part:

Next we get a common denominator. $\dfrac{4}{7} - \dfrac{4}{9} = \dfrac{36}{63} - \dfrac{28}{63}$

Now we can add as normal. $\dfrac{36}{63} - \dfrac{28}{63} = \dfrac{8}{63}$

This means the result would be $6 + \dfrac{8}{63} = 6\dfrac{8}{63}$.

b) $-2\dfrac{5}{6} - 5\dfrac{7}{9}$

Whole Part:
$-2 - 5$

$= -7$

Fraction Part:

Next we get a common denominator. $-\dfrac{5}{6} - \dfrac{7}{9} = -\dfrac{15}{18} - \dfrac{14}{18}$

Now we can add as normal. $-\dfrac{15}{18} - \dfrac{14}{18} = \dfrac{-19}{18}$

Convert improper fraction to a mixed number. $\dfrac{-19}{18} = -1\dfrac{1}{18}$

This means the result would be $-7 - 1\dfrac{1}{18} = -8\dfrac{1}{18}$.

Let's look at one more example and show how each method would work. This example illustrates that each method has its advantages and disadvantages.

Example 8: Subtract $10\dfrac{3}{8} - 7\dfrac{7}{12}$.

Solution:

Method #1: Convert to Improper Fractions:

Convert mixed numbers to improper fractions.

$$10\frac{3}{8} - 7\frac{7}{12} = \frac{83}{8} - \frac{91}{12}$$

Find LCM and make equivalent fractions.

$$= \frac{3 \cdot 83}{3 \cdot 8} - \frac{91 \cdot 2}{12 \cdot 2}$$

$$= \frac{249}{24} - \frac{182}{24}$$

Now we can add as normal.

$$\frac{249}{24} - \frac{182}{24} = \frac{67}{24}$$

Convert improper fraction to a mixed number.

$$\frac{67}{24} = 2\frac{19}{24}$$

Our final answer is $2\frac{19}{24}$.

Method #2: Subtract the Whole and Fraction Parts:

Notice Subtracting the fractional parts results in a negative. To avoid this we rewrite the mixed number $10\frac{3}{8}$ as follows:

$$10\frac{3}{8} = 9 + 1 + \frac{3}{8} = 9 + \frac{8}{8} + \frac{3}{8} = 9\frac{11}{8}$$

Whole Part: $9 - 7$

$$= 2$$

Fraction Part: $\frac{11}{8} - \frac{7}{12}$

- Find LCM.
- Make equivalent fractions.

$$= \frac{3 \cdot 11}{3 \cdot 8} - \frac{7 \cdot 2}{12 \cdot 2}$$

$$= \frac{33}{24} - \frac{14}{24}$$

- Subtract as normal

$$= \frac{19}{24}$$

Now we add the whole part with the fraction part.

$$2 + \frac{19}{24}$$

$$= 2\frac{19}{24}$$

Our final answer is:

See how this example shows the advantages and disadvantages of each method? With Method #1 you don't have to learn any new "tricks", but you may have to work with larger numbers. With Method #2, you avoid larger numbers but have to learn how to deal with certain special cases.

STOP Exercise Set - Mixed Numbers

Add or Subtract. Simplify your answer if possible.

13. $3\frac{2}{9} + 8\frac{7}{9}$

14. $2\frac{2}{5} + 6\frac{1}{5}$

15. $19\frac{8}{11} - 7\frac{7}{11}$

16. $6\frac{3}{10} - \frac{18}{25}$

17. $\frac{22}{27} + 2\frac{5}{9}$

18. $1\frac{4}{5} + 3\frac{2}{3}$

19. $5\frac{5}{6} - 1\frac{2}{9}$

20. $-3\frac{1}{6} - 4\frac{3}{4}$

21. $-3\frac{3}{10} + 6\frac{1}{4}$

22. $9\frac{5}{12} - 10\frac{2}{3}$

Solving Equations

We can now solve equations that require adding and/or subtracting fractions. When working with equations that involve improper fractions, do not convert any improper fractions to mixed numbers until you have your final answer.

Example 9: Solve.

a) $x + \dfrac{2}{3} = \dfrac{7}{8}$ b) $x - \dfrac{5}{12} = \dfrac{11}{16}$

Solution: Just like other equations we've seen so far, we isolate the variable by adding or subtracting to both side.

a) $x + \dfrac{2}{3} = \dfrac{7}{8}$

Subtract $\dfrac{2}{3}$ to both sides.

$$x + \dfrac{2}{3} = \dfrac{7}{8}$$
$$\underline{-\dfrac{2}{3} \quad -\dfrac{2}{3}}$$
$$x \ = \dfrac{5}{24}$$

Note: $\dfrac{7}{8} - \dfrac{2}{3} = \dfrac{21}{24} - \dfrac{16}{24} = \dfrac{5}{24}$

Our final answer is $\dfrac{5}{24}$.

b) $x - \dfrac{5}{12} = \dfrac{11}{16}$

Add $\dfrac{5}{12}$ to both sides.

$$x - \dfrac{5}{12} = \dfrac{11}{16}$$
$$\underline{+\dfrac{5}{12} \quad +\dfrac{5}{12}}$$
$$x \ = \dfrac{53}{48}$$

Note: $\dfrac{11}{16} + \dfrac{5}{12} = \dfrac{33}{48} + \dfrac{20}{48} = \dfrac{53}{48}$

Convert the improper fraction to a mixed number.

$$\dfrac{53}{48} = 1\dfrac{5}{48}$$

Our final answer is $1\dfrac{5}{48}$.

We can now put the ideas on solving equations together. This next example will involve equations where we will have to use the addition/subtraction properties of equality and the multiplication/division properties of equality. Recall from chapter 3, that when solving multi-step equation, we add or subtract first and then multiply or divide to isolate the variable.

Example 10: Solve $\dfrac{1}{2}x - \dfrac{3}{5} = \dfrac{7}{10}$.

Solution: Just like other equations we've seen so far, we isolate the variable by adding to both sides and dividing on both sides.

Add $\dfrac{3}{5}$ to both sides.

$$\dfrac{1}{2}x - \dfrac{3}{5} = \dfrac{7}{10}$$

$$+\dfrac{3}{5} \quad +\dfrac{3}{5}$$

Note: $\dfrac{7}{10} + \dfrac{3}{5} = \dfrac{7}{10} + \dfrac{6}{10} = \dfrac{13}{10}$

$$\dfrac{1}{2}x = \dfrac{13}{10}$$

Multiply both sides by $\dfrac{2}{1}$ the reciprocal of $\dfrac{1}{2}$.

$$\dfrac{2}{1}\cdot\dfrac{1}{2}x = \dfrac{13}{10}\cdot\dfrac{2}{1}$$

$$x = \dfrac{26}{10}$$

Simplify by the common factor of 2.

$$x = \dfrac{26}{10} = \dfrac{13}{5}$$

Convert to a mixed number and our final answer is:

$$2\dfrac{3}{5}$$

Example 11: Where in the World? A landscaper is extending a retaining wall that already has $3\dfrac{1}{4}$ feet long. The blocks that he is using are $\dfrac{7}{8}$ feet long. How many must he use to extend the wall to a total of $8\dfrac{5}{16}$ feet.

Solution:

ASSIGN A VARIABLE	We are being asked to find the number of blocks he must use, so let x = amount of blocks used
SUMMARIZE THE INFORMATION	Already had $3\dfrac{1}{4}$ feet of wall. Blocks are $\dfrac{7}{8}$ feet long.
DO THE MATH	We use our summary to create an equation: original wall adding x increments of $\dfrac{7}{8}$ ft to get a total of $8\dfrac{5}{16}$ ft. $$3\dfrac{1}{4} + x\cdot\dfrac{7}{8} = 8\dfrac{5}{16}$$
Solve the equation: • Subtract $3\dfrac{1}{4}$ from both sides. • Aside: find the LCD and make equivalent fractions. • Subtract. • Multiply both sides by $\dfrac{8}{7}$.	$3\dfrac{1}{4} + x\cdot\dfrac{7}{8} = 8\dfrac{5}{16}$ Aside: $8\dfrac{5}{16} - 3\dfrac{1}{4} = 8\dfrac{5}{16} - 3\dfrac{4}{16}$ $\quad-3\dfrac{1}{4} \qquad -3\dfrac{1}{4}$ $x\cdot\dfrac{7}{8} = 5\dfrac{1}{16}$ $x\cdot\dfrac{7}{8}\cdot\dfrac{8}{7} = 5\dfrac{1}{16}\cdot\dfrac{8}{7}$

Recall that $\dfrac{7}{8} \cdot \dfrac{8}{7} = 1$	$x = \dfrac{81}{16} \cdot \dfrac{8}{7}$
• Convert mixed number to improper fraction. • Multiply. • Convert improper fraction to mixed number.	$x = \dfrac{81}{16} \cdot \dfrac{8}{7} = \dfrac{81}{14}$ $\dfrac{81}{14} = 5\dfrac{11}{14}$
ANSWER THE QUESTION	The landscaper must use $5\dfrac{11}{14}$ more blocks.

STOP Exercise Set - Solving Equations

Solve. Simplify your answer if possible.

23. $x + \dfrac{2}{3} = \dfrac{5}{3}$

24. $\dfrac{-7}{15} = t - \dfrac{8}{15}$

25. $h + \dfrac{7}{12} = \dfrac{-5}{12}$

26. $\dfrac{3}{11} = b - \dfrac{4}{11}$

27. $\dfrac{4}{9} + x = \dfrac{2}{9}$

28. $\dfrac{11}{24} = \dfrac{3}{8} + c$

29. $\dfrac{2}{5} + \dfrac{1}{2}h = \dfrac{1}{4}$

30. $\dfrac{3}{8} = \dfrac{2}{3}x - \dfrac{3}{4}$

31. $\dfrac{3}{7}a - \dfrac{2}{7} = \dfrac{-1}{3}$

32. $\dfrac{-3}{5} = \dfrac{1}{4}x + \dfrac{11}{15}$

Good Question: Can I always convert mixed numbers to improper fraction, so I don't have to remember any rules?

Answer: We can simplify each problem in two categories.

Addition/Subtraction: We have presented two different methods, one where you have to convert to improper and one where you do not have to. It is completely up to you on how you choose to work with this type of problem

Multiplication/Division: ALWAYS convert to improper fractions.

Good Question: Can I always convert to improper fractions?

Answer: ABSOLUTELY! However, sometimes it is easier to work with mixed numbers when adding/subtracting when dealing with big denominators.

4.5 Exercise Set - Putting it ALL Together

TRUE or FALSE

33. To add or subtract mixed numbers, we can leave as mixed numbers or convert them to improper fractions.

34. The LCD of two fractions is found by multiplying the denominators together.

35. $\dfrac{a}{b} + \dfrac{c}{b} = \dfrac{a+c}{b+b}$

36. Four sevenths plus two sevenths is six sevenths.

Perform each operation.

37. $\dfrac{3}{4} - \dfrac{1}{6}$

38. $\dfrac{2}{5} + \dfrac{3}{8}$

39. $\dfrac{5}{21} + \dfrac{6}{7}$

40. $\dfrac{4}{9} - \dfrac{11}{15}$

41. $15\dfrac{2}{3} + 22\dfrac{5}{6}$

42. $4\dfrac{1}{2} + 8\dfrac{5}{8}$

43. $\dfrac{5}{12} - \dfrac{5}{18}$

44. $\dfrac{7}{9} + \dfrac{6}{7}$

45. $-\dfrac{13}{24} + \dfrac{11}{30}$

46. $23\dfrac{5}{36} - 8\dfrac{18}{45}$

47. $\dfrac{8}{11} - \dfrac{2}{5}$

48. $4\dfrac{2}{9} + 11\dfrac{4}{9}$

49. $\dfrac{26}{45} - \dfrac{2}{5}$

50. $18\dfrac{5}{7} - 10\dfrac{3}{11}$

51. $\dfrac{2}{21} + \dfrac{3}{14}$

52. $\dfrac{33}{75} - \dfrac{7}{30}$

53. $\dfrac{-3}{8} + \dfrac{1}{4}$

54. $\dfrac{5x}{11} + \dfrac{3x}{11}$

55. $\dfrac{5a}{6} - \dfrac{3a}{6}$

56. $\dfrac{5}{16r} + \dfrac{3}{16r}$

57. $\dfrac{8b}{15} + \dfrac{2b}{3}$

58. $\dfrac{4n}{26} - \dfrac{7n}{39}$

59. $\dfrac{1}{6m} - \dfrac{5}{12m}$

60. $\dfrac{x}{6} + \dfrac{4}{15x}$

61. Find the sum of $\dfrac{t}{15}$ and $\dfrac{3}{10}$.

62. Find the sum of $\dfrac{5}{21x}$ and $\dfrac{x}{14}$.

63. Subtract $6\dfrac{2}{3}$ from $4\dfrac{1}{5}$.

64. Subtract $\dfrac{2x}{18}$ from $\dfrac{1}{12}$.

Solve.

65. $p + \dfrac{5}{21} = \dfrac{-3}{7}$

66. $k - \dfrac{3}{10} = \dfrac{9}{25}$

67. $\dfrac{6}{11} = \dfrac{6}{7}x - \left(\dfrac{-5}{9}\right)$

68. $\dfrac{4}{15} = \dfrac{1}{3}x + \dfrac{-19}{30}$

69. $\dfrac{1}{2}x - \dfrac{3}{5} = \dfrac{1}{3}$

70.   A seamstress is making a dress and needs $1\frac{5}{8}$ yards of material for the bodice and $2\frac{2}{5}$ yards of material. How much total material is needed for the dress?

71.   Versel is making curtains for Dave and Martha. She needs $11\frac{4}{9}$ yards of material for the drape and $5\frac{3}{4}$ yards of material for the cornice. How much material does Versel need to buy?

72.   Pavel is building a bike shop and needs two boards that are $4\frac{7}{12}$ ft. long and $7\frac{3}{8}$ ft. long. If he plans to buy one board and cut it in two pieces, how long should the board be?

73.   Hondo needs to cut a piece of pipe that is $13\frac{7}{16}$ ft. long so that he has a piece that is $8\frac{1}{3}$ ft. long. How much pipe does he have left?

74.   Wayne is building a picture frame that will be $13\frac{2}{5}$ in. wide by $21\frac{1}{2}$ in. long. How many inches of wood does he need?   [PN: show picture]

75.   Javier is using 4 x 4 boards to enclose a triangular vegetable garden. The sides of the garden are $15\frac{4}{9}$ ft., $14\frac{1}{4}$ ft., and $20\frac{5}{6}$ ft. How many feet of board does he need? [PN: show a picture of the garden]

76.   Find the total length of the guitar.
[PN: tuning board - $6\frac{1}{2}$ ", neck - $14\frac{3}{8}$ ", body - $19\frac{7}{8}$ "]

77.   An oil drum contains $18\frac{4}{15}$ gallons of oil. If $5\frac{2}{3}$ gallons are taken out, how much oil is left over?

In music, the notes used represent a fraction of one measure. To create a measure the notes must add up to one.

78.   Do the following notes make up one full measure?
[PN: half plus eighth plus eight]
79.   Do the following notes make up one full measure?
[PN: fourth plus sixteenth plus sixteenth]
80.   Do the following notes make up one full measure?
[PN: fourth plus half plus fourth]
81.   Do the following notes make up one full measure?
[PN: eighth plus eight plus fourth plus half plus sixteenth]

Rolling Stone Magazine surveyed a group of people to see how many hours a week the average person spends enjoying various forms of entertainment. The results are below. Answer the questions that follow. *Source: Rolling Stone Magazine*

Entertainment	Hours
Listening to Music	$11\frac{1}{2}$
Watching TV	$7\frac{9}{10}$
Social Networking	$4\frac{2}{5}$
Reading	3
Playing Video Games	$2\frac{4}{5}$

82. How many hours per week does the average person spend on Music and TV combined?
83. How many hours per week does the average person spend on Reading and Playing Video Games combined?
84. How many hours per week does the average person spend on Social Networking and Music combined?
85. How many hours per week does the average person spend on all the forms of entertainment combined?
86. How much more time do people spend watching TV than on on social networking?
87. How much more time do people spend on reading than playing video games?

The following table shows about what fraction of the Earth's land is taken up by each continent. Answer the questions that follow. *Source: www.answers.com*
[PN: I would like this to be a pie chart question]

Continent	Fraction of Earth's Land
Asia	$\frac{3}{10}$
Africa	$\frac{1}{5}$
North America	$\frac{4}{25}$
South America	$\frac{3}{25}$
Antarctica	$\frac{1}{10}$
Europe	$\frac{3}{50}$
Australia	$\frac{1}{20}$

88. What fraction of Earth's land taken up by North and South America combined?
89. What fraction of Earth's land taken up by Asia and Europe combined?
90. How much more of Earth's is taken up by Asia than North America?
91. How much more of Earth's is taken up by Europe than Australia?

Exercise Set - Chapter 4 Review

92. Solve. $\dfrac{3}{4} = \dfrac{3}{11}x$

93. Multiply. $15x\left(\dfrac{3x}{25}\right)$

94. Convert $\dfrac{45}{11}$ to a mixed number.

95. Divide. $\dfrac{14d}{35} \div \dfrac{7d^2}{25}$

96. List the first six multiples of 9.

Exercise Set - Cumulative Review

97. Translate the phrase to an equation and solve.

"three times a number is the same as the number plus eight"

98. Is $t = -5$ a solution to the equation $4(t+7) = 2t$?

99. Graph the numbers 4, 17, 23, and 13 on a number line using a scale of 5.

100. Add. $-15 + 6 + (-14)$

101. Evaluate. $7 - 5(3 - 9)$

4.5 QUIZ YOURSELF

To make sure you are ready for the EXAM, try these problems without any help. Give yourself about 20 minutes and don't check the answers until you have completely finished.

1. $\dfrac{10}{27} - \dfrac{2}{9}$

2. $\dfrac{8}{11} + \dfrac{2}{4}$

3. $\dfrac{5c}{8} + \dfrac{7c}{12}$

4. $5\dfrac{2}{7} - 2\dfrac{6}{7}$

5. $2\dfrac{1}{3} + 3\dfrac{3}{4}$

6. $15\dfrac{3}{7} + 35$

7. $x - \dfrac{3}{5} = \dfrac{12}{15}$

8. $\dfrac{1}{6} = \dfrac{31}{54} + h$

9. Barbara is making an apron. She needs $\dfrac{4}{5}$ yd. for the bid of the apron and $2\dfrac{1}{2}$ yards for the skirt. How much material does she buy total?

10. Gloria is putting a chair rail in her rectangular dinning room. The room measures $12\dfrac{1}{4}$ ft. by $16\dfrac{5}{8}$ ft. How many feet of char rail does she need?

Answers to this Quiz Yourself are on page 671.

4.6 Order Of Operations And Fractions

Topics:

- Exponents and Fractions
- Order Of Operations With Fractions
- Area for Triangles and Trapezoids
- Complex Fractions

Are You Ready?

To see if you are ready to understand this section, do the following short quiz.

1. Rewrite $(-5)^4$ in expanded form.

2. Rewrite $6 \cdot 6 \cdot 6 \cdot (-3)(-3)$ using exponents.

3. Simplify. -3^4

4. Use the order of operations to find $(3-5)^2 + 7(-2)$.

Answers to Are You Ready?

(1) $(-5) \cdot (-5) \cdot (-5) \cdot (-5)$ *(2)* $6^3 \cdot (-3)^2$ *(3)* -81 *(4)* -10

Exponents and Fractions

Recall that exponents are shorthand notation for repeated multiplication. Exponents can also used for fractions.

$$\underset{\text{This is called}\atop\text{exponential form.}}{\left(\frac{a}{b}\right)^{n}} = \overbrace{\frac{a}{b} \cdot \frac{a}{b} \cdots \frac{a}{b} \cdot \frac{a}{b}}^{n \text{ times}}$$

base → exponent ; This is called expanded form.

Examples of Fractions with Exponents

$$\left(\frac{2}{5}\right)^4 = \frac{2}{5} \cdot \frac{2}{5} \cdot \frac{2}{5} \cdot \frac{2}{5} \qquad\qquad \left(\frac{3x}{4y}\right)^2 = \frac{3x}{4y} \cdot \frac{3x}{4y}$$

It is important when writing exponential form you put the fraction base in parentheses. Otherwise, the exponent only applies to the numerator.

$$\left(\frac{3}{4}\right)^5 = \frac{3}{4} \cdot \frac{3}{4} \cdot \frac{3}{4} \cdot \frac{3}{4} \cdot \frac{3}{4} \text{ but } \frac{3^5}{4} = \frac{3 \cdot 3 \cdot 3 \cdot 3 \cdot 3}{4}$$

Example 1: Rewrite each expression in exponential form. Do not evaluate.

a) $\dfrac{11}{15} \cdot \dfrac{11}{15} \cdot \dfrac{11}{15} \cdot \dfrac{11}{15} \cdot \dfrac{11}{15}$ b) $4 \cdot 4 \cdot 4 \cdot \left(-\dfrac{6}{7}\right) \cdot \left(-\dfrac{6}{7}\right)$

Solution:

a) $\dfrac{11}{15} \cdot \dfrac{11}{15} \cdot \dfrac{11}{15} \cdot \dfrac{11}{15} \cdot \dfrac{11}{15} = \left(\dfrac{11}{15}\right)^5$

b) $4 \cdot 4 \cdot 4 \cdot \left(-\dfrac{6}{7}\right) \cdot \left(-\dfrac{6}{7}\right) = 4^3 \cdot \left(-\dfrac{6}{7}\right)^2$

Example 2: Rewrite each expression in expanded form. Do not evaluate.

a) $\left(-\dfrac{9}{13}\right)^2$ c) $\left(-\dfrac{2}{3}\right)^2 \cdot 5^4 \cdot \left(\dfrac{4}{7}\right)^3$

Solution:

a) $\left(-\dfrac{9}{13}\right)^2 = \left(-\dfrac{9}{13}\right)\left(-\dfrac{9}{13}\right)$

c) $\left(-\dfrac{2}{3}\right)^2 \cdot 5^4 \cdot \left(\dfrac{4}{7}\right)^3 = \left(-\dfrac{2}{3}\right)\left(-\dfrac{2}{3}\right) \cdot 5 \cdot 5 \cdot 5 \cdot 5 \cdot \left(\dfrac{4}{7}\right)\left(\dfrac{4}{7}\right)\left(\dfrac{4}{7}\right)$

Example 3: Evaluate each expression.

a) $\left(-\dfrac{2}{3}\right)^3$ b) $4^2 \cdot \left(\dfrac{1}{2}\right)^4$

Solution: In each case, we follow these steps:

a) Rewrite the expression in expanded form. $\left(-\dfrac{2}{3}\right)^3 = \left(-\dfrac{2}{3}\right) \cdot \left(-\dfrac{2}{3}\right) \cdot \left(-\dfrac{2}{3}\right)$

Write the multiplication as a single fraction. $\dfrac{(-2) \cdot (-2) \cdot (-2)}{3 \cdot 3 \cdot 3}$

Look for common factors to simplify.   This expression does not simplify.

Multiply to get the final answer. $\dfrac{-8}{27}$

b) Rewrite the expression in expanded form. $4^2 \cdot \left(\dfrac{1}{2}\right)^4 = 4 \cdot 4 \cdot \left(\dfrac{1}{2}\right)\left(\dfrac{1}{2}\right)\left(\dfrac{1}{2}\right)\left(\dfrac{1}{2}\right)$

Write the multiplication as a single fraction. $= \dfrac{4 \cdot 4 \cdot 1 \cdot 1 \cdot 1 \cdot 1}{2 \cdot 2 \cdot 2 \cdot 2}$

Look for common factors to simplify. $$= \frac{\overline{4} \cdot \overline{4} \cdot 1 \cdot 1 \cdot 1 \cdot 1}{\overline{2} \cdot \overline{2} \cdot \overline{2} \cdot \overline{2}}$$

Multiply to get the final answer. $$= 1$$

Finally, the parentheses we use are very important when a fraction is the base of an exponent. A fraction raised to a power must be in parentheses.

$$\left(\frac{5}{7}\right)^3 = \frac{5}{7} \cdot \frac{5}{7} \cdot \frac{5}{7} \text{ but } \frac{5^3}{7} = \frac{5 \cdot 5 \cdot 5}{7}$$

Example 4: Evaluate $\left(\dfrac{3}{4}\right)^2$ and $\dfrac{3^2}{4}$.

$$\left(\frac{3}{4}\right)^2 = \frac{3}{4} \cdot \frac{3}{4} = \frac{9}{16} \text{ and } \frac{3^2}{4} = \frac{3 \cdot 3}{4} = \frac{9}{4}$$

STOP Exercise Set - Exponents and Fractions

Rewrite each expression in exponent form. Do not evaluate.

1. $\dfrac{1}{2} \cdot \dfrac{1}{2} \cdot \dfrac{1}{2} \cdot \dfrac{1}{2}$

2. $\dfrac{-2}{3} \cdot \dfrac{-2}{3} \cdot \dfrac{-2}{3}$

3. $\dfrac{-4}{5} \cdot \dfrac{-4}{5} \cdot \dfrac{-4}{5} \cdot \dfrac{-4}{5} \cdot \dfrac{-4}{5}$

4. $-\dfrac{3}{7} \cdot \dfrac{3}{7} \cdot \dfrac{3}{7} \cdot \dfrac{3}{7} \cdot \dfrac{3}{7} \cdot \dfrac{3}{7} \cdot \dfrac{3}{7}$

Rewrite each expression in expanded form. Do not evaluate.

5. $\left(\dfrac{2}{3}\right)^2$

6. $\left(\dfrac{-4}{5}\right)^4$

7. $\left(\dfrac{-1}{2}\right)^5$

8. $-\left(\dfrac{2}{7}\right)^8$

Evaluate each expression.

9. $\left(\dfrac{1}{2}\right)^4$ 10. $\left(\dfrac{-3}{5}\right)^3$ 11. $-\left(\dfrac{-2}{3}\right)^4$ 12. $\left(\dfrac{2x}{7y}\right)^2$

13. Evaluate $\left(\dfrac{2}{3}\right)^3$ and $\dfrac{2^3}{3}$

14. Evaluate $\left(\dfrac{4}{7}\right)^2$ and $\dfrac{4^3}{7}$

Succeed in Math!   I want to improve, but I can't do ALL this stuff.

Practice Tests

Study Group

Learning Styles

Office Hours

Tutor Center

Math XL

Notecards

Highlighters

NOBODY does ALL this. You do whatever WORKS for YOU. Just pick what sounds good and try it. If it doesn't work, try something else.

Order Of Operations With Fractions

The order of operations is the same for fractions as for integers or whole numbers:
- Work inside grouping symbols such as parentheses first.
- Perform any exponents in the expression.
- Do multiplication and division moving left to right.
- Do addition and subtraction from left to right.

Example 5: Use the order of operations to evaluate each expression.

a) $\dfrac{2}{3} - \dfrac{5}{6} \cdot \dfrac{3}{10}$

b) $\left(\dfrac{5}{12} - \dfrac{11}{18}\right) \div \dfrac{5}{6}$

c) $\left(\dfrac{1}{3} + \dfrac{3}{4}\right)^2 - 2\dfrac{1}{12}$

Order of Operations
• **P**arentheses (grouping symbols)
• **E**xponents
• **M**ultiplication and **D**ivision
• **A**ddition and **S**ubtraction

Solution: We have summarized the order of operations to the right as a guide for these examples.

a) $\dfrac{2}{3} - \dfrac{5}{6} \cdot \dfrac{3}{10}$

Multiply first.
Simplify by the common factors 3 and 5.

$$\dfrac{2}{3} - \dfrac{5}{6} \cdot \dfrac{3}{10} = \dfrac{2}{3} - \dfrac{\overline{5}}{2 \cdot \overline{3}} \cdot \dfrac{\overline{3}}{2 \cdot \overline{5}} = \dfrac{2}{3} - \dfrac{1}{4}$$

Now subtract.
- Find the LCD and make equivalent fractions.

$$= \dfrac{2}{3} \cdot \dfrac{4}{4} - \dfrac{1}{4} \cdot \dfrac{3}{3} = \dfrac{8}{12} - \dfrac{3}{12}$$

- Subtract.

$$= \dfrac{5}{12}$$

The final answer is:

$$\dfrac{5}{12}$$

b) $\left(\dfrac{5}{12} - \dfrac{11}{18}\right) \div \dfrac{5}{6}$

Since the subtraction is inside parentheses we subtract first.
- Find the LCD and make equivalent fractions.

$$\left(\dfrac{5}{12} - \dfrac{11}{18}\right) \div \dfrac{5}{6}$$

$$= \left(\dfrac{5}{12} \cdot \dfrac{3}{3} - \dfrac{11}{18} \cdot \dfrac{2}{2}\right) \div \dfrac{5}{6} = \left(\dfrac{15}{36} - \dfrac{22}{36}\right) \div \dfrac{5}{6}$$

- Subtract.

$$= \left(-\dfrac{7}{36}\right) \div \dfrac{5}{6}$$

Now divide.
- Multiply by the reciprocal.

$$\left(-\frac{7}{36}\right) \div \frac{5}{6} = \left(-\frac{7}{36}\right) \cdot \frac{6}{5}$$

- Simplify by the common factor of 6.

$$= -\frac{7}{30}$$

The final answer is:

$$-\frac{7}{30}$$

c) $\left(\frac{1}{3}+\frac{3}{4}\right)^2 - 2\frac{1}{12}$

First we add inside the parentheses.

$$\left(\frac{1}{3}+\frac{3}{4}\right)^2 - 2\frac{1}{12}$$

- Find a common denominator.

$$\left(\frac{4}{12}+\frac{9}{12}\right)^2 - 2\frac{1}{12}$$

$$= \left(\frac{13}{12}\right)^2 - 2\frac{1}{12}$$

- Add.

Now we apply the exponent.
- Rewrite in expanded form.

$$= \frac{13}{12} \cdot \frac{13}{12} - 2\frac{1}{12}$$

$$= \frac{169}{144} - 2\frac{1}{12}$$

- Multiply.

Finally we add.
- Find a common denominator.

$$= \frac{169}{144} - \frac{25}{12} \cdot \frac{12}{12} = \frac{169}{144} - \frac{300}{144}$$

- Make single fraction and subtract

$$= \frac{169-300}{144} = \frac{-131}{144}$$

Our final answer is $-\frac{131}{144}$.

Example 6: Infinity's End is an art and poster shop that specializes in custom framing. A customer comes in to have an art piece framed that is $10\frac{3}{4}$ inches by $16\frac{5}{8}$ inches. What is the perimeter of the artwork?

Courtesy of Fotolia

Solution:
SUMMARIZE THE INFORMATION
Since we are framing a picture, we can use the perimeter formula for a rectangular.

$$P = 2w + 2l$$

DO THE MATH
Now substitute the values into this formula, where the length is $10\frac{3}{4}$ and the width is $16\frac{5}{8}$.

$$P = 2\left(10\frac{3}{4}\right) + 2\left(16\frac{5}{8}\right)$$

Now we simplify the expression by using order of operations.

Convert mixed numbers to improper fractions.

$$P = 2\left(\frac{43}{4}\right) + 2\left(\frac{128}{8}\right)$$

Rewrite the whole numbers as fractions.

$$= \frac{2}{1} \cdot \left(\frac{43}{4}\right) + \frac{2}{1} \cdot \left(\frac{128}{8}\right)$$

Reduce by dividing out any common factors in each fraction and multiply.

$$= \frac{43}{2} + \frac{128}{4}$$

Add.
- Find LCD and make equivalent fractions.

$$= \frac{43}{2} \cdot \frac{2}{2} + \frac{128}{4} = \frac{86}{4} + \frac{128}{4}$$

- Add

$$= \frac{214}{4}$$

Reduce and convert to a mixed number.

$$= \frac{107}{2} = 53\frac{1}{2}$$

ANSWER THE QUESTION

The perimeter of the artwork is $53\frac{1}{2}$ inches or $53\frac{1}{2} in$.

 Exercise Set - Order Of Operations With Fractions

Use the order of operations to evaluate each expression.

15. $\dfrac{2}{5} \cdot \dfrac{3}{4} - \dfrac{7}{10}$

16. $\dfrac{9}{10} \div \dfrac{3}{5} \cdot \dfrac{1}{2}$

17. $\dfrac{3}{7} + \dfrac{1}{2} - \dfrac{3}{14}$

18. $\dfrac{2}{5} + \dfrac{8}{15} \div \dfrac{1}{10}$

Evaluate the following expressions.

19. $\dfrac{25}{48} \div \dfrac{5}{12} \cdot \dfrac{4}{15}$

20. $\dfrac{22}{35} \cdot \dfrac{3}{4} \div \dfrac{33}{70}$

21. $\dfrac{5}{6} \cdot \dfrac{3}{4} - \left(\dfrac{1}{3}\right)^2$

22. $\left(\dfrac{1}{2}\right)^2 \cdot \dfrac{4}{5} - \dfrac{13}{20}$

23. $x + 2y - xy$; $x = \dfrac{8}{9}, y = \dfrac{9}{10}$

24. $x^2 + y^2$; $x = \dfrac{3}{4}, y = \dfrac{2}{3}$

25. $a + b - c$; $a = \dfrac{5}{6}, b = \dfrac{7}{12}, c = \dfrac{11}{14}$

26. $x - y \cdot z$; $x = 2\dfrac{8}{21}, y = \dfrac{5}{7}, z = \dfrac{1}{6}$

Area of Triangles and Trapezoids

Understanding how the order of operations is used with fractions allows us to explore area formulas for triangles and trapezoids.

To find the Area of a Triangle: Multiply $\frac{1}{2}$ times the *base* times the *height*.

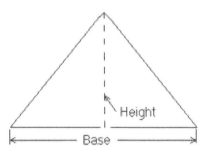

$$\text{Area} = \frac{1}{2} \cdot \text{base} \cdot \text{height}$$

$$A = \frac{1}{2}bh$$

Example 7: Find the area.

Solution: We use the formula $A = \frac{1}{2}bh$.

$$A = \frac{1}{2}bh = \frac{1}{2} \cdot 4 \cdot 3\frac{2}{5} = \frac{1}{2} \cdot \frac{4}{1} \cdot \frac{17}{5} = \frac{4 \cdot 17}{2 \cdot 5} = \frac{34}{5} = 6\frac{4}{5}$$

So the area is $6\frac{4}{5}$ square inches or $6\frac{4}{5}in^2$.

To find the Area of a Trapezoid: Multiply $\frac{1}{2}$ times the sum of the *bases*.

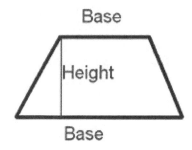

Base

Height

Base

$$\text{Area} = \frac{1}{2} \cdot \text{height} \cdot (\text{upper base} + \text{lower base})$$

$$A = \frac{1}{2} h (B + b)$$

Example 8: Where in the World? A brick mason is asked to cover a patio shaped like a trapezoid. The patio is pictured to the left. How many square feet does the patio cover?

[PN: the patio has bases of 40 and 24 feet and a height of $7\frac{1}{2}$]

Solution: We use the formula $A = \frac{1}{2} h (B + b)$.

$$A = \frac{1}{2} h (B + b) = \frac{1}{2} \cdot 7\frac{1}{2} \cdot (40 + 24) = \frac{1}{2} \cdot \frac{15}{2} \cdot (64) = \frac{1}{2} \cdot \frac{15}{2} \cdot \frac{64}{1} = 240$$

So the patio covers 240 square feet or $240\ ft^2$

Exercise Set - Area for Triangles and Trapezoids

Find the area of each figure.

27. [PN: triangle with base 5ft height 7]

28. [PN: triangle with base 14cm height 13]

29. [PN: triangle with base $\frac{2}{5}$ in height $\frac{3}{14}$]

30. [PN: triangle with base $2\frac{1}{2}$ yd height $1\frac{3}{4}$]

31. [PN: trapezoid with bases 5m and 8 height 4]

32. [PN: trapezoid with bases 11ft and 20 height 5]

33. [PN: trapezoid with bases $\frac{1}{7}$ in and $\frac{7}{14}$ height $\frac{1}{2}$]

34. [PN: trapezoid with bases $3\frac{1}{3}$ yd and $2\frac{1}{5}$ height $2\frac{3}{4}$]

35. A family is considering having their shake siding replaced with stucco. The contractor must find the total area of the walls. Find the area of the triangular area to the right. [PN: base $6\frac{3}{4}$ feet height $5\frac{1}{8}$ feet]

36. A business is having their parking lot repaved. Find the total area of the lot. [PN: lot has bases $13\frac{4}{5}$ yards and $20\frac{1}{2}$ yards height $8\frac{4}{7}$ yards]

Complex Fractions

Recall that a fraction bar can represent division. Because of this, it is common in math to have a fraction bar separate two fractions. This type of fraction is called a *complex fraction*.

A **complex fraction** is a fraction that has fraction(s) in the numerator and/or denominator.

Here are some examples of complex fractions.

$$\text{numerator} \rightarrow \left. \begin{cases} \dfrac{4}{7} \\ 5\dfrac{1}{2} \end{cases} \right. \leftarrow \text{denomintor} \qquad \text{numerator} \rightarrow \left. \begin{cases} \dfrac{1}{2} \\ \dfrac{3}{5} \end{cases} \right. \leftarrow \text{denomintor} \qquad \text{numerator} \rightarrow \left. \begin{cases} 5 \\ -\dfrac{2}{3} \end{cases} \right. \leftarrow \text{denomintor}$$

Complex fractions are easy to handle if you just remember that a fraction bar can be interpreted as division. That is,

Rewrite the complex fraction as a division problem.	$\dfrac{\frac{4}{7}}{5\frac{1}{2}} = \dfrac{4}{7} \div 5\frac{1}{2}$
Rewrite the mixed number as an improper fraction.	$= \dfrac{4}{7} \div \dfrac{11}{2}$
Rewrite the division problem as multiplication.	$= \dfrac{4}{7} \cdot \dfrac{2}{11}$
Multiply and the final answer is $\dfrac{8}{77}$.	

Example 9: Simplify each complex fraction.

a) $\dfrac{-\frac{3}{14}}{\frac{10}{21}}$

b) $\dfrac{8}{\frac{5}{9}}$

Solution:

a)

Rewrite the complex fraction as a division problem.	$\dfrac{-\dfrac{3}{14}}{\dfrac{10}{21}} = -\dfrac{3}{14} \div \dfrac{10}{21}$
Rewrite the division problem as multiplication.	$= -\dfrac{3}{14} \cdot \dfrac{21}{10}$
Rewrite the product as a single fraction and prime factor the numerator and denominator.	$= \dfrac{3 \cdot 3 \cdot 7}{2 \cdot 7 \cdot 2 \cdot 5}$
Reduce, there are common factors of 2 and 7 in the numerator and denominator.	$= \dfrac{3 \cdot 3 \cdot \overline{7}}{2 \cdot \overline{7} \cdot 2 \cdot 5}$
Multiply.	$= \dfrac{9}{20}$
The final answer is $\dfrac{9}{20}$.	

b)

Rewrite the complex fraction as a division problem.	$\dfrac{8}{\dfrac{5}{9}} = 8 \div \dfrac{5}{9}$
Rewrite the whole number as a fraction.	$= \dfrac{8}{1} \div \dfrac{5}{9}$
Rewrite the division problem as multiplication.	$= \dfrac{8}{1} \cdot \dfrac{9}{5}$
Rewrite the product as a single fraction and prime factor the numerator and denominator.	$= \dfrac{2 \cdot 2 \cdot 2 \cdot 3 \cdot 3}{1 \cdot 5}$
Multiply, since there are no common factors.	$= \dfrac{72}{5}$
Rewrite the improper fraction as a mixed number.	$= 14\dfrac{2}{5}$

STOP Exercise Set - Complex Fractions

Simplify each complex fraction.

37. $\dfrac{\frac{3}{4}}{\frac{2}{5}}$

38. $\dfrac{\frac{1}{6}}{\frac{2}{7}}$

39. $\dfrac{\frac{4}{15}}{3}$

40. $\dfrac{\frac{14}{7}}{12}$

41. $\dfrac{2\frac{1}{2}}{-\frac{5}{11}}$

42. $\dfrac{4\frac{1}{5}}{28}$

43. $\dfrac{16}{-5\frac{1}{3}}$

44. $\dfrac{11\frac{1}{2}}{4\frac{1}{7}}$

45. $\dfrac{-1\frac{5}{9}}{-4\frac{3}{4}}$

4.6 Exercise Set - Putting it ALL Together

TRUE or FALSE

46. I use PEMDAS to help with order of operations. That means I always multiply before I divide.

47. $\dfrac{a^n}{b} = \underbrace{\dfrac{a}{b} \cdot \dfrac{a}{b} \cdots \dfrac{a}{b}}_{n \ times}$

48. In the expression $\dfrac{4}{7} - \dfrac{1}{2}\left(\dfrac{3}{16} + \dfrac{1}{3}\right)$ addition is the first operation to perform.

Simplify using order of operations.

49. $\left(\dfrac{4}{9}\right)^2$

50. $\left(\dfrac{-1}{5}\right)^3$

51. $\dfrac{2^3}{5}$

52. $-\left(\dfrac{1}{5}\right)^3$

53. $\left(\dfrac{x}{3}\right)^2$

54. $\left(\dfrac{y}{4}\right)^3$

55. $\dfrac{5}{12} - \dfrac{2}{7} \div \dfrac{3}{14}$

56. $\dfrac{3}{25} \cdot \left(\dfrac{-5}{12}\right) \div \dfrac{5}{8}$

57. $\dfrac{7}{25} + \dfrac{-9}{20} \div \dfrac{7}{15}$

58. $\left(\dfrac{1}{2}\right)^3 + \dfrac{7}{8}$

59. $\left(\dfrac{-2}{3}\right)^2 + \dfrac{1}{4}$

60. $\left(\dfrac{2}{5}\right)^3 \cdot \left(-\dfrac{3}{8}\right)$

61. $\left(-\dfrac{1}{2}\right)^4 \div \dfrac{-5}{6}$

62. $\dfrac{-4}{5} \cdot \dfrac{3}{8} + \dfrac{3}{4}$

63. $\dfrac{2}{3} + \dfrac{1}{4} - \dfrac{5}{6}$

64. $\dfrac{-2x}{21} + \dfrac{5x^2}{7y} \cdot \dfrac{14}{15x}$

65. $\dfrac{4x}{15} \div \left(\dfrac{1}{3} + \dfrac{7}{12}\right)$

66. $\left(\dfrac{4}{5} - \dfrac{7}{15}\right) \cdot \left(-\dfrac{3y}{7x}\right)$

Evaluate the following expressions and simplify.

67. $\dfrac{2}{5}x - 4$, $x = 5$

68. $-2x + \dfrac{1}{7}$, $x = \dfrac{3}{4}$

69. $2x + 3y$; $x = \dfrac{1}{2}, y = \dfrac{2}{3}$

70. $-4x + 6y$; $x = \dfrac{3}{4}, y = \dfrac{-1}{2}$

71. $xy + 3x$; $x = \dfrac{5}{6}, y = -\dfrac{1}{3}$

72. $ab^2 + c$; $a = \dfrac{4}{5}, b = \dfrac{1}{2}, c = \dfrac{7}{10}$

73. $x^2 - y^2$; $x = \dfrac{5}{6}, y = \dfrac{1}{3}$

74. $x^2 + y^2$, $x = -\dfrac{3}{4}, y = \dfrac{2}{5}$

75. $b^2 - 4ac$; $a = \dfrac{-1}{2}, b = \dfrac{5}{6}, c = -3$

76. $b^2 - 4ac$; $a = \dfrac{2}{3}, b = \dfrac{3}{4}, c = \dfrac{1}{2}$

77. $mx + b$; $m = -\dfrac{1}{3}, x = 6, b = -\dfrac{5}{12}$

78. $mx + b$; $m = \dfrac{2}{3}, x = -2, b = \dfrac{5}{9}$

79. Dave is enclosing a flower bed with two types of stones. One stone is $\dfrac{5}{6}$ ft. wide and the other one is $\dfrac{5}{8}$ ft. wide. If he is alternating the stones and he uses a total of 12 stones (6 each), how wide is his flower bed?

80. Chad is tiling his bathroom floor. He uses 22 tiles that measure $1\dfrac{3}{8}\, ft^2$ for the center of the floor and 35 tiles that measure $\dfrac{7}{16}\, ft^2$ to border the floor. What is the total area of Chad's bathroom?

81. The Ruby-Throated Hummingbird is the only hummingbird that nests east of the Mississippi River. The wingspan of four hummingbirds are: $8\dfrac{2}{3}$ cm., $9\dfrac{12}{15}$ cm., $10\dfrac{1}{4}$ cm., and $9\dfrac{3}{5}$ cm. Find the average wingspan.

82. The California Condor is the largest flying land bird in North America. The wingspan of three Condors are: $9\dfrac{5}{12}$ ft., $10\dfrac{3}{4}$ ft., and $11\dfrac{1}{6}$ ft.

83. Find the area of a triangle with base $6\dfrac{1}{4}$ cm. and height $3\dfrac{1}{5}$.

84. A triangle has a base of $12\dfrac{2}{3}$ m. and a height of $8\dfrac{1}{4}$ m. Find the area of the triangle.

85. A trapezoid has base measures of $7\dfrac{1}{4}$ in. and $5\dfrac{1}{3}$ in. and a height of $2\dfrac{4}{5}$ in. Find the area of the trapezoid.

86. A trapezoid has base measures of $8\dfrac{1}{2}$ yd. and $4\dfrac{5}{6}$ yd. and a height of $3\dfrac{3}{5}$ yd. Find the area of the trapezoid.

87. Explain the differenced between $\left(\dfrac{a}{b}\right)^3$ and $\dfrac{a^3}{b}$.

88. Explain in your own words what a complex fraction is.

Exercise Set - Chapter 4 Review

89. Add. $\dfrac{7}{10}+\dfrac{3}{25}$

90. Graph $-\dfrac{1}{2}, \dfrac{3}{4},$ and $2\dfrac{4}{7}$ on a number line.

91. Divide. $12 \div 2\dfrac{5}{6}$

92. Build up the fractions so they have a least common denominator. $\dfrac{1}{6}, \dfrac{3}{4}, \dfrac{5}{7}$

93. Solve. $d+\dfrac{3}{4}=-\dfrac{1}{4}$

Exercise Set - Cumulative Review

94. Of the following numbers, which represent integers? $\left\{\dfrac{1}{2}, 6, -9, 4\dfrac{3}{7}, 0, \dfrac{5}{2}\right\}$

95. Solve. $-43 = m + 22$

96. Subtract. $5,624 - (-987)$

97. Find the area. [PN: rectangle 12ft by 14 feet]

98. Find the prime factorization of 72.

4.6 QUIZ YOURSELF

To make sure you are ready for the EXAM, try these problems without any help. Give yourself about 20 minutes and don't check the answers until you have completely finished.

1. $\left(\dfrac{2}{5}\right)^3$

2. $\left(\dfrac{-2xy^2}{3}\right)^4$

3. $\dfrac{9}{15}+1\dfrac{2}{3}\cdot\dfrac{6}{25}$

4. $\dfrac{3}{8}\div 3\dfrac{7}{12}\cdot(-6)$

5. $\left(\dfrac{1}{3}\right)^3\cdot\dfrac{3}{8}$

6. b^2-4ac ; $a=\dfrac{2}{3}, b=\dfrac{2}{3}, c=\dfrac{8}{15}$

7. Find the area of the following figure.

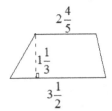

$2\dfrac{4}{5}$

$1\dfrac{1}{3}$

$3\dfrac{1}{2}$

Answers to this Quiz Yourself are on page 671.

Chapter 4 Summary_____

Section 4.1: More Fraction Fundamentals

Processes and Important Notes	Examples
Reviewing the Basics: • **Add/Subtract with common denominator:** Add/subtract numerator, keep denominator. Reduce if possible. • **Multiply:** Multiply numerators, multiply denominators. Reduce if possible. • **Divide:** Multiply by the reciprocal of the second fraction. **Be Careful!** Remember not to change the denominator. The denominator tells us the number of parts it takes to make a whole!	**Multiply.** $\dfrac{27}{55} \cdot \dfrac{22}{45}$ **Solution:** $$\dfrac{27}{55} \cdot \dfrac{22}{45} = \dfrac{27 \cdot 22}{55 \cdot 45} = \dfrac{3 \cdot 9 \cdot 2 \cdot 11}{5 \cdot 11 \cdot 5 \cdot 9} = \dfrac{3 \cdot 2}{5 \cdot 5}$$ $$= \dfrac{6}{25}$$ **Divide.** $\dfrac{7}{24} \div \dfrac{21}{32}$ **Solution:** $$\dfrac{7}{24} \div \dfrac{21}{32} = \dfrac{7}{24} \cdot \dfrac{32}{21} = \dfrac{7 \cdot 2 \cdot 2 \cdot 2 \cdot 2 \cdot 2}{2 \cdot 2 \cdot 2 \cdot 3 \cdot 3 \cdot 7} = \dfrac{2 \cdot 2}{3 \cdot 3}$$ $$= \dfrac{4}{9}$$
Proper Fractions, Improper Fractions and Mixed Numbers: • If the numerator of a fraction is less than the denominator then the fraction is called a **proper fraction**. • If the numerator of a fraction is larger than the denominator then the fraction is called an **improper fraction**. • A **mixed number** involves a whole part and a fraction. • Fractions that include variables are called **algebraic fractions** or **rational expressions**. **Remark:** A fraction that involves a variable should never be written as a mixed number.	**Proper Fractions** $\dfrac{1}{2}, \dfrac{4}{5}, \dfrac{89}{132}, \dfrac{-23}{45}$ **Improper Fractions** $\dfrac{7}{3}, \dfrac{-18}{7}, \dfrac{56}{-3}, \dfrac{917}{36}$ **Mixed Numbers** $2\dfrac{4}{5}, 16\dfrac{9}{11}, -71\dfrac{1}{18}$ **Algebraic Fractions** $\dfrac{-5x}{16}, \dfrac{17x^2 y^3}{28z^5}, -\dfrac{a^3 b^4}{3cd^3 e}$
Fractions that involve 1 or 0: From any non-zero integer a: $\dfrac{0}{a} = 0$ $\qquad$ $\dfrac{a}{0}$ is undefined $\dfrac{a}{1} = a$ $\qquad$ $\dfrac{a}{a} = 1$	**Simplify.** (a) $\dfrac{3}{3}$ $\quad$ (b) $\dfrac{5}{0}$ $\quad$ (c) $\dfrac{0}{-8}$ **Solution:** (a) $\dfrac{3}{3} = 1$ (b) $\dfrac{5}{0}$ is undefined (c) $\dfrac{0}{-8} = 0$

Graphing Fractions and Mixed Numbers:	Graph $3\frac{2}{5}$ on a number line.
• Use the whole part to locate the number on the graph. If the whole part is 0, then the number is between 0 and 1. • Use the denominator to divide each whole up into equal parts. Use the numerator to plot the point.	**Solution:** 1. Start at 3 on the number line. 2. Divide the section between 3 and 4 into 5 equal parts since the denominator is 5. 3. From 3, go over 2 tick marks since the numerator is 2. The number plotted is $3\frac{2}{5}$. [PN. Plot this]

Convert to an improper fraction:

1. $7\frac{3}{4}$
2. $-3\frac{2}{9}$
3. $-8\frac{1}{5}$
4. $11\frac{3}{7}$

Convert to a mixed number:

5. $\frac{23}{4}$
6. $\frac{77}{9}$
7. $\frac{-82}{5}$
8. $\frac{-75}{6}$

Perform the indicated operation:

9. $-\frac{27}{66}$

10. $\frac{56b^3c^2}{84bc^2}$

11. $\frac{17}{24}-\frac{3}{24}$

12. $\frac{4}{25}+\frac{-19}{20}$

13. $\frac{-8a}{27}-\left(\frac{-5a}{27}\right)$

14. $\frac{-9x}{14}-\frac{3x}{14}$

15. $\frac{-14b^2}{15}\div\frac{49ab}{27a^3}$

Section 4.2: Multiplying Fractions

Processes and Important Notes	Examples
Understanding Fraction Multiplication: • Draw a picture of the second fraction using a rectangle. • Use denominator of the first fraction to draw horizontal lines and shade the numerator of fraction being multiplied to get product.	**Use a picture to multiple** $\frac{2}{3}\cdot\frac{3}{4}$ **Solution:** [PN: 1. draw $\frac{3}{4}$ using a box with 4 vertical parts and 3 shaded 2. Use the drawing above and draw 3 horizontal parts and 2 shaded 3. Use a darker color to emphasize the overlap which is the product]
Multiplying Fractions: • With fractions that involve larger numbers, we rewrite the product as a single fraction then reduce before multiplying the numbers together. • To reduce a fraction that involves variables with exponents, use expanded form.	**Multiply.** $\frac{6x^2}{35y}\cdot\frac{15xy^3}{21x^4}$ **Solution:** $\frac{6x^2}{35y}\cdot\frac{15xy^3}{21x^4}=\frac{6x^2\cdot15xy^3}{35y\cdot21x^4}=\frac{2\cdot3\cdot x\cdot x\cdot3\cdot3\cdot x\cdot y\cdot y\cdot y}{5\cdot7\cdot y\cdot3\cdot7\cdot x\cdot x\cdot x\cdot x}$ $=\frac{18y^2}{145x}$
Multiplying Mixed Numbers: • To multiply mixed numbers you must change them to *improper fractions* first.	**Multiply.** $-5\frac{3}{4}\cdot8\frac{2}{5}$

	Solution:
• Recall that the **reciprocal** of $\dfrac{a}{b}$ is $\dfrac{b}{a}$. • Sometimes we can multiply both sides of an equation by a reciprocal to isolate a variable.	$-5\dfrac{5}{11}\cdot 4\dfrac{2}{5}=\dfrac{-60}{11}\cdot\dfrac{22}{5}=\dfrac{-5\cdot 12}{11}\cdot\dfrac{2\cdot 11}{5}$ $=-24$
Solving Equations: • To isolate the variable, make sure you multiply both sides by the **reciprocal of the coefficient** attached to the variable. The variable may be on either side of the equation.	Solve. $\dfrac{3}{8}x=-\dfrac{4}{5}$ Solution: $\dfrac{8}{3}\cdot\dfrac{3}{8}x=-\dfrac{4}{5}\cdot\dfrac{8}{3}$ $x=\dfrac{-32}{15}=-2\dfrac{2}{15}$

Multiply.

16. $\dfrac{7}{12}\cdot 2\dfrac{2}{5}$

17. $-3\dfrac{1}{5}\cdot 1\dfrac{1}{4}$

18. $2\dfrac{3}{4}\cdot\left(-3\dfrac{3}{11}\right)$

19. $4\dfrac{2}{9}\cdot(-6)$

20. $\dfrac{21a}{45}\cdot\dfrac{-18}{35b}$

21. $\dfrac{22}{51x}\cdot\dfrac{17x^3}{33}$

Solve.

22. $\dfrac{x}{6}=\dfrac{-4}{5}$

23. $\dfrac{y}{12}=\dfrac{-35}{36}$

24. $\dfrac{2}{7}x=-\dfrac{3}{14}$

25. $\dfrac{-14}{75}x=\dfrac{-2}{15}$

26. $\dfrac{3x}{22}=-3\dfrac{3}{4}$

27. $\dfrac{7a}{13}=-1\dfrac{9}{26}$

28. Summer and Josh drove for $3\dfrac{5}{8}$ hours at 56 miles per hour. How far did they drive?

29. Find the area of a rectangle with width $4\dfrac{1}{3}$ ft. and length $\dfrac{6}{7}$ ft.

Section 4.3: Dividing Fractions

Processes and Important Notes	Examples
Dividing Fractions: • To divide fractions, simply multiply by the reciprocal of the divisor. • Common variable factors can be reduced the same way as common numeric factors. CAUTION: Recall from Section 1.1 (page #) that $0\div b=0$ but $b\div 0$ is undefined.	**Divide.** $\dfrac{12x^4}{35y^2}\div\dfrac{24x^2}{21y^4}$ Solution: $\dfrac{12x^4}{35y^2}\div\dfrac{24x^2}{21y^4}=\dfrac{12x^4}{35y^2}\cdot\dfrac{21y^4}{24x^2}=\dfrac{12x^4\cdot 21y^4}{35y^2\cdot 24x^2}$ $=\dfrac{2\cdot 2\cdot 3\cdot x\cdot x\cdot x\cdot x\cdot 3\cdot 7\cdot y\cdot y\cdot y\cdot y}{5\cdot 7\cdot y\cdot y\cdot 2\cdot 2\cdot 2\cdot 3\cdot x\cdot x}$ $=\dfrac{x\cdot x\cdot 3\cdot y\cdot y}{5\cdot 2}=\dfrac{3x^2y^2}{10}$
Dividing Mixed Numbers: • As with fraction multiplication, mixed numbers must be converted to improper fractions before they are divided.	**Divide.** $7\dfrac{6}{7}\div\left(-1\dfrac{5}{6}\right)$ Solution:

$$7\frac{6}{7} \div \left(-1\frac{5}{6}\right) = \frac{55}{7} \div \left(\frac{-11}{6}\right) = \frac{55}{7} \cdot \frac{-6}{11} = \frac{5 \cdot 11}{7} \cdot \frac{-6}{11}$$

$$= \frac{5}{7} \cdot \frac{-6}{1} = \frac{-30}{7} = -4\frac{2}{7}$$

Use pictures to illustrate and answer each division problem.

30. $\dfrac{2}{3} \div \dfrac{1}{4}$

31. $\dfrac{7}{9} \div \dfrac{1}{2}$

32. $8 \div \dfrac{1}{3}$

Simplify or Solve.

33. $\dfrac{13a}{22} \div \dfrac{-26}{55}$

34. $\dfrac{28x}{27} \div \dfrac{42}{51x}$

35. $2\dfrac{1}{6} \div \left(-1\dfrac{1}{4}\right)$

36. $-3\dfrac{2}{5} \div 1\dfrac{3}{17}$

37. $\dfrac{12xy^2}{13y} \div \dfrac{6y}{7x^2y}$

38. $\dfrac{15a^3b}{19b} \div \dfrac{10a}{11b^2}$

39. $\dfrac{21a^2b^2}{24a} \div \left(-\dfrac{7b}{8ab}\right)$

40. $\left(-\dfrac{40xy^4}{49}\right) \div \left(-\dfrac{16y^2}{21xy}\right)$

Section 4.4: LCM And LCD

Processes and Important Notes	Examples
LCM of Integers and Algebraic Expressions: • The **multiples** of a number are the values we get from multiplying the number by the natural (counting) numbers. • The **least common multiple (or LCM)** of two or more integers is the smallest multiple they have in common.	Find the LCM of 5 and 12 by listing the multiples of each number. **Solution:** 5, 10, 15, 20, 25, 30, 35, 40, 45, 50, 55, 60 12, 24, 36, 48, 60 So, the LCM of 5 and 12 is 60. Find the LCM of 15, 24, and 27 by using the prime factorizations. **Solution:** $15 = 3 \cdot 5$, $24 = 2^3 \cdot 3$, $27 = 3^3$ LCM $= 2^3 \cdot 3^3 \cdot 5 = 1080$
Building Up Fractions: • A common factor can be multiplied into the numerator and denominator of a fraction to give an equivalent fraction. $\dfrac{a}{b} = \dfrac{a \cdot c}{b \cdot c}$	Write $\dfrac{7}{12}$ as an equivalent fraction with a denominator of 36. **Solution:** $\dfrac{7}{12} = \dfrac{?}{36} \qquad \dfrac{7 \cdot 3}{12 \cdot 3} = \dfrac{21}{36}$
LCD of Two or More Fractions: • The **least common denominator (LCD)** of two or more fractions is the least common multiple of their denominators.	Find the least common denominator between the given fractions. $\dfrac{3}{7}$ and $\dfrac{14}{15}$ **Solution:** Using prime factorization of the denominators: $7 = 7 \qquad 15 = 3 \cdot 5$ LCD $= 7 \cdot 3 \cdot 5 = 105$
Ordering Fractions: • **To compare two fractions with the inequality symbol like < or >:**	Fill in the blank with the symbol <, >, or =.

| a. Build the fractions up to have a common denominator.
b. Compare the numerators.

• Remember that < means "is less than" and > means "is greater than". | $\dfrac{3}{5} \,\rule{1cm}{0.4pt}\, \dfrac{5}{9}$

Solution:
a. $\dfrac{3}{5} \cdot \dfrac{9}{9} \,\rule{1cm}{0.4pt}\, \dfrac{5}{9} \cdot \dfrac{5}{5}$ or $\dfrac{27}{45} \,\rule{1cm}{0.4pt}\, \dfrac{25}{45}$

b. Since $27 > 25$ then $\dfrac{3}{5} \,\rule{0.6cm}{0.4pt}\, > \,\rule{0.6cm}{0.4pt}\, \dfrac{5}{9}$. |

Find the following.

41. Find the least common multiple for 12 and 16.
42. Find the least common multiple for 5, 21, and 14.

Find the least common denominator between the given fractions. Then rewrite each fraction so that it has the LCD as the denominator.

43. $\dfrac{5}{9}$ and $\dfrac{6}{7}$

44. $\dfrac{3}{11}$ and $\dfrac{7}{22}$

45. $\dfrac{8}{21}$ and $\dfrac{17}{40}$

46. $\dfrac{4x}{7}$ and $\dfrac{5}{8}$

47. $\dfrac{13}{18x}$ and $\dfrac{11y}{15}$

48. $\dfrac{9}{55}$ and $\dfrac{75}{132}$

49. $\dfrac{3}{5}, \dfrac{24}{39},$ and $\dfrac{57}{65}$

50. $\dfrac{9}{14}, \dfrac{34}{175},$ and $\dfrac{113}{250}$

In each case, fill in the blank with the symbol <, >, or =.

51. $\dfrac{5}{14} \,\rule{1cm}{0.4pt}\, \dfrac{3}{8}$

52. $\dfrac{-9}{17} \,\rule{1cm}{0.4pt}\, \dfrac{-5}{11}$

Section 4.5: Adding And Subtracting Fractions

Processes and Important Notes	Examples
Adding and Subtracting Unlike Fractions: • **To Add or Subtract Fractions with Different Denominators: Using Prime Factorizations** a. Rewrite each denominator using its prime factorization. b. Build up each fraction so that all the denominators have the same prime factorization. c. Multiply the numerators and denominators back together. d. Add or Subtract as normal. e. Reduce the final answer if possible.	Add. $\dfrac{5}{12} + \dfrac{8}{15}$ **Solution:** a. $\dfrac{5}{2 \cdot 2 \cdot 3} + \dfrac{8}{3 \cdot 5}$ b. $= \dfrac{5 \cdot 5}{2 \cdot 2 \cdot 3 \cdot 5} + \dfrac{8 \cdot 2 \cdot 2}{3 \cdot 5 \cdot 2 \cdot 2}$ c. $= \dfrac{25}{60} + \dfrac{32}{60}$ d. $= \dfrac{57}{60}$ e. Already in lowest terms.
Mixed Numbers: **To Add or Subtract Mixed Numbers:** a. Get a common denominator for the fractional part of the mixed numbers. b. Add or Subtract the whole parts, and the numerators of the fractional parts. c. Reduce the final answer if possible.	Add. $-1\dfrac{5}{14} + 4\dfrac{17}{35}$ **Solution:**

When working with equations that involve improper fractions, do not convert any improper fractions to mixed numbers until you have your final answer.	a. $4\dfrac{17}{35} = 4\dfrac{34}{70}$ $\dfrac{-1\dfrac{5}{14} = -1\dfrac{25}{70}}{}$ b. $\qquad 3\dfrac{9}{70}$ c. Already in lowest terms.
Solving Equations: • Use the Properties of Equality with Addition and Subtraction.	Solve. $x - \dfrac{13}{25} = \dfrac{-13}{15}$ **Solution:** $x - \dfrac{11}{34} = \dfrac{-5}{34}$ $\dfrac{+\dfrac{11}{34} \quad +\dfrac{11}{34}}{}$ $x = \dfrac{6}{34} = \dfrac{3}{17}$

Add or Subtract.

53. $\dfrac{8}{15} + \dfrac{5}{9}$

55. $\dfrac{-5}{24} - \left(-\dfrac{11}{16}\right)$

57. $\dfrac{-17}{39} + \left(-\dfrac{8}{15}\right)$

59. $4\dfrac{7}{12} + 13\dfrac{5}{9}$

54. $\dfrac{7}{10} + \left(-\dfrac{13}{25}\right)$

56. $\dfrac{-5}{12} - \dfrac{14}{15}$

58. $\dfrac{25}{156} - \dfrac{37}{144}$

60. $27\dfrac{3}{16} + \left(-6\dfrac{7}{12}\right)$

Solve.

61. $x + \dfrac{5}{9} = \dfrac{-3}{4}$

63. $2\dfrac{3}{5} - x = -4\dfrac{5}{8}$

62. $x - \dfrac{13}{20} = \dfrac{15}{36}$

64. $y + 22\dfrac{1}{3} = 17\dfrac{3}{4}$

Section 4.6: Order Of Operations And Fractions

Processes and Important Notes	Examples
Exponents and Fractions: Parentheses are important for when a fraction is the base of an exponent.	Write in expanded form. $\left(-\dfrac{1}{2}\right)^2 \cdot \left(\dfrac{3}{7}\right)^3$ **Solution:** $\left(-\dfrac{1}{2}\right)^2 \cdot \left(\dfrac{3}{7}\right)^3 = \left(-\dfrac{1}{2}\right)\left(-\dfrac{1}{2}\right)\left(\dfrac{3}{7}\right)\left(\dfrac{3}{7}\right)\left(\dfrac{3}{7}\right)$
Order of Operations with Fractions: **Order Of Operations:** ▪ Parenthesis(grouping symbols) ▪ Exponents ▪ Multiplication and Division Addition and Subtractions	Simplify. $\left(\dfrac{17}{24} - \dfrac{3}{8}\right)^2 + \dfrac{1}{6}$ **Solution:** $\left(\dfrac{17}{24} - \dfrac{3}{8}\right)^2 + \dfrac{1}{6} = \left(\dfrac{17}{24} - \dfrac{9}{24}\right)^2 + \dfrac{1}{6} = \left(\dfrac{8}{24}\right)^2 + \dfrac{1}{6}$

	$= \left(\dfrac{1}{3}\right)^2 + \dfrac{1}{6} = \dfrac{1}{9} + \dfrac{1}{6} = \dfrac{6}{54} + \dfrac{9}{54} = \dfrac{15}{54} = \dfrac{5}{18}$
	Simplify. $\dfrac{-2}{15} \div \dfrac{4}{9} + \dfrac{4}{5} \cdot \left(-\dfrac{1}{2}\right)^2$ **Solution:** $\dfrac{-2}{15} \div \dfrac{4}{9} + \dfrac{4}{5} \cdot \left(-\dfrac{1}{2}\right)^2 = \dfrac{-2}{15} \div \dfrac{4}{9} + \dfrac{4}{5} \cdot \dfrac{1}{4} = \dfrac{-2}{15} \div \dfrac{4}{9} + \dfrac{1}{5}$ $= \dfrac{-2}{15} \cdot \dfrac{9}{4} + \dfrac{1}{5} = \dfrac{-2}{3\cdot5} \cdot \dfrac{3\cdot3}{2\cdot2} + \dfrac{1}{5} = \dfrac{-3}{10} + \dfrac{1}{5} = \dfrac{-3}{10} + \dfrac{2}{10}$ $= \dfrac{-1}{10}$
Area for Triangles and Trapezoids: • **Triangle:** $\quad$ Area $= \dfrac{1}{2} \cdot$ base $\cdot$ height $\qquad A = \dfrac{1}{2}bh$ • **Trapezoid:** $\quad$ Area $= \dfrac{1}{2} \cdot$ height $\cdot$ (upper base + lower base) $\qquad A = \dfrac{1}{2}h(B+b)$	**Find the area of a trapezoid with bases 16 ft. and 22 ft. and a height of $4\dfrac{2}{3}$ ft.** **Solution:** $A = \dfrac{1}{2}h(B+b) = \dfrac{1}{2}\left(4\dfrac{2}{3}\right)(22+16)$ $= \dfrac{1}{2}\left(\dfrac{14}{3}\right)\left(\dfrac{38}{1}\right) = \dfrac{1}{\cancel{2}}\left(\dfrac{\cancel{2}\cdot7}{3}\right)\left(\dfrac{38}{1}\right) = \dfrac{266}{3}$ $A = 88\dfrac{2}{3}\ ft^2$
Complex Fractions: A **complex fraction** is a fraction that has fraction(s) in the numerator and/or denominator. Note: When simplifying a complex fraction, rewrite as the fraction numerator DIVIDED by the fraction denominator.	**Simplify.** $\dfrac{\dfrac{2}{5}}{-\dfrac{13}{18}}$ **Solution:** $\dfrac{5}{6} \div \dfrac{-13}{18} = \dfrac{5}{6} \cdot \dfrac{18}{-13} = \dfrac{5}{6} \cdot \dfrac{3\cdot6}{-13} = \dfrac{5}{1} \cdot \dfrac{3}{-13} = -\dfrac{15}{13}$ $= -1\dfrac{2}{13}$

Simplify.

65. $\left(-\dfrac{3}{5}\right)^2$

66. $\left(-\dfrac{1}{3}\right)^3$

67. $-5\cdot\left(-\dfrac{7}{10}\right)^2$

68. $\dfrac{9}{10} \div \left(\dfrac{4}{5}+\dfrac{1}{6}\right)$

69. $\dfrac{5}{6}\cdot\left(\dfrac{-4}{15}\right)+\dfrac{3}{12}$

70. $\dfrac{-7}{12} \div \dfrac{1}{8} + \left(\dfrac{1}{2}\right)^2$

Evaluate.

71. $mx+b$ for $b=4$, $m=\dfrac{1}{2}$, $x=-4$

72. b^2-4ac for $a=\dfrac{5}{6}$, $b=-\dfrac{2}{3}$, $c=\dfrac{1}{2}$

73. $a + b - c$; $a = \dfrac{5}{6}$, $b = \dfrac{7}{12}$, $c = \dfrac{11}{14}$

74. $x - y \cdot z$; $x = 2\dfrac{8}{21}$, $y = \dfrac{5}{7}$, $z = \dfrac{1}{6}$

75. Find the area of a trapezoid with height 7m and bases $4\dfrac{2}{5}$ m and $9\dfrac{1}{6}$ m.

76. A triangle has a base of $8\dfrac{2}{3}$ ft. and a height of $4\dfrac{5}{7}$ ft. Find the area of the triangle.

TEST YOURSELF
CHAPTER 4

You should give yourself about 90 minutes to complete these problems. DO NOT use notes, your book or any outside source of help, ONLY YOURSELF. Put question marks by the problems you are unsure about, but TRY all of the problems. Once your time is up, check your answers on page #.

1. Write $11\frac{4}{5}$ as an improper fraction.

2. Write $\frac{153}{7}$ as a mixed number.

3. Evaluate $b^2 - 4ac$ for $a = \frac{-7}{8}, b = \frac{1}{2}, c = -\frac{3}{14}$

4. Find the LCD of $\frac{33}{56x}$ and $\frac{5x}{24}$. Then rewrite the fractions so that each one has the LCD as its denominator.

5. Compare: $\frac{-16}{72}$ _____ $\frac{-7}{18}$

Perform the indicated operations:

6. $\frac{3}{5} + \frac{5}{9}$

7. $\left(\frac{-21}{26}\right)\left(\frac{-39}{50}\right)$

8. $\frac{7}{12} - \left(-\frac{2}{9}\right)$

9. $\frac{-1}{18} - \frac{3}{4}$

10. $\frac{8}{121} - \frac{91}{132}$

11. $\frac{24a^2b}{81a} \cdot \frac{18bc^3}{35abc}$

12. $\left(-\frac{1}{5}\right) \div \left(\frac{7}{10}\right)$

13. $\left(8\frac{2}{5}\right) \div \left(-\frac{14}{15}\right)$

14. $-5\frac{1}{4} + 3\frac{7}{8}$

15. $\left(\frac{-2}{5}\right)^2 + \frac{3}{10} \cdot \left(\frac{-8}{9}\right)$

16. $\frac{35}{48} \div \frac{5}{8} \cdot \left(\frac{-8}{15}\right)$

Solve.

17. $n + \frac{1}{9} = \frac{-3}{7}$

18. $\frac{2}{3} = x - \frac{16}{21}$

19. $\frac{-4}{5}x = \frac{-22}{25}$

20. $\frac{-3}{11}m = \frac{3}{11}$

21. Find the area of a triangle with base $8\frac{2}{3}\,in.$ and a height of $5\frac{1}{2}\,in.$

22. Find the area of a trapezoid with bases $4\frac{2}{3}\,cm.$ and $9\frac{1}{5}\,cm.$ and a height of $7\frac{2}{3}\,cm..$

23. A recipe calls for $2\frac{2}{3}$ cups of flour. How many cups of flour would you need for $\frac{1}{2}$ the recipe?

24. There were 2391 participants in a 10K run. If $\frac{1}{3}$ of them were over the age of 40, how many were under the age of 40?

CUMULATIVE REVIEW   CHAPTER 4

1. Find the prime factorization of 312.
2. Find two factors of -28 that give a sum of -12.
3. Write 17,891 in words.
4. Round 345,601 to the nearest thousand.

5. Write using exponential notation: $\dfrac{3 \cdot 3 \cdot 3 \cdot 3}{17}$

6. Write $4\dfrac{6}{15}$ as an improper fraction.

7. Graph the following points on a number line. $-3, \dfrac{2}{5}, 0, 2\dfrac{1}{3}, 5\dfrac{3}{4}, -1\dfrac{1}{2}$

8. Compare. $\dfrac{12}{17} \underline{\qquad} \dfrac{2}{3}$

Simplify if possible. Write improper fractions as mixed numbers.

9. $\dfrac{25}{95}$

10. $\dfrac{-312}{56}$

11. $\dfrac{9m}{2}$

12. $\dfrac{-35xy^3}{49x^2 y^2}$

13. -2^5

14. $\dfrac{-28}{0}$

Perform indicated operation.

15. $-17 + 18 - 36$

16. $28 - (-321)$

17. $58 + 7 \cdot (-9)$

18. $27 + 3\left(15 - 3^2\right) \div 9$

19. $\dfrac{14}{19} \cdot 0$

20. $|7 - 9| + |7| - |9|$

21. $2^3 \div 4 \cdot (-2) - (27 + 15)$

22. $\dfrac{5}{12} + \dfrac{3}{12}$

23. $4\dfrac{2}{7} - \left(-3\dfrac{4}{5}\right)$

24. $-6\dfrac{3}{8} \div 2\dfrac{1}{4}$

25. $\dfrac{16x^3 y}{25y} \cdot \dfrac{5xy^2}{24}$

Solve.

26. $18 - m = 47$

27. $5a = -75$

28. $-4y + 13 = 29$

29. $3n - 2(n + 5) = 17$

30. $4y + 5y + 3 = -11 + 2y$

31. $\dfrac{-8y}{15} = \dfrac{4}{5}$

32. $\dfrac{2m}{13} = -\dfrac{7}{8}$

33. $\dfrac{5x}{9} = -3\dfrac{2}{3}$

34. $\dfrac{-8x}{11} = -5\dfrac{5}{7}$

35. $x + \dfrac{1}{4} = -\dfrac{3}{7}$

36. $\dfrac{1}{3}x + \dfrac{1}{4} = -\dfrac{1}{6}$

37. Evaluate. $\dfrac{-b}{2a}$ for $a = 7, b = -8$

38. Evaluate. $\dfrac{4x^2 y}{-3y}$ for $x = -2, y = 7$

39. Evaluate. $x + 2y - xy$; $x = \dfrac{8}{9}, y = \dfrac{9}{10}$

40. Evaluate. $x^2 + y^2$; $x = \dfrac{3}{4}, y = \dfrac{2}{3}$

Write an algebraic equation and solve the problem.
41. eleven subtracted from a number is eight-two.
42. Julia is taking her 4th grade class to the zoo on a fieldtrip. If admission for each child is $29, how much is needed for the 26 children.
43. Grace has test scores of 89, 92, 93, 81, and 100. What is her test average?

Geometry Corner: Write an algebraic equation and solve the problem.
44. Find the area of a triangle with base 15m and height 28m.
45. Find the area of a rectangle with width 38 ft. and length 14 ft.
46. Find the area of a square if each side measures 8 cm.
47. Find the area of a trapezoid with a height of $2\frac{3}{4}$ in. and bases that measure 28 in. and 11 in.
48. The first angle in a triangle is 10 more than the second angle. The third angle is two less than twice the first. Find the measure of each angle.
49. A rectangular garden requires 117 ft. of fencing. If the length is three more than five times the width, find the measurements of the garden.
50. Find the area of the garden in problem #49

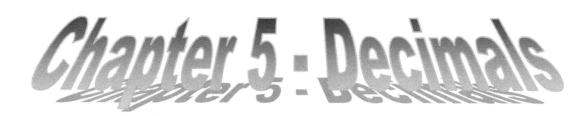
Chapter 5 - Decimals

Chapter 5 is about working with decimal numbers.

Pre-algebra (vertical side text)

What's Inside?!

2.053	3 decimal places
×0.06	+2 decimal places
.12318	5 decimal places

Courtesy of Fotolia

In this Chapter we will look at tips for how a college student can stay organized. Being organized is a HUGE part of being successful in math and in college.

So my average time is

$$\frac{55.3 + 54.7 + 53.7 + 52.3 + 55.3}{9} = \frac{271.3}{5} \approx 54.3$$

PLUS! Learn how world cycling champ Lance Armstrong uses statistics to evaluate his performance.

Time Results (in minutes)				
55.3	54.7	53.7	52.3	55.3

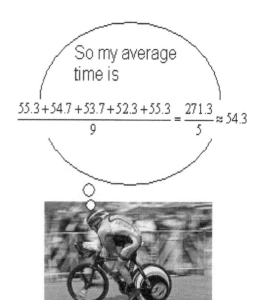

5.1 Introduction To Decimals

Topics:
* Reading And Writing Decimal Numbers
* Ordering Decimals
* Writing A Decimal Number As A Fraction
* Rounding Decimals

Are You Ready?
To see if you are ready to understand this section, do the following short quiz.
1. Write 12,512 in words.
2. Fill in the blank with a < or >: $13,498 \_\_\_ 13,513$.
3. Reduce the fraction $\dfrac{15}{100}$.
4. Round 56,856 to the nearest hundred.

Answers to Are You Ready?

(1). twelve thousand, five hundred twelve   *(2). <*   *(3)* $\dfrac{3}{20}$ *(4) 56,900*

Reading And Writing Decimal Numbers

Like fractions and mixed numbers, decimal notation is another way to represent numbers that involve part of a whole.

Improper Fractions: $\dfrac{13}{4}$ Mixed Numbers: $3\dfrac{1}{4}$ Decimal Notation: 3.25

The following decimal place value chart will help you to read and write decimal numbers. The last place value of the decimal number determines how the decimal number is read.

Ten-Thousands	Thousands	Hundreds	Tens	Ones	Decimal Point	Tenths	Hundredths	Thousandths	Ten-thousandths	Hundred-thousandths
6	3	8	0	2	.	7	5	3	0	9
Whole Part						Decimal Part				

Example 1: In the decimal number 51.0956, what digit is in the thousandths place?

Solution: Referencing the chart we see that 5 is in the thousandths place.

Decimal numbers are read similar to fractions.

To Read a Decimal Number:

- Read the whole part of the number.
- Use the word "and" for the decimal.
- Read the number after the decimal as if it were a whole number then say the last decimal place value.

Example 2: How would each decimal number be read?
a.) 0.0008   b.) −7.905

Solution:
a.) Since the last digit is in the ten-thousandths place 0.0008 is read "eight ten-thousandths"

b.) Don't forget to indicate that the number is negative.

−7.905
[PN: arrows pointing out whole, "and", and decimal parts]
"negative seven and nine hundred five thousandths"

Understanding place values is also important for writing decimal numbers. For example, suppose your professor says "eight thousandths"…

"eight thousandths"
- the "th" at the end means she is referring to a decimal number
- saying "thousandths" means that the number is out to the third place value beyond the decimal

So "eight thousandths" refers to the number 0.008 .

Ten-Thousands	Thousands	Hundreds	Tens	Ones	Decimal Point	Tenths	Hundredths	Thousandths	Ten-thousandths	Hundred-thousandths
6	3	8	0	2	.	7	5	3	0	9

| Whole Part | | | | | | Decimal Part | | | | |

As you may have noticed, we always put a zero to the left of the decimal as a placeholder if the number has no whole part. Let's look at a few more examples of writing decimal numbers.

Example 3: How would each phrase be written as a decimal number?
a.) "five tenths"
b.) "negative five thousandths"
c.) "nine hundred sixty seven hundred-thousandths"

Solution:
a.) "Five tenths" is written 0.5 .

b.) First of all the number is negative.   −0.___
Thousandths is the third place value for
decimals, so the number should have three
decimal places.
"Five" is the number part given. Write it in so   −0.<u>005</u>

that it sits in the last decimal place. Use zeros
as place holders for the other place values.

−0.005

c.) Hundred-thousandths is the fifth place value   0._ _ _ _ _
for decimals, so the number should have five
decimal places.

"Nine hundred sixty seven" is the number part   0.<u>00967</u>
given. Write it in so that it sits in the last
decimal places. Use zeros as place holders for
the other place values.

0.00967

Example 4: Where in the World? Write all the decimal numbers used in the following statement.

"The length of the Hubble Telescope is *thirteen and thirty five hundredths* meters. An
image can be sent from Hubble to Earth in *thirteen millionths* of a second."
Source: NASA

Solution: The decimal numbers given are "thirteen and thirty five hundredths" and
"thirteen millionths".

"thirteen and thirty five hundredths" is written as 13.35 .

"thirteen millionths" is written as 0.000013 .

STOP Exericse Set - Reading And Writing Decimal Numbers

1. In the decimal number 15.0865 what digit is in the hundredths place?
2. In the decimal number 0.00497 what digit is in the ten-thousandths place?

How would you read the following decimal numbers?
3. 5.3
4. 0.0087
5. -0.051
6. 8.341

How would each phrase be written as a decimal number?
7. eight and five tenths
8. negative thirty-two and five hundredths
9. negative eleven and thirty-four thousandths
10. eighty-nine and thirteen ten-thousandths

11. Write all the decimal numbers used in the following statement.
"The weight of a single bacteria is *one hundred eighty seven hundred-thousandths* of an ounce and the
volume is about *five millionths* of a cubic centimeter."

12. Write all the decimal numbers used in the following statement.
"A typical plant cell is about *twenty-five thousandths* of a centimeter long while a typical animal cell is
only about *eighty-seven hundred- thousandths* of a centimeter."

Courtesy of Fotolia

To succeed in math and college you have to get organized. The days of cramming your papers into your book are gone. You need a three-ring binder to organize your class materials.

Embrace it...and SUCCEED!

In this chapter we will give some tips on how to organize a three-ring binder for your math class.

Ordering Decimals

Using inequality symbols $<, \le, >, \ge$ is generally easier for decimals than for fractions. It is done the same way as with whole numbers.

To Order Two Decimal Numbers: Begin at the far left of the numbers and compare their place values until you find a difference. The number with the higher value in that place value is the greater number.

Example 5: TRUE or FALSE?
a.) $135.681 > 135.69$ b.) $0.0007 \le 0.0019$

Solution:
a.) $135.681 > 135.69$
This is FALSE. That fact that the number on the left has more decimal places does not make it greater. The numbers use the same values until the hundredths place, where the number on the right has a higher value. So it is greater. The expression should be $135.681 < 135.69$.

b.) $0.0007 \le 0.0019$
This is TRUE. The numbers have the same values until thousandths place, where the number to the right has a higher value. So it is greater.

Example 6: Fill in each blank with a < or >.
a.) 119.034___119.09   b.) 13.48723____13.48713

Solution:
a.) $119.039 \underset{\raise2pt=}{<} 119.04$

All the place values are the same until the thousandths place. The number to the right has a higher value in the hundredths place, since $3 < 4$. Therefore, the left side is less than the right side.

b.) $13.48723 \underset{\raise2pt=}{>} 13.48713$

All the place values are the same except for the ten-thousandths place, which is greater on the left side since $2 > 1$. Therefore the left side is greater than the right side.

Example 7: Where in the World? Solar Solutions Inc. has created a solar panel in which each solar cell only weighs 2.035 grams. Their competition, Sun Power has created a similar type of panel where each cell weighs 2.0318 grams. Use an inequality expression to compare the two weights. Which company uses a heavier weight cell?

Solution: The weights given are 2.035 grams and 2.0318 grams. As an inequality we have $2.035 > 2.0318$. Solar Solutions uses a heavier cell weight.

STOP Exercise Set - Ordering Decimals

TRUE or FALSE?
13. $23.451 > 23.452$
14. $613.527 > 613.54$
15. $13.91 < 1.392$
16. $7.23409 > 72.331$

Fill in each blank with a <, >, or =.
17. 17.2___17.8
18. 65.4___64.4
19. 231.071___231.07
20. 31.167___311.67

21. A biologist has two cell samples. The mass of sample A is 0.0752 grams while the mass of sample B is 0.0761 grams. Use an inequality symbol to compare the two samples. Which sample weighs more?

22. A quarter is about 1.75 inches thick. A Japanese 5-yen coin is about 1.734 inches thick. Use an inequality symbol to compare the thickness of the two coins. Which country's coin is thicker?

Writing A Decimal Number As A Fraction

The decimal number 0.19 is read "nineteen hundredths". Notice that "nineteen hundredths" could also be written as the fraction $\dfrac{19}{100}$. This is always true of decimal numbers. Here is another example...

"sixty eight thousandths" could be written as a decimal number.	"sixty eight thousandths" could be written as a fraction.
0.068	$\dfrac{68}{1000}$

This is also true for decimals that have a whole part.

"Five and seven tenths" could be written as a decimal number.	"Five and seven tenths" could be written as a mixed number.	"Five and seven tenths" could be written as an improper fraction.
5.7	$5\dfrac{7}{10}$	$\dfrac{57}{10}$

In the examples above notice the denominator of the fraction is given by the last place value of the decimal. This gives us a way to quickly convert decimals to fractions.

To Convert a Decimal Number to a Proper or Improper Fraction: The numerator is just the number given written without the decimal. The denominator is the power of ten (as in 10, 100, 1000, 10000, 100000, etc.) that corresponds to the decimal number's last place value. Don't forget to reduce if possible.

Example 8: Convert each decimal number to a proper or improper fraction in lowest terms.
a.) 0.009 b.) 6.08

Solution: For each number we follow the instructions above.
a.) 0.009 is read nine thousandths, since it goes to the third place value. So we use 1000 as the denominator, and 9 as the numerator.

$$0.009 = \frac{9}{1000}$$

This fraction is already in lowest terms.

b.) 6.08 is read six and eight hundredths, since it goes to the second place value. We use 100 as the denominator and 608 as the numerator.

$$6.08 = \frac{608}{100}$$

Now we reduce: $\dfrac{608}{100} = \dfrac{4 \cdot 152}{4 \cdot 25} = \dfrac{\cancel{4} \cdot 152}{\cancel{4} \cdot 25} = \dfrac{152}{25}$

It is common to see expressions that contain both a fraction and a decimal number. In the next example we add the numbers by converting the decimal to fraction notation.

Example 9: Convert the decimal number to a fraction to add: $\dfrac{7}{15} + 0.8$

Solution:

First we convert the decimal number to a fraction.

$$\frac{7}{15} + 0.8 = \frac{7}{15} + \frac{8}{10}$$

The second fraction will simplify: $\dfrac{8}{10} = \dfrac{2 \cdot 4}{2 \cdot 5} = \dfrac{4}{5}$

$$= \frac{7}{15} + \frac{4}{5}$$

Now we get a common denominator.

$$= \frac{7}{15} + \frac{4 \cdot 3}{5 \cdot 3} = \frac{7}{15} + \frac{12}{15}$$

Add the numerators and keep the same denominator.

$$= \frac{7 + 12}{15} = \frac{19}{15}$$

If a decimal number has a whole part then we can convert it to a mixed number. For example, 15.73 could be expressed as $15\dfrac{73}{100}$.

To Convert a Decimal to a Mixed Number: Convert the decimal part of the number to a proper fraction and keep the same whole part.

Example 10: Convert each decimal number to a mixed number in lowest terms.
a.) 3.8   b.) 27.015

Solution:

a.) 3.8 can be written as $3\dfrac{8}{10} = 3\dfrac{4}{5}$.

b.) 27.015 can be written as $27\dfrac{15}{1000} = 27\dfrac{3}{200}$.

Example 11: Where in the World? When this Tidus Final Fantasy X toy was created, the engineers used decimals to provide the following specifications for the new toy:

Height: 11.25 inches
Width: 2.375 inches

But marketers know that consumers don't want to see decimals on the box for the toy. Consumers prefer to see fractions on the toy's box. Convert the given specifications to mixed numbers.

Solution: The decimal numbers given were 11.25 and 2.375. Let's convert them fractions.

$$11.25 = 11\frac{25}{100} = 11\frac{1}{4} \qquad\qquad 2.375 = 2\frac{375}{1000} = 2\frac{3}{8}$$

So, on the box for the toy the specifications will be presented this way:

Height: $11\dfrac{1}{4}$ inches   Width: $2\dfrac{3}{8}$ inches

STOP Exercise Set - Writing A Decimal Number As A Fraction

Convert each decimal number to a proper or improper fraction in lowest terms.

23. 0.01   24. 0.0049   25. 4.6   26. 3.45

Convert each decimal number to a mixed number in lowest terms.

27. 4.2   28. 8.75   29. 17.0815   30. 38.912

Convert each decimal number to a fraction and add or subtract.

31. $\dfrac{5}{6} + 0.5$ 32. $6.5 - 5\dfrac{3}{4}$

33. The specifications for a new snow board design have the dimensions of the board as 0.75 feet wide and 2.8 feet long. For the marketing presentation these should be expressed as fractions. Convert the decimals to fractions.

34. The focal length for a new microscope has a range of 0.65 inches to 1.405 inches. Convert these decimal numbers to fraction notation.

Rounding Decimals

Rounding decimal numbers is very similar to rounding whole numbers.

To Round a Decimal Number to a Given Place Value: Look at the value to the left of the place value given for rounding. If that value is 5 or more, round up. If it is 4 or less, round down.

Example 12: Round 708.102468 to the nearest ten-thousandth.

Solution: We use the procedure given above.

$$708.102438$$

To round to the nearest ten-thousandth we look at the value in the hundred-thousandth place.

Since the value in the hundred-thousandths place is 4 or less, we round down at the ten-thousandths place.

So the rounding value is 708.1024 .

Example 12: Where in the World? You have probably heard of $\pi \approx 3.14$. Another famous number you will see in your Algebra classes is $e = 2.71828183...$ Round e to the nearest hundredth.

Solution: To round e to the nearest hundredth we look at the value in the thousandth place.

$$e = 2.71828183...$$

Since the value in the thousandth place is 5 or more, we round up at the hundredth place.

So e rounded to the nearest hundredth is $e \approx 2.72$.

Good Question: When rounding whole numbers we replaced the numbers behind the place value rounded with zeros. However, when rounding decimals the place values to the right are deleted, why?

Answer: When rounding decimal numbers, you could still replace the place values with zeros. However, it is not necessary.

Consider the number 0.4317 rounded to the nearest hundredths place. This number rounded could be written as 0.4300 or as we presented 0.43. Notice that these two decimal numbers represent the same value since...

$$0.4300 = \frac{4300}{10000} = \frac{43}{100} \qquad 0.43 = \frac{43}{100}$$

(STOP) Exercise Set - Rounding Decimals

Round 789.345781 to the following place values.

35. tenths
36. hundredths

37. thousandths
38. hundred thousandths

39. Given $\pi \approx 3.14159$, round π to the nearest thousandths place.
40. Given $e \approx 2.718281828$, round e to the nearest millions place.

5.1 Exercise Set - Putting it ALL Together

Represent each scenario with a positive or negative decimal number.

41. The company has a debt of $5,785.35.
42. Wayne's checking account is overdrawn by $75.41.
43. The base of the mountain starts at 52.8 feet above sea level.
44. The temperature of the chemical must be exactly 12.8 degrees below freezing.

Write each decimal number in words.

45. 8.7
46. -9.25
47. -0.0007
48. 19.04
49. 0.845

50. -14.87
51. 600.5
52. 8000.009

Write the decimal number given.
53. five and six tenths
54. five and six hundredths
55. five and six millionths
56. negative twenty-eight and twelve hundredths
57. negative one hundred thirteen and fifteen hundredths
58. ninety seven and five hundred three thousandths

59. Complete the check by writing in the amount of the check as a decimal number.

[PN: Check in the amount of "thirty-nine and $\dfrac{7}{100}$"]

60. In a math course you might hear a statement like this: "To estimate the number π, we use *three and fourteen hundredths*." Write the number given as a decimal number.

61. In a nursing course you might hear a statement like this: "There should be exactly *five thousandths* of a gram in the solution." Write the number given as a decimal number.

62. In a science course you might hear a statement like this: "The weight of one of these molecules is *three millionths* of an ounce." Write the number given as a decimal number.

63. In a physics course you might hear a statement like this: "The wave length of green light is only *fifty-five ten-thousandths*". Write the number given as a decimal number.

64. In business course you might hear a statement like this: "A change of just *seventy-five thousandths* in the value of a currency can be significant for a country". Write the number given as a decimal number.

Convert the following decimals to fractions or mixed numbers.
65. 0.88   67. -0.0075   69. 17.8   71. -237.272
66. 0.245   68. 0.144   70. 29.35   72. 532.25

Convert each decimal number to a fraction and add or subtract.

73. $\dfrac{7}{12} + 0.3$

74. $\dfrac{13}{25} - 0.13$

75. $9.27 - \dfrac{9}{10}$

76. $\dfrac{2}{3} + \dfrac{4}{5} - 0.7$

77. $\dfrac{3}{5} + 0.48 + \dfrac{7}{15}$

78. $8.75 - \dfrac{1}{6} + 0.4$

Fill in each blank with a <, >, or =.
79. 5.061____5.06
80. −0.318_____−0.532
81. 0.097____0.1
82. 0.6____0.600
83. 0.8____0.008
84. −8.4_____−8.04

85. Cell phone microchips made in a manufacturing plant have to be monitored closely for quality. Each chip created is carefully measured. In order to be used in a phone the width of a chip must be between 0.031 and 0.034 inches. Of the following chips, which be used?

Chip	#1	#2	#3	#4
Width (inches)	0.0301	0.0335	0.0342	0.0319

86. Cell phone microchips made in a manufacturing plant have to be monitored closely for quality. Each chip created is carefully measured. In order to be used in a phone the width of a chip must be between 0.076 and 0.081 inches. Of the following chips, which be used?

Chip	#1	#2	#3	#4
Width (inches)	0.077	0.0751	0.082	0.0805

Round the following numbers to the given place values.

87. 0.98; tenths

88. 89.456; hundredth

89. 123.009; tenths

90. 23.7892; tenths

91. 5678.145; hundredths

92. 1.923564; ten thousandths

93. 0.2385407; thousandths

94. 14.7821; thousandths

95. Five friends went out to dinner and decided to split the bill equally between them. The total of $126.97 divided five ways comes to $25.394. Round this answer to the nearest cent (hundredth).

96. Three friends share a cab and the fare totals $31.30 with tip. One friend has a calculator and divides the fare into three and finds that each friend should pay $10.4333333 each. Round $10.4333333 to the nearest cent (hundredth).

Given $a = -4.56$, $b = 4.6$, $c = -4.06$, **and** $d = -4.7$, **identify if the following statements are TRUE or FALSE.**

97. $a > b$

98. $c > d$

99. $b > c$

100. $d < a$

101. $c < a$

The following graph gives sales in the entertainment industry. Answer the questions that follow.

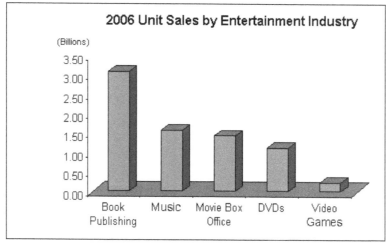

102. Which is the best approximation for the number of units sold in the music industry?
    a.) 0.9 billion   b.) 1.6 billion   c.) 3.3 billion

103. Which is the best approximation for the number of units sold for DVDs?
    a.) 1.8 billion   b.) 0.5 billion   c.) 1.4 billion

Exercise Set - Cumulative Review

104. Add. $-9+13+(-6)+6$

105. Solve. $-8 = x+5$

106. Round 14,598 to the nearest hundred.

107. Reduce. $\dfrac{24}{36}$

108. Divide. $\dfrac{-\dfrac{5}{6}}{-\dfrac{3}{8}}$

 # 5.1 QUIZ YOURSELF

To make sure you are ready for the EXAM, try these problems without any help. Give yourself about 20 minutes and don't check the answers until you have completely finished.

1. Write 67.891 in words.
2. Write -34.02 in words.
3. Write 'seventy-five ten thousandths' as a decimal.
4. Write 'four hundred and thirty five thousandths' as a decimal.
5. Round 8.1238 to the nearest hundredths.
6. Given $e \approx 2.718281828$, round e to the nearest ten thousandths place.

Fill in the blank.
7. 91.7 ___ 91.73
8. 579.34 ___ 57.934

9. Convert the decimal 5.75 to a mixed number and reduce if possible.

10. Convert the decimal to a fraction and subtract: $\dfrac{2}{3} - 0.4$

Answers to this Quiz Yourself are on page 682.

Succeed in Math! Being Organized

"We are what we repeatedly do. Excellence then, is not an act, but a habit."
ARISTOTLE, *Greek philosopher*

It is very important to be organized to succeed in college. I'm talking about things where you keep your homework, notes, and assignments that handed back. I'm also talking about how organized and neat you keep these things. A lot of students shove

Picture of Slop Book and Binder – Expecting this to work in college is like hoping a pile of junk will make itself into an engine. Some students can get away with it, but most can't.

Picture of Three Ring Binder – This is a thing of beauty. Students who take the time to do this SUCCEED.

"But I'm just not organized." Copout! You can get organized if you stick to it.

Your Class Notebook
Before we begin the discussion on how to organize your course materials, it will be good for you to reflect on your current organizational style.

EXERCISE #1   Assessing Your Organization
Make an honest assessment of your current level and/or style of organization. Be honest! Also, tell how these habits either help you or hinder you in your math class.

We cannot say enough about the importance of being organized in a math class. Being organized with your class materials, homework, and exams will turn math from an ocean of confusion to a discrete, ordered set of concepts that can be accessed for reference exactly when you need them. This chapter will address how you can set up a notebook that will keep you organized in a way that will make the course much more manageable and enjoyable.

If you are already organized with your college materials, good for you! If you are "just not an organized person", you can do it! Try it and see what a difference it makes!

Three Rings... No Circus
Organization requires the use of a three-ring binder. In my students' experience, the thinner ones are actually easier to keep neat. Do not use this binder for any other class besides math. Let's look at how to get organized!

The first page of your notebook should be a title page. This page is a good chance to store some important information that you may need to refer to during the semester. **The first page should have information about your instructor, resources for assistance in your class, peer contacts, and a space to record your exam grades.**

The rest of the notebook should be divided into five sections. Each section should be separated from the rest by a labeled divider. This way you can navigate your notebook quickly and efficiently. Otherwise, you will waste time and become frustrated trying to find things. Here is a breakdown of each section.

1.) Handouts. This section is where you keep any handouts that are given in class, like the course syllabus, class schedule, and whatever else your professor hand out. If you miss a class, be sure to get any handouts you missed from the instructor or make copies of a fellow student's handouts.

2.) Class notes. Include all your notes from class in chronological order. Each day's notes should be started on a new page with the date and section(s) covered on the top right-hand corner. We have tips for note-taking in Chapter 6.

3.) Homework. This section holds assigned homework. Start every new section on a new sheet of paper. If your instructor collects homework assignments, simply take out the homework assignment to turn it in and put it back when it is handed back. TAKE PRIDE IN YOUR HOMEWORK THE WAY YOU WILL TAKE PRIDE IN DOING YOUR DREAM JOB! Show every step. Do not write in pen.

If you are the kind of student who uses extra practice problems beyond the assigned homework to help you study, that is awesome! But store those extra problems somewhere other than this notebook. The homework assignments given by your instructor usually represent everything you are expected to know. Often when students keep every single problem done, they wind up a messy notebook stuffed full of scrap paper. In the long term, only very neat, relevant homework should be kept in this section.

4.) Exams and quizzes. In this section, put each exam or quiz in order as you take them and get them back. Correct each problem you missed on every exam or quiz. The "Exams and Quizzes" section in your notebook is going to help retain information. Making corrections will help with retention and understanding, particularly for the problems you missed. The exam section will also serve as a wonderful tool for the final exam (which is usually cumulative and based on these previous exams).

5.) Glossary. In this section, create a list of definitions that come up in math.

- Most professors write vocabulary words on the board. Whenever they do this, you can either turn to the glossary and make a quick entry right then or, if you don't have time to do that, circle the word in your notes so you will remember to make it an entry in the glossary later when you review your notes.
- From the textbook as you study. These are the **boldfaced** words.
- As you do your homework, pay attention to key words that appear in the instructions or in finding solutions. If you have not done so already, you should add these words to the glossary.
- Try your best to write the definition "in your own words." It will be easier for you to assimilate the definitions if they are worded in a way that you can relate to. But make sure that your definitions are accurate. Remember that the goal is for you to get better at speaking the language of math.

General Remarks about Math Notebooks

One of the best things about the three-ring binder is that everything is right at your fingertips. Students often ask instructors questions about the course that are answered in the syllabus. This will not happen to you. You will never find yourself saying, "I know I have that somewhere." It's all right there. And there is a place for everything that could come up. Just find a place on your campus where there is a three-hole punch, or buy one for yourself.

Speaking of a three-hole punch, make sure you do not get into the habit of putting loose-leaf pages in the pouches at the front of the notebook. Anything worth putting into the notebook is worth being punched and put into the appropriate section.

Having just one spiral notebook is simply not enough for a math class:
- Where do you put your syllabus and course schedule?
- Where do you put returned homework?
- Where do you put returned tests?
- What do you do if you want to let classmates borrow notes or you need to photocopy theirs?

Spiral notebooks are not versatile enough to organize all the information and material involved with being an excellent math student. Your mindset should be that your notebook is like a portfolio. It is very important that it not fall into disarray. Do not let the notebook get into a state where sheets are sporadically sticking out. You will learn much better from a notebook that you are proud of.

Bring your notebook to class with you every day. Show your notebook to your professor to get tips on effective studying for his or her class. The professor is likely to be so impressed that he or she will give away good information about tests.

I believe in this notebook system so much that I impose it on every algebra student I teach. The most common compliment I get from past students is that they now use a similar notebook system in all their other classes and that it makes a world of difference.

EXERCISE #2   Exploring the Notebook Format

Referring to the format for the class notebook outlined above, list the five sections again here and explain why you think they would or would not make a difference in your ability to succeed in your math course. Don't be afraid to be honest.

Section 1: _____

_____

_____

_____

Section 2: _____

_____

_____

_____

_____

Section 3: _____

_____

_____

_____

_____

Section 4: _____

_____

_____

_____

Section 5: _____

_____

_____

_____

"What If My Notebook Gets Too Full or Starts to Get Cluttered?"

It happens to the best math students. In an effort to be the best they can be in math class, they accumulate so much material that their notebooks become bloated and unmanageable. Here are some tips to help keep you on track:

- If you take up a lot of space when you do homework and/or take class notes, consider removing the old assignment(s) and/or notes. Use a paper clamp to bind a chapter's worth of material together and store it somewhere you can find it easily later if needed. This will not be necessary for exams and the glossary since they don't take up much space.
- If the holes in some of your pages are tearing and causing the pages to stick out, make an assessment of whether the page(s) really need to be in the notebook or could be filed away. Or consider transferring the information to another page. Stay on top of these loose pages; nothing will make you lose interest in your notebook faster than ugly loose pages sticking out of it.
- Remember, your notebook is not a "catch all" storage space; keeping it clean and lean will make it the effective tool that it should be.

Be persistent in keeping your notebook neat and organized. It is very common for students to start out with a nice notebook and have it deteriorate over the semester. This is often a reflection of their performance in the course. Spend time with your notebook. Take pride in it. Love it and it will love you back.

5.2 Adding And Subtracting Decimals

Topics:
- Adding and Subtracting Decimal Numbers
- Working with Positive and Negative Decimal Numbers
- Solving Equations

Are You Ready?
To see if you are ready to understand this section, do the following short quiz.
1. Subtract: $45,692 - 17,015$
2. Find the sum: $(-8) + 13 + (-5) + (-7)$
3. Solve: $x + 23 = -77$
4. Solve: $-12 + x + 31 = 38$

Answers to Are You Ready?
(1)28,677   *(2)-7*   *(3) $x = -100$*   *(4) $x = 19$*

Adding and Subtracting Decimal Numbers

Adding and subtracting decimal numbers is like adding and subtracting whole numbers in that we line up the place values to add. For decimals numbers we line the place values by lining up the decimal points.

To Add or Subtract Decimals Numbers: Line up the place values by lining up the decimal points, putting zeros in missing place values as necessary. Then add or subtract using the same method as for whole numbers. Bring the decimal straight down for the answer.

Example 1: Add or subtract.
a) $35.749 + 9.8$ b) $13.3 - 7.45$

Solution: Do these processes look familiar? If not, you may want to look in the Appendix at the decimal review.

$$
\begin{array}{r}
{}^{1}{}^{1} \\
35.749 \\
a.) \quad +\ 9.800 \\
\hline
45.549
\end{array}
\qquad
\begin{array}{r}
13.30 \\
b.) \quad -\ 7.45 \\
\hline
5.85
\end{array}
$$

[PN: I failed miserably trying to mark the subtraction up in Math Type]

Now we want to incorporate adding and subtracting decimal numbers into what we have learned about things like positives and negatives and combining like terms.

Example 2: Simplify $3.4x + 2.5 - 0.13x + 7$.

Solution: There are four terms in the expression. We can simplify by combining like terms.

Rearrange the terms to group like terms.

$$3.4x + 2.5 - 0.13x + 7$$
$$= 3.4x - 0.13x + 2.5 + 7$$

Combine like terms.

$$\underbrace{3.4x - 0.13x}_{3.27x} + \underbrace{2.5 + 7}_{9.5}$$

Our final answer is $3.27x + 9.5$.

> **Scratch Work:**
>
> | | |
> |---|---|
> | 3.40 | 2.5 |
> | -0.13 | $+7.0$ |
> | 3.27 | 9.5 |
>
> [PN: perhaps by hand?]

Example 3: Where in the World? One of the most common uses of decimal addition and subtraction is in book-keeping. Consider the spreadsheet to the right. First, estimate the new balance in the account by rounding each amount given to the nearest hundred. Then find the actual new balance.

Balance	**$2053.07**
Deposit	**$78**
Withdrawal	**$509.14**
Deposit	**$1215.67**
New Balance:	**?**

Solution: This calculation takes three steps. Keep in mind that a deposit means *adding* money of an account and withdrawing means *subtracting* money out of an account.

Estimated Value
For this calculation each number has been rounded to the hundreds place.

2000	2100	1600
$+100$	-500	$+1200$
2100	1600	2800

[PN: Can we have arrows pointing from the result to the top of the next step?]

So the new balance should be about $2800.

Actual Value
For this calculation we use the actual values given.

2053.07	2131.07	1621.93
$+78.00$	-509.14	$+1215.67$
2131.07	1621.93	2837.60

[PN: Can we have arrows pointing from the result to the top of the next step?]

So the resulting balance should be exactly $2837.60.

Notice that the estimated value is very close to actual value, meaning it is a good approximation.

STOP Exercise Set - Adding and Subtracting Decimal Numbers

Add or Subtract.
1. $7.89 + 89.3$
2. $1.00345 + 17.34$
3. $28.3 - 16.8$
4. $708.62 - 315.3$
5. $8.108 - 2.452$
6. $1.045 + 18.324$

Simplify
7. $5.2x + 1.2 - 3.1x + 8.9$
8. $13.78x - 5.23x + 7.8 + 19.23$
9. $2.346 + 9.32 - 19.82x$
10. $45.6 + 34.91x + 25.22x$

11. Consider the spreadsheet to the right. First, estimate the new balance in the account by rounding each amount given to the nearest whole dollar. Then find the actual new balance.

Balance	$896.23
Deposit	$817.92
Withdrawal	$576.10
Deposit	$249

12. Consider the spreadsheet to the right. First, estimate the new balance in the account by rounding each amount given to the nearest whole dollar. Then find the actual new balance.

Balance	$1596.72
Deposit	$2249.86
Withdrawal	$2134.89
Deposit	$350.19

Working With Positive and Negative Decimal Numbers

Of course, decimal numbers can be negative. For example, the temperature at which ordinary gasoline freezes is about -97.241 degrees Fahrenheit.

In fact, when I was in college my bank account almost always had a negative decimal number as the balance. The printout would say something like BALANCE: $-\$45.92$, which meant I had overspent.

Rules about adding and subtracting with negative numbers can be applied to decimal numbers.

Example 4: Add or subtract.
a.) $(-4.5)+(-8.9)$
b.) $-5.73-(-12.6)$

Solution: We can use the **Review of Rules for Signed Numbers** to the right as a guide for how to deal with decimals.

a.) Since these are both negative, we add their absolute values and make the result negative.

$(-4.5)+(-8.9)=-13.4$

Scratch Work:
4.5
+8.9
13.4

b.) Subtracting a negative is equivalent to adding a positive. Subtract the absolute values and make result positive.

$-5.73-(-12.6)=-5.73+12.6$

$= 6.87$

Scratch Work:
12.6
-5.73
6.87

5.73

Example 5: Where in the World? The formula $P = R - C$ is used by a company to determine their profit or loss where P represents the profit or loss, R represents the company's revenue and C represents the company's cost. Find the profit given a revenue of $R = \$11.30$ and a cost of $C = \$39.56$.

Solution: We are to find P given $R = \$11.30$ and $C = \$39.56$. Substituting, we have $P = 11.30 - 39.56 = -28.26$. So the company has a profit of $-\$28.56$, which means a loss of $\$28.56$.

STOP Exercise Set - Working With Positive and Negative Decimal Numbers

Add or Subtract.

13. $-21.5 + 78.1$

14. $-1.56 + (-3.72)$

15. $-67.923 + (-34.45)$

16. $-901.57 + 423.871$

17. $5.3 - 8.23$

18. $-9.83 - 17.24$

19. $73.4 - (-34.5)$

20. $-15.31 - (-21.87)$

21. The formula $P = R - C$ is used by company's to determine their profit or loss where P represents the profit or loss, R represents the company's revenue and C represents the company's cost. Find the profit given a revenue of $R = 11.29$ and a cost of $C = 39.25$.

22. The formula $P = R - C$ is used by company's to determine their profit or loss where P represents the profit or loss, R represents the company's revenue and C represents the company's cost. Find the profit given a revenue of $R = 67.13$ and a cost of $C = 53.45$.

Solving Equations

When solving equations, do not forget that your first steps should be to simplify each side separately.

Example 6: Solve .

a) $x + 13.72 = 25.89$

b) $4.5 + x - 9.7 = -15.2$

Solution:

a) $x + 13.72 = 25.89$

Subtract 13.72 from both sides.

$$x + 13.72 = 25.89$$
$$\underline{-13.72 \quad -13.72}$$
$$x = 12.17$$

b) $4.5 + x - 9.7 = -15.2$

We can combine like terms on the left side of the equation.

$$4.5 + x - 9.7 = -15.2$$
$$x - 5.7 = -15.2$$

Now we add 5.7 to both sides.

$$x - 5.7 = -15.2$$
$$\underline{+5.7 \qquad +5.7}$$
$$x = -9.5$$

Example 7: Where in the World? The profit a company makes is determined by the formula $P = R - C$ where P is profit, R is revenue (total sales), and C is cost. Zertech Supplies wants to make a profit of $5.37 million dollars. They anticipate their cost will be $1.61 million dollars. Use the formula $P = R - C$ to find what their revenue must be to succeed.

Solution: We will use the application solving steps discussed in Section 3.6 to help solve this problem.

ASSIGN A VARIABLE	Since we have the formula $P = R - C$, variables have already been assigned in this application: $P = $ profit, $R = $ revenue, $C = $ cost
SUMMARIZE THE INFORMATION	"profit of $5.37" means $P = 5.67$ "cost will be $1.61" means $C = 1.61$

DO THE MATH

- Substitute 5.67 for P and 1.61 for C in the equation.

$$P = R - C$$
$$5.67 = R - 1.61$$

- Solve the Equation:
Add 1.61 to both sides.

$$5.67 = R - 1.61$$
$$\underline{+1.61 \qquad +1.61}$$
$$7.28 = R$$
$$R = 7.28$$

ANSWER THE QUESTION   The resulting revenue is $7.28 million dollars.

 STOP Exercise Set - Solving Equations

Solve.

23. $21.3 + b = 18.4$
24. $a + 12.8 = 45.8$
25. $18.43 = p - 11.5$
26. $-31.6 = x + 15.4$

27. $4.3 + n - 3.1 = 34.7$
28. $6.78 + b + 15.34 = -28.93$
29. $-3.2 - 11.8 = 16.9 + x$
30. $-15.6 + 12.7 = y - 29.3$

31. Stores use the formula $C = P + T$ to find a customer's total charge for buying an item where C is the total charge, P is the price of the item and T is the tax on the item. Suppose a customer buys an item and pays a tax of $6.89. If the total charge is $91.47 what was the price of the item?

32. Cheap T-Shirts Inc. wants to make a profit of $3.8 million dollars. They anticipate their cost will be $1.21 million dollars. Use the formula $P = R - C$ to find what their revenue must be to succeed.

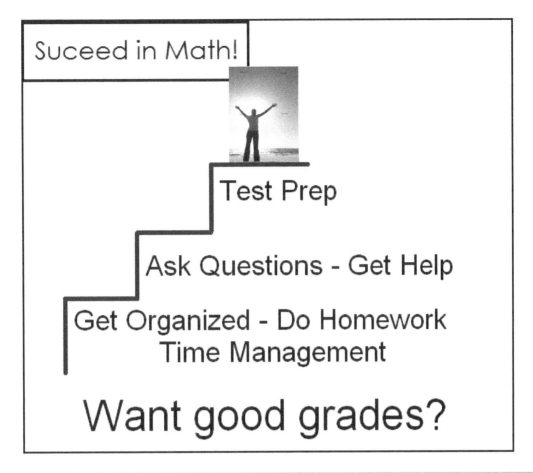

Suceed in Math!

Test Prep

Ask Questions - Get Help

Get Organized - Do Homework
Time Management

Want good grades?

5.2 Exercise Set - Putting it ALL Together

Add or Subtract.

33. $873.45 + 231.901$

34. $-1.0045 + 45.01$

35. $27.8 - 14.3$

36. $-13.891 - 45.376$

37. $17.34 + (-45.6)$

38. $673.82 - (-5.19)$

Simplify.

39. $-1.1a - 2.7a - 9.3$

40. $3.7 + 8.19 - 27.9x$

41. $2.4 + 7.8w - 6.3w + 15.01$

42. $6.83k + 28.29k - 81.203 + (21.8)$

43. $93.4 - (-36.71q) + 2.05q$

44. $18 - 3.4x - 1.8x + 3.4$

45. Is $a = 3.06$ a solution to the equation $a - 1.93 = 1.33$?

46. Is $x = 5.3$ a solution to the equation $6.9 + x = 12.2$?

47. Is $B = 3$ a solution to the equation $5.7 + B = 8.7 - B$?

48. Is $y = -4.6$ a solution to the equation $6.9 + y = y + 2.3$?

Solve.

49. $x - 3.78 = 14.91$

50. $g - 67.3 = -81.4$

51. $m + 6.5 = -12.3$

52. $1.65 + x = 17.327$

53. $8.9 + p = -19.457$

54. $-28.91 = x + 16.8$

55. $-7.924 = x - 8.3$

56. $y - 701 = -85.4$

57. $80.102 - 43.8 = x - 72.07$

58. $7+0.08 = x-(-3.42)$

59. George has \$647.82 in his checking account. He deposits \$127.19 and then makes a withdrawal of \$60.00. How much money is in his account after the deposit and withdrawal?

60. ▮ Camille has \$934.67 in her checking account. She makes a deposit of \$352.73, and then writes checks for \$67.13, and \$825. How much money is in her account after the deposit and checks?

61. ▮ Jay has \$78.45 in his pocket. He needs \$145.78 for the Spam-A-Lot tickets he wants. How much more money does he need to get the tickets?

The following table gives the total rainfall for Seattle, Washington over a period of several years. Answer the questions that follow.

Year	Rainfall (in inches)
2006	23.94
2007	22.84
2008	17.94
2009	21.19
2010	28.01

62. What is the combined rainfall for the two rainiest years?

63. What is the combined rainfall for years 2007, 2008 and 2009?

64. What is the difference in rainfall between the years with the highest and lowest level of rain?

65. What is the difference between levels for the years 2006 and 2009?

The following bar graph gives the total worldwide gross (in millions of dollars) for several movies. Answer the questions that follow. (Source: www.the-numbers.com)

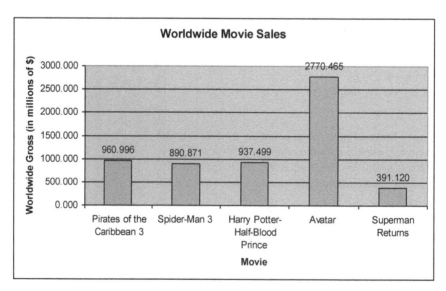

66. How many millions of dollars were made by Superman Returns and Spider 3 combined?

67. How much more money did Pirates of the Caribbean 3 make than Harry Potter?

68. Use rounding to get an idea of whether or not Avatar made more money than the other four movies combined.

Find the perimeter of each figure. Make sure to include units in your answer.

69. [PN: triangle - 7.9, 4.8, 6 inches]
70. [PN: triangle - 0.45, 0.7, 0.76 feet]
71. [PN: rectangle - 7.8 by 5.3 meters]
72. [PN: rectangle - 0.07 by 0.12 feet]
73. [PN: 5-sides with 5.1, 3.8, 9.5, 6.8, 1.8 centimeters]
74. [PN: 6-sided with 2.4, 5, 4.3, 2, 2.8, 1.5 inches]

75. Evaluate $a - b + c$ for $a = 0.09$, $b = -0.7$, and $c = -0.92$
76. Evaluate $x + y + 34.5$, for $x = 3.12$ and $y = -19.2$.
77. Evaluate $y_2 - y_1$ for $y_1 = 0.8$ and $y_2 = 1.4$.
78. Evaluate $x_2 - x_1$ for $x_1 = 2.3$ and $x_2 = 5.9$.

79. Cycle wants to make a profit of $175.62 thousand dollars. They anticipate their cost will be $63.18 thousand dollars. Use the formula $P = R - C$ to find what their revenue must be to succeed.

80. A new business makes a profit of $3.67 for each product it sales. If the cost of making the product is $6.83. Use the formula $P = R - C$ to find the revenue generated by each product sold.

81. The formula $P = R + M$ is used to determine the price a store charges for an item where P is the store price, R is the retail price, and M is the store's mark-up. Suppose the local camping store sales a tent at a store price of $149.98. You research online and find that the retail price is $59.39. Use the formula $P = R + M$ to find the amount of the mark-up.

82. The formula $P = R + M$ is used to determine the price a store charges for an item where P is the store price, R is the retail price, and M is the store's mark-up. Suppose the school book store sales a book at a store price of $98.17. You research online and find that the retail price is $79.65. Use the formula $P = R + M$ to find the amount of the mark-up.

83. In a quality control test, a statistician estimates that the average weight of Droid X cell phones is 4.6367 grams. She is confident that this estimate is not of by more than 0.0072 grams (this is called the margin of error). What range of values is she giving for the average? (Hint: add and subtract the margin of error from the estimate).

84. Engineers have determined that for a computer chip to function properly it must be within 0.0685 inches of the target length. The table below gives the target length for two different types of chips. Fill in the chart with the acceptable length range.

Chip	Target Weight (in inches)	Lowest Acceptable Length	Highest Acceptable Length
Megulon	0.9678		
Pentium	1.3721		

Exercise Set - Chapter 5 Review

85. Round 34.08736 to the nearest thousandth.
86. Fill in the blank with <, >, or = to make the statement true. 6.79 ___ 6.79000
87. Write the phrase "fifty-five and fifteen ten-thousandths as a decimal number.
88. Write 3.4 as an improper fraction and reduce if possible.
89. Write 0.006 as an improper fraction and reduce if possible.

Exercise Set - Cumulative Review

90. Multiply. $(-8)(-5)(2)$

91. Subtract and reduce if possible. $\dfrac{1}{6} - \dfrac{3}{4}$

92. Simplify. $(6-2)^2 + 5 \cdot 3$

93. Divide. $\dfrac{4x}{15} \div \dfrac{2x^2}{5}$

94. Evaluate. 3^4

 # 5.2 QUIZ YOURSELF

To make sure you are ready for the EXAM, try these problems without any help. Give yourself about 20 minutes and don't check the answers until you have completely finished.

Add or Subtract.
1. $67.901 + 472.85$
2. $98.17 - (-34.86)$
3. $-101.73 + (-34.598)$
4. $81.32 - 7.418$
5. $15x - 7.82x + 78.3$
6. $1.0345 - 8.35x + 17.93x - 102.45$

Solve.
7. $x + 187.34 = -89.301$
8. $567.32 = x - 192.007$

9. Sophie has $279.85 in her checking account. She pays her utility bill of $78.12 and cell phone bill of $86.71 online. She then deposits here paycheck of $782.98. What is the new balance of her checking account?
10. Surfboards Unlimited wants to make a profit of $2.67 million dollars. They anticipate their cost will be $1.013 million dollars. Use the formula $P = R - C$ to find what their revenue must be to succeed.

Answers to this Quiz Yourself are on page 682.

5.3 Multiplying Decimals

Topics:
- Multiplying Decimals
- Multiplying by Powers of Ten
- Decimals and Exponents
- Circumference and Area of a Circle

Are You Ready?
To see if you are ready to understand this section, do the following short quiz.
1. $25(-46)$
2. $-3 \cdot (-12)^2$
3. -2^4
4. Find the area of a rectangle with width 13 ft. and length 37 ft.

Answers to Are You Ready?

(1) -1150   *(2) -432*   *(3) -16*   *(4) 487 ft^2*

Multiplying Decimals

Multiplication with decimal numbers is similar to multiplication with whole numbers. In fact, to multiply decimal numbers we just multiply as if they were whole numbers then decide where the decimal point should go in the product.

To Multiply Decimal Numbers:
- Ignore the decimals and multiply the factors as whole numbers.
- Include as many decimal places in the product as there are decimal places in all the factors together.

Example 1: Multiply.

a.) $0.8(5.25)$ b.) $(0.3)(-0.7)(-0.05)(-0.02)$

Solution: In each case we will multiply the same way we do whole numbers and put a decimal point in the final answer.

a.) $0.8(5.25)$

5.25	2 decimal places
×0.8	+1 decimal place
4.200	3 decimal places

b.) $(0.3)(-0.7)(-0.05)(-0.02)$

There are three points to note to do this product:

- The product has three (an odd number) of negatives so the product is negative.
- Ignoring the decimals: $3 \cdot 7 \cdot 5 \cdot 2 = 210$.
- There are $1 + 1 + 2 + 2 = 6$ decimal places in the factors, so there should be 6 decimal places in the product.

.000210.

We fill in the missing place values with zeros. Our final answer is expressed 0.00021 .

Good Question: Why do we multiply decimal numbers this way?

It has to do with place values and the fact that decimals can be written as fractions. Let me show you an example.

Consider the following product. $0.13(0.005)$

Rewrite the decimals as fractions. $0.13(0.005) = \dfrac{13}{100} \cdot \dfrac{5}{1000}$

The fraction multiplication shows why our decimal multiplication works.

$$\underbrace{\dfrac{13}{100}}_{\substack{2\ \text{decimal} \\ \text{places}}} \cdot \underbrace{\dfrac{5}{1000}}_{\substack{3\ \text{decimal} \\ \text{places}}} = \underbrace{\dfrac{65}{100000}}_{\substack{5\ \text{decimal} \\ \text{places}}}$$

Notice that we multiply as whole numbers. The number of decimal places is determined by the denominators, which represent the place values.

$$\underbrace{\dfrac{65}{100000}}_{\substack{5\ \text{decimal} \\ \text{places}}} = 0.\underbrace{00065}_{\substack{5\ \text{decimal} \\ \text{places}}}$$

Next is an example that ties decimal multiplication to our work with variables.

Example 2: Simplify.

a) $0.3(x + 5.2)$ b) $-2(x - 6.7) + 9.2x$

Solution: In each case we will use the distributive property to simplify the expressions.

a) $0.3(x + 5.2)$

Distribute. $0.3(x + 5.2)$ [PN: distribution arrows]

                                    $= 0.3x + 0.3(5.2)$

Multiply. $= 0.3x + 1.56$

b) $-2(x - 6.7) + 9.2x$

Distribute. $-2(x - 6.7) + 9.2x$

$$= -2x - (-2)(6.7) + 9.2x$$

$$= -2x + 13.4 + 9.2x$$

Combine like terms $= 7.2x + 13.4$

Example 3: Where in the World? Vince has designed a logo for a company that makes dog toys. The front of the business cards is shown to the right. To put this design on a flyer the dimensions of the image need to be increased by a factor of 2.4. What will the new dimensions be?

2.7 in

1.3 in

Solution: Recall that when we refer to the dimensions of a rectangle we are referring to the length and width. So the phrase "the dimensions of the image need to be increased by a factor of 2.4" means that we need to multiply the length and width by 2.4.

$2.7(2.4) = 6.48$ and $1.3(2.4) = 3.12$

So the new dimensions for the flyer will be 6.48 inches by 3.12 inches.

STOP Exercise Set - Multiplying Decimals

Multiply.

1. $(9)(0.3)$

2. $(0.07)(1.5)$

3. $(-2.6)(0.09)$

4. $(6.702)(-7)$

5. $(0.4)(-6)(-0.2)$

6. $(-0.5)(-0.7)(-0.01)$

Simplify.

7. $7.1(x + 0.3)$

8. $-2(x + 1.8)$

9. $-8.5(2x - 0.1) + 14.5x$

10. $0.79 - 0.04(4x - 3.5)$

11. Belinda has designed a flyer for a boat trailer company. The front of the flyers is 8.5 in. by 11 in. To put this design on a poster board the dimensions of the image need to be increased by a factor of 3.5. What will the new dimensions be?

12. Rob has designed a logo for a local bike shop. The front of the business cards is 1.3 in by 2.7 in. To put this design on a sign the dimensions of the image need to be increased by a factor of 30.6. What will the new dimensions be?

Multiplying by Powers of Ten

The numbers 10, 100, 1000, 10000, 100000,... are called powers of ten. Multiplying by powers of 10 is very common and can be done easily without actually having perform a stacked multiplication. To understand, observe what happens if we multiply 5.63 by two powers of ten.

5.63 2 decimal places

5.63 2 decimal places	×1000
×10	000
000	000
563	000
56.30 2 decimal places	563
=56.3	5630.00 2 decimal places
	=5630

Powers of Ten:

$10^1 = 10$

$10^2 = 100$

$10^3 = 1,000$

$10^4 = 10,000$

$10^5 = 100,000$

$10^6 = 1,000,000$

$10^7 = 10,000,000$

Note that the power is the same as the number of zeros.

Notice that the same products can be found by just moving the decimal point to the right the same number of places as there are zeros in the power to ten.

$5.63 \cdot 10$ $5.63 \cdot 1000$

5.6.3   5.630.

56.3   5630

To Multiply a Number by a Power of Ten: Move the decimal point to the right as many places as there are zeros in the power of 10.

Example 4: Find each product.
a.) $3.785 \cdot 100$ b.) $0.084 \cdot 100,000$

Solution:

a.) $3.785 \cdot 1\underbrace{00}_{\substack{2 \text{ decimal} \\ \text{places}}} = 3.78.5 = 378.5$ b.) $0.084 \cdot \underbrace{100,000}_{\substack{5 \text{ decimal} \\ \text{places}}} = 0.084 \underbrace{00}_{\substack{\text{fill in zeros} \\ \text{for new} \\ \text{places values}}} . = 8400$

Example 5: Where in the World? Scientific notation uses powers of ten to help express very large numbers. For example, the age of the Earth is about 4.6×10^9 years. Multiply 4.6×10^9 to give the age of Earth as a whole number.

Solution: We need to multiply 4.6×10^9. The exponent 9 in the form 10^9 means nine zeros, so $10^9 = 1,\underbrace{000,000,000}_{9 \text{ zeros}}$. That is,

$4.6 \times 10^9 = 4.6 \times 1,000,000,000$. We can perform this multiplication just by moving the decimal nine places to the right.

$$4.\underbrace{600000000}_{\substack{9 \text{ decimal} \\ \text{places}}} . = 4,600,000,000$$

So the Earth is 4,600,000,000 years old.

STOP Exercise Set - Multiplying by Powers of Ten

Find the product.

13. $3.456 \cdot 10$
14. $9.82 \cdot 100$
15. $439 \cdot 1000$

16. $892 \cdot 1000$
17. $0.089 \cdot 100$

18. $18.007 \cdot 100000$

19. $4.0019 \cdot 10$

20. $9214.904 \cdot 1000000$

21. Consumers bought 11.4 million i-phones in fiscal 2008. This means that Apple sold $11.4 \cdot 10^6$ i-phones or $(11.4)(1,000,000)$ in 2008. Multiply to find the number of i-phones sold as a whole number.

22. Consumers bought 16 million Blackberry cell phones in fiscal 2008. This means that consumers bought $16 \cdot 10^6$ or $(16)(1,000,000)$ Blackberry cell phones in 2008. Multiply to find the number of Blackberry cell phones sold as a whole number.

Exponents and Decimals

Of course, exponents can be applied to decimal numbers to express repeated multiplication. Remember that to raise a negative number to a power to a power it must be in parentheses.

$$(-5)^2 = (-5)(-5) = 25 \qquad\qquad -5^2 = -(5 \cdot 5) = -25$$

The same distinction applies when decimal numbers are involved.

Example 6: Perform the indicated operations.

a) $(3.14)^2$

b) -5.2^2

c) $(-0.3)^4$

Solution: The same rules apply for decimals as they did in section 2.5 when working with negatives.

a) $(3.14)^2$

Rewrite exponent into standard form.

$$(3.14)^2 = (3.14) \cdot (3.14)$$

Multiply. Note that the product will have four decimal places.

$$= 9.8596$$

b) -5.2^2

Rewrite exponent into standard form. Notice that the negative is not being squared.

$$-5.2^2 = -(5.2 \cdot 5.2)$$

Multiply. Note that the product will have two decimal places.

$$= -27.04$$

c) $(-0.3)^4$

Rewrite exponent into standard form.

$$(-0.3)^4 = (-0.3)(-0.3)(-0.3)(-0.3)$$

Multiply. Note that the product will $= 0.0081$
have four decimal places.

Example 7: Where in the World? The screen on the LG Dare touch-screen cell phone is a square with a side length of 2.7 inches. Find the area of the screen in square inches.

Solution:
Recall that the area of a square is found by raising the side length to the second power.

$A = s^2 = (2.7)^2 = 7.29$.

The area of the screen is 7.29 square inches or $7.29 \ in^2$.

STOP Exercise Set - Exponents and Decimals

Perform the indicated operations.

23. 2.1^2

24. 5.2^3

25. $(-0.14)^2$

26. -3.7^2

27. -5.01^2

28. $(-0.8)^4$

29. $5.1(0.03)^2$

30. $-0.01(8.3)^2$

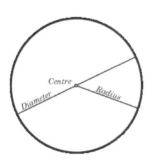

Here's the simplest formula you will learn all semester...
Determination + Hard Work = Success

Circumference and Area of a Circle

We have been working for a while with finding the perimeter and area of objects. Being able to work with decimals allows use to extend these ideas to *circles*. Here is a reminder of the terminology used to explore circles.

The distance from the center to a point on the circle is called the **radius**. We use the variable r for the radius of a circle.

The distance across the circle through the center is called the **diameter**. The diameter is always twice a long as the radius. We use the variable d for the diameter of a circle.

Finding the area and circumference both involve using the number π, pronounced "pie". The number π is a never ending, non-repeating decimal, but can be approximated as the decimal using $\pi \approx 3.14$ or as a fraction using $\pi \approx \dfrac{22}{7}$.

Strictly speaking, the word "perimeter" refers to the sum of the edges of an object. Since a circle has no edges, we use the word "circumference" instead. although they really mean the same things: the distance around the object.

The Circumference of a Circle: The distance around the circle is found using the one of the following formulas.

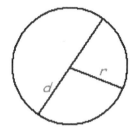

$$\text{Circumference} = \pi \cdot \text{diameter} \quad \text{or} \quad \text{Circumference} = 2 \cdot \pi \cdot \text{radius}$$
$$C = \pi d \qquad\qquad\qquad C = 2\pi r$$

$$\pi \approx 3.14 \text{ or } \pi \approx \frac{22}{7}$$

Example 8: Find the circumference of the circle using its diameter. Leave π in your answer to show the exact value then use $\pi \approx 3.14$ to find an approximation.

[PN: circle with diameter 8 inches and radius 4 inches]

Solution: Since the diameter is 8 inches we substitute $d = 8$ and into the formula $C = \pi d$.

$C = \pi d$
 $= \pi(8)$
 $= 8\pi$

So the exact value for the circumference is 8π inches. To get an approximation we substitute 3.14 in for π.
$C = \pi d$
 $\approx (3.14)(8)$ (we use $\approx$ here since our value of π is an approximation)
 $= 25.12$

So the circumference of the circle is about 25.12 inches.

Recall that area measures how many square units (like square feet ft^2 or square miles mi^2) an object takes up. Notice that a circle can be cut into pieces that can be put together like a parallelogram.

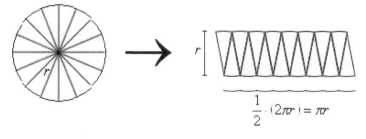

$$A = b \cdot h$$

In this case the formula $A = b \cdot h$ becomes $= r \cdot \pi r$.

$$= \pi r^2$$

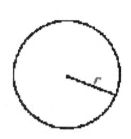

The Area of a Circle: The number of square units in a circle is found using the following formula.

$$\text{Area} = \pi \cdot (\text{radius})^2$$

$$A = \pi r^2$$

Example 9: Find the area of the following circle. Leave π in your answer to give an exact value. Then use $\pi \approx 3.14$ to get an approximation for the area.

Solution: In this figure we are given the diameter of the circle. Our area formula $A = \pi r^2$ relies on the radius. Since the diameter is always twice the radius we have the radius is 5 inches. So we substitute $r = 5$ into the formula $A = \pi r^2$.

$$A = \pi r^2 = \pi(5)^2 = \pi(25) = 25\pi$$

So the exact area is 25π square inches or $25\pi \, \text{in}^2$. To get an approximation we substitute in $\pi \approx 3.14$.

$$A = \pi r^2 = (3.14)(5)^2 = 3.14(25) = 78.5$$

So the area of the circle is about 78.5 square inches or $78.5 \, \text{in}^2$.

Example 10: Where in the World?
An agriculture specialist has a square plot of land to plant crops on. The square plot is 72 yards on each side, but the crop will be planted in a circle. Which of the following plans will provide more crop area?

    One large crop circle   Four smaller, equally sized crop circles

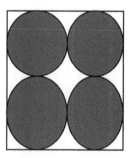

[PN: label radius of large circle 36 yards, radius of smaller circles 18 yards]

Solution:
Let's find the total area in each situation.

One large circle:
The radius of the large crop circle is 36 yards so we substitute $r = 36$ into the area formula:

$$A = \pi r^2$$
$$= \pi (36)^2$$
$$\approx 3.14 \cdot 1296$$
$$= 4069.44 \, yd^2$$

Four smaller equal circles:
The radius of each smaller crop circle is 18 yards, so to find the area of one of the four we substitute $r = 18$ into the are formula:

$$A = \pi (18)^2$$
$$\approx 3.14(324)$$
$$= 1017.36 \, yd^2$$

Since there are four circles in this plan we multiply this area by 4:
$$(4)1017.36 = 4069.44$$
So the total area for the four circles is $4069.44 \, yd^2$

So either plan produces the same area.

STOP Exercise Set - Circumference and Area of a Circle

Find the circumference of each circle. Leave π in your answer to show the exact value then use $\pi \approx 3.14$ to find an approximation. Do not forget to include units in your answer.

31. [PN: A circle with r =6in]

32. [PN: A circle with d=0.8ft]

Find the area of each circle. Leave π in your answer to show the exact value then use $\pi \approx 3.14$ to find an approximation. Do not forget to include units in your answer.

33. [PN: A circle with d=16.8cm]

34. [PN: A circle with r=4.2ft]

Find both the area and circumference of each circle. Leave π in your answer to show the exact value then use $\pi \approx 3.14$ to find an approximation. Do not forget to include units in both your answers.

35. [PN: A circle with r=9]
36. [PN: A circle with d=0.8]

37. A standard compact disc has a diameter of 4.5 inches but all the digital information is along the edge. Find the circumference. Use $\pi \approx 3.14$ to approximate your answer.

38. No planes are allowed to fly within three miles of a military base. How many square miles are covered by the "no fly" zone? Use $\pi \approx 3.14$.

5.3 Exercise Set - Putting it ALL Together

Multiply.

39. $7(8.4)$

40. $0.97(8)$

41. $(-0.4)(-0.8)$

42. $0.09(0.5)$

43. $(1.5)(-0.03)$

44. $0.3(0.7)(0.5)$

45. $(0.02)(-0.8)(0.03)$

46. $(-0.9)(2.45)$

47. $(0.025)(307)$

48. $4.5(-1003.8)$

49. $800(0.3)$

50. $14,000(0.05)$

51. $6.548 \cdot 100$

52. $761.45 \cdot 100$

53. $17.8192 \cdot 100000$

54. $78.4 \cdot 10$

55. $(-0.4)^3$

56. -0.9^2

57. $(-8.1)^2$

58. $(-0.07)^3$

59. $(0.01)^4$

60. $-2.1 \cdot (0.8)^2$

61. $-0.9 \cdot (0.3)^3$

62. It is common in algebra to take an expression and evaluate it repeatedly for different variable values. This can be organized using a table. Finish filling in the table below.

x	$0.5x$
1.2	$0.5(1.2) = 0.6$
-0.4	
0.6	
-2.5	

63. It is common in algebra to take an expression and evaluate it repeatedly for different variable values. This can be organized using a table. Finish filling in the table below.

x	x^2
-0.7	$(-0.7)^2 = 0.49$
-0.9	
0.06	
-1.5	

64. In Jay and Chrissie's neighborhood, they have decided to plant a community garden. The plot for the garden is a rectangle measures 40.8 ft by 78.9 ft. Find the total area of the garden. (Hint: Recall that the area of a rectangle is found by $A = LW$)

65. The dimensions of Apple's i-pad screen are 9.6inches by 7.5 inches. Find the area of the screen. (Hint: Recall that the area of a rectangle is found by $A = LW$)

66. Many companies that sell stock shares will send their shareholders a check each year based on the number of stock they have. These are called *dividends*. Dave has 1200 shares of stock in IBM. If they decide to pay a dividend of $0.08 per share, how much movie will Dave be sent?

67. Mike has 2700 shares of stock of Intel. One day, Mike checks the markets to see that the value of his stock has increased by $0.10 per share. How much did Mike earn in that day?

68. One bar of Hershey's milk chocolate has about 13.2 grams of fat. If you eat you bar a day for a week, how many grams of fat have you eaten?

69. One serving of Ben and Jerry's Froyo has 1.5 grams of saturated fat. How many grams of fat are in 6 servings?

70. Sound travels at a rate of 0.211 miles per second. How many miles will a sound travel in 8 seconds?

71. Apple sold 9.75 million Macs in fiscal 2008. This means that Apple sold $(9.75)(1,000,000)$ Macs. Multiply to find the number of Macs sold in standard form.

72. The RPM gauge in a car shows how many times per minute the engine is turning in revolutions per minute (RPM). The part of the gauges that says "$RPM \times 1000$" indicates that the numbers on the gauge should be multiplied by 1000 to get the number of revolutions per minute. How many times per minute is an engine turning if the RPM reads 3.9?

73. Nintendo sold overall 10.17 million Wii consoles in 2008 in the United States alone. This means that Nintendo sold $(10.17)(1,000,000)$ Wii consoles. Multiply to find the number of Wii consoles sold in standard form.

74. The distance (in miles between the Earth and the sun is about 9.3×10^6 miles. Multiply to find the distance between the Earth and the sun as a whole number.

75. Erin bought a new car and is making monthly payments. If the monthly payments are $315.67 for 4 years (48 months), how much does she pay for the car?

76. Morgan installed ADT home security in her home. Each month, she pays $46.79 for service. How much does she pay for the full year (12 months)?

77. Real estate agents are paid by charging fee based on the price of a house. Sandy Lutz, for example, is an agent who determines the fee by multiplying the sale price by 0.06. If she sales a house for $157,000 what fee will she charge?

78. An office supply store charges $0.014 per copy made. If a costumer requests 5000 copies, what will the total charge be?

Find the perimeter and area of each square. Make sure to provide units with your answer.

79. [PN: square with side length 1.6ft]   80. [PN: square with side length 0.08in]

Find the circumference of each circle. Use $\pi \approx 3.14$. Remember to include units with your answer.

81. [Circle with radius 6in]
82. [Circle with diameter 10cm]
83. [Circle with diameter 0.056ft]
84. [Circle with radius 8.4m]

Find the area of each circle. Use $\pi \approx 3.14$. Remember to include units with your answer.

85. [Circle with radius 2ft]
86. [Circle with radius 10mm]
87. [Circle with diameter 0.86in]
88. [Circle with radius 1.75mi]

Find the circumference and area of each circle. Use $\pi \approx 3.14$**. Remember to include units with your answer.**

89. [Circle with radius 3ft]

90. [Circle with diameter 200cm]

91.  [Circle with radius 0.9yd]

92. [Circle with radius 4.3m]

93. A regulation NBA basketball hoop has a diameter of 18 inches. Find the area and circumference of the basket.

94. The Kicker Coaxial Speaker head has a radius of 6 inches. Finds the area and circumference of the speak head.

The following bar graph shows the number of pounds of different types of waste generated by each person in the United States each day (Source: Environmental Protection Agency - www.epa.gov).

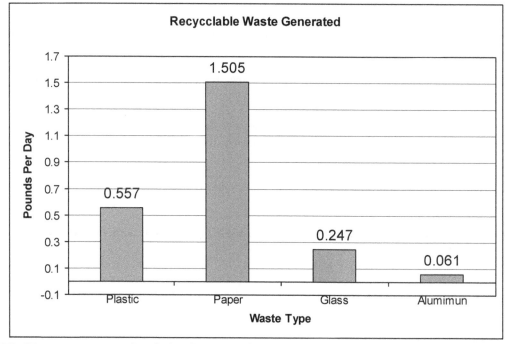

95. How many pounds of plastic waste does each person produce in a week?

96. How many pounds of glass waste does a person produce in a 30-day month?

97. How many pounds of paper and plastic waste combined does each person produce?

98. How much more paper waste does each person produce than plastic waste?

99. How may pounds of plastic waste does the average person produce in one year (365 days)?

100. How may pounds of paper waste does the average person produce in one year (365 days)?

101. 🖩 A community garden has been planted in Jenny's neighborhood. The plot measures 12.17 yd. by 37.09 yd. Find the total area of the garden. (Hint: Recall that the area of a rectangle is found by $A = LW$)

102. 🖩 A manufacturer making a large number of nutrition bars has placed orders for ingredient shown in the table below. Use multiplication to fill in the cost column for the order.

Ingredient	Price per Pound	Pounds Ordered	Cost
Peanuts	$1.47	485	
Chocolate	$3.25	250	
Oatmeal	$0.93	365	
Sugar	$2.14	250	

103. 🖩 A builder estimates that building a house will cost $65.75 per square foot. What will be the total cost of building a 1350 square foot house?

104. 🖩 Students hate carrying around a ton of books, so book makers are very careful about how thick a book will be once it is published. If one page is 0.0036 inches, how thick will a book be that has 978 pages?

Exercise Set - Chapter 5 Review

105. Add. $5.3 + (-9.8)$
106. Solve. $k - 0.06 = 0.073$
107. Round -6.893 to the nearest tenth.
108. Simplify $7.3g + 5.3w - 3.1g + 13$
109. Is $t = 4.5$ a solution to the equation $6.7 = t - 12.8$?

Exercise Set - Cumulative Review

110. Translate the following phrase into a math expression: *"three times some number plus seven"*.
111. What is the difference between an equation and an expression?
112. Simplify -5^2 and $(-5)^2$.
113. Subtract and reduce if possible. $\dfrac{4y}{15} - \dfrac{y}{15}$
114. Simplify. $9 - 3(8 - 3)$.

5.3 QUIZ YOURSELF

To make sure you are ready for the EXAM, try these problems without any help. Give yourself about 20 minutes and don't check the answers until you have completely finished.

1. $(-67.8)(-127.19)$
2. $789.4502 \cdot 100$
3. $(0.7)(-1.4)(-8.3)$
4. -0.89^2
5. $(2.37)^2$
6. $-7.5 \cdot (-2.7)^3$
7. Steve makes 8 payments of $145.67 for a new bike. What was the price of the bike?
8. Find the area of a daisy garden that is rectangular and measures 6.25 ft. by 3.45 ft.
9. Sales of PlayStation 3 hardware have grown during the second quarter in 2009 to 3.2 million. Multiply $3.2(1,000,000)$ to find the number of gaming systems sold in standard form.

Answers to this Quiz Yourself are on page 682.

5.4 Dividing Decimals

Topics:
- Dividing Decimal Numbers
- Dividing by Powers of Ten
- Solving Equations

Are You Ready?
To see if you are ready to understand this section, do the following short quiz.

1. Divide $14\overline{)602}$.

2. Multiply $4.78 \cdot 10^3$.
3. Solve $2(x-4)+3x = 7x+12$.

Answers to Are You Ready?
(1)43   *(2)4,780*   *(3)x = -10*

Dividing Decimal Numbers

The topic of dividing decimals will be easier if we review the vocabulary used for division. Please review the diagram to the right as we will be using these words to explain decimal division.

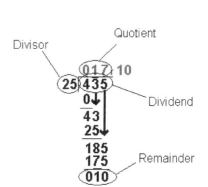

To Divide With Decimal Numbers:

- Set up long division as normal.
- If the divisor is a decimal, move the decimal point in both the divisor and the dividend until the divisor is a whole number.
- Write the decimal point in the quotient above its position in the dividend.
- Add zeros to the dividend to allow the division to continue until you have no remainder or you have divided enough to round the answer.

Here is a series of examples that show the cases that can come up in decimal division.

Example 1: Dividing Whole Numbers that Result in a Decimal Quotient
Divide. $885 \div 25$

Solution: The long division is set up to the right.

Notice that the decimal point in the quotient is directly above the decimal point in the dividend.

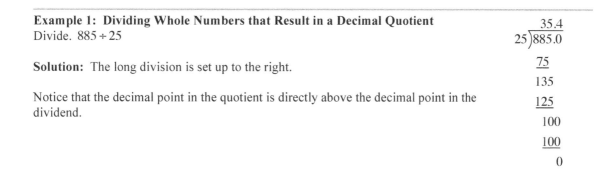

To continue the division we bring a zero down.

A remainder of zero means we are done.

The result is $885 \div 25 = 35.4$.

Example 2: Dividing a Decimal Number by a Whole Number
Divide $4.57 \div 12$. Round your answer to the nearest thousandth.

Solution: To round to the nearest thousandth we need to take the quotient to the ten-thousandths place, which is the 4th decimal place. The long division is set up to the right.

Again the decimal point in the quotient is directly above the decimal point in the dividend.

$$\begin{array}{r} 0.3808 \\ 12\overline{)4.5700} \\ \underline{36} \\ 97 \\ \underline{96} \\ 10 \\ \underline{0} \\ 100 \\ \underline{96} \\ 4 \end{array}$$

For this division we have to bring two zeros down.

We stop since we have enough place values to round to the nearest thousandth.

To the nearest thousandth, our answer is 0.381 .

Example 3: Dividing a Decimal Number by a Decimal Number
Divide $0.1494 \div 0.018$.

$$0.018\overline{)0.149.4}$$
$$\downarrow$$
$$18\overline{)149.4}$$

Solution: The divisor must be whole number. So to do the long division we must move the decimal point in the divisor and the dividend three places to the right. The long division is set up to the right.

$$\begin{array}{r} 8.3 \\ 18\overline{)149.4} \\ \underline{144} \\ 54 \\ \underline{54} \\ 0 \end{array}$$

Our result is $0.1494 \div 0.018 = 8.3$.

Example 4: Dividing a Decimal Numbers and Negatives

Divide $0.2605 \div (-0.05)$.

$$
\begin{array}{r}
5.21 \\
5\overline{)26.05} \\
\underline{25} \\
10 \\
\underline{10} \\
05 \\
\underline{5} \\
0
\end{array}
$$

Solution: Recall that a positive divided by a negative is negative, so we will neglect the signs and do the division first. The divisor must be whole number. So to do the long division we must move the decimal point in the divisor and the dividend two places to the right. The long division is set up to the right.

$$0.05.\overline{)0.26.05}$$

$$\downarrow$$

$$5\overline{)26.05}$$

Our result is $0.2605 \div (-0.05) = -5.21$.

Example 5: Rounding a Quotient

Divide $5.63 \div 4.8$. Round your answer to the nearest hundredth.

Solution: If we want to round to the nearest hundredth (2 decimal places) then we need to see the digit in the third decimal place.

$$
\begin{array}{r}
1.172 \\
4.8.\overline{)5.6.3}
\end{array}
$$

We could keep going with the division but we don't need to. Since we have the quotient to three decimal places we can round it off to two places.

$$1.172 \approx 1.17$$

Good Question: Why does the divisor have to be a whole number and why does it work to just move the decimal point in both numbers?

Answer: First...Why moving the decimal points works. Consider $0.1494 \div 0.018$ in a fraction form. Since we can multiply the numerator and denominator of a fraction by any nonzero number, multiply by 1000.

$$\frac{0.1494}{0.018} = \frac{0.1494 \cdot 1\,000}{0.018 \cdot 1\,000} = \frac{149.4}{18}$$

(3 decimal places marked over $1\,000$ in numerator; 3 decimal places marked under $1\,000$ in denominator)

This can be done for any problem that involves a decimal divisor.

Now...Why it's necessary to do decimal division this way.

$$0.18\overline{)0.1494}$$

$$\downarrow$$

$$18\overline{)149.4}$$

There is actually an alternative method for decimal division. But the alternative method is difficult to explain and difficult to remember. Making the divisor a whole number is far and away the easiest approach.

Example 6: Where in the World? Engineers have designed a cell phone battery that holds 8.45 watts. If one minute of cell phone use drains 0.037 watts from the battery, how many minutes should the cell phone be able to operate until the battery needs to be charged? Round your answer to the nearest tenth place.

Solution: The total power is 8.45 watts and one minute drains 0.037 watts. To find the total number of minutes the battery will last we should divide $8.4 \div 0.03$.

$$0.03. \overline{)8.50.} \rightarrow 3\overline{)850.00} \quad \text{(quotient: } 283.33)$$

We can stop since we have enough place values to round.

So the phone should operate for 283.3 minutes before a recharge is needed.

STOP Exercise Set - Dividing Decimals

Divide.

1. $71 \div 4$
2. $127 \div 5$
3. $10.92 \div 0.8$

4. $(-253.5) \div (-0.3)$
5. $5.819 \div 2.3$

6. $0.315 \div 4.41$

7. Divide $6.44 \div 0.13$. Round the quotient to the nearest tenth.
8. Divide $-0.6186 \div (0.52)$. Round the quotient to the nearest hundredth.

9. A biologist has a mass of plant cells that weighs 32.22 grams. If one plant cell weights about 0.009 grams, how many cells should in the entire mass?

10. Every small machine uses 0.016 liters of fuel per minute. If the engine has 1.155 liters of fuel left, how many minutes will it run?

Dividing by Powers of Ten

Recall that multiplying by a power of ten can be resolved by moving a decimal point to the right.

$$4.057 \cdot 10^4 = 4.057 \cdot \underbrace{10,000}_{\text{4 zeros}} = 4.\underbrace{0570}_{\substack{\text{4 decimal} \\ \text{places} \\ \text{right}}} = 40,570$$

A similar approach can be used for *division* by a power of ten. To understand, observe what happens if we divide a decimal number by powers of ten.

$$\begin{array}{r} 0.563 \\ 10\overline{)5.630} \\ \underline{50} \\ 63 \\ \underline{60} \\ 30 \\ \underline{30} \\ 0 \end{array}$$

$$\begin{array}{r} 0.00563 \\ 1000\overline{)5.63000} \\ \underline{5000} \\ 6300 \\ \underline{6000} \\ 3000 \\ \underline{3000} \\ 0 \end{array}$$

$10^1 = 10$
$10^2 = 100$
$10^3 = 1{,}000$
$10^4 = 10{,}000$
$10^5 = 100{,}000$
$10^6 = 1{,}000{,}000$
$10^7 = 10{,}000{,}000$
Note that the power is the same as the number of zeros.

Notice that same quotients can be found by just moving the decimal point to the *left* the same number of places as there are zeros in the power to ten.

$5.63 \div 10$

.5.63

0.563

$5.63 \div 1000$

.005.63

0.00563

To Divide a Number by a Power of Ten: Move the decimal point to the left as many places as there are zeros in the power of 10.

Example 7: Divide.

a.) $7.6 \div 100$

b.) $0.047 \div 100{,}000$

Solution: Since we are dividing we will move the decimal to the left, filling in zeros for new place values.

a.) $7.6 \div 1\underbrace{00}_{\text{2 zeros}} = .\underbrace{07}_{\substack{\text{2 decimal} \\ \text{places} \\ \text{left}}}.6 = 0.076$

b.) $0.047 \div 1\underbrace{00{,}000}_{\text{5 zeros}} = .\underbrace{00000}_{\substack{\text{5 decimal} \\ \text{places} \\ \text{left}}}.047 = 0.00000047$

Example 8: Where in the World? Scientific notation uses powers of ten to express very large and small numbers. For example, the acid level in a chemical might be expressed as $\dfrac{8.3}{10^3}$. Divide to express this division as a decimal number.

Solution: We are asked to divide $\dfrac{8.3}{10^3}$.

First, let's use our understanding of division and powers of ten to express the division in a more recognizable form.

$$\frac{8.3}{10^3} = 8.3 \div 10^3 = 8.3 \div 1000$$

So we're just dividing by a power of ten.

$$8.3 \div 1000 = .008.3 = 0.0083$$

Our final result is $\dfrac{8.3}{10^3} = 0.0083$.

Good Question: Why are powers of ten used this way? Why not always write numbers in decimal form like 0.0083 instead of $\dfrac{8.3}{10^3}$?

Answer: We're just warming you up to this topic. In Beginning Algebra you will explore it more using much higher powers of ten. For example, the width of a single strand of human DNA is 0.00000000012 centimeters. In scientific notation that's $\dfrac{1.2}{10^{10}}$.

$\dfrac{1.2}{10^{10}}$ → This power tells you how many decimal places the number has. This exponent form is just easier than counting up decimal placesin the form 0.00000000012.

In fact, of all the topics you study in math, scientific notation is one of the most likely you will see in other classes.

STOP Exercise Set - Dividing by Powers of Ten

Divide.

11. $782.39 \div 10$

12. $937.15 \div 1000$

13. $5.67 \div 100$

14. $186.5 \div 100000$

15. $0.817 \div 1000$

16. $0.064 \div 100$

17. A single silicon molecule weighs $\dfrac{2.02}{10^4}$ grams. Divide to express the weight as a decimal number.

18. A molecule of isopentyl acetate ($C_7H_{14}O_2$) weighs $\dfrac{8.0}{10^9}$ grams. Divide to express the weight as a decimal number.

Solving Equations with Decimals

Now that we know how to perform all four operations on decimals, we can solve any equation that has decimal numbers in it. Here is a recap of our steps for solving equations.

Steps for Solving an Equation:

1. Simplify each side separately by distributing and/or combining like terms
2. Add or Subtract to both sides of the equations so that terms with a variable are on the same side and terms with no variable are on the other side
3. Multiply or Divide both sides of the equation by the reciprocal of the variable's coefficient.

Example 9: Solve each equation.
a.) $0.5b + 5.74 = 6.928$
b.) $-4(0.7x + 0.5) + 13 = 7.2x$

Solution:

a.) $0.5b + 5.74 = 6.928$

Subtract 5.74 from both sides. $0.5b + 5.74 = 6.928$
$$\underline{-5.74 \quad -5.74}$$
$$0.5b \quad = 1.188$$

Divide both sides by 1.5. $$\frac{0.5b}{0.5} = \frac{1.188}{0.5}$$
$$b = 2.376$$

b.) $-4(0.7x + 0.5) + 13 = 7.2x$

Distribute −4 on the left side. $-4(0.7x + 0.5) + 13 = 7.2x$
$$-2.8x - 2 + 13 = 7.2x$$

Combine like terms on the left side. $-2.8x - 2 + 13 = 7.2x$
$$-2.8x + 11 = 7.2x$$

Add 2.8x to both sides. $-2.8x + 11 = 7.2x$
$$\underline{+2.8x \qquad +2.8x}$$
$$11 = 10x$$

Divide both sides by $$\frac{11}{10} = \frac{\cancel{10}x}{\cancel{10}}$$
$$\frac{11}{10} = x$$
$$x = 1.1$$

Example 10: Where in the World? A cab charges $2.40 to start plus $0.65 for each mile after. If a costumer is concerned about being overcharged and wants to verify. If the total fee is $18, how many miles was the trip?

Solution:

ASSIGN A VARIABLE   We are asked find the number of miles of the trip.
                                 m = miles driven on the trip

SUMMARIZE THE   cab charges 2.40 plus 0.65 per mile
INFORMATION   total fee is $18

DO THE MATH   cab charges 2.40 plus 0.65 per mile
                                 $2.40 + 0.65m$

                                 total fee is $18
                                 $2.40 + 0.65m = 18$

Solve the Equation:

$$2.40 + 0.65m = 18.00$$

- subtract 2.4 from both sides

$$\underline{-2.40} \qquad\qquad \underline{-2.40}$$
$$0.65m = 15.6$$

- divide both sides by 0.65

$$\frac{0.65m}{0.65} = \frac{15.6}{0.65}$$
$$m = 24$$

ANSWER THE QUESTION   The total distance for the trip should be 24 miles.

STOP Exercise Set - Solving Equations with Decimals

Solve.

19. $0.7x = 4.2$
20. $3.6 = -0.02x$

21. $\dfrac{-x}{8.6} = 2.45$

22. $\dfrac{x}{0.06} = -7.8$

23. $0.3x + 6.7 = 12.9$
24. $-2.51 = -1.6 + 1.3x$

25. $-0.15x + 1.35 = -70.2$

26. $2.1(x + 3.4) = -8.4$

27. A scientist studying a sample of bacteria notes that the sample weighed 1.5 grams on the first day and is gaining weight at a rate of 0.4 grams per day. How many days should it take for the sample to reach a weight of 3.9 grams?

28. Research suggests that while exercising a person's maximum target heart rate (in beats per minute) can be found by using the expression $206 - 0.9a$ where a is the person's age. If a doctor suggests that a person should have a maximum heart rate of 154 beat per minute, predict the person's age.

5.4 Exercise Set - Putting it ALL Together

Check: Fill in each blank with a word from our Vocabulary Checklist to the right. Each word is used exactly once.

Vocabulary Checklist:
divisor
dividend
quotient

29. In the decimal division $0.07\overline{)28.014}$ the decimal must be moved two places because the _____ has two decimal places.

30. To perform decimal division we may need to add zeros to the end of the _____.

31. To establish the decimal place for the _____ we just bring the decimal straight up from the dividend.

Perform the necessary operation.

32. $123.1 \div (0.003)$

33. $657.85 \div (0.05)$

34. $\dfrac{78.2}{-3.2}$

35. $-113.92 \div (-4)$

36. $\dfrac{-85.505}{-1.45}$

37. $214.578 \div (-91.7)$

38. $-89.453 \div 10000$

39. $-913.7 \div 100$

Solve.

40. $6.7x = 57.1041$

41. $18.375 = -\dfrac{3}{8}x$

42. $\dfrac{1}{4}x = -76.25$

43. $2.15x = -13.631$

44. $2.1x + 5.8 = -6.8$

45. $53.05 = -8.3x + 1.175$

46. $\dfrac{x}{0.3} = -17.4$

47. $-2x + 18.72 = -46.9$

48. $4.01 = 3x - 7.23$

49. $-8.5 = \dfrac{x}{0.05}$

50. $-9.1(2.1x + 8.74) = 371.462$

51. $67.298 = 1.9(2.1x - 4.9)$

52. $26.14 = 0.2(x - 4.1) + 10.8$

53. $0.3(x - 5.5) - 2.7 = -18.54$

54. $6.5 = x - 12.35$

55. $\dfrac{x - 16.3}{4.5} = -7.18$

56. $\dfrac{7.8 - x}{1.3} = -0.5$

For exercises # to #, use division to answer the question.

57. Jack bought a car for $7,849.95 and financed it for 2 years (24 months). How much is the monthly payment? Round your answer to the nearest cent.

58. Ellie bought a new computer for $1459.29. She financed it for 6 months. How much is her monthly payment? Round your answer to the nearest cent.

59. One gallon of semi-gloss paint can cover about 35 ft^2. Edgar's three bedrooms have a total surface area of 812 ft^2. How many gallons of paint should he buy?

60. Glenn and Sharon are painting the exterior of their house. The square footage they need to cover is 1771 ft^2. One drum of exterior paint can cover about 73 ft^2. How many gallons of paint should they buy?

61. Reed went to BestBuy and bought 13 DVD's. If the total cost was $114.27, how much did each DVD cost?

62. Wayne, Alan and David go to Comic-Con and find 8 rare Marvel toys. They spent a total of $148.72. How much did each toy cost?

63. Carmelina and Javier go to Disneyland and spend $417.10 for annual passports. Over the course of the year they go to Disneyland a total of 14 times. How much does it cost for each visit to Disneyland?

64. Shannon and Rory have San Diego Zoo annual passes for $101.05. Over the course of the year they go to zoo a total of 28 times. How much does it cost for each visit the zoo?

65. Rick buys some songs off the internet for $0.79 each. He spends a total of $18.17. How many songs did he buy?

66. The highest volume setting on a Hartke Bass Amplifier is 12. It produces a sound level (in decibels) of 91.2 decibels. If all 12 volume setting are equally spaced, how many decibels does each level produce?

67. To escape the Earth's gravitational field, a rocket must be traveling at a speed of 417.6 miles per minute. How many miles per second is this?

68. The fastest recorded speed by man was achieved in a SR-71 Blackbird jet at 2178 miles per hour. How many miles per minute is this speed?

69. A waste management truck can processes 45.6 tons of waste per day. If each day the truck makes 8 trips to and from a landfill, how many tons does it carry in each load?

70. The following table gives the total amount for a loan, the length of the loan (in months), and the monthly payments due. Use multiplication or division to fill in each missing cell. Round to the nearest cent if necessary.

California Finance Company		
Total Amount of Loan	Term of the Loan (in months)	Monthly Payments
$15,370	18	$\frac{\$15,370}{18} = \$853.89$
$7,804	10	?
$684	?	$45.60
?	20	$152.05

71. The following table gives the total size of a file download (in megabytes), the number of minutes it took for the file to download, and the download speed (in megabytes per minute). Use multiplication or division to fill in each missing cell. Round to the nearest tenth where necessary.

Megaware Computing Systems		
Total File Size (in MB)	Download Time (in minutes)	Download Speed (in MB per minute)
126	15	$\frac{126}{15} = 8.4$
220.8	24	?
?	42	7.5
54.6	?	1.2

72. A construction company must lay pipe that moves to and from several buildings. The length of each pipe segment is show below. If the construction crew can dig and lay down 9.2 yards of pipe per day, how many days should it take them to complete the project?

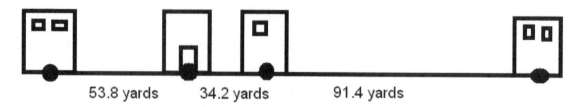

53.8 yards   34.2 yards   91.4 yards

73. A fencing company has a contract to fence in a rectangular area that is 56.3 feet by 42.5 feet. If each section of fencing is exactly 6.3 feet long, how many sections of fencing will it take to complete the project? [PN: corresponding picture]

74. Here are the American League's batting leaders for Major League Baseball's 2010 season.

Player	Batting Record
1. Josh Hamilton, TEX	.359
2. Miguel Cabrera, DET	.328
3. Joe Mauer, MIN	.327
4. Adrian Beltre, BOS	.321

Find the average of the batting records.

75. If the length of a rectangle is 4.5 feet and the total area is 30.6 square feet, what is the width? [PN: picture]

76. If the width of a rectangle is 9 inches and the total area is 77.4 square inches, what is the length? [PN: picture]

77. If the perimeter of a square is 10.4 yards, what is the length of one side? [PN: picture]

78. If the perimeter of a square is 63.2 meters, what is the length of one side? [PN: picture]

For exercises # to #, create an equation to answer the question and solve.

79. King palm trees grow at a rate of about 1.3 feet per year. If a king palm tree is currently 3.6 feet tall, how long will it take for it to grow to 20 feet? Round your answer to the nearest whole number.

TRUE or FALSE?

80. Dividing by a power of 10 can be done easily by moving the decimal place to the right.

81. In decimal division both the divisor and the dividend have their decimal places moved to the right, when necessary.

82. A negative decimal number divided by a positive decimal number will result in a negative quotient.

83. The division $0.3\overline{)4.05}$ is equivalent to $3\overline{)405}$.

84. The value $x = 4.48$ is the solution to the equation $\dfrac{x}{0.08} = 56$.

85. Write, using no numbers but only words how you would perform the division $0.5\overline{)0.37}$.

86. Without actually performing the division, explain the process for how you would round the quotient of $1.3\overline{)68.07}$ to the nearest hundredth.

87. In your own words, describe how to divide by a power of 10.

88. In what ways is dividing decimal numbers (like $15.6 \div 0.02$) different than dividing whole numbers (like $156 \div 2$)?

Exercise Set - Chapter 5 Review

89. Multiply. $(0.08)(-0.003)$

90. Investors use the formula $A = P + I$ to find the total amount in an investment account where A represents the total amount in the account, P represents the initial amount invested (called the *principle*), and I represents the interest earned. Find the total amount in an account if the principle is 405.94 and the interest earned is 56.70.

91. Add. $-4.3 + 13.8$

92. Convert the decimal number to a fraction to subtract. $0.05 + \dfrac{1}{6}$

Exercise Set - Cumulative Review

93. Divide. $(-42) \div (-6)$

94. Rewrite the exponent expression 6^4 in expanded form.

95. Divide. $\dfrac{-5a^3}{14b} \div \dfrac{4a^2b}{7b^2}$

96. Subtract. $14 - (-9)$

97. Use an integer to represent the information given including a unit: *"A deep sea diver is 252 feet below sea level"*.

5.4 QUIZ YOURSELF

To make sure you are ready for the EXAM, try these problems without any help. Give yourself about 20 minutes and don't check the answers until you have completely finished.

Perform the necessary operations.

1. $879.54 \div 5$
2. $394.64 \div 100$
3. $103.6288 \div (-18.4)$
4. Write the decimal 16.78 as a fraction. Reduce if possible.
5. The Alaskan pipeline can move 14.21 millions barrels of oil in one week. How many barrels can it move in one day?
6. Asha buys 4 Mighty Muggs from Comics-N-Stuff and spent a total of $61.96. How much did each Mighty Mugg cost?

Solve.

7. $2.3x = -13.547$
8. $\dfrac{-3}{5}x = 37.24$
9. $2.6x - 18.6 = 6.36$
10. $-3.4(6.2x - 39.4) + 76.4 = -39.612$

Answers to this Quiz Yourself are on page 682.

5.5 Fractions and Decimals, Order of Operations

Topics:

- Writing a Fraction as a Decimal
- Order Of Operations and Decimals
- Expressions and Formulas

Are You Ready?

To see if you are ready to understand this section, do the following short quiz.

1. Multiply. $(-3.8)(1.27)$
2. Subtract. $109.834 - 98.1496$
3. Multiply. $(2.1)\cdot(2.1)\cdot(2.1)$
4. Simplify. $4^2 - 7\cdot 6$
5. Simplify. $16 \div 4\cdot(-2)$

Answers to Are You Ready?

(1)-4.826   *(2)11.6844*   *(3)9.261*   *(4) -26*   *(5)-8*

Writing a Fraction as a Decimal Number

We have already discussed how to change a decimal number to a fraction:

$$0.8 = \frac{8}{10} = \frac{4}{5}$$

tenth's place → 10 as denominator

$$0.455 = \frac{455}{1000} = \frac{91}{200}$$

thousandth's place → 1000 as denominator

Now let's look at how to turn a fraction into a decimal number. The key is in the fact that the fraction bar can be interpreted as a division bar:

$$\frac{5}{8} = 5 \div 8 = 8\overline{)5.0}$$
$$\frac{14}{11} = 14 \div 11 = 11\overline{)14.0}$$

Since we have already studied decimal division, we know how to do these divisions.

To Rewrite a Fraction as a Decimal: Use decimal division to divide the numerator by the denominator.

Example 1: Convert each fraction to a decimal.

a.) $\dfrac{5}{8}$

b.) $5\dfrac{3}{11}$

Solution:

a.) $8\overline{)5.000}$ with 0.625 above

So we have $\dfrac{5}{8} = 0.625$.

b.) The whole part of the number is 5. To get the decimal part we convert $\dfrac{3}{11}$ to a decimal number.

$11\overline{)3.00000}$ with 0.27272 above

The pattern will never stop, so we use a repeating bar over the part of the decimal that

repeats. $5\dfrac{3}{11} = 5.272727... = 5.\overline{27}$

Good Question: Is there a way to tell when a decimal number is going to be a repeating decimal, like $\dfrac{6}{11} = 0.5454545... = 0.\overline{54}$?

Answer: Yes, there is. A *reduced* fraction will be a repeating decimal if its denominator has any factors other than 2 or 5. So, for example, $\dfrac{3}{16}$ WILL NOT be a repeating decimal since the only prime factor in the denominator is 2 ($16 = 2 \cdot 2 \cdot 2 \cdot 2$). But $\dfrac{5}{12}$ WILL be a repeating decimal since the denominator has a prime factor of 3 ($12 = 2 \cdot 2 \cdot 3$).

Often students want to convert ALL fractions to decimals to avoid fraction work. This gets them in trouble when the fractions turn out to be repeating decimals.

Example 2: Without actually converting to decimals, determine whether the following fractions will be repeating decimals.

a.) $\dfrac{13}{44}$

b.) $\dfrac{3}{20}$

Solution: A fraction will be a repeating decimal if the denominator has a prime other than 2 or 5. So let's look at the prime factorization for each denominator.

a.) $\dfrac{13}{44}$ $\quad 44 = 2 \cdot 2 \cdot 11$ $\qquad$ Since the denominator has a prime factor of 11 this fraction will be a repeating decimal.

b.) $\dfrac{3}{20}$ $\quad 20 = 2 \cdot 2 \cdot 5$ $\qquad$ Since the denominator's only prime factors are 2 and 5 this fraction will not be a repeating decimal.

Example 3: Where in the World? In a survey of 60 students, 14 of them same they spend more than 5 hours a week on social networks like facebook.com. Express the number of students that spend more than 5 hours on a social network as a fraction. Convert the fraction to a decimal number, round to the nearest hundredth.

Solution: The survey found 14 out of 60 students study more than 5 hours, so the fraction is $\frac{14}{60}$. To

convert we divide 14 by 60. $60\overline{)14.0}^{0.2\overline{3}}$. So $\frac{14}{60} \approx 0.23$.

STOP Exercise Set - Writing a Fraction as a Decimal

Write the following fractions and mixed numbers in decimal notation. Use a repeating bar if necessary.

1. $\dfrac{1}{2}$ 3. $-\dfrac{13}{5}$ 5. $-\dfrac{7}{4}$ 7. $\dfrac{7}{3}$ 9. $3\dfrac{7}{8}$

2. $7\dfrac{3}{4}$ 4. $-\dfrac{3}{8}$ 6. $-\dfrac{11}{12}$ 8. $\dfrac{5}{11}$ 10. $5\dfrac{2}{7}$

Remember a fraction will be a repeating decimal number if the denominator has any prime factors other than 2 or 5. Without actually converting to decimal notation, determine whether the following fractions will be repeating decimals.

11. $\dfrac{15}{8}$ 12. $\dfrac{7}{56}$ 13. $\dfrac{25}{6}$ 14. $\dfrac{17}{125}$

15. Out of 20 homes surveyed, 13 say they recycle. Express the number of homes that recycle as a fraction. Convert the fraction to a decimal number and round to the nearest tenth.

16. In a sample of 14 Droid phones, 2 of them are found to have a defect. Express the number of phones with a defect as a fraction. Convert the fraction to a decimal number and round to the nearest tenth if necessary.

Order of Operations and Decimals

Recall the order of operations.

The Order of Operations:

- Work inside grouping symbols such as parentheses first.
- Perform any exponents in the expression.
- Perform multiplication and division moving left to right.
- Perform addition and subtraction from left to right.

Example 4: Use the order of operations to simplify. Convert any fractions to decimal numbers.

a) $4.7(0.2)^3$ b) $15.8 - 1.8(4.6 + 2.4)$

Solution:

a.) Perform the exponent first.

$$4.7 \cdot (0.2)^3$$
$$= 4.7(0.008)$$

Multiply.

$$= 0.0376$$

b.) Recall it is tempting to do the subtraction first on this exercise since it is sitting in front. But the 1.8 is being multiplied to the parentheses so we have do deal with that first.

Add inside the parentheses.

$$15.8 - 1.8(4.6 + 2.4)$$
$$= 15.8 - 1.8(7)$$

Multiply.

$$= 15.8 - 12.6$$

Subtract.

$$= 3.2$$

If both fractions and decimals are present in an order of operations problem then before you begin, convert all the numbers to fractions or convert all the numbers to decimals.

Example 5: In each exercise convert all fractions to decimal numbers then simplify.

a) $4.8 \cdot \dfrac{3}{4} - 14.9$

b) $16.5 \div \dfrac{1}{2} + \left(\dfrac{27}{5} \right)^2$

> If an expression contains both fractions and decimals, convert the numbers to either all fractions or all decimals before you proceed.

Solution:

a) Convert the fraction to a decimal:

$\dfrac{3}{4} = 0.75$

$$4.8 \cdot \dfrac{3}{4} - 14.9$$
$$= 4.8 \cdot (.75) - 14.9$$

Multiply.

$$= 3.6 - 14.9$$

Subtract.

$$= -11.3$$

b) Convert both the fractions to decimals:

$\dfrac{1}{2} = 0.5 \qquad \dfrac{27}{5} = 5\overline{)27.0}\,^{5.4}$

Now we can continue with the order of operations.

$$16.5 \div \dfrac{1}{2} + \left(\dfrac{27}{5} \right)^2$$

$$= 16.5 \div 0.5 + (5.4)^2$$

Exponents first.

$$= 16.5 \div 0.5 + 29.16$$

Divide.

$$= 33 + 29.16$$

Add.

$$= 62.16$$

Example 6: In each exercise convert all decimal numbers to fractions and simplify. Express your answer as a fraction or mixed number.

a.) $\dfrac{1}{6}(0.8)+\dfrac{2}{5}\cdot 3$ b.) $\left(-2\dfrac{1}{2}+1.6\right)^2-\dfrac{7}{8}$

Solution:

a.) Convert the decimal number to a fraction:

$$\dfrac{1}{6}(0.8)+\dfrac{2}{5}\cdot 3$$

$$0.8=\dfrac{8}{10}=\dfrac{4}{5}$$

Now we can continue with the order of operations.

$$=\dfrac{1}{6}\left(\dfrac{4}{5}\right)+\dfrac{2}{5}\cdot 3$$

Multiply.

$$=\dfrac{1}{6}\left(\dfrac{4}{5}\right)+\dfrac{2}{5}\cdot\dfrac{3}{1}$$

Scratch Work:

$$\dfrac{1}{6}\left(\dfrac{4}{5}\right)=\dfrac{1\cdot 4}{6\cdot 5}=\dfrac{\cancel{2}\cdot 2}{\cancel{2}\cdot 3\cdot 5}=\dfrac{2}{15}$$

$$=\dfrac{2}{15}+\dfrac{6}{5}$$

Add.

$$=\dfrac{2}{15}+\dfrac{6\cdot 3}{5\cdot 3}$$

$$=\dfrac{2}{15}+\dfrac{18}{15}$$

$$=\dfrac{20}{15}=\dfrac{4}{3}$$

Convert to a mixed number.

$$=1\dfrac{1}{3}$$

b.) $\left(-2\dfrac{1}{2}+1.6\right)^2-\dfrac{7}{8}$

In this case, convert the decimal number to a mixed number:

$$\left(-2\dfrac{1}{2}+1.6\right)^2-\dfrac{7}{8}$$

$$1.6=1\dfrac{6}{10}=1\dfrac{3}{5}$$

$$=\left(-2\dfrac{1}{2}+1\dfrac{3}{5}\right)^2-\dfrac{7}{8}$$

Add inside parentheses.

$$=\left(-\dfrac{9}{10}\right)^2-\dfrac{7}{8}$$

Apply the exponent.

$$=\dfrac{81}{100}-\dfrac{7}{8}$$

Subtract.
Scratch Work:

LCD for $\dfrac{81}{100}$ and $\dfrac{7}{8}$:

$100 = 2 \cdot 2 \cdot 5 \cdot 5$
$8 = 2 \cdot 2 \cdot 2$ $LCM = 2 \cdot 2 \cdot 5 \cdot 5 \cdot 2 = 200$

$$= \dfrac{81 \cdot 2}{100 \cdot 2} - \dfrac{7 \cdot 25}{8 \cdot 25}$$

$$= \dfrac{162}{200} - \dfrac{175}{200}$$

$$= -\dfrac{13}{200}$$

Example 7: Where in the World? In a survey on study habits, five full-time students are asked to tell how many hours a day they study for their college classes. Here are the results:

Study Times: $6\dfrac{1}{2}$, 8, 5.3, 3.8, $7\dfrac{3}{4}$

Find the average study time given.

Solution: To find the average we first convert all the fractions to decimal numbers.

$6\dfrac{1}{2} = 6.5$, $7\dfrac{3}{4} = 7.75$

The average is given by the expression

$$\dfrac{6.5 + 8 + 5.3 + 3.8 + 7.75}{5}$$

$$= \dfrac{31.35}{5}$$

$$= 6.27$$

So the average study time is 6.27 hours.

STOP Exercise Set - Order of Operations and Decimals

Perform the order of operations.

17. $-0.7(6.2) + 15.3$

18. $7.5 \div (-0.5)(3)$

19. $0.37(5.6) + 1.63$

20. $16.79 - 7(-0.04)$

21. Convert the fraction to a decimal number to simplify the expression. $\dfrac{2}{5} \cdot (-0.4) + 9.13$

22. Convert the fraction to a decimal number to simplify the expression. $\dfrac{1}{8} \cdot (0.5 - 0.2) + 2.37$

23. Convert the decimal numbers to fractions to simplify the expression. $0.25 \div \dfrac{3}{4} + 0.6$

24. Convert the decimal numbers to fractions to simplify the expression. $\dfrac{1}{2} + 0.7(-1.3)$

25. The following table gives the water level for a reservoir over several weeks. Find the average level for the 4 week period.

Week	1	2	3	4
Level (in feet)	4.9	-3.2	-2.4	2.5

Find the average level for the 4 week period.

26. A group of patients are scored between are scored from -10 to 10 on a test. Here are the results.

-5.6   4.2   -1.5   7.8   0.8

Find the average score.

Expressions and Formulas

We have already had several examples in this chapter that involved evaluating formulas. But formulas are such an important part of math that we want to take this time to look at some more formulas that involve carefully executing the order of operations.

Example 8: Use a calculator to help evaluate each formula for the variable values given.

a.) $-gt^2 + vt$ for $g = 16.1$, $v = 50$, and $t = 0.4$

b.) $2(3.14)r(r+h)$ for $r = 0.5$ and $h = 1.2$

Solution:

a.) $gt^2 + vt$ for $g = -16$ for $v = 50$, and $t = 1.5$

$$gt^2 + vt$$

Substitute in the variable values given.
Now we can use the order of operations to simplify.

$$-16(1.5)^2 + 50(1.5)$$

Perform the exponent.

$$= -16(2.25) + 50(1.5)$$

Multiply.

$$= -36 + 75$$

Add.

$$= 39$$

b.) $2(3.14)r(r+h)$ for $r = 0.5$ and $h = 1.2$

$$2(3.14)r(r+h)$$

Substitute in the variable values given.
Now we can use the order of operations to simplify.
Perform the addition inside parentheses.
Multiply.

$$= 2(3.14)(0.5)(0.5+1.2)$$
$$= 2(3.14)(0.5)(1.7)$$
$$= 5.338$$

Example 9: The BIG Picture. The formula $Ax + By = C$ is very popular in Beginning and Intermediate Algebra. Determine whether the values given below make $Ax + By = C$ a TRUE or FALSE equation.

$A = 4.2$, $B = -3.5$, $C = 16.2$, $x = 7$, $y = 4$

Solution:

Substitute in the variables values given:

$A = 4.2$, $B = -3.5$, $C = 6.2$, $x = 7$, $y = 4$

$$Ax + By = C$$
$$4.2(7) + (-3.5)(4) = 16.2$$

Now we use the order of operations to simplify the left side:

- Multiply

- Add

$$4.2(7) + (-3.5)(4) = 16.2$$
$$29.4 + (-14) = 16.2$$
$$15.4 = 16.2$$

This is a FALSE equation.

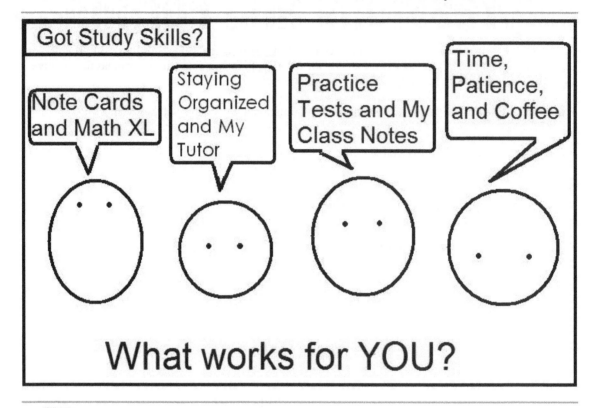

Got Study Skills?

Note Cards and Math XL

Staying Organized and My Tutor

Practice Tests and My Class Notes

Time, Patience, and Coffee

What works for YOU?

STOP Exercise Set - Expressions and Formulas

Evaluate the following expressions for the following values.

27. $x^2 - 3x + 24$, for $x = 0.6$

28. $x^2 + 7x - 11$, for $x = -0.2$

29. $4x - 8y$, for $x = 7.8$, $y = -1.5$

30. $3x + 8y$, for $x = 0.9$, $y = 0.04$

31. $17.8x - 4.1y^2$, for $x = 11.4$, $y = 2.08$

32. $3xy + x^2$, for $x = -3.2$, $y = 6.8$

33. $-7ab^2 + 1.2b$, for $a = -5$, $b = 0.91$

34. $b^2 - 4ac$, for $a = 0.1$, $b = 0.5$, $c = 2$

35. $b^2 - 4ac$, for $a = 6$, $b = -3.1$, $c = 0.09$

36. $mx + b$, for $m = \dfrac{-3}{5}$, $x = 1.4$, $b = 23.1$

37. $mx + b$, for $m = \dfrac{7}{2}$, $x = 7.016$, $b = -19.3$

The formula $Ax + By = C$ is very popular in Beginning and Intermediate Algebra. For exercises 38 and 39, determine whether the values given below make $Ax + By = C$ a **TRUE** or **FALSE** equation.

38. $Ax + By = C$ for $A = -1.7$, $B = 3.2$, $C = -6.82$, $x = 1$, $y = 1.6$

39. $Ax + By = C$ for $A = 7.9$, $B = -4.23$, $C = -40.62$, $x = 3$, $y = -4$

5.5 Exercise Set - Putting it ALL Together

Simplify, following the instructors given where appropriate.

40. $8.9 + (7.6)(-0.2)$

41. $(0.09)(1.5) + (6)(3.5)$

42. $(6.8)^2 \div (-0.2)$

43. $93.4 - (-5)^2$

44. $13.965 \div 1.5 \cdot (-3.2)$

45. $-14.122 \div 2.3 \cdot (5.1)$

50. $\dfrac{16.1 + 5.532}{7.2}$ - Round to the nearest thousandth.

51. $\dfrac{36.7 - 8.5}{(1.2)(-4.5) + 0.2}$ - Round to the nearest hundredth.

46. $\dfrac{1}{2} \cdot (-6.78) + 2.84$ - Work with decimals.

47. $\dfrac{2}{5}(-0.4 - 6.3)$ - Work with decimals.

48. $(0.6)^2 + \dfrac{3}{4}$ - Work with fractions.

49. $\dfrac{1}{2}(0.3) + \dfrac{2}{5}(0.8)$ - Work with fractions.

Evaluate the following expressions. Express all answers as decimal numbers.

52. $3x - 2.1x^2 + 4.5$; $x = 2.5$

53. $0.2x^2 - 5.4x + 29.34$; $x = 3.07$

54. $\dfrac{3}{2}RT$; $R = 0.8$, $T = 1.5$

55. $\dfrac{1}{2}bh$; $b = 2.3$, $h = 9$

56. $q + w$; $q = 415.67$, $w = 136.2$

57. $q \cdot r$; $q = -435.8$, $w = -85.61$

58. $\dfrac{-b}{2a}$; $b = 8.1$, $a = -0.5$

59. $\dfrac{1}{2}h(b + 9)$; $h = 6$, $b = 4.9$

60. πr^2 ; $\pi = 3.14, r = 0.7$

61. $4\pi r^2$; $\pi = 3.14, r = 3.05$

62. $\dfrac{4}{3}\pi r^3$; $\pi = 3.14, r = 2.9$

63. $6x^3$; $x = 0.1$

64. $x^2 + y^2$; $x = 0.04$, $y = -0.2$

65. $r^2 - x^2$; $r = 12.3$, $x = 3.45$

66. $mx + b$; $m = \dfrac{1}{2}, x = 3.1, b = 4.5$

67. $mx + b$; $m = \dfrac{-3}{5}, x = 7, b = -17.3$

68. The number π is sometimes approximated by the fraction $\dfrac{22}{7}$. Express this fraction as decimal number rounded to the nearest hundredth.

69. Use the formula $P = 2w + 2L$ to find the perimeter of the rectangle.
    [PN: rectangle with L = 6.6 and W = 9.8]

70. Use the formula $P = 2w + 2L$ to find the perimeter of the rectangle. Express your answer as a decimal number.
    [PN: rectangle with L = 6.6 and W = 9.8]

In 2010 Rolling Stone magazine surveyed 169 people to see which artists were the most influential in the history of rock and roll. The results are below. Answer the questions that follow. *Source: Rolling Stone*

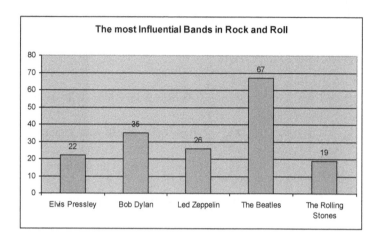

71. Write the fraction of voters that preferred Elvis as a decimal number. Round to the nearest thousandth.

72. Write the fraction of voters that preferred The Beatles as a decimal number. Round to the nearest thousandth.

73. Write the fraction of voters that preferred either Led Zeppelin or The Rolling Stones as a decimal number. Round to the nearest thousandth.

74. Write the fraction of voters that preferred either Elvis or Bob Bylan as a decimal number. Round to the nearest thousandth.

75. Without actually dividing to write it as a decimal number, how do you know that the number $\dfrac{112}{105}$ is greater than the number 1?

76. Without actually dividing to write it as a decimal number, how do you know that the number $\dfrac{75}{76}$ is greater than the number 1?

Fill in each blank with <, >, or = to make a true statement.

77. $\dfrac{7}{3}$ ___ 2.86

78. 0.48 ___ $\dfrac{1}{2}$

79. 0.098 ___ $0.0\overline{98}$

80. $0.\overline{3}$ ___ 0.3

81. $\dfrac{5}{7}$ ___ $0.\overline{71}$

82. $0.8\overline{3}$ ___ $\dfrac{5}{6}$

83. $\dfrac{478}{65}$ ___ 7.368

84. 18.906 ___ $\dfrac{9453}{500}$

85. An i-tunes shoppers buys seven songs for $1.29 each, three movies for $9.99 each, and two audio books for $24.59 each. Without actually finding the total charge, create an expression that would be used to find the total charge.

86. A snow ski rental store charges $12.65 for skis per day, $9.45 for a snow suit per day along with a flat fee of $15.95. Without actually finding the total charge, create an expression that would be used to find the total charge.

Exercise Set - Chapter 5 Review

87. Write the number 5.83 in words.
88. The Quick Sound MP3 player weighs 4.8 grams while an i-pod Nano weighs 3.1 grams. How much more does Quick Sound weigh?
89. Write the phrase "thirty-seven thousandths" as a decimal number.
90. Simplify. $5(0.9t - 0.4)$
91. Solve. $0.07x - 0.1 = 0.25$

Exercise Set - Cumulative Review

92. Simplify. $3|-7| + 3(-7)$
93. Solve. $2(3x - 7) - 4x = 6$
94. Round 69,634,713 to the nearest million.
95. Divide. $\dfrac{27}{28} \div \dfrac{4}{21}$
96. Add. $52 + 18$

5.5 QUIZ YOURSELF

To make sure you are ready for the EXAM, try these problems without any help. Give yourself about 20 minutes and don't check the answers until you have completely finished.

1. Write $\dfrac{7}{8}$ as a decimal.

2. Write $\dfrac{10}{13}$ as a decimal. Round your answer to the nearest thousandths place.

3. Simplify. $2.3 \div 0.5 + 16.7$

4. Simplify. $16.75 - (-3.6)^2$

5. Simplify. $-19.34 \div (0.2) + \dfrac{1}{4} \cdot (18.31)$

6. Evaluate $b^2 - 4ac$ for $a = 3.4, b = -2.1, c = \dfrac{1}{4}$

7. Evaluate $\dfrac{1}{2}hb$, for $h = 18.5, b = 38.17$

8. Evaluate $2\pi r^2 + 2\pi rh$, for $\pi = 3.14, r = 3.1, h = 8.92$

Find the perimeter and area of the following composite shape.

9. [PN: rectangle sides 17.92 ft. and 9.52 ft. with a triangle on top, sides 14.91 ft. and 11.05 ft. with height 12.3 ft.]

Answers to this Quiz Yourself are on page 682.

5.6 Statistics: Mean, Median and Mode

Topics:
- Finding the Mean of a Data Set
- Finding the Median of a Data Set
- Finding the Mode of a Data Set

Are You Ready?
To see if you are ready to understand this section, do the following short quiz.

1. $4\frac{2}{3} + 5\frac{3}{4} + 3\frac{5}{8}$

2. $\dfrac{14.5 + 18.3 + 23.5 + 20.1}{4}$

3. Find the average test score if Melody's test scores in her Chemistry are 78, 92, 88, 83 and 89.

Answers to Are You Ready?

(1) $14\frac{1}{24}$ *(2)29.1*   *(3)86*

Finding the Mean of a Data Set

Answering questions in the real world often means dealing with a large set of numbers.

Statistics is the branch of math that deals with collecting, organizing, and interpreting real-world data. As an example of how statistics is used, consider the following scenario.

A coach for a pro cycling team wants to know which is better for the bikers: a 15" gear or a 17" gear. To decide, he will send the riders for several rides using each gear. Suppose they get the following results.

Time results using a 15" gear (in minutes)				
55.3	54.7	53.7	52.3	55.3

Time results using a 17" gear (in minutes)				
56.2	53.4	52.3	51.4	53.5

These are two examples of data sets.

A **data set** is a collection of numbers.

So which gear performed better? This is where statistics comes in. One way to decide is to use what are called *measures or central tendency.*

A **measure of central tendency** is a number that reflects the "middle" or "expected value" of a data set.

There are three common measures of central tendency: *mean*, *median*, and *mode*. The most common used of these is the one that we have already been working with in this book: mean (or average).

To find the mean (or average) of a data set: Take the sum of the numbers and divide by the number of numbers in the data set.

Example 1: Where in the World? The following data set gives time (in minutes) on a bike ride using a 15" gear. Find the average of the data set. Round your answer to the nearest tenth.

Time result using a 15" gear (in minutes)				
55.3	54.7	53.7	52.3	55.3

Solution: $\dfrac{55.3+54.7+53.7+52.3+55.3}{9} = \dfrac{271.3}{5} \approx 54.3$

So the mean time for the 15" gear is 54.3 minutes.

Find the mean of the following list of numbers:

1.   45, 58, 67, 39, 45, 52

2.   11.3, 15.8, 23.8, 19.2, 29.3

3.   ▤ 118, 278, 167, 121, 145, 197, 188, 106

4.   ▤ 2.415, 3.115, 2.865, 1.079, 2.871

5. $5\dfrac{1}{2}, 4\dfrac{2}{3}, 5\dfrac{1}{3}, 3\dfrac{3}{5}, 4\dfrac{4}{5}, 3\dfrac{2}{3}$

6. $1\dfrac{1}{4}, 1\dfrac{7}{8}, 1\dfrac{4}{5}, 2\dfrac{1}{6}, 2\dfrac{2}{9}$

Finding the Median of a Data Set

The second most common measure of central tendency is called the *median*.

To find the median of a data set:

- List the numbers in order from smallest to largest. The **median** is the number exactly in the middle.
- If there are an even number of numbers in the data set, then the median is the average of the two numbers that fall in the middle.

Example 2: Where in the World? The following data set gives time (in minutes) on a bike ride using a 17" gear. Find the median of the data set. Round your answer to the nearest tenth.

Time results using 17" gear (in minutes)				
56.2	53.4	52.3	51.4	53.5

Solution: We list the numbers in order. The median is the number in the middle.

$$51.4 \qquad 52.3 \qquad 53.4 \qquad 53.5 \qquad 56.2$$

So the median time for the rides was 53.4 minutes.

Example 3: Where in the World? The following data set gives the wing span of 6 humming birds.

Hummingbird wing spans (in inches)	$4\frac{3}{8}$	$4\frac{1}{8}$	$3\frac{1}{2}$	$3\frac{7}{8}$	$4\frac{3}{4}$	$5\frac{1}{4}$

Solution: We list the numbers in order. Notice that since there are an even number of data points there are two numbers that fall in the middle.

$$3\frac{1}{2},\ 3\frac{7}{8},\ 4\frac{1}{8},\ 4\frac{3}{8},\ 4\frac{3}{4},\ 5\frac{1}{4}$$

To find the median we take the average $4\frac{1}{8}$ and $4\frac{3}{8}$. To do this we add them together and divide by 2:

We need to find the average of $4\frac{1}{8}$ and $4\frac{3}{8}$.

$$\dfrac{4\frac{1}{8}+4\frac{3}{8}}{2}$$

On the top, add the whole and fraction parts separately.

$$=\dfrac{8\frac{4}{8}}{2}=\dfrac{8\frac{1}{2}}{2}$$

Convert to an improper fraction for division.

$$=\dfrac{\frac{17}{2}}{\frac{2}{1}}$$

Reciprocate the second fraction and multiply.

$$=\frac{17}{2}\cdot\frac{1}{2}$$

$$=\frac{17}{4}=4\frac{1}{4}$$

So the median wing span of the hummingbirds is $4\frac{1}{4}$ inches.

STOP Exercise Set - Finding the Median of a Data Set

Find the median of the following list of numbers:

7. 45, 58, 67, 39, 45, 52
8. 118, 278, 167, 121, 145, 197, 188, 106
9. 11.3, 15.8, 23.8, 19.2, 29.3
10. 2.45, 3.15, 2.85, 1.79, 2.87
11. $5\frac{1}{2}, 4\frac{2}{3}, 5\frac{1}{3}, 3\frac{3}{5}, 4\frac{4}{5}, 3\frac{2}{3}$
12. $1\frac{1}{4}, 1\frac{7}{8}, 1\frac{4}{5}, 2\frac{1}{6}, 2\frac{2}{9}$

Finding the Mode of a Data Set

The last and least common measure of central tendency is the mode.

The **mode** of a data set is the value in the set that occurs the most number of times. A data set can have more than one mode (if more than one value occurs frequently) or no mode (if no value is repeated).

Example 4: Where in the World? The data set below was taken from a crash. Eleven cars were tested to determine what collision speed caused significant damage. Find the mode of the speeds given in miles per hour below.

Collision speeds (in miles per hour): 24, 15, 18, 20, 18, 22, 24, 26, 18, 26, 24

Solution: To organize the data set, we write the value in order.

15, 18, 18, 18, 20, 22, 24, 24, 24, 26, 26

Since 18 and 24 both occur three times, the modes are 18 and 24 miles per hour.

STOP Exercise Set - Finding the Mode of a Data Set

Find the mode of the following list of numbers:

13. 45, 58, 67, 39, 45, 52, 44, 56, 59, 66
14. 118, 120, 125, 132, 120, 118, 119, 127, 120, 145, 116, 105
15. 11.3, 15.8, 23.8, 19.2, 10.8, 23.8, 11.8, 12.9
16. 15.45, 13.25, 18.13, 14.83, 18.92, 15.78
17. $\frac{7}{8}, \frac{9}{11}, \frac{2}{3}, \frac{5}{6}, \frac{14}{16}, \frac{6}{9}, \frac{4}{6}, \frac{5}{6}$ (Hint: reduce each fraction first.)
18. $3\frac{1}{4}, 4\frac{3}{8}, 3\frac{4}{5}, 3\frac{1}{2}, 4\frac{3}{8}$

Exercise Set - Putting it ALL Together

19. The temperatures for a given week in Playa Dominical, Costa Rica are 82, 88, 91, 87, 86, 88, 92. Find the median temperature for the given week. What is the mode temperature?

20. The cost of five different brands of a jar of peanut butter is $2.45, $3.15, $2.85, $1.79, $4.87. Find the mean cost and the median cost of a jar of peanut butter.

21. On a Chemistry exam that had 12 questions, the following is the number correct for 15 students: 10, 9, 5, 11, 12, 7, 8, 9, 10, 11, 6, 12, 10, 11, 4. Find the mean correct answers on this Chemistry exam.

22. Use the data in # to find the median and mode of the exam grades.

23. A math professor takes a sample of homework grades from her students. The sample is below.

| Sample Homework Scores | 76 | 0 | 55 | 100 | 100 | 75 | 85 | 60 |

Find the mean, median and mode of the data set. Between the mean, median, and mode, which one do think is a bad indicator for the "middle value" and why?

24. A math professor takes a sample of homework grades from her students. The sample is below.

| Sample Homework Scores | 89 | 95 | 100 | 0 | 76 | 0 | 81 | 100 |

Find the mean, median and mode of the data set. Between the mean, median, and mode, which one do think is a bad indicator for the "middle value" and why?

A track coach measures the heart rate of ten members of her team after a long run. The results are below. Answer the questions that follow.

| Pulse | 120 | 146 | 105 | 112 | 105 |
| Rates | 105 | 115 | 109 | 115 | 98 |

25. Find the mean of the heart rates.
26. Find the mode of the heart rates.
27. Find the median of the heart rates.
28. How many team members have a heart rate that is above the mean?
29. How many team members have a heart rate that is below the mean?

Exercise Set - Chapter 5 Review

30. Find the perimeter of the triangle. [PN: triangle with sides 5.3in, 2.7in, 4in]
31. The TI-83 calculator has a rectangular screen that is 2.4 by 1.5 inches. Find the perimeter and area of the screen.
32. Wayne and Bethanie have theatre passes that cost $453.35. If the passes include 5 shows, how much is the price of each show?
33. Write $-\dfrac{7}{4}$ as a decimal number.
34. Solve. $\dfrac{x+0.8}{-1.5} = 7$

Exercise Set - Cumulative Review

35. Add and reduce if possible. $\dfrac{5}{6} + \left(-\dfrac{1}{6} \right)$

36. Graph the following list of numbers on a number line: -5, 3, 0, -1
37. Find the prime factorization of 42.
38. Evaluate the expression $mx + b$ for $m = 5$, $b = 3$, and $x = 6$.
39. Multiply. $2\dfrac{6}{7} \cdot \dfrac{14}{20}$

 # 5.6 QUIZ YOURSELF:

To make sure you are ready for the EXAM, try these problems without any help. Give yourself about 20 minutes and don't check the answers until you have completely finished.

1. Find the mean, median, and mode of the following data set: 6, 15, 7, 12, 22, 8, 7
2. Find the mean, median, and mode of the following data set: 0.9, 7.8, 4.5, 3.6
3. Find the mean, median, and mode of the following data set: $\dfrac{1}{2}, \dfrac{4}{5}, \dfrac{3}{10}, \dfrac{4}{5}, \dfrac{1}{4}$

4. The following data set represents a sample of the tallest and shortest NBA players. Find the median and mode of the data set. *Source: www.NBA.com*

Yao Ming, Houston	7'6"
Zydrunas Ilgauskas, Cleveland	7'3"
Mile Ilic, New Jersey	7'2"
Primoz Brezec, Charlotte	7'1"
Tyson Chandler, NO/Okla City	7'1"
Jerome James, New York	7'1"
Shaquille O'Neal, Miami	7'1"
T.J. Ford, Toronto	5'11"
Andre Barrett, Chicago	5'10"
Brevin Knight, Charlotte	5'10"
Mike Wilks, Seattle	5'10"
Brian Chase, Utah	5'9"
Nate Robinson, New York	5'9"
Earl Boykins, Denver	5'5"

5. A sample of 8 cartons of chocolate chip ice cream is taken and the amount of chocolate in each container is weighed. The results are below. Find the mean of the data set and round to the nearest hundredth.

Weight (in grams)	1.0	1.1	1.6	0.9	1.4	0.9	0.1	1.7

Chapter 5 Summary and Review_____

Section 5.1: Introduction to Decimals

Processes and Important Notes	Examples

Reading and Writing Decimal Numbers:
• **To read the decimal part of a number:** Read the number as if it were a whole number then say the last place value as the end.
• **To Read a Number with a Whole Part and Decimal Part:** Read the whole part first, use the word "and" for the decimal point, and then read then decimal part.
	How would each phrase be written as a decimal number?
	  a. Two and fifteen thousandths
	  b. Five hundred six ten thousandths
	
	Solution:
	  a. 2.015
	  b. 0.05016

Ordering Decimals:
• **To Order Two Decimal Numbers:** Begin at the far left of the numbers and compare their place values until you find a difference. The number with higher value in that place value is the greater number.
	Fill in each blank with a < or >.
	  a. 10.13 _____ 101.31
	  b. 3.476 _____ 3.467
	
	Solution:
	  a. 10.13 _ < _ 101.31
	  b. 3.476 _ > _ 3.467

Writing a Decimal as a Fraction:
 	
• **To Convert a Decimal to a Proper or Improper Fraction:** The numerator is just the number given written without the decimal. The denominator is the power of ten (as in 10, 100, 1000, 10000, 100000, etc.) that corresponds to the decimal numbers last place value. Don't forget to reduce if possible.
• **To Convert a Decimal to a Mixed Number:** Convert the decimal part of the number to a proper fraction and keep the same whole part.
	Convert each decimal number to a proper or improper fraction in lowest terms.
	  a. 0.16 $\frac{16}{100}$ $17\frac{345}{1000}$
	  b. 17.345
	
	Solution:
	  a. 0.16 is read sixteen hundredths or $\frac{16}{100}$, which can be reduced to $\frac{4}{25}$.
	  b. 17.345 is read seventeen and three hundred forty-five thousandths or $17\frac{345}{1000}$, which can be reduced to $17\frac{69}{200}$.

Rounding Decimals: • **To Round a Decimal Number to a Given Place Value:** Look at the value to the left of the place value given for rounding. If that value is 5 or more, round up. If it is 4 or less, round down.	Round 0.53917 to the nearest thousandths. Solution: Since the thousandths place is the 3rd decimal place, we look at the number in the ten thousandths place or the 4th decimal place, which is 1. Since 1 is less than 5, we replace with zeros. Therefore 0.53917 rounded is 0.539.

Write the following decimals in words.
   1. 0.75   2. 1.8   3. 78.17   4. 932.49

Write the following decimals as fractions.
   5. 0.375   6. 5.6   7. 127.48   8. 628.62

Order the following decimals.
   9. 0.234 _____ 0.433   11. -11.056 ___ -11.065
   10. 5.071 ___ 5.710   12. -78.1 ___ -7.81

Round the following decimals to the place value given.
   13. 1.357 ; tenths   15. 35.352 ; hundredths
   14. 0.0983 ; thousandths   16. 62.947 ; tenths

Section 5.2: Adding and Subtracting Decimals

Processes and Important Notes	Examples

Adding and Subtracting Decimals:
To Add or Subtract Decimals Numbers:
  • Line up the place values by lining up the decimals, putting zeros in missing place values as necessary. Then add or subtract using the same method as for whole numbers.
	Add. $16.405 + 812.01$
	
	Solution:
	   16.405
	$+812.01$
	   828.415

Working with Positive and Negative Decimals:
Review of Addition/Subtraction Rules for Signed Numbers:
  • <u>To add two negatives</u>, add their absolute value and make the result negative.
  • <u>To add a negative and a positive</u>, take the difference between their absolute values and give the result the same sign as the number with higher absolute value.
	Subtract. $-34.26 - (-5.708)$
	
	Solution:
	Rewrite as addition. $= -34.26 + (+5.708)$
	Rewrite with largest 34.26
	Number in absolute 1st. $\underline{-5.708}$
	                   28.552
	Final answer is negative. -28.552

Solving Equation:	**Solve.** $n + 6.07 = 14.35$
	
	Solution:
	        $n + 6.07 = 14.35$
	        $\underline{-6.07\quad -6.07}$
	              $n = 8.28$

Add or Subtract.
   17. $16.8 + 23.1$ 20. $-88.75 - 103.8$
   18. $17.85 - 9.23$ 21. $-7 + 3.677$
   19. $102.034 - (-50.92)$ 22. $-54.391 - (-1.9047)$

Simplify.
   23. $2.1x + 5.4x + 18.9$ 25. $-3.45a - 7.8 - 2.89a - (-1.67)$
   24. $23.1m - 67.08m + 37.9$ 26. $-19.95 + 56.8n - 3.97n + (-54.22)$

Solve.

27. $x - 17.1 = 5.3$ 29. $16 + x = 15.4 - 12.7$

28. $x + 4.5 = 3.09$ 30. $-18.9 + 34.6 = m + 2.18$

31. Lucille had $567.29 in her checking account. She went shopping and spent $23.17, $35.83, and $18.91 at a few clothing shops. How much money is left in her account after her day of shopping?

32. Buster had $892.16 in her checking account. She deposited her paycheck of $378.01 and then paid here rent of $345, electric bill of $48.28, insurance bill of $135.27, and credit card bill of $246.26. How much money does she have left in her checking account?

Section 5.3: Multiplying Decimals

Processes and Important Notes	Examples
Multiplying Decimals: **To Multiply Decimal Numbers:** • Ignore the decimals and multiply the factors as whole numbers. • Include as many decimal places in the product as there are decimal places in ALL the factors.	**Simplify.** $(3.41) \cdot (2.9)$ **Solution:** 　3.41　　**2 decimal places** $\times 2.9$　　**1 decimal place** 　3069 　682$\times$ 9.889　Move decimal to left three place values. **Simplify.** $-7.8(0.04x - 39.01)$ **Solution:** $-7.8(0.04x - 39.01) = -7.8 \cdot 0.04x - (-7.8) \cdot 39.01$ $= -0.312x + 304.278$
Multiplying by Powers of Ten: • Move the decimal point to the right as many places as there are zeros in the power of 10.	**Multiply.** $107.349 \cdot 100$ **Solution:** Move decimal to right twice since there are 2 powers of 10. So, 　　$107.349 \cdot 100 = 10734.9$
Exponents and Decimals: • Recall: The exponent tells how many times the base is multiplied by itself. • Recall: In an expression like -5.2^2 the exponent only applies to the number 5.2, *not* the negative sign.	**Perform indicated operation:** $(-2.1)^3$ **Solution:** $(-2.1)^3 = (-2.1) \cdot (-2.1) \cdot (-2.1)$ 　　　　$= 4.41 \cdot (-2.1)$ 　　　　$= -9.251$
Area and Circumference of a Circle: • A **circle** is the set of all points that are the same distance from a given point (called the **center**). • The **radius** of a circle is the distance from the center of the circle to a point on the circle. • The **diameter** of a circle is the distance between points on the circle through the center. • The **circumference** of a circle is the	**Find the radius of a circle given the diameter is 16.89 ft.** Since $d = 2r$ 　　$\dfrac{16.89}{2} = \dfrac{2r}{2}$ So, $r = 8.445$ *ft.* **Find the area and circumference of a circle with a radius of 6.1 m. Use $\pi \approx 3.14$.** Area: $A = \pi r^2$

distance around the circle and can be found using the formulas $C = 2\pi r$ or $C = \pi d$. • The **area** of a circle can be found using the formula $A = \pi r^2$	$A = 3.14 \cdot (6.1)^2$ $A = 3.14 \cdot (37.21)$ $A = 116.8394 \ m^2$ Circumference: $C = 2\pi r$ $C = 2 \cdot 3.14 \cdot 6.1$ $C = 6.28 \cdot 6.1$ $C = 38.308 \ m$

Multiply.

33. $5.5 \cdot 7$
34. $-38.05 \cdot 18.5$
35. $6.7(-0.4)$
36. $7.0946 \cdot 100$
37. $-35.87 \cdot 10$

38. $209.1 \cdot 0.25$
39. $(-9.07)(-14.8)$
40. $-0.00067 \cdot 1000$
41. 3.8^3

42. $(-5.1)^2$
43. -1.1^4
44. $-7.7 \cdot 5.1^2$

For the following problems, use $\pi \approx 3.14$.

45. Find the circumference of a circle with radius 5.2 m.
46. Find the area of a triangle with base 24.3in. and height 18.7in.
47. Dave wants to mulch the circular area around the apple tree he just planted in his backyard. The diameter of the circular area he wants to mulch is 6 ft. Find the area of how much space he needs to mulch.

48. [calculator icon] Katie works for a national park and needs to rope off a circular section of trails for re-growth. The diameter of the park has a diameter of 36.2 ft. Find the amount of rope needed to protect the section.

Section 5.4: Dividing Decimals

Processes and Important Notes	Examples
Dividing Decimal Numbers: • Set up long division as normal. • If the divisor is a decimal, move the decimal point in both the divisor and the dividend until the divisor is a whole number. • Write the decimal point in the quotient above its position in the dividend. • Add zeros to the dividend to allow the division to continue until you have no remainder or you have divided enough to round the answer.	**Divide.** $11.282 \div 0.2$ **Solution:** $0.2\sqrt{11.282}$ $\phantom{0.2\sqrt{}}56.41$ $2\sqrt{112.82}$ $\underline{-10} \downarrow\downarrow\downarrow \quad$ bring down the 2 12 $\underline{-12} \downarrow\downarrow \quad$ bring down the 8 08 $\underline{-8} \downarrow \quad$ bring down the 2 02 $\underline{-2}$ 0
Dividing by Powers of Ten: • Move the decimal point to the left as many places as there are zeros in the power of 10.	**Divide.** $459.034 \div 1000$ **Solution:** Since there are 3 powers of 10, move the decimal place to the left 3 times to get: $459.034 \div 1000 = 0.459034$

Solving Equations:	Solve. $-3.5(0.2x-1.2)+0.8=5.6x-1.3$
a. Simplify each side separately by distributing and/or combining like terms b. Add or Subtract to both sides of the equations so that terms with a variable are on the same side and terms with no variable are on the other side c. Multiply or Divide both sides of the equation by the reciprocal of the variable's coefficient.	**Solution:** a. $-0.7x+4.2+0.8=5.6x-1.3$ $\qquad -0.7x+5.0=5.6x-1.3$ b. $\qquad \underline{\quad -5.0 \qquad\qquad -5.0\quad}$ $\qquad -0.7x=5.6x-6.3$ $\qquad \underline{-5.6x \quad -5.6x\qquad\qquad}$ $\qquad \dfrac{-6.3x=-6.3}{}$ c. $\qquad \dfrac{-6.3 \quad -6.3}{}$ $\qquad\qquad x=1$

Divide.

49. $34.73 \div 2.3$

50. $-4.4516 \div 0.62$

51. $\quad$ 🖩 $\quad 9749.874 \div (-156.7)$

52. $-282.0325 \div (-18.5)$

53. $456.12 \div 100$

54. $-9.0034 \div 1000$

Solve.

55. $\dfrac{x}{3.4} = 9.1$

56. $\dfrac{m}{-67.3} = 18.45$

57. $\dfrac{-2x}{3} = -17.6$

58. $2.1x = -8.4$

59. $0.2m = 16.94$

60. 🖩 $\quad 5.18y = -4.662$

61. Barron has been saving money for the last 5 months and has a total of $893.51 in his saving account. On average, how much did he save each month? Round to the nearest cent.

62. 🖩 Desmond puts $29.76 worth of gas in his car. If gas costs $2.83 per gallon, how many gallons of gas did he buy? (Round to the nearest tenths place)

63. Rich runs a 5K (3.1 miles) in 19.22 minutes. How fast did he run each mile? (Round to the nearest tenths place)

64. Keith bikes a 50.7 mile race in 2.61 hours. What was his average speed on the bike during the race? (Round to the nearest tenths place)

Section 5.5: Fractions, Decimals, Order of Operations

Processes and Important Notes	Examples
Writing a Fraction as a Decimal: • **To Write a Fraction as a Decimal:** Use decimal division to divide the numerator by the denominator.	Write $\dfrac{3}{8}$ as a decimal. **Solution:** • **Divide denominator into numerator.**

	$\begin{array}{r} .375 \\ 8\overline{\smash{\big)}3.000} \\ \underline{24} \\ 60 \\ \underline{56} \\ 40 \\ \underline{40} \\ 0 \end{array}$
Order of Operations: • Work inside grouping symbols such parentheses first. • Perform any exponents in the expression. • Do multiplication and division moving left to right. • Do addition and subtraction from left to right.	**Simplify.** $\left(4\dfrac{1}{2}-1.8\right)^2 - \dfrac{3}{8}(0.8)$ **Solution:** $= (4.5-1.8)^2 - 0.375\cdot(0.8)$ Convert to decimals $= (2.7)^2 - 0.375\cdot(0.8)$ Parentheses $= 7.29 - 0.375\cdot(0.8)$ Exponents $= 7.29 - 0.3$ Multiplication $= 6.99$ Subtraction
Expressions and Formulas: To evaluate an expression, replace the value for the variable into the expression and simplify using order of operations.	**Evaluate the formula for the variable values given.** b^2-4ac for $a=2.3, b=-2.1, c=5$ **Solution:** $b^2-4ac = (-2.1)^2 - 4(2.3)(5)$ $\quad = (-2.1)^2 - 4(2.3)(5)$ $\quad = 4.41 - 4(2.3)(5)$ $\quad = 4.41 - (9.2)(5)$ $\quad = 4.41 - 46$ $\quad = -41.59$

Write as a decimal. Round your answer to the nearest thousandths if necessary.

65. $\dfrac{1}{5}$ 66. $\dfrac{13}{20}$ 67. $\dfrac{7}{8}$ 68. $\dfrac{7}{15}$ 69. $\dfrac{5}{6}$ 70. $\dfrac{17}{45}$

Simplify using order of operations.

71. $0.5\cdot(5.1)+4.8$

72. $-8.7+(2.7)(-0.4)$

73. $5.1(16.8-29.7)+2.3$

74. $-4.5\cdot(8.3)+(-13.55)$

75. $-3.2^2+16.4$

76. $\dfrac{4.8-6.3}{0.8}$

77. $29.15-(-2.1)^2$

78. $\left(\dfrac{1}{2}\right)^3 - 27.5$

79. $-\dfrac{3}{5}\div 1.8+17.3$

80. $-\dfrac{2}{5}(7.4+13.9)$

Evaluate the following.

81. $3x + 5; x = 5.6$

82. $x^2 - 2x + 7; x = 0.9$

83. $mx + b; b = 0.6, m = \dfrac{3}{4}, x = 1.8$

84. $b^2 - 4ac; a = 3.1, b = 5, c = -12.8$

Solve the following word problems.

85. Mike works as a landscape foreman and gets 4 weekly paychecks in a month of $1325.45 each. Mike's bills add up to $1456.91. How much money does Mike deposit into his checking account? Estimate his new checking account balance and then find the accurate balance?

86. Cycle NC is a 7 day bike ride across the state of NC starting in the mountains of Asheville, NC and ending at Ocean Isle Beach, NC. The first day Keith biked 47.8 miles, the second day he biked 59.1 miles, the third day 52.3 miles, the fourth day 65.4 miles, the fifth day 100 miles, the sixth day 66.7 miles and the last day he biked 53.4 miles into Ocean Isle Beach, NC. Find the average number of miles Keith biked each day.

Section 5.6: Mean, Median, and Mode

Processes and Important Notes	Examples
Finding the Mean of a Data Set: • A **data set** is a collection of numbers. • A **measure of central tendency** is a number reflects the "middle" or "expected value" of a data set. • **To find the mean (or average) of a data set:** Take the sum of the numbers and divide by the number of numbers in the data set.	Find the mean of the following data set: **28, 19, 31, 56, 41** Solution: Find the sum: $28 + 19 + 31 + 56 + 41 = 175$ Divide by 5: $175 \div 5 = 35$ The mean is 35.
Finding the Median of a Data Set: To find the median of a data set: • List the numbers in order from smallest to largest. • If there are an even number of numbers in the data set, then the median is the average of the two numbers that fall in the middle.	Find the median of the following data set: **16, 23, 45, 33, 19, 25, 38** Solution: Rewrite the list in numerical order: 16, 19, 23, **25**, 33, 38, 45 Find the number that is in the middle : **25**
Finding the Mode of a Data Set: • The **mode** of a data set is the value in the set that occurs the most number of times. A data set can have more than one mode (if more than one value occurs frequently) or no mode (if no value is repeated).	Find the mode of the following data set: **17, 20, 16, 18, 17, 22, 16, 17, 23** Solution: Organize the data set by writing the numbers in order. 16, 16, **17, 17, 17**, 18, 20, 22, 23 Look for the number that occurs the most: 17 The mode is 17.

Find the mean, median, and mode of the following list of numbers.

87. 15, 20, 15, 17, 12, 11

88. 42, 35, 37, 47, 48, 37

89. 13.2, 16.2, 19.1. 20.2, 16.2, 14.5, 18.2

90. 34.5, 44.7, 23.9, 44.5, 34.2, 34.5, 44.1, 34.5

91. $\dfrac{3}{5}, \dfrac{2}{6}, \dfrac{1}{3}, \dfrac{7}{8}, \dfrac{1}{2}$

92. There are 22 students taking an evening PreAlgebra class. Their ages are as follows: 18, 19, 20, 18, 18, 19, 20, 34, 45, 21, 20, 56, 23, 24, 21, 18, 20, 23, 25, 22, 21, 19. Find the mean age for this class.

93. Use the data in # to find the mode and median age for this evening class.

94. The temperatures for a given week in Paris, France are 43, 52, 53, 55, 53, 54, 56. What is the median temperature for this week in Paris?

95. Find the median height of the following presidents of the United States.

President	Height
Abraham Lincoln	6 ft 4 in
George Washington	6 ft 2 in
John Adams	5 ft. 7 in
Lyndon B Johnson	6 ft. 4 in
Gerald Ford	6 ft.
Thomas Jefferson	6 ft. 3 in
Ronald Reagan	6 ft. 1 in
George W. Bush	5 ft. 11 in
James A. Garfield	6 ft
James Madison	5 ft. 4 in
Bill Clinton	6 ft. 2 in
Richard Nixon	5 ft. 11 in
Barack Obama	6 ft. 1 in
Jimmy Carter	5 ft. 10 in
George H. W. Bush	6 ft. 2 in.
James Monroe	6 ft
John F Kennedy	6 ft

96. Use the chart in # to find the mode of the given presidents of the United States.

CHAPTER 5 - TEST YOURSELF

To make sure you are ready for the EXAM, try these problems without any help. Give yourself about an hour and don't check the answers until you have completely finished.

1. Write the number in words: 7,624.091
2. Write the number in words: 0.0035
3. Write the number as a decimal: three and five hundredths
4. Write the number as a decimal: seventeen thousand, twenty six millionths.
5. It is common to approximate the number $\pi \approx \dfrac{22}{7}$. Write this approximation as a decimal and round to the nearest hundredths..

6. $135.87 + 34.276$
7. $-98.7 + (-4.002)$
8. $(-4.5)(1.27)$
9. $(0.09)(-3.01)$

10. $(-0.008)^2$
11. $-34.08 + 14.8 \div 0.02(-7.1)$
12. $-5(0.3)^2 + 15.75 \div (-1.5)$

Convert.

13. To a decimal: $\dfrac{7}{8}$

14. To a decimal: $\dfrac{5}{11}$

15. To a fraction in reduced form: 0.78
16. To a fraction in reduced form: 6.00275

Compare the following numbers:

17. $\dfrac{3}{5}$ _____ 0.61

18. $\dfrac{1}{9}$ _____ 0.118

19. 0.445 _____ $0.\overline{4}$

Evaluate.

20. $mx + b$; $b = 17.9$, $m = -7.9$, $x = -5$

21. $\dfrac{-b}{2a}$; $a = -3.1$, $b = 18.6$

22. Hung has $671.29 in his checking account. He gets his paycheck of $389.10 directly deposited into his account. He pays bills of $78.19, $23.90, and rent of $635. He also buys groceries for $45.17. What is his new account balance?

23. Christy has been saving and putting $195.28 in her saving account each month for the past 18 months. How much has she saved?

24. Rob and Dannette purchase a house for $276,000. They get a 25 year loan and will pay $528,000 in interest over the term of the loan. What is the amount of their monthly mortgage payment?

25. At the beginning of a new semester Jodi buys books for the 4 classes she is taking. Her accounting book is $98.17, the English book is $57.29, the History book is $72.13 and her Sociology book is $34.89. Find the average cost of her books.

26. On a History exam that had 17 questions, the following is the number correct for 13 students: 16, 11, 7, 10, 15, 17, 13, 8, 16, 15, 17, 6, 15, 14, 12, 13. Find the mean, median and mode of the correct answers on this History exam.

Chapters 1 to 5 Cumulative Review

Translate to an algebraic expression or equation. Solve if it is an equation.

1. fifteen added to twice a number
2. six times the difference of a number and seven
3. twice the sum of a number and five is the same as the sum of the number and twelve
4. the quotient of three times a number and four yields forty-five

Perform the indicated operation.

5. $\dfrac{-2^2}{5}$

6. $(-0.2)^4$

7. $48 \div 8 - 3^2 \cdot 2$

8. $23 - 2 \cdot (-5)^2 \div 10$

9. $314.5 - 89.34$

10. $\dfrac{7}{15} + \dfrac{3}{10}$

11. $\dfrac{17}{30} - \left(-\dfrac{8}{27}\right)$

12. $5\dfrac{2}{7} + 6\dfrac{4}{21}$

13. $-4\dfrac{2}{3} + 8\dfrac{3}{5}$

14. $-17\dfrac{5}{6} - \left(-11\dfrac{7}{8}\right)$

15. $\dfrac{24x^2}{35} \cdot \dfrac{14y}{15x}$

16. $-\dfrac{14x^2 y}{45x} \div \dfrac{21y^3}{65x^2 y}$

17. $-2 \cdot \dfrac{5}{8} + 7.12$

18. $34 \cdot \dfrac{3}{17} - 15 \div (-5) \cdot 3$

19. $1.2(17.8 - 32.5) - (-3.1)^2$

20. $2 \cdot \left\{\left[8 + 3\left(4 + \sqrt{49}\right)\right] - 15 \div 3\right\} + 1$

21. $\left(\sqrt{87 - 6} + 7\right) \cdot 2$

Evaluate the following expressions for values given.

22. $\dfrac{-b}{2a}$, $a = \dfrac{1}{3}$, $b = -\dfrac{4}{7}$

23. $\dfrac{2A}{b}$, $A = 32.4$, $b = 4$

24. $b^2 - 4ac$, $a = \dfrac{4}{5}$, $b = -1.2$, $c = 3.5$

25. $2\pi rh + \pi r^2$, $h = 17.1cm$, $r = \dfrac{1}{2}cm$
    Use $\pi \approx 3.14$.

Solve.

26. $x + 17 = 54$

27. $-17g = 34$

28. $-3(x - 7) + 1 = 19$

29. $-3.1m = -9.3$

30. $4x - 23.8 = -32.2$

31. $x + \dfrac{9}{25} = -\dfrac{8}{15}$

32. $\dfrac{-3}{7}b = 4\dfrac{1}{5}$

33. $\dfrac{x}{3} - 7\dfrac{2}{6} = -12\dfrac{2}{5}$

34. $2\left[3(x + 2) - 5\right] - 4x = -5$

Find the following.

35. Find the LCM of 27 and 14.
36. Find the prime factorization of 452.
37. What factors of 72 have a difference of -1?
38. Find the LCD of $\dfrac{4}{15}$ and $\dfrac{23}{39}$ and make equivalent fractions with the LCD.

39. Rewrite as a decimal (round to the nearest thousandths if necessary). $\dfrac{7}{11}$

40. Rewrite as a fraction. 9.354

Write an algebraic equation and solve the following problem.

41. Dave is buying fruit trees to put around his house. He buys 8 trees at $39.95 each. How much did he spend on the trees?

42. Admission to an amusement park is $19 plus $4 per ride. If you have $64, how many rides can you ride?

43. Find the area of a rectangle with width 3.5m. and length 17m.

44. Find the area of a triangle with base $6\dfrac{2}{3}$ in. and height $4\dfrac{1}{5}$ in.

45. A circular rose garden has a diameter of 8.52 ft. Find the area of the garden. Use $\pi \approx 3.14$.

46. Two angles are supplementary. One angle is 24° more than twice the other angle. Find the measure of the two angles.

47. Wayne ran a ½ marathon (13.1 miles) in 1 hour 55 minutes. How long did it take him to run each mile on average? (round to the nearest hundredth of a minute)

48. Carrie has quiz grades 79.2, 68, 98, 54.7, 88.3. Find her quiz average. Round to the nearest ones.

49. Eight college students were polled on their hourly pay and are listed in the table below. Find the mean , median and mode of their hourly pay.

Student	Hourly pay
Joy	$8.23
Jermaine	$15.41
Brett	$10.78
Ray	$17.89
Michellie	$23.90
Vince	$8.23
Richard	$10.55
Chermaine	$16.13

50. Phil Mickelson is a professor golfer. Below is his score for the 4 days of the US Open Championship at Pebble Beach, CA. Find the mean, median and mode of the daily score for this championship.

Championship	Score
US Open Championship '10 Day 1	75
US Open Championship '10 Day 2	66
US Open Championship '10 Day 3	73
US Open Championship '10 Day 4	73

Chapter 6 - Ratios and Proportions

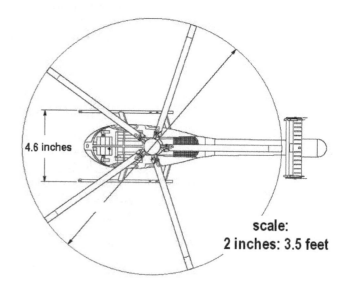

4.6 inches

scale:
2 inches: 3.5 feet

6.1 Introduction To Ratios and Rates

Topics:
- Introduction To Ratios
- Simplifying Ratios
- Introduction To Rates
- Unit Rates

Are You Ready?!
To see if you are ready to understand this section, do the following short quiz.

1. Simplify. $\dfrac{21}{56}$

2. Simplify. $\dfrac{2\frac{3}{5}}{4\frac{3}{10}}$

3. Fill the blank in with < or > to make the statement true: 0.0245_____0.0253

Answers to Are You Ready?

(1) $\dfrac{3}{8}$ *(2)* $\dfrac{26}{43}$ *(3)* 0.0245___<___0.0253

Introduction To Ratios

There is a mathematical notation and technique for comparing two quantities. Suppose, for example, a scientist has tried an experiment several times. The experiment was unsuccessful 8 times and successful 14 times. The comparison of unsuccessful attempts to successful attempts is 8 to 14. In math, a comparison like this is called a ratio.

A **ratio** is a comparison between two quantities.

A ratio can be expressed several ways:

Use words by separating the quantities with the word "to":	**Ratio Notation** uses a colon to separate the quantities:	**Fraction Notation** uses a bar to separate the quantities:
"8 to 14"	8 : 14	$\dfrac{8}{14}$

The most common of these notations for ratios is fraction notation.

Example 1: In each case a ratio is expressed in one of the three notations above. Express the ratio in the same using the other two notations.

a.) In millions of people, the ratio between the United States' population to China's population is 308 to 1338.

b.) In the United States the ratio of successful businesses to failed businesses is about 2:3.

Solution: In each case we express the ratio given in the other two forms.

a.) The ratio "308 to 1338" can be expressed as 308:1338 or $\frac{308}{1338}$.

a.) The ratio 2:3 can be expressed as "2 to 3" or $\frac{2}{3}$.

We often form ratios from real world information given in a graph or chart, as in the next example.

Example 2: Where in the World? The table to the right gives the average math SAT scores for several states. Write a ratio that compares the following scores in ratio notation and fraction notation.

a.) Colorado's average score to Iowa's average score.

b.) Tennessee's average score to Idaho's average score.

State	Average SAT Score
Colorado	553
Idaho	539
West Virginia	514
Tennessee	557
Iowa	602

Solution:

a.) Using the values given on the chart the ratio for Colorado to Iowa is 553:602 or $\frac{553}{602}$.

b.) Using the values given on the chart the ratio for Tennessee to Idaho is ratio is 557:539 or $\frac{557}{539}$.

Courtesy of Fotolia

STOP Introduction To Ratios Homework

In each case a ratio is expressed in one of the three notations above. Express the ratio using the other two notations.

1. $42 : $126
2. 8 weeks to 44 weeks
3. 17 to 35
4. 5 miles to 14 miles
5. $\frac{8}{26}$

6. 10 km to 60 km
7. 9 minutes : 12 minutes
8. 6 hours to 15 hours
9. $\frac{12 \text{ carbon atoms}}{23 \text{ helium atoms}}$
10. 8 tomatoes plants to 6 squash plants

Simplifying Ratios

As we mentioned, it is most common for ratios to be written in the same notation as fractions. This is because ratios can be simplified the same way that fractions are simplified to lowest term.

For example, the comparison "1 tutor to 2 students" is equivalent to the comparison "5 tutors to 10 students" is equivalent to the comparison "26 tutors to 52 students" in that in all of them the second quantity is twice as much as the first one.

$$\frac{1 \text{ tutor}}{2 \text{ students}} = \frac{5 \text{ tutors}}{10 \text{ students}} = \frac{26 \text{ tutors}}{52 \text{ students}}$$

Ratios are simplified the same way as fractions: remove common factors in the top and bottom by factoring.

Example 3: Write each ratio in fraction notation and reduce to lowest terms.

a.) 24 to 15   b.) 45:75

Solution:

a.) 24 to 15 can be written as $\dfrac{24}{15} = \dfrac{\cancel{3} \cdot 8}{\cancel{3} \cdot 5} = \dfrac{8}{5}$

b.) 45:75 can be written as $\dfrac{45}{75} = \dfrac{3 \cdot \cancel{3} \cdot \cancel{5}}{\cancel{5} \cdot 5 \cdot \cancel{3}} = \dfrac{3}{5}$

That ratios can be simplified like fractions makes it tempting to interpret ratios as fractions, but they completely different concepts.

Fractions: part of a whole
$\dfrac{3}{5}$ $\begin{array}{l} \rightarrow \text{we have 3 parts} \\ \rightarrow \text{5 parts make up a whole} \end{array}$

Ratio: comparing two numbers
$\dfrac{3}{5}$ $\begin{array}{l} \rightarrow \text{first number} \\ \rightarrow \text{second number} \end{array}$

So, while ratios do behave like fractions in regards to simplifying they do not behave like fractions in other respects. We never write a ratio as a mixed number. We don't express a final answer as a mixed number. Also, with fractions we would write $\dfrac{5}{1} = 5$ but since a ratio compares *two* quantities we often leave it as $\dfrac{5}{1}$.

Finally, since ratios are a comparison it is possible that one or both of the numbers in a ratio be either mixed numbers or decimal numbers. The goal when reducing a ratio that involves mixed numbers or decimals is to rewrite the ratio as a ratio of two whole numbers.

Example 4: Write each ratio in fraction notation and reduce it to lowest terms.

a.) $2\dfrac{3}{4}$ to $3\dfrac{1}{7}$ b.) 5.6 to 1.84

Solution: We begin each problem writing the ratio in fraction. Then we will have to think about it should be reduced to lowest terms.

a.) "$2\frac{3}{4}$ to $3\frac{1}{7}$" can be written as $\dfrac{2\frac{3}{4}}{3\frac{1}{7}}$. For the purpose of reducing this can be treated as a complex fraction.

First rewrite each mixed number as an improper fraction.

$$\frac{2\frac{3}{4}}{3\frac{1}{7}} = \frac{\frac{11}{4}}{\frac{22}{7}}$$

This is just like fraction division. We reciprocate the second fraction and multiply.

$$= \frac{11}{4} \cdot \frac{7}{22}$$

$$= \frac{11 \cdot 7}{4 \cdot 22}$$

We can reduce by a common factor of 11.

$$= \frac{\cancel{11} \cdot 7}{4 \cdot 2 \cdot \cancel{11}}$$

$$= \frac{7}{8}$$

This result shows why this process is important. The ratio "$2\frac{3}{4}$ to $3\frac{1}{7}$" is equivalent to "7 to 8", which is a much simpler way to express the comparison.

b.) The ratio "5.6 to 1.84" can be written as $\dfrac{5.6}{1.84}$. Recall that our goal is to rewrite this as a ratio of whole numbers.

As with fractions, we can clear decimals from the top and bottom of this ratio by multiplying top and bottom by 100.

$$\frac{5.6}{1.84} = \frac{5.6 \cdot 100}{1.84 \cdot 100}$$

$$= \frac{560}{184}$$

We can reduce by a common factor of 4.

$$= \frac{\cancel{4} \cdot 140}{\cancel{4} \cdot 46}$$

$$= \frac{140}{46}$$

There is still a common factor of 2.

$$= \frac{\cancel{2} \cdot 70}{\cancel{2} \cdot 23}$$

$$= \frac{70}{23}$$

So the ratio $\dfrac{5.6}{1.84}$ simplifies to $\dfrac{70}{23}$.

There are even real-world situations where one number in the ratio is a mixed number and one is a decimal, as in the next example.

Example 5: Where in the World? An engineer is ready do new work on a machine designed years ago and needs to know what the scale is for the old blue prints. He knows that a certain part of the engine is 7.5 inches. He measures and finds that on the blueprints that part is $2\frac{1}{4}$ inches. So the ratio of the blueprint to the actual machine is $2\frac{1}{4}$ to 7.5 . Reduce this ratio to lowest terms.

Solution: In fraction notation the ratio is $\dfrac{2\frac{1}{4}}{7.5}$. To reduce we should rewrite so that these numbers are either both decimals or both mixed numbers. Either approach will work. Let's look at both.

Using Mixed Numbers:

Rewrite the decimal as a fraction.

$$\frac{2\frac{1}{4}}{7.5}=\frac{2\frac{1}{4}}{7\frac{5}{10}}=\frac{2\frac{1}{4}}{7\frac{1}{2}}$$

Convert to improper fractions.

$$=\frac{\frac{9}{4}}{\frac{15}{2}}$$

Rewrite as multiplication.

$$=\frac{9}{4}\cdot\frac{2}{15}$$

Multiply and reduce.

$$=\frac{9\cdot2}{4\cdot15}=\frac{\cancel{3}\cdot3\cdot\cancel{2}}{\cancel{2}\cdot2\cdot\cancel{3}\cdot5}=\frac{3}{10}$$

Using Decimals:

Rewrite the mixed number as a decimal number.

$$\frac{2\frac{1}{4}}{7.5}=\frac{2.25}{7.5}$$

Multiply by $\dfrac{100}{100}$ to clear decimals.

$$=\frac{2.25\cdot100}{7.5\cdot100}=\frac{225}{750}$$

Reduce.

$$=\frac{\cancel{75}\cdot3}{\cancel{75}\cdot10}=\frac{3}{10}$$

In both case the ratios reduces to $\dfrac{3}{10}$. This means that 3 inches on the blueprint will translate into 10 inches on the actual machine.

STOP Simplifying Ratios Homework

Write each ratio in fraction notation and reduce to lowest terms.

11. 6 to 39
12. 16 to 48
13. 35 : 95
14. 26 : 65
15. $\dfrac{5}{12}$ to $\dfrac{7}{20}$

16. $4\frac{1}{6}$ to $1\frac{3}{5}$
17. 3.2 : 6.5
18. 0.49 to 6.3

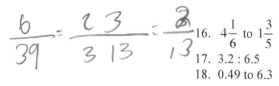

$$\frac{6}{39}=\frac{2\ \ 3}{3\ \ 13}=\frac{2}{13}$$

$\dfrac{13}{3\,\sqrt{39}}$

19. An engineer is ready do new work on a machine designed years ago and needs to know what the scale is for the old blue prints. He knows that a certain part of the engine is $3\frac{1}{2}$ inches. He measures and finds that on the blueprints that part is 4.8 inches. So the ratio of the blueprint to the actual machine is 4.8 to $3\frac{1}{2}$. Reduce this ratio to lowest terms.

20. A graphic designer has two different prints for a design. The width of the larger print is labeled as $5\frac{1}{4}$ inches. The width of the smaller print is labeled as 4.2 inches. Give the ratio of the widths in lowest terms.

Introduction To Rates

A rate is a special type of ratio.

A **rate** is a ratio that compares numbers with two different units

Here are some common rates that you see every day:

"miles to gallons"   "dollars to hours"   "pounds to dollars"

Understandably, it can be difficult when your professor is throwing around the terms ratio and rate in class so let's make sure you understand the difference.

Example 6: Do the following situations involve a rate or just a ratio. Explain.
a.) A scientist observes that 1000 bacteria collect over a 4 hour period.
b.) An investor compares and sees that Apple, Inc has sold 15,000 units of stock while Microsoft has sold 16,500 units of stock.
c.) A carpet store has a sale of $45 per 8 square feet of carpet.

Solution:
a.) In this situation the units are number of bacteria and time in hours. Since these units are different, this is describing a rate.
b.) The units here are units of stock to units of stock. So the units are the same this is describing an ordinary ratio.
c.) The units here are dollars and square feet. Since these units are different, this describing a rate.

Rates can be reduced just like regular ratios. However, for rates it is important to include the units throughout the process.

Example 7: Write each rate in fraction form and reduce if possible.
a.) 459 miles in 9 hours
b.) 35.5 pounds for $7

Solution: Note that for rates we include units throughout the reducing process and in the final answers.

a.) 459 miles in 9 can be written as $\dfrac{459 \text{ miles}}{9 \text{ hours}} = \dfrac{153 \cdot \cancel{3} \text{ miles}}{3 \cdot \cancel{3} \text{ hours}} = \dfrac{153 \text{ miles}}{3 \text{ hours}}$

b.) In this rate we have to clear the decimals in the top number.

$$\dfrac{35.5 \text{ pounds}}{\$7} = \dfrac{35.5 \cdot 10 \text{ pounds}}{\$7 \cdot 10} = \dfrac{355 \text{ pounds}}{\$70} = \dfrac{\cancel{5} \cdot 71 \text{ pounds}}{\$\cancel{5} \cdot 14} = \dfrac{71 \text{ pounds}}{\$14}$$

There are so many real-world applications of rates that it is difficult to decide which one to use for our Where in the World example. We will go with the one that most people deal with every day…gas mileage.

Example 8: Where in the World? Hank fills up the gas tank in his car with 12 gallons of gas by the time the tank is empty he has driven 228 miles. Write the rate of miles to gallons in fraction notation and reduce it to lowest terms.

Solution: We are asked for the rate miles to gallons.

$$\dfrac{\text{miles}}{\text{gallons}} = \dfrac{282 \text{ miles}}{12 \text{ gallons}} = \dfrac{\cancel{2} \cdot \cancel{3} \cdot 47 \text{ miles}}{\cancel{2} \cdot 2 \cdot \cancel{3} \text{ gallons}} = \dfrac{47 \text{ miles}}{2 \text{ gallons}}$$

The reduced ratio is $\dfrac{47 \text{ miles}}{2 \text{ gallons}}$. This means the car is going 47 miles for every 2 gallons of gas used.

Do the following situations involve a rate or a ratio? Explain.
21. In a chemistry class, there are 18 girls and 17 boys.

22. Chad is able to drive for $5\frac{1}{2}$ hours on 12 gallons of gas.

23. Chrissie bikes 112 miles in 5.2 hours.
24. A company finds makes $4.53 in revenue for every $2.95 they have in costs.

Write a rate for each scenario in fraction form and reduce if possible.
25. Paul rode his bike 72 miles in 5 hours.
26. Summer drove 345 miles in 6 hours.
27. 18 boxes of oranges from 6 trees
28. 4 cashiers for 38 customers

Unit Rates

A unit rate is a special type of rate that we deal with every day.

A **unit rate** is a rate in which the second quantity is 1.

Consider the simple example of miles per hour. If a person drive 258 miles in 6 hours, then their rate can be expressed as $\dfrac{258 \text{ miles}}{6 \text{ hours}}$. Let's reduce this rate to lowest terms.

$$\frac{258 \text{ miles}}{6 \text{ hours}} = \frac{\cancel{6} \cdot 43 \text{ miles}}{\cancel{6} \cdot 1 \text{ hours}} = \frac{43 \text{ miles}}{1 \text{ hour}}$$

$\dfrac{43 \text{ miles}}{1 \text{ hour}}$ is a unit rate that can be expressed any of the following ways…

$$43\frac{\text{miles}}{\text{hour}} \qquad 43 \text{ miles per hour} \qquad 43 \text{ miles/hour}$$

We could have gotten the same result by dividing 258 by 6.

```
      43
   6)258
      24
      18
      18
       0
```

Here are some other rates that we encounter in our daily lives.

"dollars per pound"   "miles per gallon"   "pounds per square inch"

As mentioned, you can turn any given rate into a unit rate just by dividing. This is handy if the unit rate turns out to be decimal.

Example 9: Divide to find the unit rate indicated.
a.) A new song has 336 beats in 4 minutes. What is its rate in beats per minute?
b.) A worker is given $106.80 for 8 hours of work. What is his pay rate in dollars per hour?
c.) A car goes 259 miles on 14 gallons of gas. What is its gas mileage rate in miles per gallon?

Solution: In each case will show how the rate would be set up then divide to get the unit rate.

a.) As a rate this would be $\dfrac{336 \text{ beats}}{4 \text{ minutes}}$. To get the unit rate we divide 336 by 4.

```
      84
   4)336
```

So the rate of the song is 84 beats per minute.

b.) As a rate this would be $\dfrac{\$106.80}{8 \text{ hours}}$. To get the unit rate we divide 106.80 by 8.

$$\begin{array}{r} 13.35 \\ 8\overline{)106.80} \end{array}$$

So the pay rate is $13.35 per hour.

c.) As a rate this would be $\dfrac{259 \text{ miles}}{14 \text{ hours}}$. To get the unit rate we divide 106.80 by 8.

$$\begin{array}{r} 18.5 \\ 14\overline{)259.0} \end{array}$$

So the gas mileage is 18.5 miles per gallon.

One very popular rate has to do with shopping or purchasing supplies for a business: finding the cost per unit of an item. Any time the first number in a unit rate is money the unit rate called a unit cost.

Example 10: Where in the World? Stephan runs a gaming store and has two offers to buy memory cards in bulk. Game On will sell him 8 cards for $71.60. Wholesale Fun will sell him 14 cards $135.10. Which is the better deal?

Solution: To find which offer is the better deal we just look at the unit cost in dollars per card. We find the unit cost by dividing.

Game On:
$$\dfrac{\$71.60}{8 \text{ cards}}$$

$$\begin{array}{r} 8.95 \\ 8\overline{)71.60} \end{array}$$

This company wants to charge Stephan $8.95 per card.

Wholesale Fun:
$$\dfrac{\$135.10}{14 \text{ cards}}$$

$$\begin{array}{r} 9.65 \\ 14\overline{)135.10} \end{array}$$

This company wants to charge Stephan $9.65 per card.

Game On is making the better offer at $8.95 per card.

STOP Unit Rates Homework

Find the unit rate for each of the following situations. Include units in your answer. Round to the nearest hundredth if necessary.

29. It costs $3.49 for 64 oz. of spaghetti sauce.
30. $13,590 paid over 15 years
31. $21.59 for 24 packages of sports beans.
32. Azar drives 547.3 miles with one tank of gas that is 13 gallons.
33. Marathan Organic Peanut Butter sells for $4.99 per jar, which is 32 oz.

34. Chelsea bought 1.4 lbs. of chocolate covered almonds and the total was $9.79. What is the cost per pound?

35. Tidal Creek Food Coop. is running a special on nuts. One option is a 48oz. of cashews for $9.75. And the other option is a 64 oz bag of cashews for $13.30. Which is the better deal?

36. For a cell phone company, plan A is $59.99 a month for 700 minutes and another plan that costs $69.99 for 800 minutes. Which is the better deal?

Exercise Set - Putting it ALL Together

For exercises #37 to 47, state whether the information given indicates is a rate or ratio. Then write the rate or ratio in lowest terms.
37. $55 to $105
38. 16 days to 14 days
39. 5 months to 8 months
40. 12 feet in 36 seconds
41. 5 miles in 45 minutes
42. 8 hours to 16 hours
43. 26 revolutions in 4 minutes
44. 21 out of 3458 are defective
45. $1400 for 5 days
46. $108 for 5 adjustments
47. 150 miles on 4.5 gallons of gas.

For exercises #48 to 54 find the indicated ratio. Reduce if possible.

48. Kelly answered 14 out of 17 problems correct on the test. What was the ratio of correct to incorrect answers?

49. Chaz answered 18 out of the 24 homework problems correctly. What was the ratio of correct to incorrect answers?

50. In a slice of whole wheat bread, there are 16 carbohydrates, 5 grams of fiber and 3 grams of sugar. Write the ratio of sugar to carbohydrates in one slice of bread.

51. The Nutz Over Chocolate Luna bar has 180 calories, 24 grams of carbohydrates, 12 grams of sugar and 10 grams of protein. What is the ratio of protein to carbohydrates.

52. The Nutz Over Chocolate Luna bar has 180 calories, 24 grams of carbohydrates, 12 grams of sugar and 10 grams of protein. What is the ratio of sugar to carbohydrates.

53. In a local high school, there are 12 math teachers for the 408 11th grade students. What is the ratio of teachers to students?

54. There are 25 instructors for the 2800 English students. What is the ratio of instructors to students?

Use the following chart to answer questions #55 to #58.

County in NC	Population(thousands)
New Hanover	192
Brunswick	103
Buncombe	228
Stanly	60
Wake	864
Rowan	139

55. Find the ratio of the population of Stanly to New Hanover.
56. Find the ratio of the population of Rowan to Wake.
57. Find the ratio of the population of Brunswick to Buncombe.
58. Find the ratio of the population of Buncombe to Wake.

For exercises #59 to 66, express each rate in fraction notation and then as a unit rate.

59. $375,000 for 2500 square feet of house.

60. $154,000 for 1,400 square feet of house.

61. Texas is 268,600 square miles and has a population of 24,326,974. Find the population per square mile.

62. California is 163,710 square miles and has a population of 36,756,666. Find the population per square mile.

63. An 8 oz. bag of frozen peas sells for $1.29. Find the unit cost in cents per ounce.

64. A 5 lb. bag of potatoes sells for $3.79. Find the unit cost in cents per pound.

65. A high speed train travels from San Francisco to Los Angeles, a distance of 344 miles in 2.4 hours. Find the rate of the train in miles per hour.

66. A plane flies from San Diego, CA to Charlotte, NC, a distance of 2,384 miles in 5.8 hours. Find the rate of the plane in miles per hour.

67. A bottle of ibuprofen with 90 tablets sells for $8.59 and a bottle with 120 tablets sells for $11.25. Which is the better buy?

68. A 64 oz jar of peanut butter for $4.99 or 2 – 24 oz jars for $3.80. Which is the better buy?

69. A 12 oz can of soda sells for $0.99 and a 16 oz bottle of soda sells for $1.29. Which is the better buy?

70. The 21 lb. bag of dog food sells for $42.99 and the 12.5 lb. bag of dog food sells for $32.99. Which is the better buy?

71. Jacob's car registered 316 miles on 13.4 gallons of gas, while Eduardo's truck registered 218.3 miles on 15.4 gallons of gas. Who gets better gas mileage?

72. Tarah drove 466.2 miles in 7.4 hours, while Keesha drove 520.8 miles in 9.3 hours. Who is traveling at a faster rate?

Exercise Set - Cumulative Review

73. Subtract and simplify. $\dfrac{7x}{10} - \dfrac{3x}{10}$

74. Add. $7{,}632 + 980$

75. Fill in the blank with > or <. $-19\_\_\_\_19$

76. Reduce. $\dfrac{26}{65}$

77. Is $b = 8$ a solution to the equation $2b - 10 = -2(5 - b)$

6.1 QUIZ YOURSELF:

To make sure you are ready for the EXAM, try these problems without any help. Give yourself about 20 minutes and don't check the answers until you have completely finished.

Find the ratio or rate in reduced form.

1. Express the ratio "78 defective : 7062 non-defective" two different ways and reduce the ratio to lowest terms.

2. A classroom has 16 males and 12 females. What is the ratio of males to total students?

3. Darrin drove 349 miles on 15.3 gallons of gas. What is his gas rate in miles per gallon?

4. Lance ran the Boston Marathon (26.2 miles) in 2 hours, 50 min or 170 min. Find his unit rate in minutes per mile.

5. Michael is a market research analyst and conducts research on different markets to estimate the business potential for an organization's marketing and promotional efforts. He works 38 hours per week and is paid $1284.02. What is his rate of pay in dollars per hour?

6. Janet is a student at a college in Wilmington, NC. She is currently taking 9 units which cost her $1011.60. Jeremy is taking 5 units at a college in Tempe, AZ which cost him $491.55. Which student pays less per unit for school?

Answers to this Quiz Yourself are on page 690

Succeed in Math!   Test-Taking

Test-taking is the area in your math class where you stand to make the greatest gains. Most students who are not passing math are not passing because of their exam grades. Often, you can get a good homework grade even if you don't really understand the material at the level you should. The answers are, after all, in the back of book. But you can't fool an exam. An exam will show for sure whether or not you understand the material. It's just you, a pencil, and your brain.

EXERCISE - Your Current Approach
In the space below, explore how you are currently preparing for exams. Discuss timetable and any special techniques you use.

_____
_____
_____
_____
_____

The most common misconception about test taking is that doing homework alone should provide a student with the skills he or she needs to pass a test. But think about all the resources available when you attempt your homework that are not there for an exam! Don't misunderstand what I'm saying; homework is the most important thing you will do in a math class, but homework and preparing for an exam are not quite the same thing.

THE PLAY'S THE THING

A good analogy for the distinction between homework and test preparation is that of the theatrical play. Taking a test is like performing on opening night of a play. When you do your homework, you are using the script—that is, your book and notes. This is an important process. You can't have a play without a script. But, any actor will tell you that just studying a script does not ensure a good performance on opening night. In fact, if actors rely too much on a script it becomes a crutch and they don't really learn their lines at all. To bridge the gap between the script and the actual performance, actors use a dress rehearsal. Every actor knows that this is crucial because even when you think you have everything ready, something usually goes wrong at the dress rehearsal. But that's okay because then there's time to fix it. For most students, the "dress rehearsal" is what is missing from their exam preparation. They study their homework and book endlessly, without realizing that those materials can become a crutch. You have to put down the homework and textbook BEFORE the test to make sure you can do it on your own. Because when the curtain goes up, it's just you and your pencil.

▪▪▪ Your Dress Rehearsal: The Practice Test

Nothing will improve your test scores more than taking a practice test. And I'll bet you have a practice test at the end of every chapter in your textbook. You should use this test to give yourself a dress rehearsal. A day or two before the exam, when your homework is done, you will be ready to take the practice test. Find a quiet place with no distractions, and give yourself about as much time as you'll have for the real exam. **Do not use your book or notes while you are taking a practice test.** If you do, you will be completely defeating the purpose. After you have finished the test or your time is up, go to the back of the book and grade yourself. In regular sections, the book only has the answers to the odd problems. But for the practice test it has all the answers (because they want you to be able to do this exercise). Circle the problems you missed. Now you can review the problem types you missed. Look back over the examples and notes to see what you did wrong.

Students often report that when they try taking a practice test they feel anxious or uncomfortable. If you do, that's great! Those are feelings that would normally come up as math anxiety on the day of the exam. You are working them out in advance, so that when the real test comes you will feel confident. Students also report that they thought they knew the material, but they bombed on the practice test and had to take another approach to last-minute studying. That's GREAT! It's much better than bombing the real test.

Taking a practice test can be a little challenging when you first try it. Frankly, it's easy to give up and start using the book or your notes. To get yourself used to it, start out by taking a practice test using every odd problem. This would give you two practice tests: one from the odds and one from the evens. You could try every third problem (1, 3, 6, 9, 12, ...) or every fifth problem (1, 5, 10, 15, ...). As you become more comfortable with quizzing yourself you can make the practice test longer.

EXERCISE

Taking a Practice Test

This is another exercise that will have to wait until two or three days before your next exam. It is one of the most important exercises in this whole book (if not the most important), so make sure to give it your attention. Try taking a practice test for your next exam following the guidelines given above. In the space below, reflect on what you thought of the exercise both before and after the exam.

Before the Exam: How was your experience in taking the practice test?

_____
_____
_____
_____
_____

After the Exam: Was taking the practice test an effective method of preparation?

_____
_____
_____
_____
_____

OTHER IDEAS ON PREPARING FOR TESTS

You need to start studying for the exam the day you start the new chapter. The first step in this process is doing your homework. As mentioned before, unfortunately, a popular trend among people who struggle in math is to stop there and spend the time between then and the exam forgetting how to do the techniques they learned in homework. You need other techniques that will help you retain the information by transferring it into solid long-term memory. This can be accomplished by note cards, vocabulary lists, reviewing notes frequently, or other methods mentioned in this book.

One week before the exam, it's time to step it up a notch. If you normally review your chapter notes and homework for 15 minutes a day, increase it to 30 minutes. Also, use your class notes and the textbook to make a list of potential exam questions. Anticipate questions that you think will be on the exam. Go to your instructor and bounce some of your ideas off of him or her. Ask for suggestions on what to study. Take the problems that you have had a hard time doing, and ask if they are "fair game" for the test.

Two or three days before the exam, take a practice test. This will give you plenty of time to review the problem types that you miss. It will also give you some time to compensate and vary your approach if you do poorly on it. Make sure you take your practice test far enough in advance so that you can interact with your professor about the results.

The day before the exam, ideally you should just be doing last-minute tune-ups and not trying to cram material into your head.

TEST DAY

Okay! Nice work. You've been diligent in applying good study habits. Now the big day is here. Here is your test-day checklist:

_____Get a good night's sleep.

_____Have a good breakfast that balances protein, carbohydrates, and sugar from fruit.

_____Review all the material on the cheat sheet you have created.

_____Briefly review your notes and any problem types that you have struggled with.

_____Bring everything you need to the exam:

_____Two pencils

_____Eraser

_____Ruler

_____Calculator (if you're allowed to use one)

_____Scratch paper

_____Bottled water and perhaps coffee or a soda

_____Hard candy

Arrive at the exam 10 minutes early. This will ensure that nothing unexpected happens that will make you start late. It will also give you a good chance to settle into your environment. DO NOT spend these 10 minutes feverishly looking over your notes. This usually creates a state of anxiety. You have done your job. Talk to the other students who have come early. Now would be a good time to ask them about that new movie or where they are from. This will help you relax. If you don't feel like talking, then try some deep breathing and maybe use one of your success mantras or just amuse yourself with positive self-talk: "I am a mathematical candy store. I make math look like riding a tricycle. This test is my friend. Happy test." This may sound silly, but it sure beats freaking out! Speaking of which...

When you get to an exam early you may encounter other students who are busy stressing out about the test and trying to do last-minute studying. If their negative "vibe" starts to make you feel anxious, set your stuff on your desk so you're ready to go, then step outside and get away from the madness.

▪▪▪ During the Exam

Test time. The tests are passed out and you're ready to show the world what your new approach to study skills has accomplished. You have done very well with your preparation, but there are certain things you should know that will make you a better test taker.

How to Take an Exam: Do the exam using these steps in this order to maximize your potential.

1. **Do a brain dump.** The second you get the test turn to a blank page or use scratch paper to write down all the things you are afraid you might forget during the test (particularly any formulas). This step will loosen you up and give you confidence.

2. **Survey the test.** Next, read through every problem on the test. Reading through a math test is like looking at a summary of the chapter. The material will quickly start to come back to you.

3. **Do a second brain dump.** If, after reading through the test, you see there is another formula you want to put down, do it now before you get started.

4. **Do the easiest problems first.** Starting at the beginning, go through the entire test and do all the problems that you can do quickly and easily. Skip the hard problems. This is a very important approach that many students neglect. Doing the easy problems first gets your mind warmed up and builds your confidence.

5. **Now do the hard problems**—but not necessarily in numerical order. Survey these problems again and start with the one you feel you know best how to solve.

6. **Be mindful of your time.** You should be aware of when half your time is up and gauge how much of the test you have done. This will tell you if you're on the right track or need to speed up.

7. **Review the test.** You should use every available minute you are given for the test. Do not second guess yourself, but you should spend any extra time double checking your arithmetic and looking over your solutions.

When the test is over, do your best to leave the test behind and not stress over the results. You did the best you could, and now it's time to reward yourself.

▪▪▪ After the Exam

Once you get the exam back it is very important that you don't just stuff it into your notebook and let it sit. Use the exam as a tool for greater retention and skill development. Go through the exam and pat yourself on the back as you review the problems you did correctly. Then go back and redo the problems that you missed. Feel free to get help on those problems from your professor, classmates, or a tutor. But make sure that you really understand how to do those problems for yourself. Put these corrections on a separate piece of paper, staple them to the exam, three-hole punch it all, and then file it in the Exam Section in your notebook, as we mentioned in Chapter 6: Your Class Notebook. This will make a world of difference in your ability to retain the information long term, especially when it comes time for the final exam.

EXERCISE

Putting It All Together

Of the techniques discussed in this section, which do think will be the most effective in helping you with preparing for and taking exams? Are there techniques you don't think you will use? Why?

_____

_____

_____

_____

6.2 Proportions

Topics:
- Introduction To Proportions
- Determining If A Proportion Is True Or False
- Solving Proportions

Are You Ready?!
To see if you are ready to understand this section, do the following short quiz.
1. Write the rate as a fraction and simplify. 738 feet in 36 seconds.
2. Find the unit rate. $52.37 for 12.1 gallons of gas.
3. Solve. $6x = 136$
4. Solve. $\dfrac{3}{5}x = \left(2\dfrac{1}{3}\right)\left(\dfrac{-6}{7}\right)$

Answers to Are You Ready?

(1) $\dfrac{738\,ft}{36\,\sec} = \dfrac{41\,ft}{2\,\sec}$ (2) $4.33 per gallon   (3) $x = 22\dfrac{2}{3}$ (4) $x = \dfrac{-10}{3} = -3\dfrac{1}{3}$

Introduction To Proportions

When applying ratios it is often necessary to work with proportions.

A **proportion** is the statement that two ratios are equal.

A proportion has the form $\dfrac{a}{b} = \dfrac{c}{d}$ where $\dfrac{a}{b}$ and $\dfrac{c}{d}$ are ratios.

As with all equations, proportions can be either true or false. We will look more at that later. For now, we want to get comfortable with setting up proportions from statements.

We have actually already been working with proportions. Here is snapshot of an example in Section 6.1:

Example: Write each ratio in fraction notation and reduce to lowest terms.
a.) 24 to 15   b.) 45:75

Solution:

a.) 24 to 15 can be written as $\dfrac{24}{15} = \dfrac{8}{5}$ → These are

proportions.

b.) 45:75 can be written as $\dfrac{45}{75} = \dfrac{3}{5}$

Example 1: For each statement write a corresponding proportion.
a.) 6 is to 10 as 21 is to 35

b.) "$2\dfrac{1}{2}$ to $1\dfrac{7}{8}$" is equivalent to "4 to 3"

Solution:

a.) $\underbrace{6 \text{ is to } 10}$ as $\underbrace{21 \text{ is to } 35}$

$$\frac{6}{10} = \frac{21}{35}$$

b.) $\dfrac{2\frac{1}{2}}{1\frac{7}{8}} = \dfrac{4}{3}$

Example 2: Where in the World? A business manager finds that for each product made the ratio between the cost and the profit is $2.73 to $7.35. Reduce this ratio and use the results to write a proportion.

Solution: First we should reduce the ratio $2.73 to $7.35.

Clear decimals from the top and bottom of this ratio by multiplying top and bottom by 100.

$$\frac{2.73}{7.35} = \frac{2.73 \cdot 100}{7.35 \cdot 100}$$
$$= \frac{273}{735}$$

Use prime factorizations to find and remove common factors.

$$= \frac{\cancel{3} \cdot \cancel{7} \cdot 13}{5 \cdot \cancel{7} \cdot 7 \cdot \cancel{3}}$$
$$= \frac{13}{35}$$

So the ratio $\dfrac{\$2.73}{\$7.35}$ is equivalent to the ratio $\dfrac{\$13}{\$35}$. We can write this as the proportion $\dfrac{2.73}{7.35} = \dfrac{13}{35}$.

STOP Introduction To Proportions Homework

For each statement write a corresponding proportion.

1. 8 is to 12 as 10 is to 15

2. 24 is to 90 as 140 is to 525

3. $\dfrac{4}{5}$ is to $\dfrac{7}{9}$ as $\dfrac{12}{25}$ is to $\dfrac{21}{45}$

4. $\dfrac{8}{9}$ is to $\dfrac{5}{6}$ as 7.2 is to 6.75

5. "$1\frac{2}{3}$ to $3\frac{1}{3}$" is equivalent to "1 to 2"

6. "$4\frac{5}{7}$ to $1\frac{2}{5}$" is equivalent to "$2\frac{5}{14}$ to $\dfrac{7}{10}$"

7. A business manager finds that for each product it makes the ratio between the cost and the profit is $4.75 to $8.50. Reduce this ratio and use the results to write a proportion.

8. The number π was discovered by carefully measuring the circumference and diameter and creating the ratio between them. Suppose the circumference of a circle is 92.4 inches and the diameter is 29.4 inches. Give the ratio of the circumference to the diameter. Reduce and use the result to write a proportion.

Determining If A Proportion Is True Or False

Just like any other equation a proportion can be true or false. A proportion is true if the two ratios included are indeed equal. One way to determine this would be to reduce both fractions to lowest terms. There is a shorter way that involves cross products.

In the proportion $\dfrac{a}{b} = \dfrac{c}{d}$ the products $a \cdot d$ and $b \cdot c$ are called **cross products**.

A proportion is true if its cross products are equal. A proportion is false is its cross products are not equal.

Example 3: Use cross products to determine if each proportion is true or false.

a) $\dfrac{3}{4} = \dfrac{6}{9}$ b) $\dfrac{12}{15} = \dfrac{4.8}{6}$ c) $\dfrac{2\frac{1}{3}}{1\frac{3}{5}} = \dfrac{7}{4\frac{4}{5}}$

Solution: In each case we find the cross products and check to see if they are equal.

a)
Write the cross products.

$$6 \cdot 4 \ = \ 3 \cdot 9$$

[PN: cross products arrows]

Since the cross products are not equal $24 \neq 27$

the proportion $\dfrac{3}{4} = \dfrac{6}{9}$ is false.

b)
Write the cross products.

$$\frac{12}{15} = \frac{4.8}{6}$$

$$15(4.8) \ \overset{?}{=} \ 12(6)$$

[PN: cross products arrows]

Since the cross products are not equal $72 = 72$

the proportion $\dfrac{12}{15} = \dfrac{4.8}{6}$ is true.

c) This exercise shows why cross products are useful. Finding the cross products to test the proportion is much faster than reducing the two fractions to see if they are equivalent.

Write the cross products.

$$\frac{2\frac{1}{3}}{1\frac{3}{5}} = \frac{7}{4\frac{4}{5}}$$

$$\left(1\frac{3}{5}\right)\cdot 7 \overset{?}{=} \left(2\frac{1}{3}\right)\left(4\frac{4}{5}\right)$$

[PN: cross products arrows]

To perform the multiplication covert each mixed number to an improper fraction.

$$\frac{8}{5}\cdot\frac{7}{1} \overset{?}{=} \frac{7}{3}\cdot\frac{24}{5}$$

Here are the products but the product on the right needs to be reduced.

$$\frac{56}{5} \overset{?}{=} \frac{168}{15}$$

Since the cross products are equal the proportion $\dfrac{2\frac{1}{3}}{1\frac{3}{5}} = \dfrac{7}{4\frac{4}{5}}$ is true.

$$\frac{56}{5} = \frac{56}{5}$$

Good Question: Examining the cross-products to see if a proportion is true is just a shortcut. Why does it work?

Answer: Begin with the proportion $\dfrac{a}{b} = \dfrac{c}{d}$. We can clear the bottom numbers in these ratios the same we would with fractions, by multiplying both sides by bd.

$$\frac{bd}{1}\cdot\frac{a}{b} = \frac{c}{d}\cdot\frac{bd}{1}$$

$$\frac{\cancel{b}da}{\cancel{b}} = \frac{cb\cancel{d}}{\cancel{d}}$$

$$ad = bc$$

So $\dfrac{a}{b} = \dfrac{c}{d}$ and $ad = bc$ are actually equivalent equations. If one is true the other is true.

Example 4: Where in the World? A company that makes breakfast cereal claims that the ratio of protein to fat in every box of its cereal is exactly 5 to 3. A consumer group wants to test the claim. In a sample of the cereal they find 12.3 grams of protein and 8.1 grams of fat. Does the company have the claimed ratio of protein to fat? That is, is $\dfrac{5}{3} = \dfrac{12.3}{8.1}$ a true proportion?

Solution: We just we to test the proportion $\frac{5}{3} = \frac{12.3}{8.1}$.

Write the cross products.

$$\frac{5}{3} = \frac{12.3}{8.1}$$

$$3(12.3) \overset{?}{=} 5(8.1)$$

[PN: cross products arrows]

Since the cross products are not equal
the proportion $\frac{5}{3} = \frac{12.3}{8.1}$ is false. For
this serving, at least, the company is
wrong about the ratio of protein to fat.

$$36.9 = 40.5$$

STOP **Determining If A Proportion Is True Or False Homework**

Use cross products to determine if each proportion is true or false.

9. $\frac{4}{7} = \frac{5}{8}$

10. $\frac{15}{20} = \frac{21}{28}$

11. $\frac{2}{17} = \frac{3.2}{27.2}$

12. $\frac{5}{31} = \frac{6.1}{37}$

13. $\dfrac{3\frac{6}{7}}{8\frac{2}{5}} = \dfrac{2\frac{1}{4}}{4\frac{2}{3}}$

14. $\dfrac{1\frac{5}{8}}{6\frac{1}{2}} = \dfrac{3}{12\frac{1}{3}}$

15. A manufacturer making parts knows that the ratio between aluminum and copper in the parts must be 7 to 2. A sample is taken and the results are 57.05 ounces of aluminum to 16.3 ounces of copper. Are these the correct amounts? That is, is $\frac{7}{2} = \frac{57.05}{16.3}$ a true proportion?

16. A private school claims their ratio of instructors to students is exactly 1 to 14. The roster shows that there are 24 instructors and 336. Is the school's claim true? That is, is $\frac{1}{14} = \frac{24}{336}$ a true proportion?

Solving Proportions

As we will see, the most powerful applications of ratios are based on the fact that if a term in a proportion is unknown we can find it. Consider the following proportion.

$$\frac{?}{6} = \frac{10}{15}$$

There is a missing term. If we use a variable to represent the missing term and set the cross products equal we have an equation that can easily be solved.

Use a variable to represent the unknown value.

$$\frac{x}{6} = \frac{10}{15}$$

In a true proportion, cross products are equal.

$$6 \cdot 10 = x \cdot 15$$
$$60 = 15x$$

Solve the equation by dividing both sides by 15.

$$\frac{60}{15} = \frac{15x}{15}$$

This gives us the missing term in the proportion.

$$4 = x$$
$$x = 4$$

Given the proportion $\dfrac{?}{6} = \dfrac{10}{15}$ the missing value MUST be 4. So the proportion must be $\dfrac{4}{6} = \dfrac{10}{15}$. No other value will make the proportion true.

This technique can be used to find a missing value in any proportion even if the proportion involves negatives, decimals or fractions.

Example 5: Solve the following proportions.

a) $\dfrac{4}{7} = \dfrac{-20}{b}$ 　　　 b) $\dfrac{1.7}{k} = \dfrac{6.8}{12.4}$ 　　　 c) $\dfrac{1\frac{2}{3}}{\frac{7}{9}} = \dfrac{y}{\frac{2}{5}}$

Solution:

a)

$$\frac{4}{7} = \frac{-20}{b}$$

[PN: cross products arrows]

In a true proportion, cross products are equal.

$$6(-20) = 4 \cdot b$$
$$-120 = 4b$$

Solve the equation by dividing both sides by 4.

$$\frac{-120}{4} = \frac{4b}{4}$$

This gives us the missing term in the proportion.

$$-30 = b$$
$$b = -30$$

b)

$$\frac{1.7}{k} = \frac{6.8}{12.4}$$

[PN: cross products arrows]

In a true proportion, cross products are equal.

$$k \cdot 6.8 = 1.7 \cdot 12.4$$
$$6.8k = 21.08$$

Solve the equation by dividing both sides by 6.8.

$$\frac{6.8k}{6.8} = \frac{21.08}{6.8}$$

This gives us the missing term in the proportion.

$$k = 3.1$$

c)

$$\frac{1\frac{2}{3}}{\frac{7}{9}} = \frac{y}{\frac{2}{5}}$$

[PN: cross products arrows]

In a true proportion, cross products are equal. Be careful with the fraction multiplication, we should convert the mixed number to an improper fraction.

$$\frac{7}{9} \cdot y = 1\frac{2}{3} \cdot \frac{2}{5}$$

$$\frac{7}{9} y = \frac{5}{3} \cdot \frac{2}{5}$$

$$\frac{7}{9} y = \frac{2}{3}$$

Solve the equation by multiplying both sides by $\frac{9}{7}$.

$$\frac{9}{7} \cdot \frac{7}{9} y = \frac{2}{3} \cdot \frac{9}{7}$$

This gives us the missing term in the proportion.

$$y = \frac{6}{7}$$

The ability to solve proportions leads to so many important real-world applications that they really need their own section. So we'll look at most of our applications in Section 6.3 - More Applications of Proportions. But here is one real-world problem to get us started.

Example 6: Where in the World?   Accel Gel is a gel packet that runners take for energy. Their motto is "4:1, it's not a ratio, it's an advantage." Actually, 4:1 is the ratio of carbohydrates (in grams) to protein (in grams) in the gel. Ron has consumed 14 grams of carbs from Accel Gel. How many grams of protein has he taken? To find out, he can solve the proportion 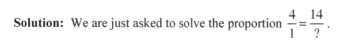 $\frac{carbs}{protien} = \frac{4}{1} = \frac{14}{?}$. How many grams of protein has Ron consumed?

Courtesy of Fotolia

Solution: We are just asked to solve the proportion $\frac{4}{1} = \frac{14}{?}$.

Use a variable to represent the unknown value. We'll use p since the unknown value represent the amount of protein consumed.

$$\frac{4}{1} = \frac{14}{p}$$

[PN: cross products arrows]

In a true proportion, cross products are equal.

$$1 \cdot 14 = 4 \cdot p$$
$$14 = 4p$$

Solve the equation by dividing both sides by 4.

$$\frac{14}{4} = \frac{4p}{4}$$

This gives us the missing term in the proportion. $3.5 = p$

$p = 3.5$

So Ron has consumed 3.5 grams of protein.

STOP Solving Proportions Homework

Solve the following proportions.

17. $\dfrac{x}{8} = \dfrac{5}{16}$

18. $\dfrac{3}{8} = \dfrac{-5}{a}$

19. $\dfrac{12}{35} = \dfrac{8}{y}$

20. $\dfrac{m}{6} = \dfrac{5}{9}$

21. $\dfrac{m}{3.5} = \dfrac{13}{17.5}$

22. $\dfrac{5.1}{p} = \dfrac{35.7}{68.6}$

23. $\dfrac{2\frac{4}{9}}{3\frac{1}{3}} = \dfrac{b}{3\frac{2}{11}}$

24. $\dfrac{\frac{3}{14}}{4\frac{5}{8}} = \dfrac{y}{2\frac{4}{7}}$

25. Jeff is reading a book for class. He has read 23 pages in 35 minutes and wants to know about how long it will take him to read the whole 145 page book. To find out he can solve the proportion $\dfrac{23}{35} = \dfrac{145}{m}$. About how long should it take him to read the whole book? Round your answer to the nearest minute.

26. A recipe for cupcakes calls for $3\frac{1}{2}$ cups of sugar to make 18 cupcakes. To find out how many cups will be needed to make a dozen cupcakes we can solve the proportion $\dfrac{3\frac{1}{2}}{18} = \dfrac{c}{12}$. How many cups of sugar will be needed to make dozen cupcakes?

6.2 Exercise Set - Putting it ALL Together

For each statement write a corresponding proportion.
27. 4 is to 7 as 8 is to 14.
28. 9 is to 12 as 51 is 68.
29. $\dfrac{5}{8}$ is to $\dfrac{1}{2}$ as 6.75 is to 3.
30. $4\frac{1}{5}$ is to 9.4 as 5.2 is to $10\frac{2}{5}$.

Determine if the following proportions are true or false.

31. $\dfrac{4}{5} = \dfrac{9}{13}$

32. $\dfrac{2}{5} = \dfrac{4}{10}$

33. $\dfrac{6}{9} = \dfrac{26}{39}$

34. $\dfrac{6}{-7} = \dfrac{-8}{9}$

35. $\dfrac{2.4}{3.9} = \dfrac{3.2}{5.2}$

36. $\dfrac{8.1}{10.8} = \dfrac{1.2}{1.6}$

37. $\dfrac{5}{8} = \dfrac{\frac{7}{8}}{1\frac{2}{5}}$

38. $\dfrac{\frac{2}{3}}{1\frac{3}{5}} = \dfrac{\frac{5}{14}}{\frac{6}{7}}$

Solve the following proportions. Give your answer as a mixed number if necessary. Only give the answer as a decimal if there are already decimals in the proportion, and round to the nearest hundredth if necessary.

39. $\dfrac{5}{8} = \dfrac{x}{24}$

40. $\dfrac{42}{70} = \dfrac{b}{35}$

41. $\dfrac{5}{6} = \dfrac{10}{m}$

42. $\dfrac{3}{7} = \dfrac{n}{9}$

43. $\dfrac{y}{13} = \dfrac{2}{15}$

44. $\dfrac{6}{11} = \dfrac{8}{y}$

45. $\dfrac{x}{18} = \dfrac{12}{-27}$

46. $\dfrac{m}{16} = \dfrac{15}{24}$

47. $\dfrac{4.2}{5.7} = \dfrac{t}{14.25}$

48. $\dfrac{0.8}{0.14} = \dfrac{3}{h}$

49. $\dfrac{-5.6}{k} = \dfrac{3.5}{1.3}$

50. $\dfrac{2\frac{1}{4}}{\frac{3}{5}} = \dfrac{x}{1\frac{1}{2}}$

51. $\dfrac{\frac{5}{6}}{1\frac{1}{3}} = \dfrac{x}{\frac{1}{4}}$

52. Sue can bike 4.1 miles in 15 minutes. How long will it take her to bike 26 miles? Solve the proportion $\dfrac{4.1}{15} = \dfrac{26}{x}$ to find how many minutes it will take.

53. Jeremiah can run 3.1 miles in 24.9 minutes. Continuing at the rate, how long will it take him to run a ½ marathon(13.1 miles)? Solve the proportion $\dfrac{3.1}{24.9} = \dfrac{13.1}{x}$ for find out how many minutes it will take Jeremiah to run the ½ marathon.

54. Julia is making chocolate chip cookies for a party. The recipe she has calls for $2\frac{1}{3}$ cups of all purpose flour and makes 50 cookies. She needs to make 80 cookies for the party. How many cups of all purpose flour does she need? Solve the proportion $\dfrac{2\frac{1}{3}}{50}=\dfrac{x}{80}$ to find how many cups of flour Julia needs.

55. Oleg is making strawberry jam with the strawberries from her garden. The recipe she is using calls for $1\frac{1}{2}$ cups of sugar for every 4 cups of strawberries. She has a total of $7\frac{1}{3}$ cups of strawberries. How many cups of sugar should she use? Solve the proportion $\dfrac{1\frac{1}{2}}{4}=\dfrac{x}{7\frac{1}{3}}$ to find how many cups of sugar she should use.

56. According to National Geographic, it requires 150 big brown bats to eat 1.3 million pest insects in one year. How many big brown bats would it require to eat 3.5 million pest insects in one year? Use the proportion $\dfrac{150}{1.3}=\dfrac{b}{3.5}$ to find the number of big brown bats?

57. According to National Geographic, it took a female elephant known as Mrs. Kamau 48 hours to streak 100 miles from Marsabit north-eastward in search of food and water. At this rate, how long did it take her to streak 72 miles? Use the proportion $\dfrac{100}{48}=\dfrac{72}{x}$ to find how long it would take her?

Exercise Set - Chapter 6 Review

58. Write the ratio "5 to 13" using two other notations.
59. Does the statement "35 miles in 7 hours" represent a regular ratio or a rate?
60. Write the ratio "18 to 54" in fraction notation and reduce if possible.
61. A college tutors center has $600 to pay 8 tutors. What is the unit rate in dollars per tutor?
62. A shopper can buy a pack of 10 computer CDs for $14.99 or 15 CDs for $24.99. Which is a better buy?

Exercise Set - Cumulative Review

63. Evaluate $\dfrac{2x}{x+7}$ for $x=3$. Reduce if possible.

64. Simplify. $(-8)^3$

65. Add and reduce. $\dfrac{1}{8}+\dfrac{5}{8}$

66. Rewrite $-\left(\dfrac{4}{5}\right)^3$ in expanded form. Do not evaluate.

67. Divide. $-154\div(-11)$

6.2 QUIZ YOURSELF:

To make sure you are ready for the EXAM, try these problems without any help. Give yourself about 20 minutes and don't check the answers until you have completely finished.

1. **True or False.** $\dfrac{6}{15} = \dfrac{21}{50}$

2. **Solve.** $\dfrac{4}{7} = \dfrac{x}{28}$

3. **Solve.** $\dfrac{18.3}{30.5} = \dfrac{y}{39.5}$

4. **Solve.** $\dfrac{m}{2\frac{1}{2}} = \dfrac{1\frac{1}{3}}{1\frac{5}{9}}$

5. To make 12 oz of an athlete's recovery drink, he needs 5 grams of protein. A group of runners get back from a run and need to make 80 oz of the recovery drink. How many grams of protein is in the mix? Solve the proportion $\dfrac{12}{5} = \dfrac{80}{x}$ to find out how many grams of protein are in the drink.

6. Jasper is hiking in the Anza-Borrego State Park. It takes her 1.8 hours to hike the 3 mile Borrego Palm Canyon Trail. If she continues at the same rate, how long will it take her to hike 5 miles of the California Hiking and Riding Trail? Use the proportion $\dfrac{1.8}{3} = \dfrac{x}{5}$ to find how long it will take.

Answers to this Quiz Yourself are on page 690

6.3 More Applications of Proportions

Topics:
* Proportions in the Real World

Are You Ready?!
To see if you are ready to understand this section, do the following short quiz.
1. Write the ratio in lowest terms as a fraction: In 130 countries there are 820 languages.
2. Find the unit rate of cost per ounce: It costs $4.67 for a 16 oz jar of organic peanut butter.
3. Solve. $\dfrac{5}{21} = \dfrac{12}{x}$

Answers to Are You Ready?

(1) $\dfrac{13}{82}$ *(2)* *$0.29/oz*   *(3)* *x = 50.4*

Proportions in the Real World

From engineering to shopping to every science to economics, proportions are used to solve real-world applications everywhere. In the following applications we will be given enough information to establish ratios and set up a proportion to find a missing value.

To help us set up the applications we will use the tips given in Section 3.6 on page # for solving word problems. Here is a review.

The KEY to getting good at word problems is to take a careful approach. Carefully follow these steps and you WILL get better at applying math:
1) **Read the Problem**
2) **Assign a Variable**
3) **Summarize the Information**
4) **Do the Math**
5) **Answer the Question**

Example 1: Blueprints
A scale is a ratio that compares the dimensions (size) of a drawing to the dimensions (size) of an actual object. Scales are used in maps and blueprints. The diagram given is of a helicopter. Notice the scale in the lower right corner indicates that 2 inches on the drawing means 3.5 feet on the actual helicopter.

If the width of the helicopter on the drawing is 4.6 inches, how wide will the actual helicopter be? Round to the nearest tenth if necessary.

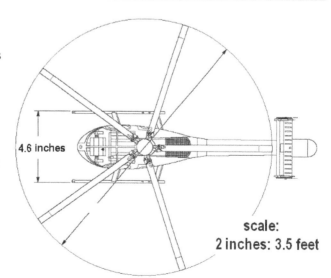

4.6 inches

scale:
2 inches: 3.5 feet

Solution: Make sure to begin by reading the problem carefully and take time to understand the drawing.

ASSIGN A VARIABLE $x =$ the width of the helicopter in feet

SUMMARIZE THE   The scale is 2 inches : 3.5 feet.
INFORMATION

The scale can be expressed as $\dfrac{2 \text{ inches}}{3.5 \text{ feet}}$.

The on the drawing is 4.6 inches.

DO THE MATH   We can set up the following proportion:

$$\frac{2 \text{ inches}}{3.5 \text{ feet}} = \frac{4.6 \text{ inches}}{x \text{ feet}}$$

$$\frac{2}{3.5} = \frac{4.6}{x}$$

Solve: $16.1 = 2x$
- Set cross products equal.
- Divide by 2 to solve.
$$x = 8.05$$

ANSWER THE QUESTION   To the nearest tenth the helicopter will be 8.1 feet wide.

Example 2: Culinary Arts

The website www.foodnetwork.com has a great recipe for baked macaroni and cheese that serves 4 people and calls for $2\frac{1}{2}$ cups of grated cheese. You are having a dinner party serving 10 people and would rather make the correct amount than deal with a ton of leftovers. How many cups of grated cheese will you need for the recipe to serve 10 people?

ASSIGN A VARIABLE $c =$ cups of cheese to serve 10

SUMMARIZE THE   recipe says $2\frac{1}{2}$ cups for 10 people, so we are comparing cups to
INFORMATION   people

$$\frac{\text{cups}}{\text{people}} = \frac{2\frac{1}{2}}{4} = \frac{c}{10}$$

DO THE MATH
Solve $\dfrac{2\frac{1}{2}}{4} = \dfrac{c}{10}$.

[PN: cross product arrows]

Solve:

- Set cross products equal.

$$4c = 2\frac{1}{2} \cdot 10$$

$$4c = 25$$

$$c = 6\frac{1}{4}$$

- Divide by 2 to solve.

ANSWER THE QUESTION

You will need $6\frac{1}{4}$ cups of grated cheese to serve 10 people.

Example 3: Business Performance
A business has seen that the ratio between its cost and its profits stays fixed from year to year. They want to use that information to predict their profit for the current year given their cost. The following chart gives information on cost and profit for last year and this year.

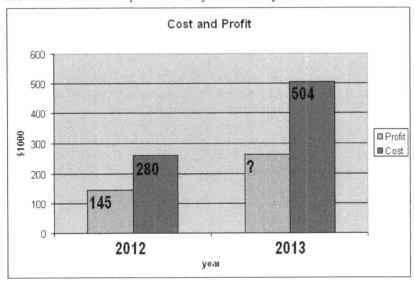

What do we predict the profits will be for the year 2013?

Solution: Make sure to begin by reading the problem carefully and take the time understand the information in the chart.

ASSIGN A VARIABLE

In math we usually use P to represent profit.

P = the company's profit for the year 2013

SUMMARIZE THE INFORMATION

From the chart:
- profit for 2012 was $145 thousand and cost was $280 thousand
- profit for 2013 is P and cost is $504 thousand

Using the proportion $\dfrac{\text{profit}}{\text{cost}} = \dfrac{\text{profit}}{\text{cost}}$ we have $\dfrac{145}{280} = \dfrac{P}{504}$.

DO THE MATH

Solve $\dfrac{145}{280} = \dfrac{P}{504}$.

[PN: cross product arrows]

Solve:

- Set cross products equal.

$$280P = 73,080$$

$$P = 261$$

- Divide by 280.

ANSWER THE QUESTION   We predict that the company's profits for 2013 will be $261 thousand or $261,000.

1. Samantha can buy 2 cantaloupes for $5. How much would 5 cantaloupes cost her?

2. Shayla can buy 7 oranges for $1.50. If she has $4.78, how many oranges can she buy?

3. An engineer is drawing up plans for making a new design of food processor. The scale for the drawing to the actual machine is 2 inches to 3 inches. If the blade on the drawing comes out to be 4 inches, what will the actual length of the blade be on the machine?

4. A manufacturer has received blueprints to build stereo speakers. The scale for the blueprints to the actual speakers is 4 inches to 1 foot. On the blueprint the height of the speaker is 10 inches. What will be the height (in feet) of the actual speaker? Express your answer as a mixed number.

5. The instructions on a bottle of liquid lawn fertilizer say to mix 5 ounces of the fertilizer with 2 gallons of water. Wayne has a watering tank that holds 8.5 gallons of liquid. How many ounces of the fertilizer should he include in the tank? Round to the nearest ounce.

6. It takes 2.7 liters of concentrated dye to make 3 gallons of paint. How many ounces of the dye will be needed to make 8 gallons of the paint?

7. A $52\frac{1}{2}$ feet wall measures $6\frac{1}{4}$ inches on a set of blueprints. How long should a $78\frac{3}{4}$ feet wall measure on the blueprints? Express your answer as a mixed number.

8. A $11\frac{7}{8}$ feet wall measures $3\frac{1}{2}$ inches on a set of blue prints. On the blueprint a second wall measures $4\frac{3}{8}$ inches. How long will actual second wall be? Express your answer as a mixed number.

9. A nuclear power plant can pump out about 7000 mega joules of usable electricity in 9 seconds. How many seconds will it take for the plant to pump out 25000 mega joules of electricity? Round to the nearest second if necessary.

10. A water treatment plant can process 25,000 gallons of water in 15 hours. How many gallons does it process in a day (24 hours)? Round to the nearest gallon if necessary.

11. An online party planner says that 9.5 pounds of cheese will serve 30 guests. How many guests will 12 pounds of cheese serve?

12. A recipe for taco soup calls for $2\frac{1}{2}$ cups of cheese and serves 8 people. How much cheese should be used to serve 6 people? Express your answer as a mixed number.

13. Imani is training for a bike race. Yesterday she biked 32 miles in 116 minutes. At the same rate how many minutes will it take her to bike 100 miles?

14. If $8\frac{1}{2}$ cubic yards of concrete costs $288, how much should it cost for 3 cubic yards? Round you answer to the nearest cent.

15. A chemist has 4 gallons of a solution that contains 18 milliliters of acid. How many gallons of the solution would be needed to have 10 milliliters of acid? Express your answer as a mixed number.

16. A 60-pound bag of fertilizer is needed to cover a crop that is 2,400 square yards. To the nearest pound, how many pounds of the fertilizer will be needed to cover a crop that is 8,750 square yards?

17. Medical patients receive a dose of a certain medicine based on their weight. A man who weighs 195 pounds receives 6.5 milligrams. How many milligrams will be given to a man who weighs 170 pounds? Round to the nearest tenth.

18. One serving of Accelerade is 12 fluid ounces. One serving contains 65 milligrams of potassium. During a race, endurance athletes loss about 435 milligrams of potassium per hour. How many fluid ounces of Accelerade will I need to drink in one hour to completely replace all the potassium lost during that hour? Round your answer to the nearest tenth.

19. For athletes doing extensive endurance training and racing, researchers recommend a daily protein intake of 4 grams of protein for every 7 pounds of body weight. How many grams of daily protein should be taken by an athlete who weighs 168 pounds? Rounds to the nearest gram.

20. To lose one pound of body weight you have burn about 3500 calories. Jogging for $\frac{1}{4}$ of an hour burns about 125 calories. How many hours will you have to jog to lose one pound?

21. To lose one pound of body weight you have burn about 3500 calories. Swimming in the ocean for 35 minutes burns about 259 calories. How many hours will you have to swim to lose one pound?

22. A lender recommends that the ratio between your monthly mortgage payment and your total monthly income be about 2 to 7. How much of a mortgage could you afford if your monthly income is $3,250?

23. A lender recommends that the ratio between your monthly mortgage payment and your total monthly income be about 2 to 7. How much of a mortgage could you afford if your monthly income is $6,105?

24. Tyronne is taking a PreAlgebra final that has 50 questions and he has 2 hours to complete it. He looks at the clock and realizes he has been working for 70 minutes and has 32 problems done. At this rate, how many problems will he have done at 2 hours(120 minutes)? Will he finish the final?

25. Jin is doing his math homework and has completed 28 of the 45 problems. He has been working for 50 minutes. At this rate, how long will it take him to finish his homework?

26. A massage therapist charges $15 for a 20-minute massage. At this rate, how much would a 75-minute massage cost?

27. Malik is planting roses in his front yard. He bought 3 bushes for $17.23. How much will it cost him to buy 9 more?

28. Aiko is planting her garden and bought 4 packs of seeds for $3.87. How much will it cost to buy 3 more packs of seeds?

29. The exchange rate for the European currency, called euros, is 11 euros is $16. June bought a leather purse in Florence, Italy for 59 euros. How much did the purse cost in American dollars?

30. The exchange rate for the Luxembourg currency, called francs, is 28 francs is $1. Alberto spent 550 francs on dinner in Luxembourg. How much did dinner cost in American dollars?

31. It takes Kishi 17 minutes to swim 750 meters. How long will it take her to swim 1000 meters at the same rate?

32. Paul swam 1.2 miles in 31 minutes. At the same rate, how long will it take him to swim 3 miles?

33. A $3\frac{1}{2}$-foot zebra weighs 440 lbs. How much would you expect a 5-foot zebra to weigh?

34. An elephant seal can weigh up to 1908 lbs. with blubber alone weighing 1450 lbs. of that. How many lbs. of blubber would you expect an elephant seal that weighs 1670 lbs. have at this same rate?

35. For every 4 American(North, Central and South America) high school students who study abroad, there are 15 European high school students that student abroad. In 2008, 16,727 European students studied abroad. How many American students studied abroad?

36. For every 81 Asian high school students who study abroad, there are 2 Oceania high school students that study abroad. In 2008, 189 Oceania students studied abroad. How many Asian students studied abroad?

Exercise Set - Chapter 6 Review

37. Reduce the ratio $\frac{14}{35}$.
38. Rewrite the ratio "8.4 to 5.2" in fraction notation and simplify.
39. Write the statement "1.5 is to 6 as 1.8 is to 7.2" as a proportion.
40. A copy center charges $42 for 525 copies. Give the unit rate in dollars per page.
41. Use cross products to determine if the proportion $\frac{5}{7} = \frac{2.2}{2.8}$ is true or false.

Exercise Set - Cumulative Review

42. Evaluate the expression $Ax + By$ for $A = -1, B = 3, x = 4$ and $y = 5$.

43. Multiply and reduce if possible. $\left(-\frac{7}{15}\right)\left(\frac{5}{6}\right)$

44. Solve. $3(x - 4) = x + 2$
45. Multiply. $(9)(0.4)$
46. Add. $4.5 + 8.1$

6.3 QUIZ YOURSELF:

To make sure you are ready for the EXAM, try these problems without any help. Give yourself about 20 minutes and don't check the answers until you have completely finished.

1. The exchange rate is 5 British pounds for $8. While shopping in the UK, Yoko buys a sweater for 69 pounds. How much did the sweater cost in dollars?

2. It takes Layla 12 minutes to swim 700 meters. At this same rate, how long will it take her to swim 1000 meters?

3. A lender recommends that the ratio between your monthly mortgage payment and your total monthly income be about 2 to 7. How much of a mortgage could you afford if your monthly income is $2,875?

4. There are about 2,190,000 deaths in the US per year. 1 in 5 of deaths is caused by smoking. How many deaths are caused by year in the US?

5. For every 8 Asian high school students who study abroad, there are 17 European high school students that student abroad. In 2008, 16,727 European students studied abroad. How many Asian students studied abroad?

Answers to this Quiz Yourself are on page 690

6.4 Similar Geometric Figures

Topics:
- Similar Triangles
- Other Similar Shapes

Are You Ready?
To see if you are ready to understand this section, do the following short quiz.

1. $\left(-3\dfrac{1}{5}\right)\left(4\dfrac{3}{8}\right)$

2. Solve. $2\dfrac{1}{3}x = \left(\dfrac{3}{5}\right)\left(\dfrac{-7}{8}\right)$

3. Solve. $\dfrac{x}{15} = \dfrac{4}{25}$

Answers to Are You Ready?

(1) -14   *(2)* $x = -\dfrac{9}{40}$ *(3)* $x = 2\dfrac{2}{5}$

Similar Triangles

In the last section we did an example and several exercises about scale drawings. The idea of an object

Similar objects have the exact same shape but necessarily the exact same size.

Here are a few examples of similar shapes.

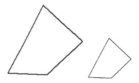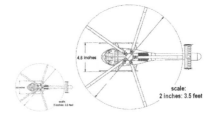

There are two properties of similar shapes that make them great for applying math to the real world.

In similar shapes, corresponding angles have the same measure and corresponding sides are proportional.

What do we mean when we say that corresponding sides are proportional? We mean that the ratio between corresponding sides is always the same. We begin our study of similarity using triangles. Here is an example of similar triangles with the sides and angles labeled.

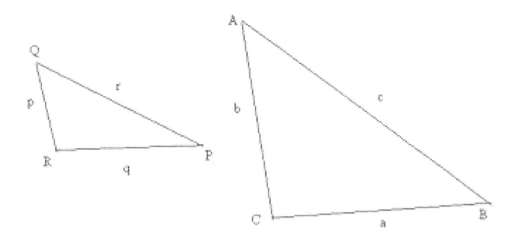

Corresponding angles have the same measure (the symbol $\angle$ refers to an angle):

$$\angle Q \text{ and } \angle A, \ \ \angle R \text{ and } \angle C, \ \ \angle P \text{ and } \angle B$$

Corresponding sides are proportional:

$$\frac{q}{a} = \frac{p}{b} = \frac{r}{c}$$

That sides are proportional in similar triangles makes it possible to find the length of a side if it is unknown. All we have to do is set up and solve the appropriate proportion.

Example 1: Using Proportions to Find Missing Values
If the triangles below are known to be similar, find the values of x and y.

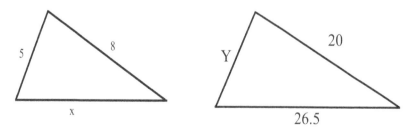

Solution:
The values of x and y can be found from the proportion of the corresponding sides:

$$\frac{5}{Y} = \frac{x}{26.5} = \frac{8}{20}$$

We use one proportion at a time:

$$\frac{x}{26.5} = \frac{8}{20}$$
$$20x = 212$$
$$x = 10.6$$

$$\frac{5}{Y} = \frac{8}{20}$$
$$8Y = 100$$
$$Y = 12.5$$

Example 2: Find x and y in the following figure.

Solution:
The figure contains two triangles that share one angle and have the other two marked as congruent. So the triangles are similar. Here are the proportions formed by the corresponding sides:

$$\frac{10}{25} = \frac{x}{10} = \frac{6}{y}$$

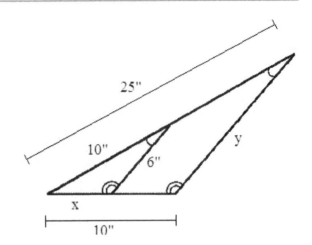

As before, we solve each proportion separately:

$$\frac{10}{25} = \frac{x}{10}, \text{ so } x = 4"$$

$$\frac{10}{25} = \frac{6}{y}, \text{ so } y = 15"$$

The proportion property of sides of similar triangles is very useful in real-world applications. As one example, if we look at triangles made by shadows of two different objects at the same time of day, the triangles are similar because the angle of elevation of the sun is the same in both triangles. This idea leads to a way to find the height of extremely tall objects relatively easily.

Example 3: Erica wants to find the height of a tall flag pole using only a yard stick. She has a friend stand perfectly still and measures the length of his shadow. The shadow is 4 feet 6 inches, or 4.5 feet. She then finds that her friend is exactly 6 feet tall. Finally, she uses the yardstick to find that the flagpole casts a shadow 24 feet long. How tall is the flagpole?

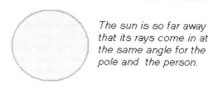

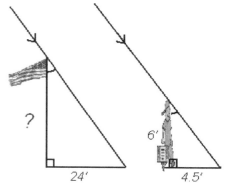

Solution: The scenario is illustrated to the right (not drawn to scale). This situation involves two similar triangles. We can establish a proportion between the corresponding sides:

$$\frac{4.5}{24} = \frac{6}{x}, \text{ so } x = 32$$

The height of the flagpole is 32 feet.

Exercise Set - Similar Triangles

The following triangles are similar. Find the unknown side.

1.

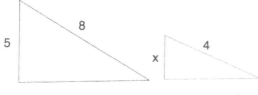

2.

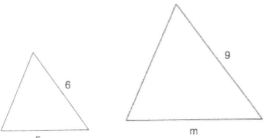

3. Given the following triangles are similar, find x and y.

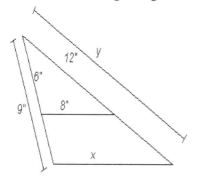

4. Given the following triangles are similar, find a and b.

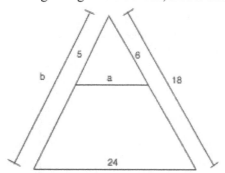

5. A forest ranger is trying to find the height of a tree. He is $5\frac{1}{2}$ feet tall. He notes that the length of his shadow is 11 feet and that the length of the tree's shadow is 23 feet. How tall if the tree?

6. A surveyor needs to know the height of a building. He is $5\frac{3}{4}$ feet tall and has a shadow of 12 feet. He observes that the shadow of the building is 80 feet long. How tall is the building?

Other Similar Shapes

We began our study of similar shapes by looking at triangles. But the same properties of similarity hold for more complicated figures: corresponding angles have the same measure and corresponding sides are proportional. We can use two generic similar shapes to illustrate what we mean about sides being proportional.

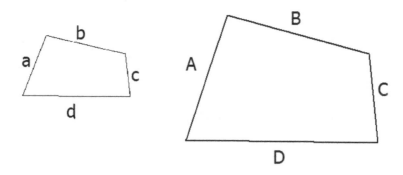

$$\frac{a}{A} = \frac{b}{B} = \frac{c}{C} = \frac{d}{D}$$

As with triangles, we can often find the length of a missing side.

Example 3: Given the following figures are similar find z.

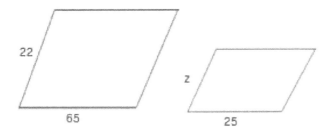

Solution:
Set up a proportion using the corresponding sides to find z.

$$\frac{25}{65} = \frac{z}{22}$$

So, $z = 8\frac{6}{13}$

Example 4: Where in the World? Devin is building a house and according to the house plan, the living room is 3" wide by 7.2" long. He knows that the width of the living room is 12'. Using a proportion, find the length of the living room.

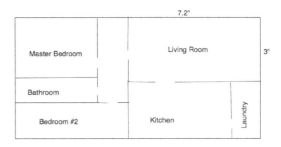

Solution:
Set up a proportion using the corresponding sides for the width and length.

$$\frac{width}{length} \qquad \frac{3}{7.2} = \frac{12}{x}$$

$$x = 28.8$$

The actual length of the living room will be 28.8 feet long.

Exercise Set - Other Similar Shapes

7.   Given the similar figures, find x.

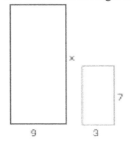

8.   Given the similar figures, find t.

9. Given the similar figures, find x, y and z.

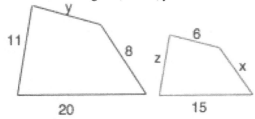

10. Given the similar figures, find k, m and n.

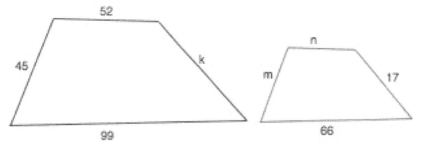

Exercise Set - Putting it ALL Together

The following triangles are similar. Find the unknown side.

11.

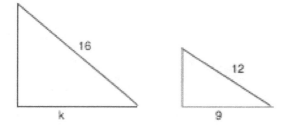

12.

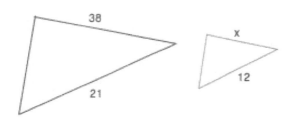

13. Find b and f.

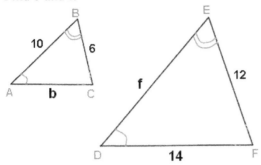

14. Find *b* and *c*.

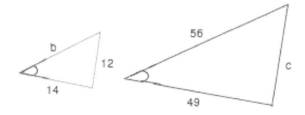

15. Given the following triangles are similar, find *m* and *p*.

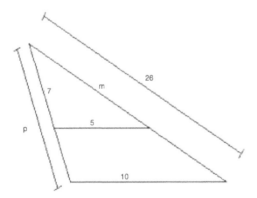

16. Given the following triangles are similar, find x and y.

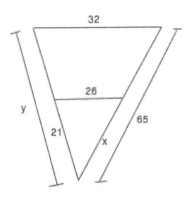

17. Given the following figures are similar, find x.

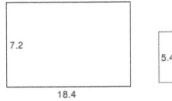

18. Given the following figures are similar, find m.

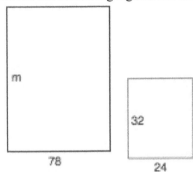

19. Given the following figures are similar, find a and c.

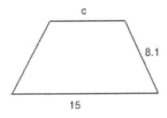

20. Given the following figures are similar, find *p*.

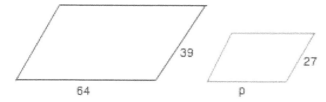

21. Given the following figures are similar, find *g* and *h*.

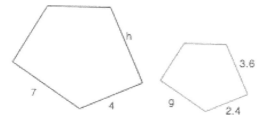

22. Given the following figures are similar, find *g* and *h*.

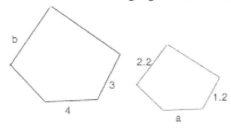

23. A tree 18 feet tall casts a shadow 10 feet long. Justino is 6 feet tall. How long is Jusitno's shadow?

24. A 25-foot flagpole casts a 9-foot shadow. A nearby building casts a shadow of 20 feet. How tall is the building?

25. A flagpole 26 feet tall casts a shadow 80 feet long. Jazmyn is 3 1/2 feet tall. How long is Jazmyn's shadow?

26. The tallest tree is a redwood in Redwood National Park is 367.8 feet tall. On a sunny day it casts a shadow of 46 feet. A nearby redwood casts a shadow of 25 feet. How tall is the nearby redwood?

27. On a floor plan, the master bedroom is 3" wide by 4" long. The actual length of the bedroom will be 16'. Using the floor plan to right, find the actual width of the master bedroom.

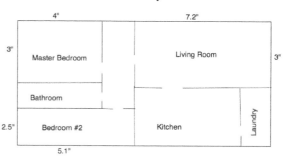

28. On a floor plan, the second bedroom is 2.5" wide by 5.1" long. The actual width of the bedroom will be 10'. Using the floor plan to right, find the actual width of the second bedroom.

Exercise Set - Chapter 6 Review

29. Reduce the ratio to lowest terms. $\dfrac{132}{165}$

30. Write as a unit rate in fraction form. 165 miles on 13.2 gallons of gas.

31. Solve. $\dfrac{k}{20} = \dfrac{34}{45}$

32. Determine if proportion is true or false. $\dfrac{18}{27} = \dfrac{26}{39}$

33. A photo shop charges $2.48 to develop 8 photos. How much would they charge to develop 25 photos?

Exercise Set - Cumulative Review

34. Find the product $(-11)(5)(0)(-18)$.

35. Add. $-\dfrac{4}{15} + \dfrac{1}{15}$

36. Solve. $6x - 5 = -47$

37. Find the area of a circle with $r = 5cm$. Use $\pi \approx 3.14$.

38. Simplify. $14 \div 2(-7) + (-1)^4$

39. Combine like terms. $\dfrac{1}{4}(16m - 24) - 9m$

6.4 QUIZ YOURSELF:

To make sure you are ready for the EXAM, try these problems without any help. Give yourself about 20 minutes and don't check the answers until you have completely finished.

Given the following similar figures, find the unknown side.

1. Find *h*.

2. Find w.

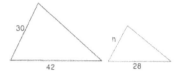

3. Find *d*.

4. Find *x*, *y* and *z*.

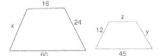

Answers to this Quiz Yourself are on page 690

6.5 Square Roots

Topics:

- Square Roots
- Expressions that Contain Radicals
- The Radical as a Grouping Symbol

Are You Ready?!

To see if you are ready to understand this section, do the following short quiz.

1. Simplify. $(-7)^2$

2. Simplify. $-3(19-21)+4^2$

3. Simplify. $\dfrac{2}{5}+\dfrac{1}{4}$

Answers to Are You Ready?

(1) 49   *(2)* 22   *(3)* $\dfrac{13}{20}$

Square Roots

We have discussed exponents at length so far. An idea closely related to exponents is the idea of a square root.

The **square root** of x is any number that, when multiplied to itself, gives x.

Example 1: What are the square roots of each number?
a) 49   b) 1   c) 81

Solution: What number, multiplied to itself gives each number?

a) The square roots of 49 are 7 and $\frac{21}{56}$ since $7 \cdot 7 = 49$ and $\frac{3}{8}$.

b) The square roots of 1 are $\frac{26}{43}$ and -1 since $1 \cdot 1 = 1$ and $(-1)(-1) = 1$.

c) The square roots of 81 are 9 and -9 since $9 \cdot 9 = 81$ and $(-9)(-9) = 81$.

The symbol $\sqrt{}$ is used to indicate a positive square root. This symbol is often called a **radical**.

Here are the first few square roots that are whole numbers.

$$\sqrt{1} = 1 \qquad \sqrt{25} = 5 \qquad \sqrt{81} = 9 \qquad \sqrt{169} = 13$$

$$\sqrt{4} = 2 \qquad \sqrt{36} = 6 \qquad \sqrt{100} = 10 \qquad \sqrt{196} = 14$$

$$\sqrt{9} = 3 \qquad \sqrt{49} = 7 \qquad \sqrt{121} = 11 \qquad \sqrt{225} = 15$$

$$\sqrt{16} = 4 \qquad \sqrt{64} = 8 \qquad \sqrt{144} = 12 \qquad \sqrt{400} = 20$$

The radical symbol $\sqrt{}$ only represents the positive square root of a number. So $\sqrt{49}$ is read "the square root of 49" and $\sqrt{49} = 7$. Be careful not to confuse a square root radical with a division bar.

To represent the negative square root there must be a negative in front of the square root symbol, as in $-\sqrt{49} = -7$.

Example 2: Find the following.

a) $\sqrt{36}$ b) $-\sqrt{25}$ c) $\sqrt{\dfrac{4}{9}}$

Solution: In each case we want a number that, when multiplied to itself, gives the number in the square root symbol. Remember the radical symbol only represents the positive square root.

a) $\sqrt{36} = 6$

b) $-\sqrt{25}$ is the opposite of the square root of 25, so $-\sqrt{25} = -5$.

c) $\sqrt{\dfrac{4}{9}} = \dfrac{2}{3}$ because $\left(\dfrac{2}{3}\right)^2 = \dfrac{2}{3} \cdot \dfrac{2}{3} = \dfrac{4}{9}$

Good Question: I don't understand what square roots have to do with exponents.

Answer: Each square root statement has a corresponding exponent form using a power of 2.

$$\sqrt{9} = 3 \text{ because } 3^2 = 9$$

$$\sqrt{49} = 7 \text{ because } 7^2 = 49$$

$$\sqrt{289} = 17 \text{ because } 17^2 = 289$$

$$\sqrt{\dfrac{36}{49}} = \dfrac{6}{7} \text{ because } \left(\dfrac{6}{7}\right)^2 = \dfrac{36}{49}$$

Example 3: Write a statement in exponent form using a power of 2 that corresponds to each square root statement.

a) $\sqrt{49} = 7$ b) $\sqrt{\dfrac{25}{121}} = \dfrac{5}{11}$ c) $\sqrt{35,721} = 189$

Solution:

a) $7^2 = 49$

b) $\left(\dfrac{5}{11}\right)^2 = \dfrac{25}{121}$

c) $189^2 = 35,721$

Not every square root comes out to be a whole number. In fact, most square roots come out to be nonterminating, non-repeating decimals called *irrational numbers*.

$$\sqrt{5} = 2.236067... \qquad \sqrt{20} = 4.472135... \qquad \sqrt{101} = 10.049875...$$

To find these square roots we use a calculator or use a table that gives approximations. When we use them in exercises we round the values off.

Example 4: Use a calculator to find each square root. Round each answer to the nearest hundredth.

a) $\sqrt{2}$

b) $-\sqrt{350}$

Solution: We use a calculator and round to two places. Your calculator either has a square root button or the square root command is the second command over the square button.

a) $\sqrt{2} \approx 1.41$

b) $-\sqrt{350} \approx -18.71$

Often when we round we use the approximation symbol $\approx$ instead of the equals sign.

STOP Exercise Set - Square Roots

What are the square roots of each number?
1. 25
2. 144

Find the following.
3. $\sqrt{16}$
4. $\sqrt{121}$
5. $-\sqrt{\dfrac{25}{49}}$
6. $-\sqrt{\dfrac{16}{81}}$

Write a statement in exponent form using a power of 2 that corresponds to each square root statement.
7. $\sqrt{289} = 17$
8. $\sqrt{262,144} = 512$

Use a calculator to approximate each square root. Round your answer to the nearest thousandth.

9. $\sqrt{5}$

10. $-\sqrt{14}$

Expressions that Contain Radicals

It is important to understand how radicals are handled when other operations are involved. In regards to the order of operations, a radical should be done at the point as exponents.

The Order of Operations:

- Work inside grouping symbols such as parentheses and radicals first.
- Perform any exponents and radicals in the expression.
- Perform multiplication and division moving left to right.
- Perform addition and subtraction from left to right.

Example 5: Simplify the following expressions.

a) $8\sqrt{25}$

b) $-4\sqrt{16}+2\sqrt{49}$

c) $\sqrt{\dfrac{4}{9}}-\sqrt{\dfrac{1}{4}}$

Solution:

a) The expression $8\sqrt{25}$ means $8\cdot\sqrt{25}$. So we simplify the radical first.

$$8\sqrt{25}$$
$$=8\cdot 5$$
$$=40$$

b)

Simplify the radicals first.

Multiply next.

Do addition last.

$$-4\sqrt{16}+2\sqrt{49}=-4(4)+2(7)$$
$$=-16+14$$
$$=-2$$

c)

Example 6: Where in the World?

The amount of time it takes for an object to free-fall a given distance can be found by the formula

$t=\sqrt{\dfrac{d}{16}}$ where t is time in seconds and d is distance in feet. How many seconds will it take for an object to free-fall a distance of 1248 feet (the height of the Empire State Building in New York)?

Solution:
We are given a distan

Simplify the radicals first.

Get a common denominator of 6 to add the fractions.

Subtract.

$$\sqrt{\dfrac{4}{9}}-\sqrt{\dfrac{1}{4}}=\dfrac{2}{3}-\dfrac{1}{2}$$
$$=\dfrac{4}{6}-\dfrac{3}{6}$$
$$=\dfrac{1}{6}$$

ce of 1248 feet so we substitute $d = 1248$ into the given formula.

$$t = \sqrt{\dfrac{d}{16}}$$

$$= \sqrt{\dfrac{1248}{16}} \qquad \text{Remember we divide before we find the square root.}$$

$$= \sqrt{78}$$

$$t \approx 8.8$$

So it will take about 8.8 seconds for an object to fall a distance of 1248 feet.

Exercise Set - Expressions that Contain Radicals

Simplify each expression.

11. $3\sqrt{16}$

12. $7\sqrt{81}$

13. $-5\sqrt{64}$

14. $-2\sqrt{121}$

15. $-6\sqrt{4} + 7\sqrt{16}$

16. $12\sqrt{9} - 5\sqrt{100}$

17. $\sqrt{\dfrac{9}{25}} - \sqrt{\dfrac{1}{4}}$

18. $\sqrt{\dfrac{36}{81}} + \sqrt{\dfrac{4}{9}}$

The formula $t = \sqrt{\dfrac{d}{16}}$ **is used to find the time** t **it will take for a free-falling object fall a distance of** d **feet (See example #).**

19. How long will it take an object to fall 400 feet? Round to the nearest tenth if necessary.
20. How long will it take an object to fall 2596 feet? Round to the nearest tenth if necessary.

The Radical as a Grouping Symbol

So radicals are evaluated at the same stage as exponents, but if there is an operation inside a radical it is done first. That means the radical is treated as a grouping symbol. For example, $\sqrt{16+9}$ is different than $\sqrt{16} + \sqrt{9}$.

For $\sqrt{16+9}$ we add first then take the square root.

$$\sqrt{16+9} = \sqrt{25} = 5$$

For $\sqrt{16}+\sqrt{9}$ we take the square root first $\sqrt{16}+\sqrt{9}=4+3=7$
then add.
This means that a radical is treated as a grouping symbol.

An operation inside a radical should be done before taking the square root.

Example 7: Simplify each expression.

a.) $\sqrt{169}-\sqrt{25}$ b.) $\sqrt{169-25}$

Solution:
a.) For this expression we take the square root first then subtract.

$\sqrt{169}-\sqrt{25}=13-5=8$

b.) For this expression we subtract inside the radical then take the square root.

$\sqrt{169-25}=\sqrt{144}=12$

Example 8: Where in the World?
As we will see in the next section, to find the missing side of right triangle, a surveyor must evaluate the

expression $\sqrt{c^2-a^2}$. Evaluate the expression for $a=7$ and $c=11$. Round the answer to the nearest
tenth if necessary.
[PN: Triangle with leg=7, hypotenuse=11 and leg=b].

Solution:
Begin by substituting $a=7$ and $c=11$ $\sqrt{c^2-a^2}=\sqrt{11^2-7^2}$
.

Perform the exponents inside the radical. $=\sqrt{121-49}$

Subtract. $=\sqrt{72}$

We must use a calculator to finds $\sqrt{72}$. ≈ 8.5
We round to the nearest tenth as
instructed.

Exercise Set - The Radical as a Grouping Symbol

Simplify the two expressions given.

21. $\sqrt{25}+\sqrt{144}$ and $\sqrt{25+144}$

22. $\sqrt{64+36}$ and $\sqrt{64}+\sqrt{36}$

23. $\sqrt{100}-\sqrt{36}$ and $\sqrt{100-36}$

24. $\sqrt{25-16}$ and $\sqrt{25}-\sqrt{16}$

25. Evaluate the expression $\sqrt{a^2 + b^2}$ for $a = 6$ and $b = 8$. Round to the nearest tenth if necessary.

26. Evaluate the expression $\sqrt{c^2 - b^2}$ for $b = 9$ and $c = 12$. Round to the nearest tenth if necessary.

Exercise Set - Putting it ALL Together

Vocabulary Check: Fill in each blank with a word from our Vocabulary Checklist to the right. Each word is used exactly once.

27. The numbers 7 and -7 are the _____ of the number 49.

28. The symbol $\sqrt{}$ is called a _____ and is used to indicate a positive square root.

Simplify.

29. $\sqrt{81}$

30. $\sqrt{121}$

31. $\sqrt{16}$

32. $\sqrt{196}$

33. $-\sqrt{9}$

34. $-\sqrt{49}$

35. $-\sqrt{144}$

36. $-\sqrt{100}$

Simplify. Round to the nearest tenth.

37. $\sqrt{6}$

38. $\sqrt{75}$

39. $-\sqrt{40}$

40. $-\sqrt{157}$

Simplify.

41. $\sqrt{\dfrac{16}{49}}$

42. $\sqrt{\dfrac{1}{9}}$

43. $\sqrt{\dfrac{49}{36}}$

44. $\sqrt{\dfrac{100}{121}}$

45. $-\sqrt{\dfrac{81}{144}}$

46. $-\sqrt{\dfrac{9}{64}}$

47. $\sqrt{\dfrac{1}{25}} - \sqrt{\dfrac{9}{25}}$

48. $\sqrt{\dfrac{9}{49}} + \sqrt{\dfrac{16}{49}}$

49. $\sqrt{\dfrac{1}{9}} + \sqrt{\dfrac{25}{36}}$

50. $\sqrt{\dfrac{81}{100}} - \sqrt{\dfrac{1}{16}}$

Simplify.

51. $\sqrt{64} + \sqrt{16}$

52. $\sqrt{121} + \sqrt{9}$

53. $\sqrt{1} - \sqrt{25}$

54. $-\sqrt{49} - \sqrt{81}$

55. $5\sqrt{36} + 7\sqrt{1}$

56. $3\sqrt{121} + 2\sqrt{144}$

57. $-7\sqrt{16} + 4\sqrt{49}$

58. $4\sqrt{9} - 3\sqrt{16}$

59. $2\left(5 + \sqrt{100}\right)$

60. $7^2 + \sqrt{49}$

61. $\sqrt{25} + 5^2$

62. $-\sqrt{81}(-3)^2$

63. $-4 + \sqrt{36}$

64. $-5\sqrt{16} + 3(7)$

65. $\sqrt{19 - 3} + 8$

66. $11 - \sqrt{85 - 4}$

67. $1 + \sqrt{20 + 35 \div 7}$

68. $-3\sqrt{77 - 2 \cdot 14} + 89$

70. $\dfrac{-8 + 16 \div 2 \cdot 3}{1 + \sqrt{3^3 - 2}}$

69. $\dfrac{6 + \sqrt{77 - 13}}{3^2 + 5 \div 1}$

71. Simplify $\sqrt{25} - \sqrt{16}$ and $\sqrt{25 - 16}$.

72. Simplify $\sqrt{25} + \sqrt{144}$ and $\sqrt{25 + 144}$.

73. Simplify $\sqrt{3^2 - 4(2)(1)}$.

74. Simplify $\sqrt{5^2 - 4(2)(2)}$.

75. Simplify the expressions $(3+7)\sqrt{16}$ and $3 + 7\sqrt{16}$.

76. Simplify the expressions $(8-6)\sqrt{25}$ and $8 - 6\sqrt{25}$.

77. Use a calculator to complete the following table.

x	$\sqrt{x}$
1	
2	
3	
4	
5	

78. Use a calculator to complete the following table.

x	$\sqrt{x}$
10	
20	
30	
40	
50	

79. Evaluate the formula $I = \sqrt{\dfrac{P}{5}}$ for P = 20.

80. Evaluate the formula $t = \dfrac{\sqrt{s}}{4}$ for s = 144.

81. Evaluate the formula $S = K\sqrt{L}$ for K = 4 and L = 25.

82. Evaluate the formula $z = \sqrt{\dfrac{x}{y}}$ for x = 49 and y = 81.

83. Evaluate $\sqrt{b^2 - 4ac}$ for a = 1, b = 6, and c = 5.

84. Evaluate $\sqrt{b^2 - 4ac}$ for a = 5, b = 7, and c = 2.

Exercise Set - Chapter 6 Review

85. Ronaldo can swim 500 meters in 8 minutes. How long should it take him to swim 1200 meters?

86. Solve the proportion. $\dfrac{x}{12} = \dfrac{3}{8}$

87. Write a rate in fraction form for " 54 miles in 12 minutes". Reduce if possible.

88. Write a ratio " $7\dfrac{1}{2}$ to $22\dfrac{1}{2}$ " in fraction form and reduce.

89. Find the missing side in the following similar triangles.

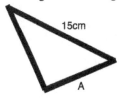

Exercise Set - Cummulative Review

90. Multiply. $(-7)(3)(-5)$

91. Solve. $t + 3 = -7$

92. Graph the numbers 5, 2, and 0 on a number line.

93. Add and reduce if possible. $\dfrac{4}{15} + \dfrac{4}{15}$

94. Add. -8 + 12 + 7 + (-10)

 # 6.5 QUIZ YOURSELF:

To make sure you are ready for the EXAM, try these problems without any help. Give yourself about 20 minutes and don't check the answers until you have completely finished.

Simplify.

1. $\sqrt{225}$

2. $-\sqrt{\dfrac{25}{81}}$

3. $8\sqrt{25} - 6\sqrt{49}$

4. $\sqrt{\dfrac{16}{25}} + \sqrt{\dfrac{121}{100}}$

5. $-6\left(\sqrt{9} + 11\right)$

6. Evaluate. $\sqrt{b^2 - 4ac}$ for a = 4, b = 13 and c = 9

7. Evaluate. $\sqrt{a^2 + b^2}$ for a = 7 and b = 5. Approximate to the nearest hundredths.

Answers to this Quiz Yourself are on page 690

Chapter 6 Summary

Section 6.1: Introduction to Ratios and Rates

Processes and Important Notes	Examples
Introduction to Ratios: • A **ratio** is a comparison between two quantities.	**Express the ratio in the same using the other two notations.** 27 boys to 40 girls Solution: $\dfrac{27}{40}$, 27:40
Simplifying Ratios: • Ratios are reduced the same way as regular fractions: remove common factors in the top and bottom by factoring.	**Write each ratio in fraction notation and reduce to lowest terms.** 70 minutes to 84 minutes Solution: $\dfrac{70}{84} = \dfrac{5}{6}$
Introduction to Rates: • A **rate** is a ratio where the units for the two quantities being compared are different. • Note that for rates we include units throughout the reducing process and in the final answers.	**Write each rate in fraction form and reduce if possible.** There are have been 214 shark attacks off the coast of South Africa in the last 100 years. Solution: $\dfrac{\text{shark attacks}}{\text{years}} = \dfrac{214}{100} = \dfrac{107\,\text{shark attacks}}{50\,\text{years}}$
Unit Rates: • A **unit rate** is a rate in which the second quantity is 1.	**Find the unit rate for each of the following situations. Include units in your answer. Round to the nearest hundredth if necessary.** A 15-ounce jar of Skippy peanut butter costs $3.49. Solution: Set up a rate and divide. $\dfrac{\$3.49}{15\ oz} = \dfrac{\$0.23}{oz}$

Decide if the following is a ratio or a rate and then write in lowest terms.

1. 132 students to 3 classes.
2. 18 minutes to 26 minutes.
3. $4.39 for 18 oz. of peanut butter.
4. $51.20 for 12 gallons of gas.
5. Shufen answered 18 of the 20 questions correct on his exam. Write the number of incorrect to number of correct as a ratio/rate.
6. Wayne ran the LA marathon (26.2 miles) in 4 hours, 24 minutes. Find his speed in minutes per mile?
7. LaShayla drove 423 miles in 6 hours. Find her speed in miles per hour?

8. A Swiss adventurer spent 19 days aloft in a hot-air balloon with 32 tanks of propane. Find the number of tanks of propane required per day.

Find the unit rate to find the best buy.
9. It costs $2.49 for 7oz. of hummus or $4.29 for 16 oz. container of hummus.
10. It costs $396 year of gym membership at YMCA and it cost $649.99 for 3-years of gym membership at 24 hour fitness. Which gym is less expensive per month?

Section 6.2: Proportions

Processes and Important Notes	Examples
Introduction to Proportions: • A **proportion** is the statement that two ratios are equal. • A proportion has the form $\dfrac{a}{b} = \dfrac{c}{d}$ where $\dfrac{a}{b}$ and $\dfrac{c}{d}$ are ratios.	**For each statement write a corresponding proportion.** 6 is to 8.4 as 25 is to 35 **Solution:** $\dfrac{6}{8.4} = \dfrac{25}{35}$
Determining if a Proportion is True or False: • In the proportion $\dfrac{a}{b} = \dfrac{c}{d}$ the products $a \cdot d$ and $b \cdot c$ are called **cross products**. • A proportion is true if its cross products are equal. A proportion is false is its cross products are not equal.	**Use cross products to determine if each proportion is true or false.** $\dfrac{4}{15} \; \dfrac{3}{13}$ **Solution:** To solve, find the cross products. $\overset{?}{}$ $4 \cdot 13 = 5 \cdot 15$ $52 \neq 75$ Therefore, the proportion is false.

Solving a Proportion:

Use a variable to represent the missing term and set the cross products equal we have an equation that can easily be solved.

Solve the following proportion.

$$\frac{3\frac{3}{5}}{7\frac{1}{2}} = \frac{m}{4\frac{2}{9}}$$

Solution:
Use cross products to solve.

$$3\frac{3}{5} \cdot 4\frac{2}{9} = 7\frac{1}{2}m$$

$$\frac{18}{5} \cdot \frac{38}{9} = \frac{15}{2}m$$

$$\frac{76}{5} = \frac{15}{2}m$$

$$\frac{2}{15} \cdot \frac{76}{5} = m$$

$$\frac{152}{75} = m$$

So, $m = 2\dfrac{2}{75}$

Determine if the following proportions are True or False.

11. $\dfrac{4}{6} = \dfrac{6}{9}$

12. $\dfrac{61}{115} = \dfrac{42}{78}$

Solve the following proportions.

13. $\dfrac{x}{15} = \dfrac{8}{25}$

14. $\dfrac{m}{8} = \dfrac{5}{12}$

15. $\dfrac{6.2}{19.5} = \dfrac{y}{29.25}$

16. $\dfrac{1\frac{2}{3}}{3} = \dfrac{m}{6\frac{2}{5}}$

17. $\dfrac{1\frac{1}{3}}{3\frac{2}{5}} = \dfrac{y}{6\frac{1}{4}}$

18. $\dfrac{2.4}{4.8} = \dfrac{n}{8.2}$

Section 6.3: More Applications of Proportions

Processes and Important Notes	Examples
Proportions in the Real World: Carefully follow these steps and you WILL get better at applying math: 1) **READ THE PROBLEM** 2) **ASSIGN A VARIABLE** 3) **SUMMARIZE THE INFORMATION** 4) **DO THE MATH** 5) **ANSWER THE QUESTION**	**Solve.** For every hour you spend in class, you should spend 2 hours studying/doing homework. If Kaitlyn is taking 9 hours of class, how many hours should she spend studying? **Solution:** Let h = hours Kaitlyn should spend studying. Set up a proportion: $\dfrac{1}{2} = \dfrac{9}{h}$ Solve: $\begin{array}{l} 1h = 2 \cdot 9 \\ h = 18 \end{array}$ So, Kaitlyn should spend 18 hours studying/doing homework.

19. A tutoring center requires that there are 2 tutors for every 15 students. If they anticipate 110 students, how many tutors should they hire?

20. Rochelle waits tables. For every 3 hours, she makes $56 in tips. She is on the schedule this week to work 16 hours. How much money should she make in tips at this rate?

21. A massage therapist charges $25 for a 15-minute massage. Find the cost for an 80-minute massage.

22. The exchange rate for the Libya currency, called dinars is 11 dinars to $9. Alfonso spent 135 dinars buying souvenirs for his family. How much did he spend in American dollars?

23. In the US, every 34 seconds someone has a heart attack because of high cholesterol. At this rate, how many people have a heart attack in an hour? (There are 3600 seconds in an hour)

24. In 2002, the birth rate per year was 13.9 for every 1000 persons. If a community has 56,000 persons, how many births did they have in 2002?

25. Google Voice charges $0.15 per minute for calls to Mexico. How much would a 36-minute phone call cost?

26. Surfing can burn 256 calories in 45 minutes. How many calories can you burn in 26 minutes surfing?

Section 6.4: Similar Geometric Figures

Processes and Important Notes	Examples
Similar Triangles: • **Similar** objects have the exact same shape but necessarily the exact same size. • In similar figures, corresponding angles have the same measure and corresponding sides are proportional. • Corresponding angles have the same measure (the symbol $\angle$ refers to an angle): • Corresponding sides are proportional.	Solve. 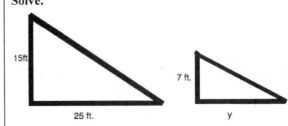 **Solution:** Set up a proportion using the corresponding sides. $\dfrac{7}{15} = \dfrac{y}{25}$ $7 \cdot 25 = 15y$ Solve using cross products. $175 = 15y$ $y = 11\dfrac{2}{3}\,ft.$

Use the similar triangles to find the missing side.

27. Find x.

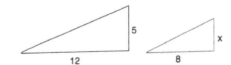

28. Find x.
29. Find y.

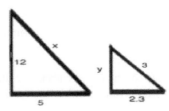

Use for problems 28-29

30. Find z.
31. Find y.

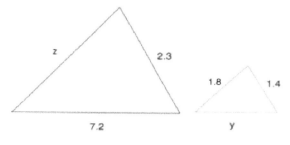

Use for problems 30-31

Section 6.5: Square Roots

Processes and Important Notes	Examples
Square Roots: • The **square root** of x is any number that, when multiplied to itself, gives x. • The symbol $\sqrt{}$ is used to indicate a positive square root. This symbol is often called a **radical**. • The symbol $-\sqrt{}$ is used to indicate a negative square root.	**What are the square roots of each number?** a. $\sqrt{81}$ b. $-\sqrt{\dfrac{1}{16}}$ c. $\sqrt{32}$ **Solution:** a. $\sqrt{81} = 9$ b. $-\sqrt{\dfrac{1}{16}} = -\dfrac{\sqrt{1}}{\sqrt{16}} = -\dfrac{1}{4}$ c. You need to use a calculator for this one: $\sqrt{32} \approx 5.657$
Expressions that Contain Radicals: **The Order of Operations:** • Work inside grouping symbols such as parentheses and radicals first. • Perform any exponents and radicals in the expression. • Perform multiplication and division moving left to right. • Perform addition and subtraction from left to right.	**Simplify.** $5\sqrt{16} + 27$ **Solution:** $5\sqrt{16} + 27$ $= 5 \cdot 4 + 27$ find the square root $= 20 + 27$ multiplication $= 47$ addition
The Radical as a Grouping Symbol: • An operation inside a radical should be done before taking the square root.	**Simplify.** $4\sqrt{25 - 16} + 7^2$ **Solution:** $4\sqrt{25 - 16} + 7^2$ $= 4\sqrt{9} + 7^2$ work inside radical first $= 4 \cdot 3 + 49$ perform exponents and radicals $= 12 + 49$ multiplication $= 61$ addition

Simplify.

32. $\sqrt{121}$

33. $\sqrt{100}$

34. $\sqrt{\dfrac{4}{49}}$

35. $-\sqrt{\dfrac{1}{25}}$

36. $3\sqrt{81}$

37. $-12\sqrt{\dfrac{25}{36}}$

38. $7\sqrt{100}+5^2$

39. $-4\sqrt{121}-3\sqrt{4}$

40. $6\cdot11-3\sqrt{45-6^2}$

41. $\dfrac{-6+\sqrt{6^2-4\cdot9}}{-2(9)}$

42. Evaluate. $\sqrt{b^2-4ac}$, a = 2, b = 9, c = 7

43. Evaluate. $xy-\sqrt{x+y}$, x = 9, y = 7

Section 6.6: The Pythagorean Theorem

Processes and Important Notes	Examples
The Pythagorean Theorem: • In any right triangle, the sum of the squares of the legs is equal to the square of the hypotenuse $(\text{leg})^2+(\text{leg})^2=(\text{hypotenuse})^2$ $a^2+b^2=c^2$	**Find the missing side in the right triangle. Round to the nearest tenth if necessary.** **Solution:** Use the Pythagorean theorem since it is a right triangle with legs 8 and 11. $a^2+b^2=c^2$ $8^2+11^2=c^2$ $64+121=c^2$ $185=c^2$ $c\approx13.6$ use a calculator to approximate $\sqrt{185}$ since it is not a perfect square.
Verifying Right Triangles: • If a triangle has sides a, b, and c, such that $a^2+b^2=c^2$ then the triangle is a right triangle.	**Is the following triangle a right triangle?** Triangle with sides 5, 16 and 13. **Solution:** To determine, use Pythagorean theorem to see if it is a true statement. So let a =5, b = 13 and c = 16 $a^2+b^2=c^2$ $5^2+13^2=16^2$ $25+169=256$ $194\neq256$ This is not true, this is NOT a right triangle.

Refer to the generic triangle to the right. Find the missing side of each triangle given the other two measures. Round to the nearest tenth if necessary.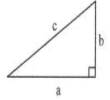

44. a = 6, b = 8

45. b = 10, c = 26

46. a = 15, c = 17

47. b = 24, c = 25

48. a = 7, b = 11

49. b = 9, c = 13

Check the following triangles to verify if they are right triangles or not.

50. a = 3, b = 4, c = 5

51. a = 5, b = 12, c = 13

52. a = 7, b = 24, c = 25

53. a = 7, b = 8, c = 15

54. a = 4, b = 9, c = 13

55. a = 11, b = 60, c = 61

Chapter 6 Test Yourself

Simplify.

1. $\sqrt{\dfrac{81}{121}}$

2. $\sqrt{64}$

3. $2\sqrt{25} + 78$

4. $\sqrt{100} - 3\sqrt{16}$

5. $-3\sqrt{49} + 13(-4)$

6. $45 \div (-3) + 2\sqrt{9+16}$

Solve the following proportions.

7. $\dfrac{m}{45} = \dfrac{17}{135}$

8. $\dfrac{2.7}{11.7} = \dfrac{k}{15.6}$

9. $\dfrac{\frac{8}{9}}{3\frac{1}{5}} = \dfrac{b}{7\frac{3}{5}}$

10. Write as a unit rate: $285,000 for 1450 square feet of house.

11. A 2 pack of paper towels costs $2.69, while an 8 pack sells for $9.79. Which is the better deal?

12. Mars has two natural satellites, Deimos which has a diameter of 7.5 miles and Phobos which has a diameter of 13.7 miles long. Earth's moon has a diameter of 2,159 miles long. Find the ratio of the diameter of Phobos to the diameter of Earth's moon.

13. A total of 2,065 verified nuclear detonations have occurred in the last 63 years. Find the number of detonations per year.

14. In 2007, volunteers donated 676,960 hours of labor to the Ozark Highlands Trail, worth $13 million. Find the rate at which the volunteers would have been paid in dollars per hour.

15. Japan's volcano Sakurajima is one of the most active volcanoes on Earth. The largest ever eruption in Japan was in January 1914. In the nearby city of Kagoshima, they experienced 417 earthquakes in the 30 hours before this eruption. Find the number of earthquakes per hour.

16. National Geographic's exhibit Tutankhamun and the Golden Age of Pharaohs drew record-breaking crowds in Los Angeles, Fort Lauderdale, Chicago and Philadelphia. Use the table below to find the following ratios.

City	Attendance
Los Angeles	937,613
Fort Lauderdale	707,534
Chicago	1,044,743
Philadelphia	1,300,700

    a.   The attendance of Los Angeles to Chicago

    b.   The attendance of Fort Lauderdale to Philadelphia

    c.   The attendance of Chicago to the attendance of all 4 cities combined

17. A case of soda (12 cans) sells for $3.49. At this rate, how much would 15 cans of soda sell for?

18. Poli can run a marathon in 3 hours 56 minutes (236 minutes) at a 9 minute per mile pace. How long would it take someone to run a marathon at an 11 minute per mile pace?

19. A triangle has sides 15m, 36 m, and 39 m. Is this triangle a right triangle? Explain why.

20. Find the missing side of the right triangle.

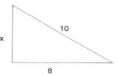

Chapters 1 – 6 Cumulative Review

Find the following:
1. The prime factorization of 732.
2. The LCM of 64 and 72.
3. Two factors of -56 whose sum is -10.
4. Rewrite 1.245 as a fraction.

Simplify.

5. $-819 - (-152)$

6. $-52 \div 0$

7. $8(-5)(0)(-11)$

8. $-72 \div (-6) \cdot 2 + 1^3$

9. $(-3)^4 + 5(-7)$

10. $7 \cdot 5 + 564 \div 8$

11. $3^2 - 26$

12. $-4|-13| + 82$

13. $\dfrac{25}{42} \div \left(-\dfrac{10}{77}\right)$

14. $9\dfrac{5}{16} - 4\dfrac{7}{12}$

15. $-\dfrac{16c^2 g^3}{55} \cdot \dfrac{35c}{24cg^4}$

16. $-3\sqrt{49} + 6 \cdot 11$

17. $6^2 \div (-9) + \sqrt{19 + 17}$

18. $5.93 + (-11.208)$

19. $(-5.7)(-17.92)$

20. $\left\{5 - 3\left[5 - \sqrt{16}\right] + 60 \div 12\right\} - 7$

Solve.

21. $x - 39 = 62$

22. $2x + 13 = 47$

23. $5x = -2x - 49$

24. $k - \dfrac{4}{5} = 2\dfrac{3}{7}$

25. $\dfrac{2}{3}m + 1 = 8\dfrac{1}{3}$

26. $b + 5.67 = 6b - (-3.22)$

27. $-3\left[2(n-4) + 7\right] + 2n = -5$

28. $\dfrac{c}{11} = \dfrac{6}{25}$

29. $\dfrac{u}{2\frac{2}{5}} = \dfrac{\frac{8}{9}}{5\frac{1}{3}}$

Simplify/combine like terms.

30. $-18x + 37x - (-45x)$

31. $-2(3m - 7) + 6n - 5(-8n + 5m)$

Evaluate.

32. $\dfrac{-b}{2a}$, $a = \dfrac{2}{5}$, $b = 4$

33. $xy + y^2$, $x = -2$, $y = -7$

34. $b^2 - 4ac$, $a = 3, b = 6, c = -5$

35. $\pi r^2 l$, $r = 5.4$, $h = \dfrac{7}{2}$. Use $\pi = \dfrac{22}{7}$.

Write an algebraic equation and solve the following problems.
36. Find the missing side of the right triangle.

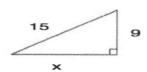

37. Find the circumference of a circle with a diameter of $\dfrac{21}{22}$ ft. Use $\pi = \dfrac{22}{7}$

38. Find the area of a circle whose radius is $4\dfrac{1}{5}$ yd. Use $\pi = 3.14$.

39. Write as a rate: Shalee drove 678 miles in 8 hours.

40. Write as a ratio: Olivia got 16 of the 20 questions correct on a quiz.

41. Rica wrote four checks for her monthly bills. She wrote two checks for her rent that were $175 each, one for her electric bill that was $47, and one for her cell phone that was $98. When she deposited $519 into her account, she has a balance of $123. What was her balance before she wrote the checks and made the deposit?

42. Find Kervin's average in his anthropology class if he has scored 76, 48, 90, 63 and 82 on his 5 exams.

43. Two angles are complementary. The second angle is 15 more than twice the first. Find the measure of the two angles.

44. Enrique is taking 11 units at the local community college. His tuition consists of $45 per unit plus health fees of $78, and a parking pass that costs $119 for the semester. Find his total cost.

45. Carmelina is buying textbooks for her 3 classes. The costs of the books are $78.19, $149.59 and $37.65. Find the cost of her books.

46. OmWhitney buys 7 books for $74.13. How much did each book cost?

47. It costs $67 for a 55-minute massage. At this rate, how much would an 80-minute massage cost?

48. A 150-lb person burns 750 calories per hour(60 minutes) swimming. At this rate, how many calories would they burn swimming for 37 minutes?

49. Which is the better buy? A package of 20 yoga classes for $210 or a package of 15 classes for $154.

50. Find the missing side.

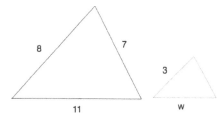

Chapter 7 - Percents

Prealgebra

Courtesy of Fotolia

We see percents in everyday life.

Courtesy of Fotolia

We will also look at probability…

In poker, the odds of getting at least a pair is 43.5%.

7.1 Introduction To Percent

Topics:
- Understanding Percents
- Percents and Fractions
- Percents and Decimals
- Introduction to Percent Statements

Are You Ready?
To see if you are ready to understand this section, do the following short quiz.

1. Divide. $8\overline{)3}$
2. Multiply. $0.65 \cdot 128$
3. Reduce. $\dfrac{25}{200}$
4. Multiply. $64 \cdot \dfrac{1}{100}$
5. Divide. $47 \div 100$

Answers to Are You Ready?

(1) .375   *(2) 83.2*   *(3) $\dfrac{1}{8}$*   *(4) $\dfrac{16}{25}$*   *(5) .47*

Understanding Percents

This entire chapter is about percents.

The word **percent** means "per one hundred". The symbol for percent is %.

You can't go anywhere in our modern world without seeing percents.

Extra 30% trade-in means that for every 100 cents you get on
trade-ins, they will add 30 more cents.

A 75% sale means that for every 100 cents an item costs they take out 75 cents.

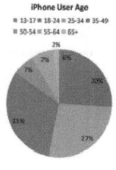

According to the pie chart to the right, 27% of i-phone users are between 25 and 34 years old. That means that for every 100 people who have an i-phone about 27 of them will be between 25 and 34 years old.

Example 1: Use a shaded figure to illustrate 87%. Represent the shaded area as a fraction.

Solution: 87% means "87 out of 100". We can use a grid with 100 squares and shade 87 of them.

"87 out of 100" can be expressed as the fraction $\dfrac{87}{100}$.

Example 2: A recent newspaper article from San Diego claims that 46 out of 200 people surveyed think the San Diego Charges need a new football stadium. What percent of people from the survey think need a new football stadium?

Solution: 46 out of 200 can be expressed as $\dfrac{46}{200} = \dfrac{\cancel{2} \cdot 23}{\cancel{2} \cdot 100} = \dfrac{23}{100}$. Since percent means per one hundred, 23 out of 100 means 23%.

Understanding Percents Homework

What percent is represented by each shaded grid?

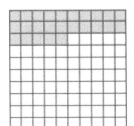

1.

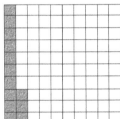

2.

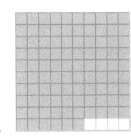

3.

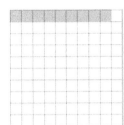

4.

5. Out of 100 people surveyed 87 of them say they do not support raising tuition costs for college students. What percent of people surveyed do not support higher tuition costs?

6. Out of 200 parts manufactured, 14 are found to have defects. What percent of the parts were defective?

Percents and Fractions

One easy way to interpret a percent is as a fraction. Take 75% as an example…

75% means 75 per 100. 75 per 100 can be expressed as the fraction $\dfrac{75}{100}$, which can be reduced:

$$\frac{75}{100} = \frac{3 \cdot 25}{4 \cdot 25} = \frac{3 \cdot \cancel{25}}{4 \cdot \cancel{25}} = \frac{3}{4}$$

So 75% is equivalent to the fraction $\dfrac{3}{4}$. Here are some other examples of how percents can be interpreted as fractions.

Percent/Fraction Statement	Percent/Fraction Connection
"50% of all people are females" is equivalent to "one-half of all people are females"	50% is equivalent to $\dfrac{1}{2}$ since $50\% = \dfrac{50}{100} = \dfrac{1}{2}$.
"a decrease of 40%" is equivalent to "a decrease of two-fifths"	40% is equivalent to $\dfrac{2}{5}$ since $40\% = \dfrac{40}{100} = \dfrac{2}{5}$.
"25% of the budget" is equivalent to "one quarter of the budget"	25% is equivalent to $\dfrac{1}{4}$ since $25\% = \dfrac{25}{100} = \dfrac{1}{4}$.

Here is the formal procedure for writing a percent in fraction form.

To Convert a Percent to a Fraction:

- Use the percent value as the numerator (without the % symbol).
- Use 100 as the denominator.
- Reduce the fraction.

The last step, "reduce the fraction" may involve decimals or even complex fractions.

Example 3: Convert each percent to fraction form and write the result using an equivalence sentence.

a.) 44%   b.) 17.5%   c.) $9\dfrac{1}{5}\%$

Solution:

a.) Use the percent value as the numerator and 100 as the denominator.

$$44\% = \frac{44}{100}$$

Reduce the fraction.

$$= \frac{\cancel{4}\cdot 11}{\cancel{4}\cdot 25}$$

$$= \frac{11}{25}$$

44% is equivalent to $\dfrac{11}{25}$.

b.) This percent involves a decimal. This just means we will have an extra step in reducing the fraction.

Use the percent value as the numerator and 100 as the denominator.

$$17.5\% = \frac{17.5}{100}$$

Reduce the fraction:
- To clear the decimal out of the numerator, multiply by 10.

- Now reduce as normal.

$$= \frac{17.5 \cdot 10}{100 \cdot 10}$$

$$= \frac{175}{1000}$$

$$= \frac{\cancel{25} \cdot 7}{\cancel{25} \cdot 40}$$

$$= \frac{7}{40}$$

17.5% is equivalent to $\dfrac{7}{40}$.

c.) The percent $9\dfrac{1}{5}\%$ involves a mixed number but it is still in percent form. To put it in the corresponding fraction form we divide by 100.

Use the percent value as the numerator and 100 as the denominator.

$$9\frac{1}{5}\% = \frac{9\frac{1}{5}}{100}$$

This is a complex fraction. Recall that we reduce complex fractions using fraction division.

$$= \frac{\frac{46}{5}}{100}$$

$$= \frac{46}{5} \div 100$$

$$= \frac{46}{5} \cdot \frac{1}{100}$$

$$= \frac{23}{250}$$

$9\dfrac{1}{5}\%$ is equivalent to $\dfrac{23}{250}$.

Just as every percent can be written as a fraction, every fraction can be written in percent notation.

To Convert a Fraction to Percent Notation:
- Multiply the fraction by 100 and add the % symbol.

- When converting fractions to percent notation final answers should be expressed as a mixed number.

Example 4: Convert each fraction to a percent notation and write the result using an equivalent statement.

a.) $\dfrac{3}{4}$ b.) $2\dfrac{1}{5}$ c.) $\dfrac{2}{11}$

Solution:

a.)

Multiply the fraction by 100 and include the percent symbol %.

$$\frac{3}{4} = \frac{3}{4} \cdot 100\%$$

Perform the multiplication.

$$= \frac{3}{4} \cdot \frac{100}{1}\%$$

$$= 75\%$$

$\dfrac{3}{4}$ is equivalent to 75%.

b.)

Multiply the fraction by 100 and include the percent symbol %.

$$2\frac{1}{5} = 2\frac{1}{5} \cdot 100\%$$

Perform the multiplication.

$$= \frac{11}{5} \cdot \frac{100}{1}\%$$

$$= 220\%$$

$2\dfrac{1}{5}$ is equivalent to 220%.

c.)

Multiply the fraction by 100 and include the percent symbol %.

$$\frac{2}{11} = \frac{2}{11} \cdot 100\%$$

Perform the multiplication.

$$= \frac{2}{11} \cdot \frac{100}{1}\%$$

- There are no common factors to reduce.

$$= \frac{200}{11}\%$$

- When converting fractions to percent notation the final percent should be expressed as a mixed number.

$$= 18\frac{2}{11}\%$$

$\dfrac{2}{11}$ is equivalent to $18\dfrac{2}{11}\%$.

Example 5: Where in the World? According to www.wikianswers.com about 9 out of 50 people on the planet have access to the internet. Covert the fraction $\dfrac{9}{50}$ to percent notation.

Solution:

$$\dfrac{9}{50} = \dfrac{9}{50} \cdot 100\% = 18\%$$

So about 18% of people on the planet have access to the internet.

 Exercise Set - Percents and Fractions

Convert each percent to fraction notation.
7.   65%
8.   78%
9.   45.5%
10. 12.5%

11. $5\dfrac{1}{2}\%$

12. $6\dfrac{1}{4}\%$

Convert each fraction to percent notation. Express the resulting percent in mixed number form if necessary.

13. $\dfrac{3}{5}$

14. $\dfrac{7}{8}$

15. $8\dfrac{7}{10}$

16. $1\dfrac{1}{2}$

17. $\dfrac{5}{7}$

18. $\dfrac{1}{12}$

19. A survey done at a community college says that 16 people out of 75 are relying on some kind of financial aid. Convert the fraction $\dfrac{16}{75}$ to percent notation.

20. Heidi does 18 training sessions on her bike. On 12 of the sessions she is able to complete the course in her target time. Convert the fraction $\dfrac{12}{18}$ to a percent.

Percents and Decimals

Just as we can convert between percent and fraction notations, we can convert between percent and decimal notations.

To Convert a Percent to Decimal Notation:

- Divide by 100 and drop the percent symbol %.
- Recall that dividing by 100 can be done by moving the decimal two places to the left.

Example 6: Convert each percent to decimal notation and write the result using an equivalent statement.
a.) 56%   b.) 370%   c.) 14.6%

Solution:
a.) $56\% = 56 \div 100 = 0.56. = 0.56$
[PN: decimal place jump arrows]

56% is equivalent to 0.56.

b.) $370\% = 370 \div 100 = 3.70. = 3.7$
[PN: decimal place jump arrows]

370% is equivalent to 3.7.

c.) Note that the percent already has a decimal place. But it is still in percent notation versus decimal notation.

$14.6\% = 14.6 \div 100 = 0.14.6 = 0.146$
[PN: decimal place jump arrows]

14.6% is equivalent to 0.146.

To Convert a Decimal Number to Percent Notation:

- Multiply by 100 and add the percent symbol %.
- Recall that multiplying by 100 can be performed by moving the decimal two places to the right.

Example 7: Convert each decimal to percent notation and write the result using an equivalent statement.
a.) 0.47   b.) 6.914   c.) 0.0083

Solution:
a.) $0.47 = 0.47 \cdot 100\% = 0.47. = 47\%$
[PN: decimal place jump arrows]

0.47 is equivalent to 47%.

b.) $6.914 = 6.914 \cdot 100\% = 6.91.4 = 691.4\%$
[PN: decimal place jump arrows]

6.914 is equivalent to 691.4%.

c.) $0.0083 = 0.0083 \cdot 100\% = 0.00.83 = 0.83\%$
[PN: decimal place jump arrows]

0.0083 is equivalent to 0.83%.

Example 8: Where in the World
The following chart gives the sales tax for several states in either decimal or percent notation. Fill in the missing values.

State	Tax Rate (Decimal Notation)	Tax Rate (Percent Notation)
California		8.25%
Utah	0.047	
Minnesota	0.06875	
Oregon		0%

Solution: in each case we are given either the decimal notation or the percent notation and need to fill in the other. Here is the chart with the missing values included.

State	Tax Rate (Decimal Notation)	Tax Rate (Percent Notation)
California	0.0825	8.25%
Utah	0.047	4.7%
Minnesota	0.06875	6.875%
Oregon	0	0%

Notice the last row means that Oregon has no sales tax.

STOP Exercise Set - Percents and Decimals

Convert each percent to decimal notation.

21. 75%

22. 23%

23. 235%

24. 614%

25. 0.136%

26. 0.083%

Convert each decimal to percent notation.

27. 0.06

28. 0.82

29. 4.12

30. 354.9

31. 0.0157

32. 0.0096

33. The following table gives the commission rate for several sales jobs in decimal and percent notations. Complete the table.

Company	Commission Rate (Decimal Notation)	Commission Rate (Percent Notation)
Solar Com	0.097	
Hi-Tech	0.159	
BioWave		0%
THR		2.51%

34. The following table gives interest rates on several different types of accounts at a bank in decimal and percent notation. Complete the table.

Account	Interest Rate (Decimal Notation)	Interest Rate (Percent Notation)
Savings	0.0471	
Checking		3.08%
Credit Card		17.45%
CD	0.0582	

Introduction to Percent Statements

Suppose Best Buy is having a 25% off sale on all console games and you are interested in a game that costs $52. To find the amount of the discount the question becomes "What is 25% of $52?". Here is the procedure for finding the amount of a percent.

To Find the Amount of a Percent:
Rewrite the percent in decimal or fraction form and translate the word "of" into multiplication.

$$25\% \text{ of } \$52$$

$$\downarrow \quad \downarrow \quad \downarrow$$

$$0.25 \cdot 52$$

$$= \$13$$

So if an item is originally $52 but there is a 25%, the store will take $13 off the price.

Example 9: Find the following percents and write the result using a percent statement.

a.) 5% of 73   b.) $8\frac{1}{3}$% of 425   c.) 0.03% of 4.8

Solution: For each exercise we convert the percent to a decimal or fraction and multiply, remembering to .write the final result as a percent statement.

a.)
$$
\begin{array}{ccc}
5\% & \text{of} & 73 \\
\downarrow & \downarrow & \downarrow \\
0.05 & \cdot & 73
\end{array}
$$
$$= 3.65$$

5% of 73 is 3.65.

b.) Trying to rewrite the mixed number as a decimal number results in a repeating decimal so it is best to

stay in fraction form for this exercise. $8\frac{1}{3}\% = \dfrac{8\frac{1}{3}}{100} = \dfrac{25}{3} \cdot \dfrac{1}{100} = \dfrac{1}{12}$

$8\frac{1}{3}$% of 425

$$
\begin{array}{ccc}
\downarrow & \downarrow & \downarrow \\
\dfrac{1}{12} & \cdot & 425
\end{array}
$$

$$= 35\frac{5}{12}$$

$8\frac{1}{3}$% of 425 is $35\frac{5}{12}$.

c.)
$$
\begin{array}{ccc}
0.03\% & \text{of} & 73 \\
\downarrow & \downarrow & \downarrow \\
0.0003 & \cdot & 4.8
\end{array}
$$
$$= 0.00144$$

0.03% of 4.8 is 0.00144.

There are so many applications to percents that it is difficult to decide which to pick first. Percents are an important topic for nearly every vocation, but particularly business and economics.

- Sale discounts
- Price mark-ups
- Taxes of all kinds
- Shipping and handling

- Interest
- Grades
- Tips

Example 10: Where in the World? Between the years 1948 to 1973, the Soviet Union killed approximately 95% of the 51,028 Humpback Whales for their meat and oil. Find the number of Humpback Whales killed.

Solution:
Notice the important part of the sentence with the percent sign:

95% of the 51,028 Humpback Whales

$.95 \cdot 51028$ Translate to a percent equation.
$= 48,477$

So, during 1948 to 1973, 48,477 Humpback Whales were killed by the Soviet Union.

STOP Introduction to Percent Statements Homework

Find the following percents. Round your answer to the nearest hundredth if necessary.
35. 7% of 65
36. 5.3% of 528
37. 90.4% of 15.3
38. 0.73% of 45.8

Find the following percents. Express your answer as a mixed number if necessary.
39. 8% of 42
40. 10% of 370

41. $5\frac{1}{2}\%$ of 64

42. $2\frac{1}{4}\%$ of 250

43. Ahbed spent 37% of his monthly income of $2180 on rent. How much is his rent each month?

44. Between 1970 and 1977, Kenya lost 50% of its 120,000 elephants for their ivory. How many elephants did they lose?

7.1 Exercise Set - Putting it ALL Together

For each exercise you are given a decimal, fraction or percent. Rewrite the given value using the other two notations.

45. $\frac{1}{4}$

46. 0.8

47. 40%

48. $10\frac{1}{2}\%$

49. 0.75

50. 58%

51. 0.006

52. $\frac{4}{5}$

53. 85%

Courtesy of Fotolia

54. 120%

55. $\dfrac{7}{10}$

56. 1.25

Find the following percents. Round your answer to the nearest hundredth if necessary.

57. 19% of 67

58. 25% of 92

59. 33% of 154

60. 51% of 729

Find the following percents. Express your answer as a mixed number if necessary.

61. $15\dfrac{1}{2}$% of 36

62. $7\dfrac{1}{4}$% of \$812

63. $5\dfrac{3}{4}$% of \$18,940

64. $2\dfrac{3}{8}$% of \$245,000

65. Over the past 5 seasons the Smith College basketball team has won 85 out of 125 games. What fraction of their games have they won? Convert the fraction to a percent. Round your answer to the nearest hundredth.

66. Over the last 7 seasons the Smith College baseball team has won 108 out of 164 games. What fraction of their games have they won? Convert the fraction to percent notation. Round your answer to the nearest hundredth.

67. A serving of soda that weighs 368 grams contains 28 grams of sugar. What fraction of the soda's weight is sugar? Convert the fraction to a percent. Round your answer to the nearest hundredth.

68. A Twinkie weighs 94 grams and contains 36 grams of fat. What fraction of a Twinkie's weight is fat? Convert the fraction to a percent. Round your answer to the nearest hundredth.

69. The following chart gives the sales tax for several states in either decimal or percent notation. Fill in the missing values.

State	Tax Rate (Decimal Notation)	Tax Rate (Percent Notation)
Kansa		6.25%
Texas	0.0775	
Nevada	0.0685	
Ohio		5%

70. The following chart gives the mortgage rate for several couples in either decimal or percent notation. Fill in the missing values.

State	Mortgage Rate (Decimal Notation)	Mortgage Rate (Percent Notation)
Contador's		11.55%
Armstrong's	0.045	
Cancellera's		3.85%
Gilbert's	0.0865	

71. Nizhnevartovsky is the oil capital of Russia. 20% of the Russian oil is extracted from this district. Write this percentage as a decimal and a fraction.

72. 85% of people exposed to poison ivy have an allergic reaction consisting of itchy, blistery bumps. Write this percentage as a decimal and a fraction.

73. Among Western Lowland gorillas, infant mortality can be as high as 50%. Write this percentage as a decimal and a fraction.

74. In Yellowstone National Park in the winter, half a mile from Old Faithful, you can hear noise from snow mobiles 68% of the day. Write this percentage as a decimal and a fraction.

75. According to National Geographic, if we can prevent all human-caused deaths to whale in the North Atlantic, the population of whales could swell 25% in 15 years. Write this percentage as a decimal and a fraction.

76. While migrating, at least 30% of the flock of Bee-Eaters will make it back to Europe for the following spring. Write this percentage as a decimal and a fraction.

77. 15% of wild turkeys are killed by hunters every year. Write this percentage as a decimal and a fraction.

78. A Haitian's diet consists of about 20% of rice. Write this percentage as a decimal and a fraction.

79. In a history class, 18% of the 46 students made A's. Find the number of students that made an A in the course.

80. In a French class, 23% of the 28 students made a C in the course. Find the number of students that made a C in the French course.

81. There was a total of 20,705 annual total of orphan visas issued by the US during the years 1996-2006. 31.5% of these 20,705 visas were awarded to China. How many visas were awarded to China orphans for adoptions?

82. In a 2001 Census, 62% of the 8,274,325 inhabitants identified themselves as indigenous Bolivian Indians. Find the number of indigenous Bolivian Indians.

Exercise Set - Cumulative Review

83. Subtract. $-89 - (-54)$

84. Solve. $7(x - 2) = 4x + 7$

85. Draw a picture to represent the fraction $\dfrac{3}{5}$.

86. The legs of a right triangle measure 5 inches and 8 inches. What is the length of the hypotenuse? Round to the nearest tenth.

87. Multiply. $(-9)(-5)(2)$

7.1 QUIZ YOURSELF:

To make sure you are ready for the EXAM, try these problems without any help. Give yourself about 20 minutes and don't check the answers until you have completely finished.

Write the following as a percent.

1. $\dfrac{3}{8}$

2. 0.079

3. 4.6

4. Write 35.8% as a decimal.

5. Write 45% as a fraction.

6. Write $7\dfrac{1}{3}\%$ as a fraction.

7. Find 20% of 78.

8. Find 27.3% of 265.

9. A senior high school class has 438 graduates. A study shows that only 69% of these graduates enrolled in college. Find the number of graduates from this high school enrolled in college.

Answers to this Quiz Yourself are on page 696.

7.2 Solving Percent Statements

Topics:
- Writing Percent Statements As Equations
- Solving Percent Statements
- Estimating Percents

Are You Ready?
To see if you are ready to understand this section, do the following short quiz.
1. Multiply. $340 \cdot 0.24$
2. Multiply. $4350 \cdot 0.06$
3. Solve. $4x = 42.36$
4. Solve. $0.15x = 84.30$
5. Solve. $\dfrac{1}{2}x = 951$

Answers to Are You Ready?
(1) 81.6   (2) 261   (3) x = 10.59   (4) x = 562   (5) x = 1902

Writing Percent Statements As Equations

In the last section we looked at how to calculate the amount of a percent and writing a percent statement, like this...

$$45 \text{ is } 26\% \text{ of } 225$$

This can also be expressed by writing

$$26\% \text{ of } 225 \text{ is } 45$$

Let's look at percent statements in more detail.

In general, a **percent statement** has the following form.

$$A \text{ is } P\% \text{ of } B \qquad \text{or} \qquad P\% \text{ of } B \text{ is } A$$

A is called the **amount**.

P is the **percent**.

B is called the **base**.

Every percent statement can be written as an equation.

For example, the statement "45 is 26% of 225" is expressed in the equation $45 = 0.26 \cdot 225$.

And the second form of the statement, "26% of 225 is 45" can be expressed as $0.26 \cdot 225 = 45$.

To Write a Percent Statement in Equation Form:
- Change the percent to decimal or fraction form
- Translate the word *of* into multiplication
- Translate the word *is* into an equal sign

$$A \text{ is } P\% \text{ of } B \qquad\qquad P\% \text{ of } B \text{ is } A$$
$$\downarrow \downarrow \downarrow \;\; \downarrow \downarrow \qquad\qquad \downarrow \downarrow \downarrow \;\; \downarrow \downarrow$$
$$A = P \cdot B \qquad\qquad P \cdot B = A$$

It is very important to remember that in the percent statement the percent is in percent form but in the equation it is in decimal or fraction form.

Example 1: Translate each percent statement into an equation.
a.) 54 is 45% of 120   b.) 325% of 145 is 471.25   c.) 5.439 is 8.4% of 64.75

Solution: For each statement we translate the word "is" into an "=", the word "of" into multiplication "$\cdot$" and use a variable to represent unknown value.

a.)
$$54 \text{ is } 45\% \text{ of } 120$$
$$\downarrow \downarrow \downarrow \;\; \downarrow \downarrow$$
$$56 = 0.45 \cdot 120$$

b.)
$$325\% \text{ of } 145 \text{ is } 471.25$$
$$\downarrow \downarrow \downarrow \;\; \downarrow \downarrow$$
$$3.25 \cdot 145 = 471.25$$

c.)
$$5.439 \text{ is } 8.4\% \text{ of } 64.75$$
$$\downarrow \downarrow \downarrow \;\; \downarrow \downarrow$$
$$5.439 = 0.084 \cdot 64.75$$

□ Note that when the percent goes into the equation it is written in decimal form.

Example 2: Where in the World?
A business woman is giving a presentation and makes the following statement:

"The total cost for making and delivering our product is $154.20. Of that cost, $53.97 goes to shipping. That means 35% of the cost just goes to shipping!"

Write a percent statement that corresponds to this scenario. Translate the percent statement into an equation and verify the equation.

Solution:
In this scenario, $154.20 is the base, 35% is the percent, and 53.97 is the amount. So the corresponding percent statement would be " $53.97 is 35% of $154.20 ". Let's translate this statement to an equation and verify that it is true:

53.97 is 35% of 154.20

$$\downarrow \downarrow \downarrow \quad \downarrow \downarrow$$

$$53.97 = 0.35 \cdot 154.20$$

$$53.97 = 53.97$$

So the statement is true.

Translate each percent statement into an equation.
1. 15% of 70 is 10.5.
2. 38% of 35 is 13.3.
3. 900 is 45% of 2000.
4. 120 is 75% of 160.

Write a percent statement that corresponds to the following scenarios. Translate the percent statement into an equation.

5. Jackie placed an order online for a new shirt. The total came to $35, of which $7 was for shipping, which is 20% of the total bill. So, the $7 shipping cost is 20% of the total bill $35.

6. Katie competed in an Ironman Triathlon, which is a total of 140.6 miles. One leg of the triathlon consists of a 26.2 mile run which is 18.63% of the whole distance. That means that 18.63% of the triathlon distance is running.

Solving Percent Statements

We now look at finding missing values in a percent statement.

[PN: Guy on TV saying this with the percent statement beside]
"68 out of 75 people say that we should not be at war. That's a high percentage!."

68 is what percent of 75?

[PN: Like a clip from a newspaper.]
"In a survey of 500 magazine subscribers, we found that 75% of them recycle their magazines."

What is 75% of 500?

[PN: A quote form the internet.]
"By 2011, 50% of Apple's profit will come from the i-phone. That will be about $7.9 billion!"

50% of what is $7.9 billion?

As these examples show, often when we see information about that would involve percents, one of the values form the

To Solve a Percent Statement:
- Translate the statement into an equation using a variable to represent the unknown value.
- Solve the resulting equation.
- If finding a percent give the final answer in percent form.

First we will look at some examples of translating statements into equations and then a few examples of following through and solving the equation.

Example 3: Translate each percent statement into an equation. Do not solve.
a.) What is 75% of 500?   b.) 4.5% of what is 13.8?   c.) What percent of 76 is 134?

Solution: In each case we translate just like before but use a variable for the unknown value. As a last step we will also rewrite the equation in a simpler form if appropriate.

a.) What is 25% of 500?
$$x = 0.25 \cdot 500$$

b.) 4.5% of what is 73.8
$$0.045 \cdot B = 73.8$$
$$0.045B = 73.8$$

c.) What percent of 76 is 134?
$$P \cdot 76 = 134$$
$$76P = 134$$

Look at part b.) from the last example and recall that to solve an equation like $0.045B = 13.8$ we divide both sides by 0.045.

$$\frac{0.045\,B}{0.045} = \frac{73.8}{0.045}$$
$$B = 1640$$

So our resulting percent statement would be "4.5% of 1640 is 73.8".

Solving a regular percent statement with an unknown value will always involve either multiplication or division.

Example 4: Solve each percent statement. Round you answer to the nearest hundredth if necessary.
a.) 6% of what number is 15?
b.) What percent of 84 is 10.5?
c.) 18.2 is 53% of what number?

Solution: Note that in part b.) we express our final answer in percent form. Note in Part c.) that we rounded our answer to the nearest hundredth.

a.)

6% of what number is 15?

$\downarrow \downarrow \downarrow \;\; \downarrow \downarrow$

$0.06 \cdot B = 15$

$0.06B = 15$

$\dfrac{0.06B}{0.06} = \dfrac{15}{0.06}$

$B = 250$

b.)

What percent of 84 is 15?

$\downarrow \downarrow \downarrow \;\; \downarrow \downarrow$

$P \cdot 84 = 10.5$

$\dfrac{P \cdot 84}{84} = \dfrac{10.5}{84}$

$P = 0.125 = 12.5\%$

c.)

18.2 is 53% of what number?

$\downarrow \downarrow \downarrow \;\; \downarrow \downarrow$

$18.2 = 0.53 \cdot B$

$\dfrac{18.2}{0.53} = \dfrac{0.53 \cdot B}{0.53}$

$34.34 = B$

$B = 34.34$

Example 5: Where in the World? An investor is confident she can make an 8.5% profit on an investment. If she wants make $500 in profit, she can find how much must be invested by solving the percent statement "$500 is 8.5% of what number?" To the nearest hundred, how much money must be invested to make the $500 profit?

Solution: We are just asked to solve the percent statement "$500 is 8.5% of what number?" and round the nearest hundred.

500 is 8.5% of what number?

$\downarrow \downarrow \downarrow \;\; \downarrow \downarrow$

$500 = 0.085 \cdot B$

$5882.352... = B$

So, to the nearest hundred, she must invest $5,900 to get a profit of $500.

STOP EXERCISE SET - Solving Percent Statements

Translate each percent statement into an equation. Do not solve.
7.   28 is what percent of 64?
8.   What is 18% of 356?
9.   16% of what is 49.92?
10. 45% of 156 is what?

Solve each percent statement. Round you answer to the nearest hundredth if necessary.
11. 39.9 is 15% of what?
12. 20% of 24 is what?
13. 51.7 is what percentage of 94?
14. 38.4 is 24% of what?

15. An investor is confident she can make a 5.75% profit on an investment. If he wants make $2300 in profit, she can find how much must be invested by solving the percent statement "$2300 is 5.75% of what number?" How much money must be invested to make the $2300 profit?

16. In a recent power outage, 573 homes were without power. This was 27.1% of the home in the area. To find the number of homes in the area affected by the power outage one can solve the percent statement "573 is 27.1% of what number?" To the nearest home, how many homes were in the area affected by the power outage?

Estimating Percents

Now that we can solve percent statements we should have pretty good understanding of what percents represent. Often it is not necessary to know a percent value exactly. Rather we may need to estimate what the value will be close to. In doing this it is helpful to interpret a percent as a fraction.

$$10\% \text{ of something is } \frac{1}{10} \text{ or "one-tenth" of it}$$

$$25\% \text{ of something is } \frac{1}{4} \text{ or "one-quarter" of it}$$

$$50\% \text{ of is } \frac{1}{2} \text{ or "one-half" of it}$$

$$75\% \text{ of something is } \frac{3}{4} \text{ or "three-quarters" of it}$$

The next few examples are multiple choice questions.

Example 6: Which of the following is the best estimate for 23% of 350?

A.) 8   B.) 80   C.) 800   D.) 8000

Solution: 23% is close to 25%, so the estimate should be close to one-quarter of 3500. So, A.) 8 is too small and C.) 800 and D.) 8000 are both way too big. The best estimate given for 23% of 350 is B.) 80.

Example 7: Which is the best estimate for 93% of 78.2?
A.) 0.72   B.) 7.2   C.) 72   D.) 720

Solution: 93% is close to 100%, which would be the full amount. So A.) 0.72 and B.) 7.2 are way too small. Similarly, 720 is way too large to be 93% of 78.2. The only reasonable estimate is C.) 72.

Example 8: Where in the World? A salesman from a company that sells heating units is trying to get you to buy a unit. He makes the following statement:

"This unit will save you 40% on your heating bill. If you spend $1200 a year on heating, that's a savings of $500!"

Is the statement reasonable? That is, is $500 a good fast estimate for 40% of $1200?

Solution: 40% is close to 50%, which is one-half. So the estimate should be under half of $1200. Half of $1200 is $600, so $500 does seem like a reasonable estimate for 40% of $1200.

17. Which of the following is the best estimate for 11% of 895?
      A.) 9   B.) 90   C.) 900   D.) 9000
18. Which of the following is the best estimate for 77% of 400?
      A.) 3   B.) 30   C.) 300   D.) 3000
19. Which of the following is the best estimate for 49% of 18?
      A.) 0.09   B.) 0.9   C.) 9   D.) 90
20. Which of the following is the best estimate for 60% of 92?
      A.) 5.5   B.) 5.5   C.) 550   D.) 55
21. Which of the following is the best estimate for 90% of 2000?
      A.) 1.80   B.) 1800   C.) 18000   D.) 180
22. Which of the following is the best estimate for 30% of 58?
      A.) 2   B.) 20   C.) 0.2   D.) 200

23. A phone company is offering bundling of cable, phone and internet.
        "Bundling the services will save you 35% on your phone bill. "If you spend $1980 a year
        on these three services, that's a savings of $700!"
    Is the statement reasonable? That is, is $700 a good fast estimate for 35% of $1980?

24. A car saleman is offering a deal on a 2004 Honda Civic that is priced at $6,800. He offers the car at
        20% off to you, which he says is a savings of $900. He then makes the following statement:
        "This offer will save you 20% on the price of the car. Buying the car today at this savings,
        will save you $900"
    Is the statement reasonable? That is, is $900 a good fast estimate for 20% of $6800?

7.2 EXERCISE SET - Putting it all Together

25. Which of the following is the best estimate for 10% of 960?
      A.) 0.96   B.) 9.6   C.) 960   D.) 96

26. Which of the following is the best estimate for 50% of 258?
      A.) 1300   B.) 130   C.) 13   D.) 1.3

27. Which of the following is the best estimate for 29% of 75?
      A.) 0.25   B.) 2.5   C.) 25   D.) 250

28. Which of the following is the best estimate for 55% of 178?
     A.) 55   B.) 100   C.) 200   D.)10

29. Which of the following is the best estimate for 200% of 38?
     A.) 8000   B.) 80   C.) 8   D.) 0.8

30. Which of the following is the best estimate for 75% of 65?
     A.) 24   B.) 48   C.) 2.4   D.) 4.8

31. Which of the following is the best estimate for 7.5% of 34?
     A.) 2.55   B.) 255   C.) 25.5   D.) 255

32. Which of the following is the best estimate for 6% of 68?
     A.) 0.02   B.) 0.4   C.) 40   D.) 4

33. Which of the following is the best estimate for 100% of 35.9?
     A.) 0.359   B.) 35.9   C.) 3.59   D.) 359

34. Which of the following is the best estimate for 16% of 37?
     A.) 3.7   B.) 37   C.) 6   D.) 60

35. Which of the following is the best estimate for 0.1% of 80?
     A.) 0.08   B.) 8   C.) 0.008   D.) 80

36. Which of the following is the best estimate for 20% of 50?
     A.) 1   B.) 10   C.) 0.1   D.) 100

Translate each percent statement into an equation and solve. Round your answer to the nearest hundredths if necessary.

37. 5 is 100% of what?
38. 50% of 182 is what?
39. 10% of 385 is what?
40. What is 300% of 56?
41. What is 400% of 1290?
42. 90 is what percentage of 180?

43. What percentage of 14 is 28?
44. 23 is 30% of what?
45. 15% of 204 is what?
46. 36 is what percentage of 120?
47. 29.2 is 20% of what?
48. 18 is what percentage of 18?

49. Lin has a loan for $3025. So far she has paid off $145 of the loan. What percentage of her loan has she paid off?

50. Rachel has student loans that amounted to $12,690. She has paid off 45% of the loan so far. How much has she paid off?

51. Lucia has paid $4,875 toward her student loans. This is 38% of the total she owed. How much did she borrow for college with these loans?

52. A trailer shop buys trailers for $2300 and sells them for $3750. The cost is what percentage of the sell price of the trailer?

53. Joanna bought a house that cost $109,000 and put down $21,800. What percentage of the house was her down payment?

54. Javier buys a house that cost $185,000 and has to pay 3% of the purchase price for closing costs. What are his closing costs?

55. Silvia bought a new car and put $2520 as a down payment. If this was 15% of the purchase price, how much did the car cost her?

56. Stephen bought a new car that retailed for $13,800 and put down $2484. What percentage of the car was his down payment?

57. In 2010, the San Diego Padres won 49.4% of the 162 games they played. Find the number of games the Padres won.

58. In 2011, the New York Yankees won 96 games. This is 59% of the total games they played. Find the number of games the Yankees played in 2011.

59. In the state of California, child actors are required to put 15% of their income in a savings account. The highest paid child actor on TV is Angus T. Jones of 'Two and a Half Men', and he makes $250,000 per episode. How much must he put in savings per episode?

60. The highest paid female child actor on TV is Miranda Cosgrove from Nickelodeon's 'iCarly'. She is paid $180,000 per episode. She also has to put 15% of her income in saving by state law. How much does she put in savings each episode?

61. Comprehensive dance lessons for the serious student of ballet can consist of 5 hours of day of dancing. What percentage of the day does a serious ballet student dance? (There are 24 hours in a day)

62. The Boban Marković Orchestra has been the leading Balkan Brass Band in Serbia for the past 17 years. Marko Markovic of the Orchestra practices 10 hours a day. What percentage of the day does he practice? (There are 24 hours in a day)

63. In 2010, there was a security breach with Sony online Entertainment via PlayStation Network. From this breach there was the chance that credit card data was taken from some 12.3 million accounts. 45.5% of these accounts were in the US. Find the number of accounts in the US that had the chance of their credit card information was stolen.

64. Female Elephant Seals off the coast of South Georgia Islands have a life expectancy of about 20 years. Satellite tracking discovered that 80% of her life was consumed with offshore odysseys. How many years of her life was she in offshore odysseys?

Exercise Set - Chapter 7 Review

65. Write $13\frac{1}{2}\%$ in fraction notation.

66. Write the fraction $\frac{4}{5}$ in percent notation.

67. Convert 35.2% to decimal notation.

68. Convert 15.7 to percent notation.

69. A Motorola Android phone retails for $200. If sales tax is 7.5% of the price, what will be the amount of the tax?

Exercise Set - Cumulative Review

70. Solve. Express your answer a s a mixed number. $\dfrac{5}{6}x = 8$

71. Evaluate. $7 - 3(1 + 2)$

72. Add and reduce if possible. $\dfrac{7}{12} + \dfrac{2}{9}$

73. Use a calculator to multiply. $15.05(-0.32)$

74. Evaluate. $\sqrt{9 + 40}$

 # 7.2 QUIZ YOURSELF:

To make sure you are ready for the EXAM, try these problems without any help. Give yourself about 20 minutes and don't check the answers until you have completely finished.

Solve the following percent equations. Round to the nearest hundredths place if necessary.

1. 20% of 820 is what?
2. 67 is 50% of what?
3. What is 47% of 81?
4. 38 is what percent of 104?
5. 65.4 is 15% of what?
6. Carlos has to write a 500-word term paper for his history class. He has written 376 word so far. What percent of the paper has Carlos written?
7. Jody is buying a house and wants to put 20% down. If the purchase price is $214,900, how much does he need for his down-payment?
8. What is the best estimate to 57% or 310?
   a. 17.5   b. 134   c. 175   d. 287

Answers to this Quiz Yourself are on page 696.

7.3 Consumer Applications of Percents

Topics:

- Discounts
- Sales Tax
- Markups
- Commission and Tips

Are You Ready?

To see if you are ready to understand this section, do the following short quiz.

1. Convert 45% into a decimal.
2. Convert 6% into a decimal.
3. $72 \cdot 0.0775$
4. Find 18% of 90.
5. What is 26% of $104.27?

Answers to Are You Ready?
(1) 0.45   (2) 0.06   (3) 5.58   (4) 16.2   (5) $27.11

Discounts

Courtesy of Fotolia

When you buy an item on sale, there is almost always a percent involved. Let's look at the math that goes into calculating sale prices. There are two calculations involved: one to find the amount of the discount and a second to find the new price of the item.

Discount is Sale Percent of Original Price

Sale Price = Original Price − Discount

So generally, first we calculate the amount of the discount by solving a percent statement then find the new price by subtracting the discount from the original price.

Example 1: Once the baseball season is over, www.MLB.com usual takes 35% off all their team jerseys. If a jersey was originally $120, what will the sale price be?

Solution:

Discount is 35% of $120

First we calculate the discount: Discount $= 0.35 \cdot 120$

$$= 42$$

Sale Price = Original Price − Discount

Now we can find the sale price: $= 120 - 42$

$$= 78$$

So the sale price for the jersey will be $78.

STOP EXERCISE SET - Discounts

Complete the chart. Round to the nearest cent.

Item Cost	Discount Rate	Amount of Discount	Discount Price
$38.95	20%	1.	2.
$459.50	30%	3.	4.
$89	25%	5.	6.

Solve the discount problems.

7. Games R Us has all new Playstation3 games on sale 25% off. Carlos picks up 2 games that total $109.90. How much will he save on his two new games?

8. Mo's Records is having a 25% off sale on all vinyl records. Charles finds several vinyl records that add up to a total of $138. How much will he save on his new records?

9. Trek Superstore has all of last year's bikes 27% off. Gino buys the Madone 5.2 and receives a discount of $1112.13. What was the original price?

10. Guitar Center is having a 20% off anniversary sale. Wayne splurges and buys the new Les Paul guitar. If the discount is $299, what was the original price?

Sales Tax

Almost every time you purchase an item from a store you pay sales tax based on a percent decided by the government.

The percent paid in sales tax a called the **tax rate**.

So there are two calculations involved in finding the total price of an item. First we calculate the sales tax using a percent statement then the total price by adding the sales tax to the original price.

Sales Tax is Tax Rate of Original Price

Total Price = Original Price + Sales Tax

Example 2: A textbook costs a student $125.99. If the sales tax rate is 8.5%, what will be the total price for the book? Round the sales tax to the nearest cent if necessary.

Solution:

Sales Tax is 8.5% of $125.99

First we calculate the sales tax: Sales Tax $= 0.085 \cdot 125.99$

$= 10.71$ (rounded to the nearest hundredth)

$$\text{Total Price } = \text{ Original Price } + \text{ Sales Tax}$$

Now we can find the total price:
$$= 125.99 + 10.71$$
$$= 136.7$$

So the total price of the textbook will be $136.70.

Example 3: Where in the World?

Sales tax in California is 8.25%. The price of a Roland TR300 drum kit is $830. To the nearest cent how much will the sales tax be? What will be the full price of the kit including tax?

Solution: To find the amount of the sales tax we find 8.25% of $830.

8.25% of $830

↓   ↓ ↓

0.0825 ·   830

= $68.475

To the nearest, the tax will be $68.48.

To find the total price we add the tax to the purchase price: $830 + $68.48 = $898.48

So the total price of the kit will be $898.48.

STOP EXERCISE SET - Sales Tax

Complete the chart. Round to the nearest cent.

Item Cost	Sales Tax Rate	Amount of Tax	Item + Tax
$67	4.5%	11.	12.
$109.80	7.75%	13.	14.
$45.85	6%	15.	16.

Solve the following sales tax problems. Round your answers to the nearest cent.

17. Jacob is buying a snowboard that costs $218. If sales tax is 7%, how much does he pay in tax and what is the total price of the board?

18. Lee is buying a SeaRay boat for the summer! The one he has decided on costs $14,580 before taxes. What will cost of the boat be after taxes if the tax rate is 6%?

19. A new pair of jeans are marked $54. If the tax rate is 8.5%, how much will they be after tax?

20. Chrissie is starting college and is shopping for a new desk. She finds one she likes for $138. How much will it be after tax, if the tax rate is 7.75%?

21. Gamestop is having a promotion where they give gamers a 30% bonus on trade ins. If a customer brings in $75 worth of games, how much of a bonus will they get? Round to the nearest cent if necessary.

22. Electronics Boutique is having a promotion where they give gamers a 25% bonus on trade-ins. If a costumer brings in $60 worth of games, how much of a bonus will they get? Round to the nearest cent if necessary. What will be the total amount for the trade-ins?

Markups

Stores buy products from a manufacturer or distributor at a *retail price*. Then they increase that price to sell the product to the customer so that they can make a profit. This is called a *markup* and the price paid by the customer is called *market price*. A markup is usually based on the retail price.

$$\text{Markup is Markup Percent of Retail Price}$$

$$\text{Market Price} = \text{Retail Price} + \text{Markup}$$

Example 4: A vendor that sells Venetian party masks uses a 15% markup to make a profit. It buys the masks at a retail price of $13 each. Find the market price for a mask.

Solution:

$$\text{Markup is } 15\% \text{ of } 13$$

First we calculate the amount of the markup: $\text{Markup} = 0.15 \cdot 13$

$$= 1.95$$

$$\text{Market Price} = \text{Retail Price} + \text{Markup}$$

Now we can calculate the market price: $= 13 + 1.95$

$$= 14.95$$

So the vendor will charge $14.95 to the customer for each mask.

STOP EXERCISE SET - Markups

Complete the chart. Round to the nearest cent.

Wholesale Price	Markup	Amount of Markup	Item + Markup
$19	50%	23.	24.
$79.35	40%	25.	26.
$213.69	35%	27.	28.

29. Martha buys red wagons from a wholesaler for $15 and uses a markup of 40% to make a profit selling them at markets. How much does she sells the wagons for?
30. Debbie buys ladies dresses from a wholesaler for $35.50 each and uses a markup of 30%. What is the market price for each dress?
31. Raul runs a local bike shop and purchases beach cruisers for $76.40 each. He uses a 50% markup to make a profit. What is the market price of the beach cruisers?
32. The markup on used cars is 22%. If a car dealer buys a car from an individual trading her car for $1675, what will the dealer turn around and sell it for?

Commission and Tips

Many people who have sales jobs are paid by commission. Commission is a percent of their sales.

Commission is a Percent of Total Sales

Example 5: The commission rate for the sales people at a car dealership is 9%. Suppose a sales person makes the following sales for a month:

Car	Price
Toyota Prius	$12,500
Honda CRV	$8,900
Ford Focus	$10,250
Toyota Tacoma	$16,500
Total Sales:	**$48,150**

Solution: The sales person had $48,150 in total sales. The commission is 9% of this amount.

Commission is Percent of Total Sales

$$\text{Commission} = 0.09 \cdot 48150$$
$$= 4333.5$$

So the sales person will be paid $4,333,50 in commission for these sales.

It is customary at restaurants to give the waiter some money (a *tip*) in addition to the bill. The tip is normally about 15% of the total bill.

Tip is a Percent of Bill

Example 6: The total bill of a meal is $57.94. If we want to leave a 15% tip, how much money should we leave for the waiter?

Solution:

Tip is a Percent of Bill

$$\text{Tip} = 15\% \text{ of } 57.94$$
$$= 0.15 \cdot 57.94$$
$$= 8.691$$

So, rounded to the nearest tenth the tip would be $8.70.

STOP EXERCISE SET - Commission and Tips

Bill	Tip %	Amount of Tip	Total Bill
$34.87	15%	33.	34.
$87.02	18%	35.	36.
$109.56	20%	37.	38.

39. A group of friends go out to dinner and the bill is $87.91. The server did a great job and they decide to leave a 20% tip. How much was the total bill after tip?

40. Mary Beth gets her hair cut and color and the total comes to $135. She gives her stylist a 15% tip. What was the total cost to get her hair done?

41. Lin has started hosting home jewelry shows for Silpada Silver. She earns 30% of free jewelry on the total sales of the show. How much free jewelry does Mary earn on a show that has total sales of $839?

42. Stuart is a car salesman and makes 5% in commission. He sold a car today for $25,490! How much does he make in commission?

EXERCISE SET - Putting it all Together

Complete the chart. Round to the nearest cent.

Item Cost	Discount Rate	Amount of Discount	Item - Discount
$78	20%	43.	44.
$348	10%	45.	46.
$47.75	15%	47.	48.
$999.20	40%	49.	50.
$287.99	25%	51.	52.

Complete the chart. Round to the nearest cent

Item Cost	Tax Rate	Tax	Item + Tax
$23.56	6%	53.	54.
$157	5.75%	55.	56.
$98.34	7.75%	57.	58.
$798.15	8.75%	59.	60.
$56	7.5%	61.	62.
$147.89	13%	63.	64.
$4675	5%	65.	66.

67. Tarah bought a dress from Anthropologie that was originally $128. There was a slight flaw on the dress that she knew she could fix. She asked for a discount and they offered her 15% off. What was the price of the dress after the discount?

68. Gabby is buying a pair of jeans that cost $78. They are on for sale 30% off. What is the sale price of the jeans?

69. JCPenny's is having their ½ yearly sale and all purses are 40% off! Claire finds a very cute bag that is originally $78. How much does she save on the bag?

70. Jinsung finds a pair of running shoes on sale for 35% off. They are originally marked as $129.90. What is the sale price of the running shoes?

71. Anna is spending the weekend at the beach and has rented an oceanfront house. The cost of the house is $1250 for the week plus tax. If the tax rate is 11%, how much does she pay for the tax and what is the total price of the house?

72. Jon and Dina are going away for the weekend and have rented a hotel room. The room is advertised for $89 per night plus tax. The tax rate on the hotel room is 9.5%. Find the amount of tax paid and the total cost of the room per night.

73. Alfonso finds a skateboard on sale for 25% off. It originally cost $145. What is the sale price of the board? What is the total price if the tax rate is 6%?

74. Israel is shopping for a new surfboard. He finds one he likes on sale that was originally marked at $549 on sale for 37% off. Find the sale price of the board.

75. Winter's Storm is having a sale on all snowboards. Leslie finds a board she likes that was originally marked at $489. It is on sale for 40% off. Find the sale price of the snow board.

76. Anderson's nursery is having a 20% off sale on all trees. Chad finds a mulberry tree that originally cost $39.99. How much will the tree be after the discount if the tax rate is 8.5%?

77. Estella is a loan originator. She makes 1.5% of every loan she makes. Her total loans for the month of May totaled $1,256,900. How much did she make in commission?

78. Enrique is a loan originator. He makes 1.5% of every loan he makes. His total loans for the month of April totaled $921,500. How much did he make in commission?

79. Ricardo is a real estate agent. He makes 3% on every home he sells. Last quarter, he sold a total of $2,590,900 worth of homes. How much did he make last month in commission?

80. Janet is a real estate agent. She makes 3% on every home she sells. Last month, she sold a total of $389,450 worth of homes. How much did she make last month in commission?

81. An online vender selling clothes adds a processing fee of 3.7% of the total sales. If a costumer's order comes to $75.24, what will the processing fee be? Round to the nearest cent.

82. In Vegas, gambling winnings are taxed at a rate of 38.2%. If a person wins $17500 on a slot machine, how much will be paid in taxes? How much of the winnings will the person get to take home?

Exercise Set - Chapter 7 Review

83. What is 75% of 96?
84. 4 is what percent of 80?
85. An NFL team has 53 players. If 19 of the players are free agents, what percent of the players are free agents? Round to the nearest whole percent.
86. Write the fraction $\dfrac{5}{6}$ as a percent. Write the percent as a mixed number if necessary.
87. Write $10\dfrac{1}{2}\%$ in decimal form.

Exercise Set - Cumulative Review

88. Graph the numbers 3, 8, 5, and 1 on a number line.
89. Solve. $0.3y + 1.7 = 3.8$
90. Add. $(-9) + (-7) + 4$
91. Divide and reduce if possible. $\dfrac{6}{7} \div \left(-\dfrac{2}{3}\right)$

92. Solve the proportion. $\dfrac{2.6}{8} = \dfrac{b}{20}$

7.3 QUIZ YOURSELF:

To make sure you are ready for the EXAM, try these problems without any help. Give yourself about 20 minutes and don't check the answers until you have completely finished.

1. Jahsead buys a new surfboard that originally cost $679 on sale for 20% off. What is the sale price of the board?

2. Koi is a loan originator. She makes 1.5% of every loan she makes. Her total loans for the last quarter totaled $2,700,500. How much did she make in commission?

3. In NYC the hotel occupancy tax is 5.85% of the room. Maeve finds a hotel for $179 a night in NYC. How much will she pay in occupancy tax per night?

4. A group of friends goes out to dinner for a birthday and the total is $118.38. If they plan to leave an 18% tip, how much should they leave? What is the total including the tip?

5. Hisoka purchases a new house for $198,900.

   a. He has to pay closing costs that are 5% of the purchase price. How much are his closing costs?
   b. He decides to put 20% down on the house. What is his down-payment?
   c. Between closing costs and his down-payment, how much did Hisoka bring to closing?
   d. His agent made 3% in commission on the sale of the house. How much did the agent earn?

Answers to this Quiz Yourself are on page 696.

7.4 Other Applications of Percents

Topics:

- Percent Increase and Decrease
- Percents and Graphs

Are You Ready?

To see if you are ready to understand this section, do the following short quiz.

1. Write $\dfrac{5}{8}$ as a decimal.
2. Write 65% as a fraction and a decimal.
3. Find 50% of 84.
4. What is 37% of 138?

Answers to Are You Ready?

(1) 0.625   (2) $\dfrac{13}{20}$ and 0.65   (3) 42   (4) 51.06

Percent Increase and Decrease

Percents can be used to express the amount of an increase or decrease. For example, a college that has 12,000 students might say they expect a 7% decrease in enrollment. This is called a percent decrease, and is calculated using a percent statement.

Amount of Increase/Decrease is a Percent of the Original Amount

This relationship can be written in equation form as...

$$\text{Amount of Increase/Decrease} = \text{Percent} \cdot \text{Original Amount}$$

Example 1: A college has 12,000 students enrolled. If they have a 7% decrease in enrollment, what be the amount of the increase? What will be the new enrollment?

Solution: The percent is 7% and the original amount is 12,000. Substituting these values into our percent statement we have...

$$\text{Amount of Decrease} = \text{Percent} \cdot \text{Original Amount}$$
$$\text{Amount of Decrease} = 7\% \cdot 12000$$
$$= 0.07(12000)$$
$$= 840$$

So the amount of the decrease is 840 students. This means the new enrollment will be $12000 - 840 = 11160$ students.

When trying to find the actual percent of an increase or decrease we must use the amount of the change in the percent statement.

Example 2: Eric has a blog online. In one year the number of subscribers to the blog went form 460 to 700. What is the percent increase? Round to the nearest whole percent.

Solution: We want to use the following equation:

$$\text{Amount of Increase} = \text{Percent} \cdot \text{Original Amount}$$

We must find the amount of the increase. The number of subscribers went from 460 to 700, so the amount of the increase is $700 - 460 = 240$. The original amount was 460. We are looking for the percent. This gives use...

$$\text{Amount of Increase} = \text{Percent} \cdot \text{Original Amount}$$
$$240 = P \cdot 460$$
$$240 = 460P$$

As with other percent statements we solve by dividing.

$$240 = 460P$$
$$P = \frac{240}{460}$$
$$P = 0.5217$$
$$P \approx 52\%$$

So the percent increase was 52%.

1. A fast food restaurant announces it has decided to decrease the amount of fat in its burgers by 25%. If the burgers originally had 32 grams of fat, how many grams of fat will the decrease be? How many grams of fat will be in the new burger?

2. An Aquafina water bottle has the statement "Now made with 20% less plastic." If the original bottle containing 20 grams of plastic, how many grams plastic has the bottle decreased by? How many grams of plastic are in the new bottle?

3. An art gallery has decided to increase the number of paintings by 30%. If they originally offered 70 paintings, how many more do they plan to add? How many paintings will they offer total?

4. The existing parking lot at a mall is 45,000 square feet. The management announces that they are going to increase the size of the parking lot by 40%. How many more square feet of parking will their parking lot be? What will be the total size of the new parking lot?

5. The value of a house goes from $94,500 to $124,700. What is the percent increase? Round to the nearest whole percent.

6. The value of a stock goes from $15.06 per share to $13.85 per share. What is the percent decrease? Round to the nearest whole percent.

Percents and Graphs

We have already been using charts and graphs in this book. It is common to organize information about percents on charts and tables.

Example 3: The following chart gives the percent of students receiving financial aid at Greenfield College over several years. If there were 5,600 students enrolled in the year 2009, how many of them received financial aid?

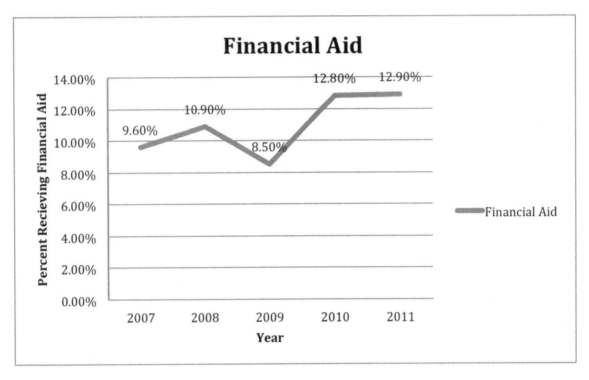

Solution: Looking at the graph we see that in 2009 there were 8.5% of students on financial aid. If there were 5600 students, this means we should find 8.5% of 5600.

$$8.5\% \text{ of } 5600$$
$$= 0.085(5600)$$
$$= 476$$

So there were 476 students on financial aid in 2009.

One type of chart that particularly popular for percents is a pie chart. Pie charts provide a way to easily compare different percents given in a scenario. For example, the pie chart to the right gives the percent of music old within each genre. The whole circle represents all music sales for the year 2009. The pie-shapes pieces represent how much of the total sales came from that genre. So, for example, 32% of the music sold in 2009 was rock music while 6% of the music sold was classical. Note that if all the percentages are added up the total is 100%:

$$15\% + 2\% + 10\% + 6\% + 6\% + 32\% + 29\% = 100\%$$

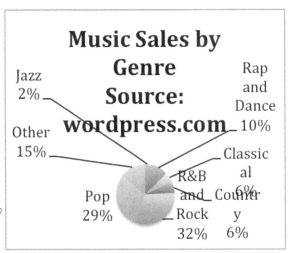

Example 4: The following pie chart gives the percent of college students in the US who work a job. If Mesa College has 20,000 students, how many of them have a full-time job?

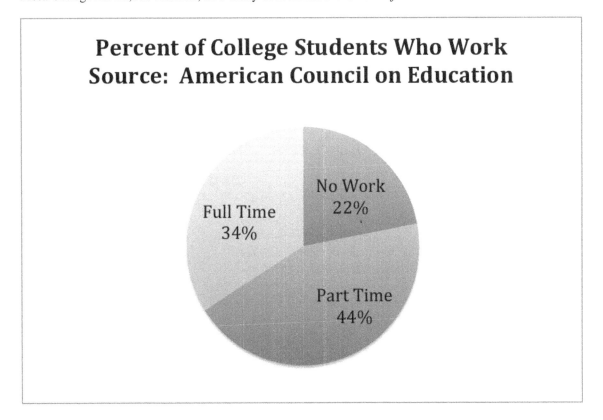

Solution: From the chart we see that 34% of students have a full-time job. Since the college has 20,000 students, we find 34% of 20,000.

$$34\% \text{ of } 20,000$$
$$= 0.34(20,000)$$
$$= 6800$$

So about 6800 students at Mesa College have a full-time job.

STOP EXERCISE SET - Percents and Graphs

The following chart gives the percent of U.S. households that own different kinds of pets.

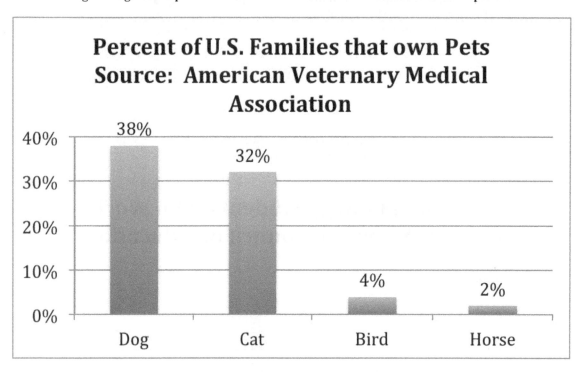

7. What percent of households own a bird?
8. What percent of households own a dog?
9. If a city has 45,000 households, how many of them own a cat?
10. If a city has 8,000 households, how many of them own a horse?

The following pie chart gives the percent of phones that use different operating systems.

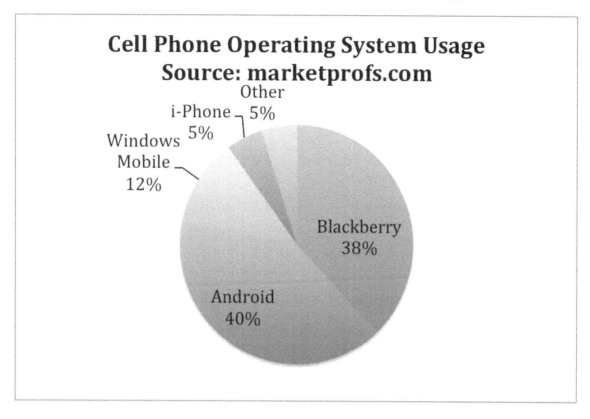

11. What percent of phone use i-Phone as their operating system?
12. What percent of phones use Blackberry as their operating system?
13. Out of 1,000 cell-phones, about how of them use Android as their operating system?
14. Out of 5,500 cell-phones, how many of them use Windows Mobile as their operating system?

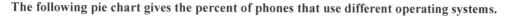

15. The original price on drum set is $650. Because of high demand, the owner of the store decides to do a 20% increase on the price. What will be the amount of the increase? What will be the new price?

16. The price of a surfboard was $595. It's the end of summer and the owner of the surf shop decided to lower the price by 30%. What is the amount of the discount? What will be the new price?

17. The number of members at a health club goes from 70 to 75. What is the percent increase? Round to the nearest tenth.

18. A company's profits go from $47,000 in one year to $40,500 in the next year. Find the percent decrease. Round to the nearest tenth.

19. The average salary of a man with a high school diploma is $28,763. Earning a Bachelor's degree will increase your salay to $50,916. Find the percent increase in your salary when you go to college and earn your Bachelor's degree.

20. In 1981 Haiti imported 18,000 tons of rice. In 2008, they imported 400,000 tons of rice annually. Find the percent increase of the tons of rice Haiti imports annually.

21. In 1968, there was on average 3,289 items of litter per mile on the highway I-370 in Maryland. In 2008, this number decresed to only 704 items of litter per mile on this same highway. Find the percent decrease of litter on the highway.

22. In London in 1925 a study was done and found 2,603 house sparrows in the city's Kensington Gardens. A follow-up study was done in 2000 and only found 8 house sparrows. Find the percent decrease of house sparrows in London.

23. An adverstisment for Rosetta Stone shows that Level 1 was originally $209 and is now on sale for $188.10. Find the percent decrease.

24. An adverstisment for Rosetta Stone shows that Level 1 & 2 was originally $339 and is now on sale for $305.10. Find the percent decrease.

25. A loaf of white bread cost went up from $1.19 a loaf to $1.37 a loaf in a year. Find the percent increase.

26. The cost of a french baquette went up from $0.70 a loaf to $1.50 in a year. Find the percent increase.

27. The water clarity at Lake Tahoe, CA has dropped from 100 ft visibility in 1968 to 72 ft visibility in 2005. Find the percent decrease of water clarity at Lake Tahoe.

28. The sale of hybrid gas-electric cars decreased from 34,000 in March 2011 to 25,000 in April 2011. Find the percent decrease in sales from March to April.

Below is a circle graph showing the percent of electonics that are recyled and don't go to the landfill.

29. What percent of all recycled electronics are TV's?

30. What percent of all recycled electronics are cell phones?

31. What percent of all recycled electronics are laptop computers?

32. What percent of all recycled electronics are monitors?

In 2005, there was a total of 1,913.5 thousand tons of recycled electonics.

33. Find how many thousand tons of desktop computers were recycled.

34. Find how many thousand tons of televisions were recycled.

35. Find how many thousand tons of cell phones were recycled.

36. Find how many thousand tons of all computers(desktop and laptop) wer recycled.

The circle graph give the percentages of what college students do to relieve stress.

37. What percentage of college students exercise to relieve stress?

38. What percentage of college students clean/organize to relieve stress?

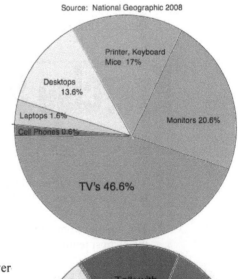

Source: National Geographic 2008

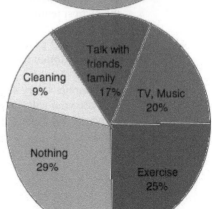

39. What percentage of college students do nothing to relieve stress?

40. What percentage of college students talk with friends or family to relieve stress?

41. At a college of 15,400 students, how many exercise to relieve stress?

42. At a college of 26,900 students, how do nothing to relieve stress?

43. At a college of 45,550 students, how many watch TV or listen to music to relieve stress?

44. At a college of 8,100 students, how many clean to relieve stress?

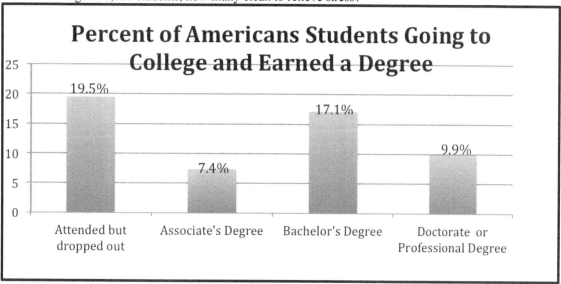

Source: College Money

45. What percentage of students earn an Associate's Degree?
46. What percentage of students earn a Doctorate or Professional Degree?
47. In a town of 18,500, how many Americans would you expect to have a Bachelor's Degree?
48. In a city of 37,920, how many Americans would you expect to have an Associate's Degree?
49. Boston, Massachusetts has a population of 559,034, how many Bostonians would you expect to have a Doctorate or Professional Degree?
50. Austin Texas has a population of 782,541, how many of them would you expect to have attended college but dropped out?

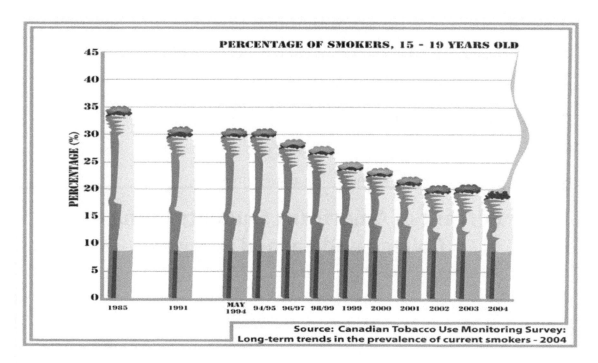

PERCENTAGE OF SMOKERS, 15 - 19 YEARS OLD

Source: Canadian Tobacco Use Monitoring Survey:
Long-term trends in the prevalence of current smokers - 2004

51. What was the percentage of smokers aged 15 – 19 in 1985?
52. What was the percentage of smokers aged 15 – 19 in 1999?
53. What was the percentage of smokers aged 15 – 19 in 2002?
54. What was the percentage of smokers aged 15 – 19 in May 1994?
55. In a community that has 5,802 people aged 15 – 19, how many would you expect to be smokers in 1999?
56. In a community that has 1,320 people aged 15 – 19, how many would you expect to be smokers in 2004?

Exercise Set - Chapter 7 Review

57. What percent of 52 is 14?
58. Write 45% in fraction notation.
59. Write 54.09 in percent notation.
60. An i-Phone sells for $199. If tax is 6.5%, what will be the total cost of the phone?
61. What 0.08% of 25?

Exercise Set - Cumulative Review

62. Find the perimeter and area of the rectangle. [PN: rectangle: 7in by 12 in]
63. Is $x = 5$ a solution to the equation $3x + 9 + x = 2(x + 13)$?

64. Reduce. $\dfrac{12x}{16x^2}$

65. Add and reduce if possible. $\dfrac{2}{3} + \left(-\dfrac{1}{6} \right)$

66. Fill in the blank with < or >. -15 ____ 12

7.4 QUIZ YOURSELF:

To make sure you are ready for the EXAM, try these problems without any help. Give yourself about 20 minutes and don't check the answers until you have completely finished.

1. The cost of tuition increased from $11 per unit to $20 per unit. Find the percent increase.

2. Because of budget cuts, a government worker is forced to take furlough days, which results in a reduction in his pay. His salary was $45,800 a year and is now $44,426. Find the percent decrease in his pay.

Use the circle graph of Juanita's monthly budget of $2,580 per month to answer the following questions.

3. What percent of Juanita's salary goes to housing?

4. What percent of her salary goes to savings?

5. How much money does she spend on her car and car insurance?

6. How much money does she put in savings?

7. How much money does she have for fun and entertainment?

8. What percent of her pay goes to bills? (housing, utilities, car, credit cards)

9. How much money does she spend each month on bills?

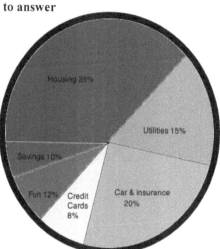

Answers to this Quiz Yourself are on page 696.

7.5 Interest

Topics:
- Simple Interest
- Compound Interest

Are You Ready?

To see if you are ready to understand this section, do the following short quiz.

1. Multiply. $120(.07)(5)$

2. Multiply. $200(.06)\left(\dfrac{1}{4}\right)$

3. Add. $550 + 550(.03)(8)$
4. Convert to a fraction: 75%
5. Convert to a decimal: 6.5%

Answers to Are You Ready?

(1) 42   *(2) 3*   *(3) 682*   *(4) $\dfrac{3}{4}$*   *(5) 0.065*

Simple Interest

When money is borrowed or invested, there is usually a pay back for the borrowed money. This payback is called *interest*.

Interest is a charge for borrowing money.

When someone borrows money from a bank they usually pay interest based on a percent of the amount borrowed and the length of time for the loan. When someone makes an investment they are often paid in a similar way: based on a percent of the amount invested and the length of time for the investment.

Principle is an amount of money borrowed or invested.

An interest rate is a percent associated with the payback of a loan or investment.

There are two ways to calculate interest: simple and compound. We will look at both beginning with simple interest.

Simple interest relies on the original principle and time alone to determine the interest owed. Here is how it is calculated.

The Simple Interest Formula

$$I = P \cdot r \cdot t$$

where

$I =$ interest earned

$P =$ principle

$r =$ interst rate (in decimal form)

$t =$ time (in years)

Example 1: Stan borrows $4500 from a bank for 3 years at an interest rate of 6%. How much interest will he pay the bank? How much money will he pay the bank back total?

Solution: The principle is $4500, the interest rate is 6%, and the amount of time is 3 years, so we have.
$P = 4500$

$r = 6\% = 0.06$

$t = 3$

So we substitute these values into the simple interest formula:
$$I = P \cdot r \cdot t$$
$$= 4500(0.06)(3)$$
$$= 810$$

Stan will pay the bank $810 in interest to the bank. To find the total Stan will pay back we can add the amount paid back from the loan to the interest.

$$\text{total paid back} = \text{principle} + \text{interest}$$
$$= 4500 + 810$$
$$= 5310$$

So Stan will have to pay the bank $5310 total.

If the amount of time is given by something other than years we use fraction notation to express the time given in years based on the fact that there are 12 months in a year:

$$6 \text{ months} = \frac{6}{12} \text{years} = \frac{1}{2} \text{year}$$

$$3 \text{ months} = \frac{3}{12} \text{years} = \frac{1}{4} \text{year}$$

Example 2: Find the simple interest that will be paid on a $3000 loan that lasts 10 months at an interest rate of 9%.

Solution: The principle is $4500, the interest rate is 6%, and the amount of time is 3 years, so we have.

$P = 3000$

$r = 9\% = 0.09$

Note that the amount of time is given in months but the formula uses years. So we use a fraction to express 10 months as a fraction of a year.

$$t = \frac{10 \text{ months}}{12 \text{ months}} = \frac{5}{6}$$

So we substitute these values into the simple interest formula:
$$I = P \cdot r \cdot t$$
$$= 3000(0.09)\left(\frac{5}{6}\right)$$
$$= 225$$

So the interest charged will be $225.

STOP EXERCISE SET - Simple Interest

In each exercise calculate the interest on a loan given the values.

1. $P = 200, r = 6\%, t = 3$ years

2. $P = 950, r = 5.3\%, t = 2$ years

3. $P = 5000, r = 4.8\%, t = 6$ months

4. $P = 200, r = 2\frac{1}{4}\%, t = 10$ months

5. Antwon is ready to invest \$3,600 at 7.3% simple interest for 8 years. Given the simple interest formula $I = \text{Pr}t$, identify the values of P, r, and t.

6. A bank is advertising a CD investment where the investor deposits \$10,000. The CD draws 2.5% interest over a period a period of 5 years.

7. Jenny borrows \$15,000 from a bank at a simple interest rate of 3.9% for 6 years. How much interest will she pay on the loan? How much will she pay the bank back in total?

8. Lauren helps finance a new car by borrowing \$8,500 from the dealer. The loan is for 20 months and has a simple interest rate of $8\frac{1}{2}\%$. How much interest will she pay the dealer? How much will she pay the dealer in total for the loan?

Compound Interest

While simple interest relies on the original principle alone to calculate interest, compound interest takes into account the interest earned on the investment or loan over time. To illustrate, suppose that \$5000 is invested at an interest rate of 6%.

After one year, the amount of interest earned is given by…

$$I = \text{Pr}t$$
$$\text{Year One:} \quad = 5000(0.06)(1)$$
$$= 300$$

So in one year, \$300 in interest has been earned. With compound interest that money is put back into the account, so the new balance is $\$5000 + \$300 = \$5300$. So for the next year, the principle is not just \$5000, it is \$5300.

For the second year, the amount of interest earned is given by…

$$I = \text{Pr}t$$
$$\text{Year Two:} \quad = 5300(0.06)(1)$$
$$= 318$$

As with the first year, this interest is then put back into the account for the third year: $\$5300 + \$318 = \$5618$. With this approach to interest the investor knows that their account is constantly being updated to reflect interest earned. The investor is literally earning interest on their interest, which is very appealing.

In fact, in today's high-tech business minded world compound interest is much more common than simple interest. Recalculating the amount owed or earned based on built-up interest is called *compounding*. Here is the formula for finding the amount of money that will be in a compounded account.

Compound Interest Formula

$$A = P\left(1 + \frac{r}{n}\right)^{nt}$$

$A =$ amount of the account

$P =$ principle

$r =$ interst rate (in decimal form)

$n =$ number of compounds per year

$t =$ time (in years)

The compound interest formula is different from the simple interest formula in that it gives the total amount in the account instead of the just the amount of the interest.

Example 3: A parent looking to invest money for their child's college education puts $750 into an account that will draw 9% interest compounded monthly. What be the balance of the account after 10 years? Round to four decimal places as needed.

Solution: If the account is compounded monthly then in one year it will be compounded 12 times. So, from the scenario given we have the following values.

$P = 750$

$r = 0.09$

$n = 12$

$t = 10$

Now we substitute these values into the compound interest formula.

Substitute in our given values.

$$A = P\left(1 + \frac{r}{n}\right)^{nt}$$

$$= 750\left(1 + \frac{0.09}{12}\right)^{12(10)}$$

Perform the division inside parentheses and multiply $12(10)$ in the exponent.

$$= 750(1 + 0.0075)^{120}$$

Add inside the parentheses.

$$= 750(1.0075)^{120}$$

Perform the exponent before multiplication! This multiplication is

$$\approx 750(2.4514)$$

rounded to four decimal places.

Finally perform the multiplication. ≈ 1838.55

So in 10 years the amount in the account will have grown to about \$1838.55.

STOP EXERCISE SET - Compound Interest

In each exercise calculate the amount A in an account given the values.

9. $P = 500, r = 4\%, t = 2$ years, compounding monthly $(n = 12)$

10. $P = 650, r = 9.8\%, t = 5$ years, compounding quarterly $(n = 4)$

11. $P = 7000, r = 8\frac{1}{2}\%, t = 8$ months, compounding annually $(n = 1)$

12. $P = 30,000, r = 18.9\%, t = 8$ years, compounding daily $(n = 365)$

13. A checking account is opened with \$10,000 that draws 3.1% interest compounded annually. Given the compound interest formula $A = P\left(1 + \frac{r}{n}\right)^{nt}$, identify the values of P, r, and n.

14. \$500 is invested at 4.7% interest compounded monthy. Given the compound interest formula $A = P\left(1 + \frac{r}{n}\right)^{nt}$, identify the values of P, r, and n.

15. A savings account is opened with \$2500 that draws 3.2% interest compounded monthly. How much money will be in the account after 4 years? Round to the nearest cent if necessary.

16. Jorge and Guadalaupe open a CD account to save for their daughter's college education. They plan to deposit \$3000 and leave it in the account for 15 years. If the CD account draws 6.1% interest compounded daily, how much money will be in the account after 15 years?

7.5 EXERCISE SET - Putting it all Together

Vocabulary Check: Fill in each blank with a word from our Vocabulary Checklist to the right. Each word is used exactly once.

17. The percent associated calculating the interest on a loan is called the
_____.

Vocabulary Checklist:
interest
principle
interest rate
simple interest
compound interest

18. The _____ of an investment is the amount of money originally invested.

19. _____ is calculated based on interest previously earned.

20. Money paid to borrow money is called _____.

21. Interest that is only based on the original principle is called _____.

Find the Interest on the following simple interest accounts.
22. P = $6000, r = 8%, t = 4 years.
23. P = $675, r = 4.5%, t = 3 years
24. P = $1500, r = 6%, t = 2 years
25. P = $8800, r = 9%, t = 5 years
26. P = $500, r = 5.5%, t = 4 months
27. P = $2300, r = 10%, t = 6 months

Find the total Amounts on the following compounded interest accounts.
28. P = $400, r = 9%, t = 2 years, compounded monthly
29. P = $850, r = 4%, t = 3 years, compounded annually
30. P = $1200, r = 5.5%, t = 5 years, compounded quarterly
31. P = $2500, r = 6.75%, t = 2 years, compounded bimonthly
32. P = $5785, r = 5.25%, t = 4 years, compounded daily
33. P = $15,000, r = 8.5%, t = 11 years, compounded monthly

34. Janelle bought a car at a used car lot for $5,495. The dealership financed the car for 4 years at a simple interest rate of 11.5%. How much interest did Janelle end up paying for the car? What was the total cost for the car including interest?

35. Cobb and Ash financed a RV for 5 years at a simple interest rate of 7%. They negotiated the price and agreed upon $25,900. How much interest did they pay for their new RV? What was the total cost for the RV including interest?

Courtesy of Fotolia

36.   Fabian financed a new bike through his local bike shop. His bike was priced at $549. He financed it for 10 months at 7% compounded monthly. What was the total cost of the bike?

37. A young photographer needs a new camera and has to finance it. The price of camera/setup kit is $1259.99. Her credit union gives her a 3-year loan at an interest rate of 6.8% compounded monthly. What will be the total cost for the camera and setup kit?

38. Mike borrows $175,000 to buy a house. He finances the house for 15 years at a simple interest rate of 4.5%. Find the interest paid on the loan and the total price paid, including interest.

39. Shayla borrows $298,000 to buy a house. She finances the house for 30 years at a simple interest rate of 5%. Find the interest paid on the loan and the total price paid, including interest.

40. Lilo invested $3700 in a simple interest account earning 3.5% for 12 years. Find the total amount in the account.

41. Robert invested $7500 in a CD for his son when his son was born for college. What is the total amount in the CD in 18 years(when his son is off to college) if the CD had a rate of 4% compounded monthly?

42. An investor wants to invest $3500 for 5 years and must decide between two investment options:

- Plan A: Draws 7.5% simple interest.
- Plan B: Draws 7.1% interest compounded daily.

Which of the plans will result in a higher earning?

43.   A family saving for retirement wants to invest $5000 for 10 years and must decide between two investment options:

- Plan A: Draws 8.7% simple interest.
- Plan B: Draws 8.5% interest compounded monthly.

Which of the plans will result in a higher earning?

Exercise Set - Chapter 7 Review

44.   Computer programmers are able to take an application that was 54 megabytes and reduce it size to 40 megabytes. What is the percent decrease? Round to the nearest tenth.

45. Convert $12\frac{1}{2}\%$ to fraction notation.

46. 18 is 45% of what?

47. Convert 0.087 to percent notation.

48. A store buys a product wholesale for $25. If the store does a 20% markup to sell the item, what will the retail price be?

Exercise Set - Cumulative Review

49. Evaluate. $(3-7)(2-9)$

50. Find the prime factorization of 130.

51. Evaluate $4x^2 + 3x$ for $x = -2$.

52. Distribute. $-3(4y-9)$

53. Simplify. $-7a + 4 - b + 6 - 2a + 4b$

7.5 QUIZ YOURSELF:

To make sure you are ready for the EXAM, try these problems without any help. Give yourself about 20 minutes and don't check the answers until you have completely finished.

1. $1700 is borrowed for 3 years at a simple interest rate of 8%. Find the interest on the loan.
2. $4800 is borrowed for 10 months at a simple interest rate of 5.5%. Find the interest on the loan.
3. $550 is borrowed for 2 years at a rate of 9% compounded monthly. Find the total amount of the loan.
4. Mason borrowed $289,000 to buy a house. He financed the loan for 20 years at a simple interest rate of 6%. Find the total amount of the loan.
5. Jackeline invested $4500 in a CD for 5 years at a rate of 4% compounded quarterly. Find the total amount of the CD in 5 years.

Answers to this Quiz Yourself on page 696.

7.6 Introduction to Probability

Topics:
- Probability
- Probability and Counting

Are You Ready?
To see if you are ready to understand this section, do the following short quiz.
1. Express 0.45 as a fraction in lowest terms.
2. Express 65% in decimal notation.
3. What is 13% of 840?
4. 14 out of 26 students are female. Write this as a fraction and a percent.

Answers to Are You Ready?

(1) $\dfrac{9}{20}$ *(2)* 0.65   *(3)* 109.2   *(4)* $\dfrac{7}{13}$, 53.85%

Probability

Probability is a math topic that goes hand in hand with statistics. For this topic we will introduce how to find the *probability of an event*.

> The **probability of an event** is a number that represents the chances of it happening. A probability can be represented as a fraction, a decimal, or a percent.

Here are some examples of probability that you may recognize.

The probability of a coin flip landing on heads is $\dfrac{1}{2}$ or 50%.	
A weather report might say, "The probability on rain today 30%".	
In poker, the probability of getting three of a kind is 2.11% or 0.0211.	

Example 1: In poker, the probability of getting a pair is 0.423. Express this probability as a percent and a fraction.

Solution: We have already learned to express decimals in fraction and percent form.

$$0.423 = \frac{423}{1000} = 42.3\%$$

Certain probabilities, like flipping a coin and getting heads or getting three of a kind, can be calculated using a simple formula.

The Probability of an Event

$$\text{probability} = \frac{\text{number of ways the event can occur}}{\text{total number of outcomes}}$$

Example 2: If a six-sided dice is rolled, what is the probability of getting a number higher than 4? Express your answer as a fraction.

Solution: If we roll a six-sided dice there are six possible outcomes: 1,2,3,4,5, and 6.

Of these outcomes, two of them result in a number higher 4, these are 5 and 6.

So out of 6 equally possible outcomes, two result in a number higher than 4.

$$\text{probability} = \frac{2 \text{ ways to get higher than four}}{6 \text{ total possible outcomes}}$$
$$= \frac{2}{6}$$
$$= \frac{1}{3}$$

Example 3: Rosita is setting up a carnival game. She puts the following balls in a bag.

[PN: green   red   red   blue   green   green   blue   green   green   blue]

The contestants will pay money to draw a ball from the bag and win a prize:

Ball Drawn	Prize
Green	Candy
Red	Free Carnival Ride
Blue	Toy

What is probability that a contestant will win candy? Express your answer as a fraction.

Solution: Since there are 10 balls in the bag, there are 10 possible outcomes. Of these 10, five of them are green.

$$\text{probability} = \frac{5 \text{ green balls}}{10 \text{ balls total}}$$

$$= \frac{5}{10}$$

$$= \frac{1}{2}$$

So the probability of playing the game and wining candy is $\frac{1}{2}$.

A probability of 0 or 0% means that an event has no chance of happening. A probability of 1 or 100% means an event will definitely happen. So probabilities are always between 0 and 1 or 0% and 100%.

Recall that a probability can be expressed as a fraction, decimal, or percent. In each case a probability is given. Express the probability two other ways.

1. The probability that a U.S. male is over 6 feet tall is about 0.145.

2. The probability that a slot machine hits a win is $\frac{23}{50}$.

3. What is the probability of the spinner hitting red?
4. What is the probability of the spinner hitting blue?
5. What is the probability of the spinner not hitting green?
6. What is the probability of the spinner not hitting yellow?

7. What is the probability of rolling a six-sided dice and getting 3 or more?

8. What is the probability of rolling a six-sided dice and getting 1 or 2?

9. In the game of roulette, players try to guess which slot a ball will land in on a spinning wheel. The wheel has 38 slots total: 2 green slots, 23 black and 23 red slots. What is the probability that a randomly placed ball will land in a black slot? Express your answer as a fraction.

10. A bag contains 15 balls: 3 blue, 5 black, and 7 white. If a ball is chosen at random, what is the probability it will be blue? Express your answer as a decimal.

Probability and Counting

To calculate a probability we have to know the total number of possible outcomes. We can often find the total number of outcomes by organizing information given in a problem. The examples that follow involve listing or at least counting outcomes.

Example 4: A coin is tossed and a six-sided dice is rolled. What is the set of all possible outcomes? How many possible outcomes are there?

Solution: We will organize all possible outcomes using brackets. For example, if heads is tossed and 4 is rolled, the outcome would be $\{H,4\}$. There are two possibilities for the coin toss: heads (H) and tails (T).

$$\{H, \ \ \}\{T, \ \ \}$$

The second position has six possibilities: 1 through 6. Here are all possible outcomes:

$$\{H,1\}\{H,2\}\{H,3\}\{H,4\}\{H,5\}\{H,6\}$$
$$\{T,1\}\{T,2\}\{T,3\}\{T,4\}\{T,5\}\{T,6\}$$

There a re a total of 12 possible outcomes.

Example 5: A deck of cards has 52 cards. There are four suits: diamonds, hearts, spades, and clubs. Each suit has 14 cards: 2,3,4,5,6,7,8,9,10, jack, queen, king, ace.

If a card is drawn at random, what is the probability that it will be an ace? Express your answer as a percent.

Solution: There are a total of 52 cards. Since each suit has one ace, there are 4 aces.

$$\text{probability} = \frac{\text{there are 4 aces}}{52 \text{ cards total}}$$
$$= \frac{4}{52}$$
$$= \frac{1}{14}$$

We were asked to express the answer as a percent: $\frac{1}{14} = 0.0714 = 7.14\%$.

STOP Exercise Set - Probability and Counting

11. Nine balls are put into a bag. There are three colors: blue, red, and yellow. For each color there are three balls numbered 1, 2, and 3. If a ball is drawn at random from the bag, list the set of all possible outcomes. How many outcomes are there total?

12. Eight balls are put into a bag. There are four colors: blue, red, yellow, and green. For each color there are two balls numbered 1 and 2. If a ball is drawn at random from the bag, list the set of all possible outcomes. How many outcomes are there total?

A deck of cards has 52 cards. There are four suits: diamonds, hearts, spades, and clubs. Each suit has 14 cards: 2,3,4,5,6,7,8,9,10, jack, queen, king, ace. Suppose that a card is drawn randomly from a deck.

13. The jack, queen, and king for each suit are called "face cards". What is the probability of drawing a face card?

14. What is the probability of drawing a 6 or a 10?

Exercise Set - Putting it ALL Together

The picture to the right shows several different kinds of dice, from 4-sided to 20-sided. In each exercise express your answer as a fraction.

15. What is the probability of rolling an eight-sided dice and getting seven?

16. What is the probability of rolling a six-sided dice and getting three?

17. What is the probability of rolling a ten-sided dice and getting a 4 or lower?

18. What is the probability of rolling a eight-sided dice and getting lower than 3?

19. What is the probability of rolling a twenty-sided dice and getting lower than 11?

20. What is the probability of rolling a twelve-sided dice and getting higher than 5?

The picture to the right shows a single suit from a deck of cards. Suppose that one card is drawn at random from the suit.

21. What is the probability of drawing a face card or an ace?
22. What is the probability of *not* drawing a face card or an ace?
23. What is the probability of drawing 5 or lower?
24. What is the probability of drawing 3 or lower?

Suppose that a single is drawn at random from the following set of cards.

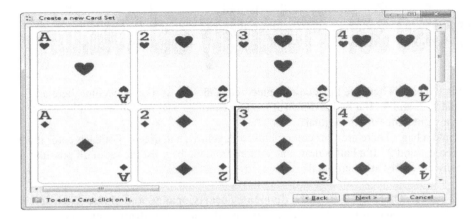

25. What is the probability of drawing an ace?
26. What is the probability of drawing a four?
27. What is the probability of drawing 3 or 4?
28. What is the probability of drawing higher than 2 or an ace?
29. What is the probability of drawing the ace of hearts?
30. What is the probability of drawing the ace of diamonds?

31. A four-sided dice is tossed and, at the same time, a coin is flipped. List the set of all possible outcomes.

32. An eight-sided dice is tossed and, at the same time, a coin is flipped. List the set of all possible outcomes.

33. Refer to exercise #31. What is the probability of getting 3 and heads? Express your answer as a percent.

34. Refer to exercise #32. What is the probability of getting 7 and tails? Express your answer as a percent.

In a carnival game, a coin is tossed and the spinner to the right is spun.

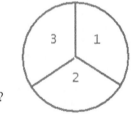

35. List the set of all possible outcomes.
36. What is the probability of getting heads on the coin and 3 on the spinner?
37. What is the probability of getting tails on the coin and 1 on the spinner?
38. What is the probability of getting heads on the coin and 2 or 3 on the spinner?

Exercise Set - Chapter 7 Review

39. 17 is what percent of 58?
40. If $2000 is interested at 9.5% simple interest for 3 years, how much interest will be earned?
41. A business grows from $45 million profit in one to $67 million profit in the next year. What is the percent increase?
42. Express $\frac{1}{8}$ in percent form.
43. A guitar sells for $250. If sales tax is 6.75%, how much tax will be charged?

Exercise Set - Cumulative Review

44. Graph the numbers 0, 5, 3 and 1 on a number line.
45. Add without a calculator. $7.05 + 0.9$

46. Add and simplify if possible. $\dfrac{3x}{14} + \dfrac{4x}{14}$

47. Solve. $x + 9 = -13$
48. Find the prime factorization of 42.

49. Solve the proportion, round to the nearest hundredth if necessary. $\dfrac{3.4}{y} = \dfrac{5.2}{7.6}$

 # 7.6 QUIZ YOURSELF:

To make sure you are ready for the EXAM, try these problems without any help. Give yourself about 20 minutes and don't check the answers until you have completely finished.

1. The probability of winning at bingo by the 20th turn is 0.023. Express the probability as a percent.

2. If one of seven keys is selected at random, what is the probability that it is the correct key? Express your answer as a fraction.

3. There are 26 letters in the alphabet. Five of them are vowels (a, e, i, o, u). If a letter from the alphabet is chosen at random, what is the probability is will be a vowel? Express your answer as a decimal.

4. What is the probability of the spinner to the right hitting green? Express your answer as a percent.

5. A bag contains the following balls/

   black   white   black   white   white   white   red

If a ball is drawn at random, what is the probability it will be white? Express your answer as a fraction.

6. A card is drawn from the following hand and the spinner is spun. How many outcomes are possible? List the possible outcomes.

    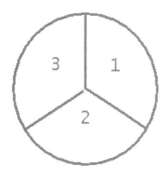

Answers to this Quiz Yourself on page 696.

Chapter 7 Summary and Review

Section 7.1: Introduction To Percents

Processes and Important Notes	Examples
Understanding Percents: • The word **percent** means "per one hundred". The symbol for percent is %.	In a green city, 67 out of 100 households recycle. Find the percent of households that recycle. **Solution:** Since percent means 'per one hundred', 67% of the households recycle.
Percents and Fractions: **To Convert a Percent to a Fraction:** • Use the percent value as the numerator (without the % symbol). • Use 100 as the denominator. • Reduce the fraction. **To Convert a Fraction to Percent Notation:** • Multiply the fraction by 100 and add the % symbol. • When converting fractions to percent notation final answers should be expressed as a mixed number.	**Convert:** **a. to a percent:** $\frac{4}{5}$ **b. to a fraction:** 15% **Solution:** **a.** $\frac{4}{5} \cdot 100\% = \frac{4}{5} \cdot \frac{100}{1}\% = 4 \cdot 20\% = 80\%$ **b.** $15\% = 15 \cdot \frac{1}{100} = \frac{15}{1} \cdot \frac{1}{100} = \frac{3}{20}$
Percents and Decimals: **To Convert a Percent to Decimal Notation:** • Divide by 100 and drop the percent symbol %. • Recall that dividing by 100 can be done by moving the decimal two places to the left. **To Convert a Decimal Number to Percent Notation:** • Multiply by 100 and add the percent symbol %. • Recall that multiplying by 100 can be performed by moving the decimal two places to the right.	**Convert:** **a. to a percent: 0.39** **b. to a fraction: 9.7%** **Solution:** **a.** $0.39 \cdot 100\% = 39\%$ **b.** $9.7\% = 9.7 \div 100 = 0.097$
Introduction to Percent Statements: **To Find the Amount of a Percent:** • Rewrite the percent in decimal or fraction form and translate the word "of" into multiplication.	**Find the following.** **17% of 89** **Solution:** 17% of 89 $= 0.17 \cdot 89$ Change percent to a decimal and 'of' to multiplication $= 15.13$

Write the following as a percent.

1. 0.076
2. 1.25
3. 0.12
4. $\dfrac{2}{5}$

5. $\dfrac{1}{3}$

6. $\dfrac{12}{35}$

Write the following as a decimal and a fraction.

7. 15%
8. 68.7%

9. 4%

10. $66\dfrac{2}{3}\%$

11. 11 out of 50 people are taking a staycation(stay at home vacation) in 2011 instead of traveling. Find the percent of people that taking a staycation.

12. According to a poll in 2005, 50 out of 200 Americans between the ages of 18 and 29 have traveled abroad. Find the percent of these Americans that have traveled abroad.

13. On an exam, Joanna got 37 out of 40 problems correct. Write a corresponding fraction for the number correct to total problems. Convert this fraction to a percent.

14. On a school bus there are 29 boys and 18 girls. Write a corresponding fraction of the number of boys to number of kids on the bus. Convert this fraction to a percent to find the percentage of boys on the bus.

Section 7.2: Solving Percent Statements

Processes and Important Notes	Examples

Writing Percent Statements as Equations:
A **percent statement** has the following form.
    A is *P*% of *B*   or   *P*% of *B* is *A*
• *A* is called the **amount**.
• *P* is the **percent**.
• *B* is called the **base**.
To Write a Percent Statement in Equation Form:
• Change the percent to decimal or fraction form
• Translate the word of into multiplication
• Translate the word is into an equal sign
	Write the following percent statement in equation form. Do not solve.
	    20% of 89 is 17.8
	
	Solution:
	Change % to decimal: 20% = .20
	Change 'of' to *
	Change 'is' to =
	
	So, 20% of 89 is 17.8 in equation form is:
	    $.20 \cdot 89 = 17.8$

Solving Percent Statements: **To Solve a Percent Statement:** • Translate the statement into an equation using a variable to represent the unknown value. • Solve the resulting equation. • If finding a percent give the final answer in percent form.	Solve. 24 is 15% of what? **Solution:** $\dfrac{24}{.15} = \dfrac{.15 \cdot x}{.15}$ $160 = x$ So, 24 is 15% of 160.

Estimating Percents: Use the following standard percents to round the given percent to when estimating. • 10% of something is $\frac{1}{10}$ or "one-tenth" of it • 25% of something is $\frac{1}{4}$ or "one-quarter" of it • 50% of is $\frac{1}{2}$ or "one-half" of it • 75% of something is $\frac{3}{4}$ or "three-quarters" of it	**Estimate the following:** Find 12% of 450. **Solution:** We can round 12% to 10% and then take $\frac{1}{10}$ of 450. So, 12% of 450 is approximately 45.

Find the following.

15. What is 21% of 56.90?
16. What is 35% of 4590?
17. What is 18.5% of 238?
18. What is $22\frac{1}{5}\%$ of 75?

19. What is $9\frac{1}{2}\%$ of 918?
20. 19 is what percent of 45?
21. 18.75 is what percent of 98?
22. 14 is 35% of what number?
23. 56 is 67% of what number?

24. There was a total of 20,705 annual total of orphan visas issued by the US during the years 1996-2006. Of these visas, 19.8% were awarded to Guatemala. How many visas were awarded to Guatemala orphans for adoptions?

25. There are 1,100 different types of bat species worldwide. Only about 4.3% of these species live in the US. How many different types of bat species live in the US?

Mental Math. Find the following without any computations.

26. What is 50% of 30?
27. What is 100% of 87?
28. What is 200% of 15?
29. What is 10% of 570.9?
30. What is 20% of 68?

Section 7.3: Consumer Applications of Percents

Processes and Important Notes	**Examples**
Discounts: • **Discount is Sale Percent of Original Price** • **Sale Price = Original Price - Discount**	**Solve.** Rack Room Shoes has a pair of Nike's on sale for 23% off. The original price was $86. Find the discount and the sale price. **Solution:** Discount = 23% of $86. = .23·86 = **$19.78** Sale Price = 86 − 19.78 = **$66.22**
Sales Tax: • The percent paid in sales tax a called the	**Solve.** The sales tax in Utah is 4.75% on clothing. Nikita

tax rate.	spent $241.73 on back to school clothes. Find how much she spent on tax and what the total cost of her clothes cost her.

Solution:
Sales Tax = 4.75% of $241.73
$= 0.0475 \cdot 241.73$
$= \mathbf{\$11.48}$

Total Price = 241.73 + 11.48
$= \mathbf{\$253.21}$ |
| • **Sales Tax is Tax Rate of Original Price**

• **Total Price = Original Price + Sales Tax** | |
| **Markups:**
• **Markup is Markup Percent of Retail Price**
• **Market Price = Retail Price + Markup** | **Solve.**
Antwon buys a bike on craigslist for $85 and then marks it up by 75% and sells it in his bikeshop. Find the markup and the market price.

Solution:
Markup = 75% of 85
$= .75 \cdot 85$
$= \mathbf{\$63.75}$
Market Price = 85 + 63.75
$= \mathbf{\$148.75}$ |
| **Commission and Tips:**
• **Commission is a Percent of Total Sales**
• **Tip is a Percent of Bill** | **Solve.**
Rica is a real estate agent and makes 2.7% commission on the total sales of homes. Last month, she sold a house priced at $345,000. What was her commission?

Solution:
Commission is commission rate of total sales
Commission = $0.027 \cdot 345000$
$= \mathbf{\$9,315}$ |

Solve the following percent word problems.

31. Hotels in San Francisco charge a 14% tax on rooms. If Terrance books a hotel room for $219, how much does he pay in tax?

32. A group of friends goes out to dinner and the bill is $67.19. If they want to leave an 18% tip, how much is the tip?

33. Every year Juan gets a 3.5% bonus of his salary at his law firm. If he currently makes $95,870 per year, what is his bonus?

34. Lizette is a real estate agent and makes 4% commission on the sell of a home when she acts as a dual agent, meaning she represents the buyers and the sellers. Lizette sold an oceanfront home for $675,000 as a dual agent. How much did she make in commission?

35. A scalper buys Charger's tickets for $55 and then marks them up 65%. Find the markup and the new price for the scalper sells the tickets for.

36. A skate shop buys skateboards for $48 and then marks them up 140%. Find the markup and the new price for the skateboards.

37. Brian bought an electric drum kit that originally cost $1675.79 on sale for 30% off. The tax rate in Brian's state is 7.5%.
    a. What with the discounted price of the drum kit?
    b. What was the tax on the discounted price?
    c. What was Brian's total at checkout?

38. Martha and Betty are renting a mountain cabin for four nights during the week that rents for $125 per night. Since they are renting through the week, they get a 20% discount off the cabin per night. The tax rate on the cabin is 12% and there is a one time $75 cleaning fee.
    a. What with the discounted price of the cabin per night?
    b. What was the tax on the discounted price?
    c. What was total cost to rent the cabin?

Section 7.4: Other Applications of Percent

Processes and Important Notes	Examples
Percent Increase and Percent Decrease: • **Amount of Increase = Current – Original** • **Amount of Decrease = Original - Current** • **Amount of Increase/Decrease = Percent of Original Amount.**	Solve. Jackie bought a house in 2005 for $278,000. The housing market crash and the home is now worth $189,000. Find the percent decrease of the home. **Solution:** **Amount of Decrease = Original – Current Price** $= 278,000 - 189,00$ $= 89,000$ **Amount of Decrease = Percent of Original** $89000 = x \cdot 278000$ $.32 = x$ **So, the percent decrease of the home is 32%**
Percents and Graphs: **Graphs are used** to organize information about percents on charts and tables. The main graphs considered are: • Circle Graphs • Bar Graphs • Line Graphs	**Use the bar graph given.** What percent of full-time undergrads receive pell grants? Percent of undergrads receiving Pell Grants at Kentucky independent colleges, 2006-07 40 percent of all AIKCU undergraduates, and 47 percent of full-time undergraduates, receive Pell Grants, the federal program for the lowest income students. **Solution:** The green bar represents the full time undergraduates. So 47% receive pell grants.

39. Keisha bought a house in 2001 for $115,000. In 2006, she sold the house for $205,00. Find the amount of increase.
40. Alexis purchased a car for $6,750. Three years later she sold it for $2900. Find the amount of decrease.
41. Find the percent increase for #39.
42. Find the percent decrease for #40.

43. In Pete's Pre-Algebra class in the fall, he had 25 students pass the class. The following semester, he had 31 students pass the class. What was the percent increase for successful students.

44. Facebook launched in 2004. By 2005, it had 5.5 million active users. Currently, in 2011, there are 750 million active users. Find the percent increase in facebook users over the last 7 years.

45. MySpace had a peak with 1,600 employees. In 2009, a major layoff happened, leaving only 1,000 employees. Find the percent decrease in the employees at MySpace.

46. The Kenyan elephant population has decreased from 167,000 elephants in 1973 to only 35,117 elephants in 2010. Find the percent decrease in elephants.

The circle graph to the right, gives the percentages of a college student's weekly activities. Use this graph to answer the following questions.

Hint: there are 168 hours in one week.

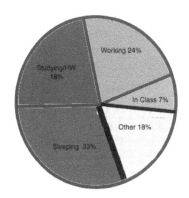

47. What percent of a week, does a college student study/do homework?

48. What percent of a week, does a college student spend working?

49. How many hours does this college student sleep a week?

50. How many hours of free time does this college student have during a typical week?

Section 7.5: Interest

Processes and Important Notes	Examples
Simple Interest: • **Interest** is a charge for borrowing money. • **Principle** is an amount of money borrowed or invested. • An **interest rate** is a percent associated with the payback of a loan or investment. • **The Simple Interest Formula** $I = P \cdot r \cdot t$	**Solve.** $4000 is borrowed for 6 years in a simple interest account with a rate of 9.5%. How much is paid in interest? **Solution:** Use: $I = \Pr t$ P = $4000 r = 9.5% = 0.095 t = 6 $I = \Pr t = 4000 \cdot 0.095 \cdot 6$ **I = $2280**
Compound Interest: • **Compound Interest Formula** $$A = P\left(1 + \frac{r}{n}\right)^{nt}$$ $A =$ amount of the account $P =$ principle $r =$ interst rate (in decimal form) $n =$ number of compounds per year $t =$ time (in years)	**Solve.** $1985 is invested in an account for 9 years at a rate of 4.8% compounded quarterly. Find the total amount in the account after 9 years. **Solution:** P = 1985 r = 4.8% = 0.048 t = 9 n = 4 (quarterly) $$A = 1985\left(1 + \frac{0.048}{4}\right)^{4 \cdot 9}$$ **A = $3049.71**

51. Bruce invested $3500 in a simple interest account for 6 years at a rate of 5.5%. How much interest did he earn?

52. Juana invested $16,750 in a simple interest account for 9 months at a rate of 4.75%. How much interest did she earn?
53. Juliet borrowed $7700 for 3 years to buy a car from her local credit union. She got a rate of 8.75% compounded monthly. What is the total amount she paid for her loan?
54. Christian borrowed $2500 for 5 years for college from his local credit union. He got a rate of 3.5% compounded monthly. What is the total amount he paid for his loan?
55. Lin invested $5000 for her son's college fund when he was born. She invested in her bank at a rate of 4.5% compounded quarterly. What is the total amount of the account when her son turns 18 years old?
56. Roberto invested $13,000 in his bank at a simple interest rate of 3% saving for his first home. He saved for 8 years when he pulled the money out as a down payment on his home. What was the amount of the account after this time?

Section 7.6: Introduction To Probability

Processes and Important Notes	Examples
Probability: The **probability of an event** is a number that represents the chances of it happening. A probability can be represented as a fraction, a decimal, or a percent. **The Probability of an Event** $$probability = \frac{\text{number of ways the event can occur}}{\text{total number of outcomes}}$$	**Find the probability.** What is the probability of drawing a jack or queen from a deck of cards. Hint: There are 52 cards in a deck of cards. **Solution:** Since there are 4 different sets and a jack and queen in each one, there are a total of 8 cards that would satisfy the criteria. $$probability = \frac{8 \text{ possible cards}}{52 \text{ total outcomes}}$$ $$= \frac{2}{13} = 0.1538 = 15.38\%$$
Probability and Counting: • **List the possible outcomes** • **Count the total outcomes**	**List all the possible outcomes.** A four-sided dice is tossed and a coin is flipped at the same time. **Solution:** **{1H, 2H, 3H, 4H, 1T, 2T, 3T, 4T}** **There are 8 possible outcomes.**

57. What is the probability of rolling a six-sided dice and getting 4 or higher?
58. What is the probability of rolling a twelve-sided dice and getting a number less than 5?
59. What is the probability of drawing a heart out of a deck of cards?
60. What is the probability of drawing an 8, 9, or 10 out of a deck of cards?
61. A bag contains 18 balls: 7 blue, 6 black, and 5 white. If a ball is chosen at random, what is the probability it will be blue? Express your answer as a decimal.
62. A bag contains 13 marbles: 2 yellow, 5 green, and 6 orange. If a ball is chosen at random, what is the probability it will be yellow? Express your answer as a fraction.
63. A six-sided dice is tossed and, at the same time, a coin is flipped. List the set of all possible outcomes.
64. The spinner to the right is spun and, at the same time, a coin is flipped. List the set of all possible outcomes.

Chapter 7 Test Yourself: PreAlgebra

Write the following as a percent.
1.   0.65
2.   3.8

3. $\dfrac{3}{8}$

4. $\dfrac{6}{11}$

Write the following as a decimal and a fraction.
5.   28%

6. $33\dfrac{1}{3}\%$

Find the following.
7.   What is 50% of 180?
8.   What is 100% of 29?
9.   What is 20% of 45?

10. What is 17.9% of 32?
11. 20 is what percent of 64?
12. 27 is 35% of what number?

Solve the following percent word problems.
13. On an exam, Joanna got 37 out of 40 problems correct. Write a corresponding fraction for the number correct to total problems. Convert this fraction to a percent.

14. Hotels in Outer Banks, NC charge a 12% tax on rooms. If Jorge books a hotel room for $199, how much does he pay in tax?

15. Every year Cynthia gets a 2.7% bonus of his salary at her accounting office. If she currently makes $73,928 per year, what is her bonus?

16. A group of friends goes out to dinner and the bill is $72.10. If they want to leave a 20% tip, how much is the tip?

17. Jawed is a real estate agent and makes 4.5% commission on the sell of a home when he acts as a dual agent, meaning he represents the buyers and the sellers. Jawed sold a mountain vacation home for $387,000 as a dual agent. How much did he make in commission?

18.   Rachel bought a new surfboard that originally cost $574.95 on sale for 25% off. The tax rate in Rachel's state is 6.25%.
     a.   What with the discounted price of the surfboard?
     b.   What was the tax on the discounted price?
     c.   What was Rachel's total at checkout?

19. What is the probability of drawing a diamond face card from a deck of cards?

20. The spinner to the right is spun and at the same time a 4-sided dice is rolled. List all the possible outcomes. How many outcomes are there?

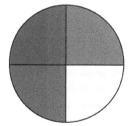

Chapters 1 to 7 Cumulative Review:

1. Is 51 prime or composite? If composite, list a factorization of the number other than 1 and itself.
2. Rewrite $-\dfrac{78}{5}$ as a mixed number and simplify if possible.
3. Find two factors of 48 that give a difference of 8.
4. Determine if 14 is a factor of $2 \cdot 5 \cdot 13 \cdot 3 \cdot 7$.

Simplify.

5. $-23 + (-19)$

6. $-20 \div 4 \cdot 2 + 3^2$

7. $\dfrac{-5}{18} + \dfrac{11}{24}$

8. $\left(-4\dfrac{1}{6}\right)\left(1\dfrac{4}{5}\right)$

9. $\dfrac{12x^3 y^2}{45x} \cdot \dfrac{25x^2}{27y^5}$

10. $-\dfrac{27}{35} \div \dfrac{18}{49}$

11. $-3\dfrac{2}{5} + 8\dfrac{4}{7}$

12. $\left(-5\dfrac{1}{2}\right) \div \left(3\dfrac{3}{10}\right)$

13. $\dfrac{7}{8} - \left(-4\dfrac{2}{3}\right)$

14. $6.025 + 27.89$

15. $(5.3)(-7.18)$

16. $153.67 - (-622.75)$

17. $\dfrac{4}{7} \cdot 2.1 - \left(\dfrac{1}{3}\right)^2$

18. $\dfrac{6\left(5 - 2^2\right) \cdot 5 \div 2}{2^3 + 7}$

Solve.

19. $x + 3 = 27$

20. $\dfrac{-3}{8}x = 51$

21. $\dfrac{5}{7} = x - \dfrac{2}{9}$

22. $m - 13.67 = -58.915$

23. $1.2n = -5128.16$

24. $3x - 5 = 19$

25. $2(3x - 1) + 4x = -13$

26. $4x - 12 = 6x + 15$

Evaluate.

27. $3x^2 + 2x - 7$, $x = -2$

28. $4xy + 3y^2$, $x = 5$, $y = -3$

29. $mx + b$, $m = \dfrac{2}{3}$, $x = -6$, $b = \dfrac{1}{7}$

30. $\dfrac{-b}{2a}$, $a = \dfrac{3}{4}$, $b = \dfrac{1}{2}$

31. $a^2 + b^2$, $a = -3$, $b = 4$

32. $b^2 - 4ac$, $a = -5$, $b = -1$, $c = 6$

Convert.

33. 0.76 to a fraction

34. $\dfrac{8}{9}$ to a decimal

35. $\dfrac{3}{8}$ to a percent

36. 68% to a decimal

37. $15\dfrac{1}{3}\%$ to a fraction

38. 1.36 to a percent

Compare the following with <, > or =.

39. $-6.815 \underline{\quad} -6.185$

40. $\dfrac{8}{9} \underline{\quad} \dfrac{6}{7}$

Solve the following word problems.

41. What is 50% of 286?

42. What is 10% of 7200?

43. What is 28% of 59?

44. 12 is 25% of what number?

45. 16 is what percent of 4?

46. Find the area of a triangle with base $12\frac{2}{5}$ in. and height $7\frac{1}{3}$ in.

47. Find the area of a circle that has a diameter of 28 m. Use $\pi \approx \frac{22}{7}$.

48. Find the circumference of a circle with radius 9.2 ft. Use $\pi \approx 3.14$.

49. Twice the sum of a number and five is the same as the number subtracted from thirteen.

50. Suppose that the total interest that will be paid on a 30-year mortgage from a home loan of $175,000 is going to be $297,000. What will be the payments each month if the payments are to pay off both the loan and the interest (to the nearest hundredth)?

51. The smallest angle in a triangle measures 15 degrees more than twice the 2nd angle. The third angle measures twice the 2nd angle. Find the measure of the angles of the triangle.

52. Two angles are complementary. One angle is thrice the other angle. Find the measure of each angle.

53. A rectangular garden requires 46 feet of fencing. If the length is 2 feet more than three times the width, what are the dimensions of the garden?

54. Zakirah currently has $187.19 in her checking account. She gets paid $518.27 and deposits the check in her account. She then writes bills for $63.11, $17.82 and $379. What is her new account balance?

55. Troy buys a new bike and does interest free financing for a year. He financed $2789.99 for the bike. How much should he pay each month so he can pay off the bike in a year and not have to pay interest?

56. Male Elephant Seals off the coast of South Georgia Islands have a life expectancy of about 14 years. Satellite tracking discovered that 80% of his life was consumed with offshore odysseys. How many years of his life was he in offshore odysseys?

57. Carol is a real estate agent and earns $2\frac{1}{2}$% commission on the sale of a house. She sales a home for $439,900. How much commission did she earn?

58. When financing a home loan, it is possible to pay 1 point or 1% in order to get a lower interest rate. If the loan is for $225,000, how much would it cost to lower the rate on the loan?

Chapter 8 - Measurement

Time to learn the metric prefix system.

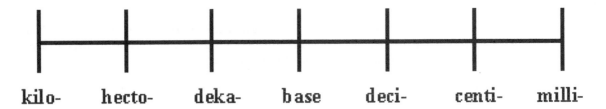

kilo-   hecto-   deka-   base   deci-   centi-   milli-

And how it compares to the way we measure in the United States.

8.1 American Measurement

Topics:
- American Units of Length
- American Units of Capacity
- American Units of Weight

Are You Ready?

To see if you are ready to understand this section, do the following short quiz.

1. Reduce the fraction. $\dfrac{75}{105}$

2. Multiply. $\dfrac{38}{1} \cdot \dfrac{1}{12}$

3. Convert $\dfrac{253}{12}$ to mixed number.

Answers to Are You Ready?

1.) $\dfrac{5}{7}$ 2.) $\dfrac{19}{6}$ 3.) $21\dfrac{1}{12}$

American Units of Length

In the United States, we commonly use the inch, foot, yard, or mile to measure lengths. In our American system (also commonly referred to as the English system) each of these units can be expressed in terms of another.

12 inches (in) = 1 foot (ft)

3 feet (ft) = 1 yard (yd)

5280 feet (ft) = 1760 yards (yd) = 1 mile (mi)

The most important topic in this section, and in the whole chapter, is how to convert from one unit to another. For example, 48 inches is equivalent to 4 feet. To understand how to convert between units, we need to understand unit fractions.

A **unit fraction** is a fraction made of two different units but that is equivalent to 1.

Here are some examples of unit fractions that involve American units of length.

$$\frac{12 \text{ inches}}{1 \text{ foot}} \qquad \frac{1 \text{ yard}}{3 \text{ feet}} \qquad \frac{5280 \text{ feet}}{1 \text{ mile}}$$

Good Question: How is $\dfrac{1 \text{ foot}}{12 \text{ inches}}$ equivalent to 1? It looks like $\dfrac{1}{12}$ to me!

Answer: The key is that the units are different. 12 inches is the same as 1 foot, so the numerator and denominator are indeed the same. Since the numerator and denominator are the same, the fraction is equivalent to 1.

You can create a unit fraction with any two units if you know how they relate. Remember that each unit fraction is equivalent to 1.

Example 1: What two unit fractions involve yards and miles?

Solution: Since 1760 yards = 1 mile, the two unit fractions are $\dfrac{1 \text{ mile}}{1760 \text{ yards}}$ and $\dfrac{1760 \text{ yards}}{1 \text{ mile}}$.

Understanding unit fractions gives us a way to easily convert between units.

To Convert Between Two Units of Measurement:

- Write the given measurement as a fraction with 1 in the denominator.
- Multiply by unit fraction(s) so that all units reduce except for the new unit.
- Express your answer as a proper fraction, mixed number, or decimal with the new units indicated.

This next example shows how this process works. In particular it shows what we mean by "reducing units".

Example 2: Use a unit fraction to convert 32 inches to feet.

Solution: Let us follow the steps given above carefully.

Write the given measurement as a fraction with 1 in the denominator.

$$32 \text{ inches} = \frac{32 \text{ inches}}{1 \text{ foot}}$$

Multiply by the unit fraction that has the new measurement in the numerator and the old given unit in the denominator.

$$\frac{32 \text{ inches}}{1} \cdot \frac{1 \text{ foot}}{12 \text{ inches}}$$

In converting, units reduce like numbers, so the units "inches" reduce.

$$\frac{32 \text{ inches}}{1} \cdot \frac{1 \text{ foot}}{12 \text{ inches}} = \frac{32}{12} \text{ feet}$$

Now we can reduce the fraction and write it as a mixed number.

$$\frac{32}{12} \text{ feet} = \frac{8}{3} \text{ feet} = 2\frac{2}{3} \text{ feet}$$

Good Question: This process seems too complicated. Can't I convert between these units by simply multiplying or dividing?

Answer: For simple problems, yes, you can convert by just multiplying or dividing. But advanced conversions, like those coming up next in this book or in a chemistry class, require unit fractions. We are trying to get you used to the idea with these simpler conversions first.

Unit fractions help us decide how to do more complicated conversions. To convert inches to miles, for example, we convert the inches to feet and then the feet to miles. Using unit fractions this can be done as a multiplication of three fractions.

Example 3: Convert 70 inches to miles. Leave your answer as a fraction if necessary.

Solution: We do not know how to convert straight from inches to miles. We can, however, convert from inches to feet and then feet to miles. This process can be done using unit fractions as follows.

$$\underbrace{\frac{70 \text{ inches}}{1}}_{\substack{\text{Here is our} \\ \text{original unit.}}} \cdot \underbrace{\frac{1 \text{ foot}}{12 \text{ inches}}}_{\substack{\text{This unit fraction} \\ \text{converts inches} \\ \text{to feet.}}} \cdot \underbrace{\frac{1 \text{ mile}}{5280 \text{ feet}}}_{\substack{\text{This unit fraction} \\ \text{converts feet to miles.}}}$$

And here is how this fraction multiplication is processed. Note that we are reducing units.

$$\frac{70 \text{ inches}}{1} \cdot \frac{1 \text{ foot}}{12 \text{ inches}} \cdot \frac{1 \text{ mile}}{5280 \text{ feet}} = \frac{70 \cdot 1 \cdot 1}{1 \cdot 12 \cdot 5280} \text{ miles}$$

Now we can simplify the resulting fraction.

$$\frac{70}{12 \cdot 5280} \text{ mile} = \frac{7}{6336} \text{ mile}$$

Example 4: Where in the World?
A family wants a fence built that would measure 56 feet. The fencing company they plan to use says they can estimate the cost as $65 per yard of fencing. What is a good estimate for the cost of the fence?

Solution: First, we should convert 56 feet to yards using the unit fraction $\frac{1 \text{ yd}}{3 \text{ ft}}$. We round to the nearest tenth.

$$\frac{56 \text{ ft}}{1} \cdot \frac{1 \text{ yd}}{3 \text{ ft}} = \frac{56}{3} \text{ yd} \approx 18.7 \text{ yd}$$

So the fence is about 18.7 yards. Since the fencing is about $65 per yard, we multiply $18.7(65) = 1215.5$. So the fencing will cost about $1215.50.

Example 5: Find the perimeter and area of the rectangle. You may need to convert to a common unit first.

35in

2.8 yd

Solution: First we should convert the yards to inches to have a common unit.

$$\left(\frac{2.8\,yd}{1}\right)\left(\frac{3\,ft}{1\,yd}\right)\left(\frac{12\,inches}{1\,foot}\right)=100.8\,inches$$

Perimeter: $P = 2l + 2w$

$\quad\quad P = 2(35) + 2(100.8)$

$\quad\quad\quad = 70 + 201.6$

$\quad\quad\quad = 271.6\,inches$

Area: $A = l \cdot w$

$\quad\quad A = (35)(100.8)$

$\quad\quad\quad = 3{,}528\,in^2$

Courtesy of Fotolia

STOP **Exercise Set - American Units of Length**

1. What two unit fractions involve feet and inches?
2. What two unit fractions involve yards and miles?

Use unit fractions to convert each measure to the unit indicated.

3. 48 inches to feet
4. 15 feet to yards
5. 13 feet to yards
6. 27 inches to feet
7. 180 inches to yards
8. 145 inches to miles

American Units of Capacity

In the United States, we use the following the fluid once, pint, quart, or gallon to measure how much space an object takes up, called capacity. Just like units of length, these measurements can be related to each other.

8 fluid ounces (fl oz) = 1 cup (c)

16 fluid ounces (fl oz) = 1 pint (pt)

2 cups (c) = 1 pint (pt)

2 pints (pt) = 1 quart (qt)

4 quarts (qt) = 1 gallon (gal)

Here are some examples of unit fractions that involve American units of capacity.

$$\frac{2 \text{ pints}}{1 \text{ quart}} \qquad \frac{1 \text{ gal}}{4 \text{ qt}} \qquad \frac{1 \text{ pt}}{16 \text{ fl oz}}$$

To convert between these units of measure we use the same process of reducing with unit fractions as with units of length.

Example 6: Convert 3.5 pints to fluid ounces.

Solution: The unit fraction that converts pints to fluid ounces is $\dfrac{16 \text{ fl oz}}{1 \text{ pt}}$. So we multiply by it.

$$\frac{3.5 \text{ pt}}{1} \cdot \frac{16 \text{ fl oz}}{1 \text{ pt}} = \frac{3.5(16 \text{ fl oz})}{1} = 56 \text{ fl oz}$$

So 3.5 pints is the same as 56 fluid ounces.

Our next example involves two unit fractions.

Example 7: Where in the World? An engine requires 74 fluid ounces of fuel but the fuel is only sold in quarts. Use unit fractions to convert 74 fluid ounces to quarts. Express your answer as a mixed number.

Solution: This conversion requires two unit fractions: one to take fluid ounces to pints and one to take pints to quarts. For convenience we will use the abbreviation for each unit.

$$\frac{74 \text{ fl oz}}{1} \cdot \frac{1 \text{ pt}}{16 \text{ fl oz}} \cdot \frac{1 \text{ qt}}{2 \text{ pt}} = \frac{74 \, \cancel{\text{fl oz}}}{1} \cdot \frac{1 \, \cancel{\text{pt}}}{16 \, \cancel{\text{fl oz}}} \cdot \frac{1 \text{ qt}}{2 \, \cancel{\text{pt}}} = \frac{74 \cdot 1 \cdot 1 \text{ qt}}{1 \cdot 16 \cdot 2} = \frac{74}{32} \text{ qt}$$

Now we reduce the fraction and express as a mixed number. $\dfrac{74}{32} = \dfrac{37}{16} = 2\dfrac{5}{16}$

So 74 fluid ounces is equivalent to $2\dfrac{5}{16}$ quarts.

STOP Exercise Set - American Units of Capacity

9. What two unit fractions involve quarts and pints?
10. What two unit fractions involve fluid ounces and cups?

Use unit fractions to convert each measure to the unit indicated.
11. 14 pints to cups
12. 52 pints to quarts
13. 24 fluid ounces to cups
14. 13 quarts to gallons
15. 37 pints to gallons

16. 75 fluid ounces to quarts

American Units of Weight

In the United States, we use the ounce, pound, or ton to measure how heavy an object is, called the weight. Here is how these units relate to each other.

$$16 \text{ ounces (oz)} = 1 \text{ pound (lb)}$$

$$2000 \text{ pounds (lb)} = 1 \text{ ton}$$

Here are some examples of unit fractions that involve American units of length.

$$\frac{1 \text{ pound}}{16 \text{ ounces}} \qquad \frac{2000 \text{ lb}}{1 \text{ ton}}$$

Example 8: Where in the World? Scrap metal sells for $150 per ton. If an old truck weighs 8,600 pounds, how much money is the scrap metal worth?

Solution: We need to convert the pounds to tons first. To convert pounds to tons we use the unit fraction $\frac{1 \text{ ton}}{2000 \text{ lb}}$.

$$\frac{8600 \text{ lb}}{1} \cdot \frac{1 \text{ ton}}{2000 \text{ lb}} = \frac{8600 \text{ lb}}{1} \cdot \frac{1 \text{ ton}}{2000 \text{ lb}} = \frac{8600 \text{ ton}}{2000} = 4.3 \text{ tons}$$

So the truck is 4.3 tons. Since the scrap metal is worth $150 per tons, the truck is worth $4.3(\$150) = \$645$.

 STOP Exercise Set - American Units of Weight

17. What two unit fractions involve pounds and ounces?
18. What two unit fractions involve pounds and tons?

Use unit fractions to convert each measure to the unit indicated.
19. 10000 pounds to tons
20. 64 pounds to ounces
21. 35 ounces to pounds
22. 4700 pounds to tons
23. 2.7 tons to ounces
24. 36,000 ounces to tons

Exercise Set - Putting it ALL Together

Fill in the blank.

25. 1 mile = _____ feet
26. _____ yards = 1 mile
27. 1 pint = _____ cups
28. 1 foot = _____ inches
29. _____ quarts = 1 gallon
30. _____ pounds = 1 ton
31. 1 pound = _____ ounces
32. _____ fluid ounces = 1 cup

Use unit fractions to convert each measure to the unit indicated. Round to the nearest hundredth when necessary.

33. 4 quarts = _____ pints
34. 7.8 feet = _____ inches
35. 75 ounces = _____ pounds
36. 5.5 pints = _____ fluid ounces
37. 72 feet = _____ yards
38. 108 fluid ounces = _____ cups
39. 6.7 tons = _____ pounds

40. $4\frac{1}{2}$ gallons = _____ quarts
41. 9 cups = _____ pints
42. 100 yards = _____ miles
43. 86 fluid ounces = _____ quarts
44. 25 pints = _____ gallons

45. The Empire State building in New York City is 1454 feet tall. Convert this to inches.

46. The largest elephant ever observed weighed about 24,000 pounds. How many tons is this?

47. The average great white shark is about 174 inches long. Convert this to feet.

48. The largest standing stone at Stonehenge weighs almost 50 tons! Convert this to pounds.

49. A camel can drink up to 80 quarts of water at a time. How many gallons is this?

50. A marathon is 26.2 miles. Convert this to feet.

51. A restaurant chief estimates she needs 15 quarts of broth. How many pints is this?

52. In his 18 year career, NFL quarterback Bret Favre threw for 71,838 yards. Convert this to miles.

53. America's nuclear reactors have generated about 72,000 tons of radioactive waste. How many pounds is this?

54. In 1953, Edmund Hillary and Tenzig Norgay became the first people to climb Mount Everest. This expedition took them to an elevation of 29,035 feet above sea level. Convert this to miles.

55. An average new-born baby weighs about 130 ounces. Convert this to pounds.

Fill the table in with the correct conversions. Round to the nearest tenth if necessary.

Object	Inches	Feet	Yards
56. Adult King Palm Tree		27	
57. Adult Giraffe			5.5
58. The Statue of Liberty	1812		
59. Length of the International Space Station		167.3	

Note that in many of the following figures the units do not match. You may have to convert to find the area and/or perimeter.

60. Find the area and perimeter. Express you answer in square feet (ft^2) and square inches (in^2).

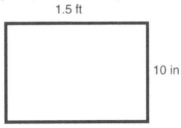

1.5 ft

10 in

61. Find the area and perimeter. Express you answer in square feet (ft^2) and square inches (in^2).

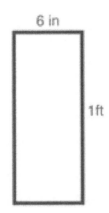

6 in

1 ft

62. Find the area and perimeter. Express you answer in square feet (ft^2) and square yards (yd^2).

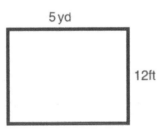

5 yd

12ft

63. Find the area and perimeter. Express you answer in square feet (ft^2) and square yards (yd^2).

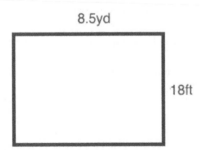

8.5yd

18ft

64. Find the area and perimeter. Express you answer in square feet (ft^2) and square inches (in^2).

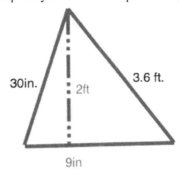

65. Find the area and perimeter. Express you answer in square feet (ft^2) and square yards (yd^2).

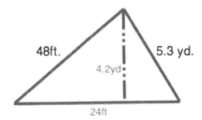

66. Find the area. Express you answer in square feet (ft^2).

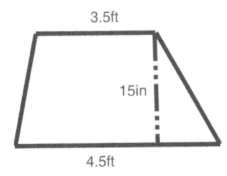

67. Find the area. Express you answer in square inches (in^2).

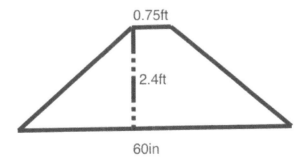

Exercise Set - Cumulative Review

68. Multiply without a calculator. $(-1.2)(0.7)$

69. Is the proportion $\dfrac{\frac{1}{2}}{4} = \dfrac{\frac{3}{4}}{8}$ true or false?

70. Find the prime factorization of 68.

71. Convert $\dfrac{4}{7}$ to a decimal without using a calculator. Round to the nearest hundredth.

72. 15 tons of steal costs $2490. How many tons of steal could you buy with $1000?

73. The Affordable Care Act has allotted $198 million towards training 1100 doctors. How much should it cost to train 300 doctors?

8.1 QUIZ YOURSELF:

Courtesy of Fotolia

To make sure you are ready for the EXAM, try these problems without any help. Give yourself about 20 minutes and don't check the answers until you have completely finished.

1. Fill in the blank: 1 mile = _____ feet
2. What unit fractions relate fluid ounces to pints?
3. Convert 30 inches to feet.
4. Convert 740 pounds to tons.
5. Convert 16 cups to quarts.
6. A recipe for calls for 3 quarts of broth. Convert this to pints.
7. Find the area. Express you answer in square feet (ft^2) and square yards (yd^2).

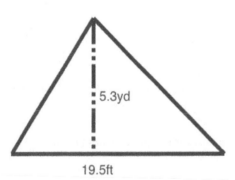

5.3yd

19.5ft

Answers to this Quiz Yourself are on page 702.

8.2 Metric Measurement

Topics:
- Introduction to the Metric System
- Converting with a Prefix Chart
- Operations with Metric Measurements

Are You Ready?
To see if you are ready to understand this section, do the following short quiz.

1. Multiply. $0.09(1000)$

2. Divide. $\dfrac{4.6}{0.01}$

3. Reduce the unit fractions. $\dfrac{3.5\,ft}{1} \cdot \dfrac{12\,in}{1\,ft}$

Answers to Are You Ready.

1.) 90   *2.) 460*   *3.) 42in*

Introduction to the Metric System

Here in the US we are used to using American units like feet, gallons, and pounds. Most other countries use a system of measurement called *the metric system*.

The metric system is simpler than the American system in that there is only one base unit for each type of measurement: length, capacity, and weight.

- **Length:** The base unit of length in the metric system is the **meter**. One meter is slightly longer than one yard.
- **Capacity:** The base unit of capacity in the meter system is the **liter**. One liter is the size of a large drinking bottle.
- **Weight:** The base unit of weight in the metric system is the **gram**. One gram is about the weight of a small paper clip.

1 liter

1 meter ▭▭▭▭▭▭▭

1 yard ▭▭▭▭▭▭▭

Example 1: In each scenario, which unit of measure (meter, liter, or gram) would be used.

a.) A surveyor is measuring the height of a building.
b.) A botanist is measuring the weight of a plant.

Solution:
a.) Since the height of a building is a distance, the surveyor would use *meters*.
b.) Since the botanist is measuring weight, they would use *grams*.

To take larger or smaller measurements, the metric system uses prefixes to express multiples of the base unit. Here are the prefixes.

Metric System Prefixes							
Prefix	kilo	hecto	deka	base unit	deci	centi	milli
Meaning	1000	100	10	-	$\dfrac{1}{10}=0.1$	$\dfrac{1}{100}=0.01$	$\dfrac{1}{1000}=0.001$

So, for example, if we put the prefix kilo with the base unit meter, we get kilometer. One kilometer is 1000 meters.

Example 2: Express each unit given as a multiply of its base unit (meters, grams, or liters).

a.) hectogram   b.) decimeter   c.) milliliter

Solution: We use the prefix chart to determine each multiple.

a.) A hectogram is 100 grams.

b.) A decimeter is $\dfrac{1}{10}$ of a meter.

c.) A milliliter is $\dfrac{1}{1000}$ of a liter.

We can organize the relationships between these units the same way as the American units in order to create unit fractions.

Common Metric Measurements		
Length	**Capacity**	**Weight**
1 kilometer (km) = 1000 meters (m)	1 kilogram (kg) = 1000 grams (g)	1 kiloliter (kL) = 1000 liters (L)
1 centimeter (cm) = 0.01 meter (m)	1 milligram (mg) = 0.001 gram (g)	1 milliliter (mL) = 0.001 liter (L)
1 millimeter (mm) = 0.001 meter (m)		

Here are some references to help you visualize how large or small these units are:

• One kilometer (1000 meters) is a little more than half of a mile.
• One kilogram (1000 grams) is a little more than two pounds.
• One millimeter (0.001 meter) is about the thickness of a penny.

That all these conversions are based on multiples of 10 makes converting in the metric system very easy. Here are examples of some unit fractions in the metric system.

$$\frac{1kL}{1000L} \qquad \frac{0.001g}{1mg} \qquad \frac{0.01m}{1cm}$$

Example 3: Use unit fractions to convert 4.5 kiloliters to liters.

Solution: As with American conversions from section 8.1, we multiply by the unit fraction that will cause the units to cancel. Since we want kiloliters (kL) to cancel we use the unit fraction $\dfrac{1000L}{1kL}$.

$$\frac{4.5kL}{1} \cdot \frac{1000L}{1kL} = \frac{4.5\cancel{kL}}{1} \cdot \frac{1000L}{1\cancel{kL}} = 4.5(1000)L = 4500L$$

Example 4: Where in the World? Antwan is an engineer listing the specifications for a new phone cell phone design. A certain part weighs 0.0853 grams. To match the other specs, the weight should be expressed in milligrams. Make the conversion.

Solution: To convert grams to milligrams we use the unit fraction $\dfrac{1mg}{0.001g}$.

$$\frac{0.0853g}{1} \cdot \frac{1mg}{0.001g} = \frac{0.0853\cancel{g}}{1} \cdot \frac{1mg}{0.001\cancel{g}} = \frac{0.0853mg}{0.001} = 85.3mg$$

STOP Exercise Set - Introduction to the Metric System

Choose the answer that matches the prefix given.

1. deka
   - a. 1000
   - b. 10
   - c. 0.001
2. centi
   - a. 100
   - b. 0.01
   - c. 0.1

3. kilo
   - a. 1000
   - b. 100
   - c. 10
4. milli
   - a. 0.01
   - b. 1000
   - c. 0.001

5. What unit fraction involves grams and kilograms?
6. What unit fraction involves meters and centimeters?

7. Use unit fractions to convert 15.7 centimeters to meters.
8. Use unit fractions to convert 6.3 kilograms to grams.

Converting with a Prefix Chart

We take the time to use unit fractions to convert within the metric system because unit fractions are very important in math and most sciences. However, all the conversions in the metric system involve a power of ten. This leads to a much easier way to convert within the metric system.

Consider a prefix chart for metric units of length.

Metric System Prefixes							
Unit (Abbreviation)	kilometer (km)	hectometer (hm)	dekameter (dam)	meter (m)	decimeter (dm)	centimeter (cm)	millimeter (mm)
Meaning	1000 meters	100 meters	10 meters	1 meter	$\frac{1}{10}$ meter	$\frac{1}{100}$ meter	$\frac{1}{1000}$ meter

To get from one unit to the next we multiply or divide by 10. Recall that multiplying or dividing by 10 is just a matter of moving the decimal to the left or right. This suggests the follow procedure for converting.

To Convert Between Units in the Metric System:
- Identify the given unit on the prefix chart.
- Identify the desired unit on the prefix chart.
- Move the decimal point the same number of places and in the same direction as it takes to go from the given unit to the desired unit.

Example 5: Convert 38 hectometers to centimeters.

Solution: Let's look at the prefix chart again and identify the given and desired units.

kilometer	hectometer	dekameter	meter	decimeter	centimeter	millimeter
	Given Unit				Desired Unit	

To get from the given unit to the desired unit we move four places to the right. So we move the decimal the same way: four places to the right.

38 hm = 38 .0000. cm = 380000 cm

four places

to the right

Example 6: Convert 98.4 milliliters to liters.

Solution: Let's look at the prefix chart again and identify the given and desired units.

kiloliter	hectoliter	dekaliter	liter	deciliter	centiliter	milliliter
			Desired Unit			Given Unit

To get from the given unit to the desired unit we move three places to the left. So we move the decimal the same way.

$$98.4 mL = 0 \ .098. \ 4L = 0.0984L$$
three places
to the left

STOP Exercise Set - Converting with a Prefix Chart

Convert as indicated using the prefix chart for meters.

kilometer (km)	hectometer (hm)	dekameter (dam)	meter (m)	decimeter (dm)	centimeter (cm)	millimeter (mm)

9.   7 dekameters to meters
10. 95 centimeters to meters
11. 8.2 mm to dm
12. 81.9 hm to km

Convert as indicated using the prefix chart for liters.

kiloliter (kL)	hectoliter (hL)	dekaliter (daL)	liter (L)	deciliter (dL)	centiliter (cL)	milliliter (mL)

13. 0.05 deciliters to dekaliters
14. 80 hectoliters to centiliters
15. 52.9 L to dL
16. 8750 cL to kL

Convert as indicated using the prefix chart for grams.

kilogram (kg)	hectogram (hg)	dekagram (dag)	gram (g)	decigram (dg)	centigram (cg)	milligram (mg)

17. 0.86 grams to decigrams
18. 63,000 milligrams to dekagrams
19. 65 hg to dm
20. 7.5 g to dag

Operations with Metric Measurements

Operations ($+,-,\cdot,\div$) with metric units show the advantage the system has over the American system. Imagine trying to add miles and feet or subtract gallons and cups. In the metric system such operations are easier because converting to the same unit is easier.

Example 7: Add $6.5dL + 6.3cL$. Express your answer in centiliters.

Solution:	$6.5dL + 6.3cL$
Since the answer should be in centiliters, we convert the first measurement to centiliters.	$65.0cL + 6.3cL$
Now we can add.	$= 71.3cL$

Example 8: Where in the World? Two chemists have made the same solution and wish to combine them. One chemist has 0.45 hectograms of the solution. The other has 130 decigrams. How many grams will there be when the solutions are combined?

Solution: The operation given is $0.45hg + 130dg$. The answer is to be expressed in grams.

$$0.45hg + 130dg$$

Convert each unit to grams. $= 45g + 13.7g$

Add. $= 58.7g$

That converting in the metric system is so straight-forward also makes it easy to compare to different measurements.

Example 9: Fill in the blank with <, >, or =.   7.91 hg _____ 7910 cg

Solution: To see the relationship, both measurements must be in the same units. We will convert hectograms (hg) to centigrams (cg)

7.91 hg _____ 7910 cg

79100 cg _____ 7910 cg

From this we see that the left side is greater so we have 7.91 hg > 7910 cg.

Add or subtract as indicated. Express your answer in either unit.
21. 9.8 dag + 400 dg
22. 5.3 hL + 7 kL
23. 0.09 km − 65 cm
24. 7.6 m + 600 cm
25. 85 cg − 45 mg
26. 56 kL − 75 hL

Fill in each blank with <, >, or =.
27. 75km _____ 700m
28. 5.6 dag _____ 5.6 hg
29. 780 hm _____ 78,000 m
30. 4.09 L _____ 500 dL

Exercise Set - Putting it ALL Together

Match each metric unit in the first column to the correct multiple of the base unit in the second column.

31. dekagram
32. deciliter
33. kiloliter
34. hectometer
35. centigram
36. millimeter
37. dekaliter
38. decigram

a.) 1000 liters

b.) $\dfrac{1}{10}$ of a gram

c.) $\dfrac{1}{1000}$ of a meter

d.) 10 grams

e.) 10 liters

f.) $\dfrac{1}{100}$ of a gram

g.) $\dfrac{1}{10}$ of a liter

h.) 100 meters

Use a prefix chart to convert as indicated.

39. 6 grams = _____ centigrams
40. 3.8 decigrams = _____ grams
41. 15.03 kiloliters = _____ milliliters
42. 0.0072 hectometers = _____ centimeters
43. 782 dag = _____ dg
44. 1680 mL = _____ cL
45. 8.5 hg = _____ cg
46. 150 dam = _____ km
47. 4.9 km = _____ m

48. 0.05 kL = _____ daL
49. 0.6 centiliters = _____ dekaliters
50. 4.09 dL = _____ cL
51. 1405 kg = _____ mg
52. 0.007 hectoliters = _____ deciliters
53. 9.75 gram = _____ kilograms
54. 0.00964 km = _____ cm
55. 0.823 centimeters = _____ decimeters
56. 0.0613 hL = _____ cL

Perform the indicated operation.

57. 500cm + 3.4 dm
58. 7.8dL – 45mL
59. 89kg + 19.3dag
60. 0.09kL – 5789mL
61. 15g – 76mg

62. 4.56hg + 820dg
63. 0.34 dam – 56 cm
64. 55L + 475 mL
65. 45 mg + 19cg
66. 0.78m – 320mm

67. European robins migrate from Scandinavia to Africa every year. That's a distance of 13,000 kilometers. Convert this to meters.

68. The world's largest aquarium is in Atlanta Georgia. It holds about 303,000 kiloliters of water. How many liters is this?

69. The hike from Haw Creek to Hare Mountain in the Ozarks takes hikers from 244 meters above sea level to 0.725 kilometers above sea level. Find the total change in altitude in meters.

70. The Android 2.0 weighs 169 grams while the i-phone 3 weighs 1.35 hectograms. Find the difference in the weights in grams.

71. One spray from a spray bottle squirts out 0.4 milliliters. If the entire bottle is 1.5 liters, about how many squirts should the bottle hold?

To find the perimeter and area of a geometric figure the lengths must be in the same units. Find the perimeter and area of each figure.

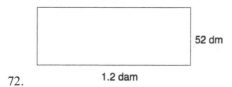

72.

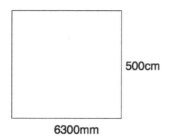

73.

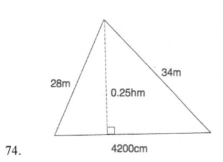

74.

75.

Fill in the blank with the correct values.
76. 8mm = _____ cm = _____ m
77. 6.7 dL = _____ L = _____ daL
78. 0.003 hm = _____ km = _____ mm
79. 8.01 cg = _____ dg = _____ dag

Exercise Set - Chapter 8 Review

80. Convert 6.5 feet to inches.
81. What two unit fractions involve quarts and gallons?
82. Convert 7,600 ounces to tons. Round to the nearest hundredth.
83. Fill in the blank. 1 pint = _____ fluid ounces
84. A Boeing 747 airplane requires 5.1 gallons of fuel for each mile it flies. Convert this to pints.

Exercise Set - Cumulative Review

85. Find two factors of 18 whose sum is 11.
86. A mobile phone can download 6 megabytes of information in 42 seconds. At this rate, how long should it take for the phone to download 20 megabytes of information? Round to the nearest second.
87. Solve. $0.2x + 0.9 = 0.5$
88. How many terms are in the expression $4x^2 + 8x - 9$?
89. Simplify $-(-5)$ and $-|-5|$.

8.2 QUIZ YOURSELF:

To make sure you are ready for the EXAM, try these problems without any help. Give yourself about 20 minutes and don't check the answers until you have completely finished.

1. What fraction or multiple of 10 does the prefix "hecto" stand for?
2. Convert 15 grams to decigrams.
3. Convert 0.07 kilometers to centimeters.
4. Convert 50.09 mL to dL.
5. The Eiffel Tower in Paris is 0.324 kilometers tall while the statue of liberty is 465 decimeters tall. Find the difference in the heights in meters.
6. Find the area and perimeter. Express you answer in meter (**m**) or square meters (m^2).

```
        4.5m
   ┌─────────────┐
   │             │
   │             │ 32dm
   │             │
   └─────────────┘
```

Answers to this Quiz Yourself are on page 702.

8.3 Conversion Between Measurement Systems

Topics:
- Converting Between The Systems
- Units Of Temperature

Are You Ready?
To see if you are ready to understand this section, do the following short quiz.
1. Use unit fractions to convert 5.5 pints to quarts.
2. Convert 0.45 kilograms to grams.
3. Evaluate the formula $y = \dfrac{2}{3}x + 5$ for $x = -9$.

Answers to Are You Ready?

1.) 2.75 qt   2.) 450 grams   3.) -1

Converting Between Measurement Systems

The American system (Section 8.1) and the metric system (Section 8.2) were created completely independently of each other, so the conversion factors between the two systems are not nice, simple numbers. They involve decimal approximations. Here are the important conversion factors.

Conversions between the American and Metric System		
Units of Length	**Units of Capacity**	**Units of Weight**
1 inch (in) = 2.54 centimeters (cm) 1 foot (ft) = 0.31 meter (m) 1 yard (yd) = 0.91 meter (m) 1 mile (mi) = 1.61 kilometers (km)	1 fluid ounce = 29.57 milliliters (mL) 1 quart (qt) = 0.95 liters (L) 1 gallon (gal) = 3.79 liters (L)	1 ounce = 28.35 grams (g) 1 pound (lb) = 0.45 kilograms (kg)

As before, we convert by using these relations to create unit fractions. When necessary we will round to two decimal places for our conversions.

Example 1: Convert 45.2 feet to meters.

Solution: Given the fraction $\dfrac{45.2\,ft}{1}$ and that we are converting to meters, we multiply by the unit

fraction $\dfrac{0.31m}{1\,ft}$.

$$\frac{45.2\,ft}{1} \cdot \frac{0.31m}{1\,ft} = \frac{45.2\,\cancel{ft}}{1} \cdot \frac{0.31m}{1\,\cancel{ft}} \approx 14.01m$$

If there is not a conversion factor that relates the two units we working with we may have to use an extra unit fraction to reach the desired unit. To do this we may rely on conversions from Sections 8.1 and/or 8.2.

Example 2: Convert 18 pints to liters.

Solution: Note that there is no conversion factor for pints and liters on our conversion chart above. There is, however, a conversion that relates quarts to liters. From Section 8.1 we have 2 pints (pt) = 1 quart (qt). We include an extra unit fraction that connects these units.

$$\frac{18\,pt}{1} \cdot \underbrace{\frac{1\,qt}{2\,pt}}_{\substack{\text{takes} \\ \text{pint to} \\ \text{quarts}}} \cdot \frac{0.95\,L}{1\,qt} = \frac{18\,\cancel{pt}}{1} \cdot \frac{1\,\cancel{qt}}{2\,\cancel{pt}} \cdot \frac{0.95\,L}{1\,\cancel{qt}} = \frac{18(0.95)}{2}L = 8.55\,L$$

Good Question: I know you can make these conversions just by multiplying or dividing, but I have a hard time figuring out which operation to do.

Answer: I do too. That is why unit fractions are so important. They make sure that you are performing the right operation. All you have to do is think about what units should cancel.

STOP Exercise Set - Converting Between Measurement Systems

Convert as indicated. Round to the nearest hundredth when necessary.

1. 6 feet to meters
2. 18 liters to quarts
3. 155 fluid ounces to milliliters
4. 7.5 kilograms to pounds
5. 24 pints to liters
6. 4500 yards to kilometers

Units of Temperature

In the American system, temperature is measured in degrees Fahrenheit (^{o}F). In the metric system, temperature is measured in degrees Celsius (^{o}C). A comparison of the two scales is shown below along with some common equivalent measurements.

- $212\,^{o}F \approx 100\,^{o}C$ Water boils
- $32\,^{o}F \approx 0\,^{o}C$ Water freezes
- $17\,^{o}F \approx -8\,^{o}C$ Average winter day in Minneapolis
- $85\,^{o}F \approx 29\,^{o}C$ Average summer day in Dallas

Temperature Scales			
Fahrenheit (F)		**Celsius (C)**	
$212^{\,o}$ F	Boiling point of water	$100^{\,o}$ C	
$194^{\,o}$ F		$90^{\,o}$ C	
$176^{\,o}$ F		$80^{\,o}$ C	
$158^{\,o}$ F		$70^{\,o}$ C	
$140^{\,o}$ F		$60^{\,o}$ C	
$122^{\,o}$ F		$50^{\,o}$ C	
$104^{\,o}$ F		$40^{\,o}$ C	
$86^{\,o}$ F		$30^{\,o}$ C	
$68^{\,o}$ F	Room temperature	$20^{\,o}$ C	
$50^{\,o}$ F		$10^{\,o}$ C	
$32^{\,o}$ F	Freezing point of water	$0^{\,o}$ C	

We have formulas that convert between the two temperatures.

Converting Fahrenheit to Celsius

$$C = \frac{5}{9}(F - 32)$$

Converting Celsius to Fahrenheit

$$F = \frac{9}{5}C + 32$$

You will derive these formulas for yourself when you get to Beginning Algebra. For now, let's look at how to use them.

Example 3: Convert $65^{\,o}$ C to Fahrenheit.

Solution: Since we are going from Celsius to Fahrenheit, we use the formula $F = \frac{9}{5}C + 32$.

$$F = \frac{9}{5}C + 32$$

Substitute 65 in for C.
$$= \frac{9}{5}(65) + 32$$

Multiply.
$$= 117 + 32$$

Add.
$$= 149$$

So 65° C is equivalent to 149° F.

Example 4: Where in the World? The coldest natural temperature ever recorded was at a Russian station in Antarctica. The temperature was -129° F. Convert this to degrees Celsius. Round to the nearest degree.

Solution: Since we are converting from Fahrenheit to Celsius we use the formula $C = \dfrac{5}{9}(F - 32)$.

$$C = \frac{5}{9}(F - 32)$$

Substitute -129 in for F.
$$= \frac{5}{9}(-129 - 32)$$

Subtract.
$$= \frac{5}{9}(-161)$$

Multiply and round to the nearest degree.
$$\approx -89^{o} \text{ C}$$

Convert. Round to the nearest degree when necessary.

7. 65° C to Fahrenheit

8. 83° C to Fahrenheit

9. 41° F to Celsius

10. 130° F to Celsius

11. The average daytime temperature on the moon is 107 degrees Celsius. Convert this to degrees Fahrenheit. Round to the nearest tenth.

12. Average human body temperature is about 37 degrees Celsius. Convert this to degrees Fahrenheit. Round to the nearest tenth.

Exercise Set - Putting it ALL Together

Fill in the blank.

13. 1 ft = _____ m

14. 1 quart = _____ liters

15. 1 mile = _____ kilometers

16. 1 lb = _____ kg

17. 1 gallon = _____ liters

18. 1 fluid ounce = _____ milliliters

Convert. Round to the nearest whole number when necessary.

19. How many liters of water are in a 5-gallon jug?

20. Dual-flush toilets can help a household save up to 39,000 liters of water each year. To the nearest gallon, how many gallons is this?

21. Photographers and scientists on assignment for National Geographic at Mexico's Naica Cave of Crystals had to endure cave temperatures of up to 44.5 degrees Celsius. Convert this to degrees Fahrenheit.

22. Turning off the water while you brush your teeth can save up to 50 gallons of water every week! How many liters is this?

23. A low-flow showerhead can save almost 10,000 liters of water in a year. How many gallons is this.

24. The surface of planet Venus can get over 860 degrees Fahrenheit. Convert this to degrees Celsius.

25. A recipe obtained from Europe states "Preheat oven to 245 degrees Celsius". What is this temperature in degrees Fahrenheit?

26. The world record for longest non-stop run is 293 kilometers miles held by Yiannis Kouros from Greece. How many miles was the run?

27. A newborn baby weighs 8.8 pounds. Convert this to kilograms.

28. Heavier sumo wrestlers can get up to 250 kilograms. How many pounds is this?

29. How many fluid ounces of soda are in a one liter bottle?

30. The average length of a king cobra snake is about 190 centimeters. Convert this to feet.

31. a lawn mower is advertised to hold 25 pints of fuel. How many liters is this?

32. A truck weighs 2.4 tons. Convert this to kilograms.

Exercise Set - Chapter 8 Review

33. Fill in the blank. 1 mile = _____ yards
34. Convert 17 quarts to gallons.
35. What unit fractions involve pounds and tons?
36. Convert 620 decimeters to millimeters.
37. Find the area of the rectangle. Give your answer in square centimeters.
    [PN: rectangle with length 16 cm and width 80 mm]

Exercise Set - Cumulative Review

38. Add without a calculator. $650 + 1520$

39. Subtract. $\dfrac{4}{7} - \left(-\dfrac{3}{7}\right)$

40. Is $d = -5$ a solution to the equation $3d = d - 10$?

41. Multiply and reduce if possible. $\dfrac{4}{9} \cdot \dfrac{3}{14}$

42. Translate the phrase "three more than twice some number" into a math expression.

8.3 QUIZ YOURSELF:

To make sure you are ready for the EXAM, try these problems without any help. Give yourself about 20 minutes and don't check the answers until you have completely finished.

1. Convert 500 milliliters to fluid ounces. Round to the nearest hundredth.
2. Convert 5.3 quarts to liters. Round to the nearest tenth.
3. Convert 56.8 feet to meters. Round to the nearest tenth.
4. Convert 67 degrees Celsius to degrees Fahrenheit. Round to the nearest degree.
5. Convert 450 degrees Fahrenheit to degrees Celsius. Round to the nearest degree.

Answers to this Quiz Yourself are on page 702.

Chapter 8 Summary and Review_____

Section 8.1: American Measurement

Processes and Important Notes	Examples

American Units of Length
 	
A **unit fraction** is a fraction made of two different units but that is equivalent to 1.
To convert between two units of measurement:
  • Write the given measurement as a fraction with 1 in the denominator.
  • Multiply by unit fraction(s) so that all units reduce except for the new unit.
  • Express your answer as a proper fraction, mixed number, or decimal with the new units indicated.
  • 1 foot = 12 inches
  • 1 yard = 3 feet
  • 1 mile = 5280 feet
  • 1 miles = 1760 yards
	Convert.
	58 yards = _____inches
	
	Solution:
	We need to use two conversions.
	  • 1 foot = 12 inches
	  • 1 yard = 3 feet
	
	$$\left(\frac{58\,yards}{}\right)\left(\frac{3\,feet}{1\,yard}\right)\left(\frac{12\,inches}{1\,foot}\right)=2088\,inches$$
	
	58 yards = **2,088 inches**

American Units of Capacity
 	
  • 8 fluid ounces (fl oz) = 1 cup (c)
  • 16 fluid ounces (fl oz) = 1 pint (pt)
  • 2 cups (c) = 1 pint (pt)
  • 2 pints (pt) = 1 quart (qt)
  • 4 quarts (qt) = 1 gallon (gal)
	At a convenient store, Marissa bought a 38 oz fountain soda. How many cups of soda did she buy?
	
	Solution:
	  • 8 fluid ounces (fl oz) = 1 cup (c)
	
	$$\left(\frac{38\,fl.oz.}{}\right)\left(\frac{1\,cup}{8\,fl.oz.}\right)=4\frac{3}{4}\,cups$$

American Units of Weight
 	
  • 16 ounces (oz) = 1 pound (lb)
  • 2000 pounds (lb) = 1 ton
	A small aircraft weights 12,500 pounds or less. How much does the aircraft weigh in tons?
	
	Solution:
	  • 2000 pounds (lb) = 1 ton
	
	$$\left(\frac{12500\,pounds}{}\right)\left(\frac{1\,ton}{2000\,pounds}\right)=6\frac{1}{4}\,tons$$

Convert to the given units.

1. 15 inches = _____ feet
2. 68 feet = _____ yards
3. 17 oz. = _____ cups
4. 62 cups = _____quarts
5. 55 oz. = _____lbs.

6. 24 qts = _____ gals
7. 16 yards = _____ in.
8. 5.1 mi = _____ ft.
9. 6320 lb = _____ton
10. 15 pts = _____ qts

11. A 10K run is 6.2 miles. How many yards is this?

12. Challenger Deep in the Mariana Trench is the deepest point in Earth's oceans at 35,840 feet below sea level. How many miles is this below sea level?

13. According to America's Blood Center, 43,000 pints of donated blood are used every day in the US and Canada. How many gallons of donated blood are used per day?

14. A newborn baby weighs 7 lbs 5 oz. How many total ounces does the baby weigh?

Section 8.2: Metric System

Processes and Important Notes	Examples
Introduction to the Metric System • **Length:** The base unit of length in the metric system is the **meter**. One meter is slightly longer than one yard. • **Capacity:** The base unit of capacity in the meter system is the **liter**. One liter is the size of a large drinking bottle. • **Weight:** The base unit of weight in the metric system is the **gram**. One gram is about the weight of a small paper clip.	**Which unit of measure would be used in each situation?** a. Distance a person runs b. The amount of caffeine in a soda c. Amount of juice you had for breakfast **Solution:** a. Kilometers b. Milligrams c. Liters
Converting with a Prefix Chart **To convert between units in the metric system:** • Identify the given unit on the prefix chart. • Identify the desired unit on the prefix chart. • Move the decimal point the same number of places and in the same direction as it takes to go from the given unit to the desired unit.	**Convert 784.5 cm to dam** **Solution:** Using the prefix chart, we see that the desired unit is 3 places to the left, so we move the decimal 3 places to the left. 784.5 cm = **0.7845 dam**
Operations with Metric Measurements • Convert all measurement to a common unit • Perform operation	**Find the perimeter of the triangle.** **Solution:** First we need to convert to the same units, cm. 103 mm = 10.3 cm 8 cm = 8 cm 1.9 dm = 19 dm The perimeter of a triangle is $P = a + b + c$, $P = 10.3 + 8 + 19 = 37.3$ **The perimeter is 37.3 cm.**

Convert to the given units.

15. 34 cm = _____mm

16. 73 hg = _____dg

17. 65.1 m = _____cm

18. 0.089 dam = _____dm

19. 5782 mL = _____ kL
20. 475.18 km = _____ hm

21. 99.3 mg = _____ g
22. 6839.24 L = _____ cL

Perform the indicated operation.

23. 99mL + 104cL
24. 2.3kg – 183g

25. 788dL + 23cL
26. 450cm – 1785mm

27. The Turkey Trot on Thanksgiving day is a 5km run. How many meters is the run?

28. A chemist has 28.6 kilograms of Carbon. How many grams of Carbon does the chemist have?

29. Clif Shot Blocks have 25 mg of caffeine in 3 blocks. Jens consumed 15 blocks on his bike ride. How many grams of caffeine did he consume from Shot Blocks?

30. Find the perimeter and area of the following rectangle.

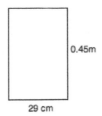

0.45m

29 cm

Section 8.3: Conversion Between Measurement Systems

Processes and Important Notes	Examples
Converting Between The Systems **Units of Length:** • 1 inch (in) = 2.54 centimeters (cm) • 1 foot (ft) = 0.31 meter (m) • 1 yard (yd) = 0.91 meter (m) • 1 mile (mi) = 1.61 kilometers (km) **Units of Capacity:** • 1 fluid ounce = 29.57 milliliters (mm) • 1 quart (qt) = 0.95 liters (L) • 1 gallon (gal) = 3.79 liters (L) **Units of Weight:** • 1 ounce = 28.35 grams (g) • 1 pound (lb) = 0.45 kilograms (kg) •	Great White Sharks have been recorded to grow as long as 6.4 meters. How long is that in feet? **Solution:** We should use the conversion that • 1 foot (ft) = 0.31 meter (m) $\left(\dfrac{6.4m}{1}\right)\left(\dfrac{1ft}{0.31m}\right) = 20.65\,ft.$ So, the longest Great White shark recorded was 20.65 feet long!
Units Of Temperature • **Converting Fahrenheit to Celsius** $C = \dfrac{5}{9}(F - 32)$ • **Converting Celsius to Fahrenheit** $F = \dfrac{9}{5}C + 32$	Methanol has a normal boiling point of $64.6°F$. Find the boiling point in degrees Celsius. **Solution:** $C = \dfrac{5}{9}(F - 32)$ $= \dfrac{5}{9}(64.6 - 32)$ $= \dfrac{5}{9}(32.6)$ $\approx 18.11°C$

	Methanol has a normal boiling point of 18.11°C

Convert to the given units.

31. 25 yards = _____ meters
32. 4.5 quarts = _____ liters
33. 8.93 liters = _____ gallons
34. 15 pounds = _____ kilograms

35. 39 liters = _____ pints
36. 120 inches = _____ cm
37. 25 km = _____ miles
38. 16 fluid ounces = _____ mL

39. The Whale shark is the biggest shark ever. It is estimated to grow to 12.2 meters long and up. These sharks do not attack humans they eat plankton. How long is the whale shark in feet?

40. The boiling point of water at Mt. Whitney, California is 87°F. What is the boiling point in degrees Celsius?

41. While visiting Paris, France over the winter Roxanna looked at the thermostat in her room to discover it read 18°C. What was the temperature in the room in degrees Fahrenheit?

42. The average weight for a 20-year old male is 56 kg. What is the average weight in pounds?

Section 8.4: Volume and Surface Area

Processes and Important Notes	Examples
Formulas for Volume The **volume** of a solid measures the amount of space it takes up.	**Find the volume of the following cone.** 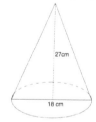

Object	Formula for Volume
Cube	$V = s^3$
Rectangular Solid	$V = l \cdot w \cdot h$
Cylinder	$V = \pi r^2 \cdot h$
Cone	$V = \frac{1}{3}\pi r^2 \cdot h$
Rectangular Pyramid	$V = \frac{1}{3} l \cdot w \cdot h$
Sphere	$V = \frac{4}{3}\pi r^3$

Solution:

Use the formula $V = \frac{1}{3}\pi r^2 h$.

h = 27cm

r = ½ diameter = ½ of 18 cm = 9 cm

$$V = \frac{1}{3}\pi r^2 h = \frac{1}{3}\pi (9)^2 (27)$$

$$= 729\pi cm^3$$

$$\approx 2,289.06 cm^3$$

Formulas for Surface Area

Surface area measures the area taken up by the surface of the object.

Object	Formula for Surface Area
Cube	$SA = 6s^2$
Rectangular Solid	$SA = 2lw + 2lh + 2wh$
Cylinder	$SA = 2\pi r^2 + 2\pi rh$
Sphere	$SA = 4\pi r^2$

Find the surface area for the rectangular solid.

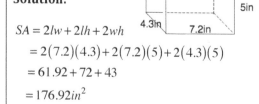

Solution:

$SA = 2lw + 2lh + 2wh$

$$= 2(7.2)(4.3) + 2(7.2)(5) + 2(4.3)(5)$$

$$= 61.92 + 72 + 43$$

$$= 176.92 in^2$$

Unit Conversions for Area and Volume			Convert to the given units.

Convert to the given units.

$2.345 cm^2 = \underline{\hspace{1cm}} mm^2$

Linear Units	Area Units	Volume Units
$3 ft = 1 yd$	$9 ft^2 = 1 yd^2$	$27 ft^3 = 1 yd^3$
$12 in = 1 ft$	$144 in^2 = 1 ft^2$	$1728 in^3 = 1 ft^3$
$1 cm = 10 mm$	$1 cm^2 = 100 mm^2$	$1 cm^3 = 1000 mm^3$
$1 meter = 100 cm$	$1 m^2 = 10,000 cm^2$	$1 m^3 = 1,000,000 cm^3$

Solution:

Use the conversion $1 cm^2 = 100 mm^2$.

$$2.345 cm^2 \left(\frac{100 mm^2}{1 cm^2} \right) = 234.5 mm^2$$

Find the following.

43. Find the surface area and volume.

44. Find the surface area and volume.

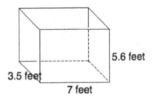

45. Find the surface area and volume.

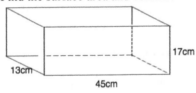

46. Find the surface area and volume.

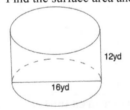

47. Find the surface area and volume.

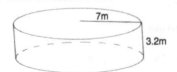

48. Find the volume.

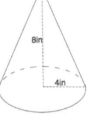

49. Find the volume.

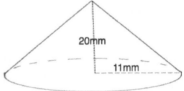

50. Find the surface area and volume.

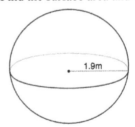

51. Find the surface area and volume.

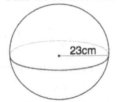

52. Find the volume.

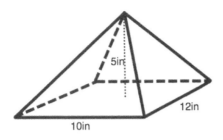

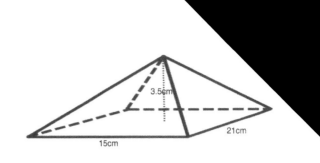

53. Find the surface area and volume.

Convert the following.

54. $6 ft^2 = $ _____ in^2

55. $3 cm^3 = $ _____ mm^3

56. $24500 km^2 = $ _____ m^2

57. $27 ft^3 = $ _____ yd^3

58. $5000 cm^3 = $ _____ dm^3

59. $8.45 m^2 = $ _____ dm^2

60. $756 in^2 = $ _____ ft^2

Test Yourself

iven units.
_____yd.
_____hl
_____lb.
= _____qts.
5.   67.8 cm = _____m
6.   0.38 km = _____mm
7.   67 in = _____dm
8.   45 gal = _____qts.

9.   400 m = _____km
10. 50km = _____miles
11. $15cm^2 =$ _____m^2
12. $48 ft^3 =$ _____yd^3
13. $0.5km^3 =$ _____m^3

14. Add. 66 feet + 12 yards
15. How tall is a 6-foot man in meters?

16. A newborn baby weighs 6lbs. 3 oz. How much does the baby weigh in ounces?

17. An 8.2 oz can of Red Bull contains 80 mg of caffeine. How many grams of caffeine does 2 cans of Red Bull contain?

18. A grocery shelf stocker has to lift boxes and then unload them and put the items on the shelves. On the outside of one of the boxes, it says 45kg. How many pounds does this box weigh?

19. Angel Falls (Salto Ángel) in Venezuela is the highest waterfall in the world. The falls are 3230 feet in height. How high are the falls in yards?

20. In August 2011, the high temperature for Venice, Italy was $35°C$. How hot was it in degrees Fahrenheit?

21. A large biofuels plant in Soperton, Ga converts 1,000 tons of wood chips and waste from Georgia's paper industry into 274,000 gallons of ethanol. How many quarts of ethanol does it produce?

22. Esmeralda is fencing her backyard, which requires 162 feet of fencing. The fencing company charges $58.75 per yard of fence. Find the cost of the fence.

23. A chemist has 4 samples of iron that she is going to melt down to make one sample. The weights of the samples are 14.5mg, 3.5cg, 26.91mg and 0.92g. What is the weight of her new sample?

24. Find the area and perimeter of the following figure. You may have to convert the units if they are not the same.

3.4cm

126 mm

25. Find the volume and surface area.

3 yd

4.1 yd

Chapters 1 to 8 Cumulative Review_____

Find the following.

1. Two factors of -48 that add up to -13.

2. Use <, >, or =. $\dfrac{3}{19}$ ____ $\dfrac{5}{26}$

3. Is 21 a factor of $2 \cdot 3 \cdot 5 \cdot 2 \cdot 7 \cdot 11$?

Simplify.

4. 99 + (-145) – (-23)

5. $\dfrac{4}{33} + \dfrac{7}{33}$

6. $-3 \cdot 10 \div 2 + 3^2$

7. $4\sqrt{25} - 5\left(-7 + (-3)\right)^2$

8. $\dfrac{7}{25} + \dfrac{8}{15}$

9. $24 \div \left(-\dfrac{6}{35}\right)$

10. $-56.89 + 34.2$

11. $(-9.1)(0.05)$

12. $17 - 5\dfrac{2}{9}$

13. $\left(\dfrac{-21x}{55y^2}\right)\left(-\dfrac{33xy}{49}\right)$

14. $-3\dfrac{2}{5} + 7\dfrac{5}{6}$

15. $\dfrac{66 \div 11 \cdot 3 - 17}{\sqrt{169 - 25} - 2^2}$

16. $-5 + \sqrt{(-5)^2 - 4(1)(4)}$

Simplify the Algebra Expressions

17. $-(5x - 9y)$

18. $\left(3x^2 + 16xy - y^2\right) \cdot 7$

19. $4(-6x + 7) + 25x$

20. $\dfrac{1}{5}(10m - 35) - \dfrac{2}{3}(-12m + 18)$

Evaluate.

21. $a + 3b$ for a = -4, b = 12

22. $mx + b$ for $b = \dfrac{5}{6}, m = \dfrac{-3}{4}, x = -\dfrac{2}{9}$

23. $-3x^2y + 7y^3 + 15$, for $x = -1, y = 2$

Solve.

24. $x + 67 = 498$

25. $\dfrac{-3k}{4} = \dfrac{12}{19}$

26. $6x + 7 = -13$

27. $x - 18.9 = -23.45$

28. $2(3c - 5) + 7 = 12c + 5$

29. $17t - 6 = 24t + 31$

Convert to the given units.

30. 45 cm = _____dm

31. 26 in = _____ft.

32. $6\dfrac{1}{2}$ qts. = _____cups

33. 13.1 miles = _____km

34. Write $\dfrac{4}{15}$ as a percentage.

35. Write 0.668 as a fraction. Reduce if possible.

36. What is 34% of 819?

37. REI is having a 25% sale on all their tents and camping gear. Dvalyn buys a tent that originally cost $239. How much did she save and what was the sale price?

38. A south San-Francisco based Solazyme supplied more than 20,055 gallons of oil to the US Navy. They charged $424 a gallon. What was the total cost of this oil to the US Navy?

39. 62% of people in North, Central and South America are overweight. Write this percent as a decimal and as a fraction.

40. Lin has $218.09 in his checking account. He pays bills online of $47.82, $167.23 and $513 and makes a deposit of $651.29. What is his new account balance?

41. Two slices of pizza has 41 grams of carbohydrates. How many grams of carbohydrates does 3 slice have?

42. The weight of a male Mexican Prairie Dog is approximately 2.6 lbs. What is his weight in kg?

43. Tarah needs to swim 1500 meters, but the local pool is measured in yards. How many yards are in 1500 meters? If one lap is 80 yards, how many laps does Tarah need to swim?

44. The atmosphere of Mar's is very thin and contains essentially no oxygen. The temperature on the surface is approximately $-60°C$. Find the temperature in degrees Fahrenheit.

45. Find the perimeter of the figure to the right.

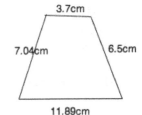

46. Find the area of a circle with diameter 49 m. Use $\pi \approx \dfrac{22}{7}$.

47. Two angles are supplementary. The second angle is twenty more than three times the first angle. Find the measure of the angles.

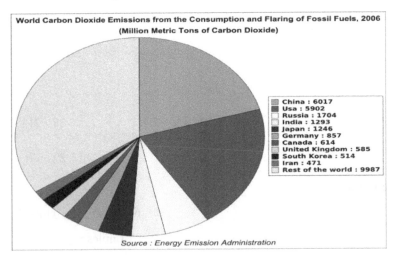

48. Find the percent of carbon dioxide emissions from the USA.

49. Which country emits the most carbon dioxide? Find the percent of the whole. (Do not consider the rest of the whole since that includes many countries.)

50. What is the percent of carbon dioxide emissions from Germany and UK combined?

9.1 Ordered Pairs and The Rectangular Coordinate System
  a) Introduction To Graphing
  b) Plotting Points
  c) Ordered Paired Solutions to Equations

9.2 Linear Equations And Their Graphs
  a) Ordered Pairs as Solutions to Equations
  b) Finding Solutions To A Linear Equation
  c) Graphing Linear Equations

So far we have seen graphs like this...

Now we'll use the same type of graphs with negative numbers...

We will graph points and straight lines from equations.

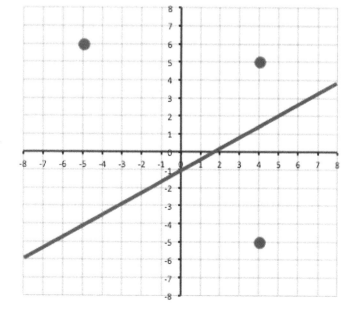

9.1 Ordered Pairs and The Rectangular Coordinate System

Topics:
- Ordered Pairs
- Plotting Ordered Pairs
- Quadrants

Are You Ready?
To see if you are ready to understand this section, do the following short quiz.
1. Graph the following numbers on a number line: $-3, 5, 0, -1, 4$

Answers to Are You Ready?

(1) graph

Ordered Pairs

Throughout this book we have looked at lots of tables and graphs. As an example, the following table and corresponding graph give the yearly profit of a new business over a period of several years.

Year	Profit
2010	-$6,000
2011	-$2,500
2012	$5,700
2013	$15,900
2014	$12,000
2015	$18,500

In the year 2010 the company made a profit of -$6000 (which is actually a loss) and in the year 2013 the company made a true profit of $15,900. Another way to organize this kind of data is to arrange it in *ordered pairs*.

> An **ordered pair** is a pair of related numbers put in parentheses and separated by a coma. In general, ordered pairs have the form (x, y).

Example: Where in the World? Organize the information in the table as ordered pairs.

Year	Profit
2010	-$6,000
2011	-$2,500
2012	$5,700
2013	$15,900
2014	$12,000
2015	$18,500

Solution: Our ordered pairs will have the form (Year, Profit).

(Year, Profit)
(2010, -6000)
(2011, -2500)
(2012, 5700)
(2013, 15900)
(2014, 12000)
(2015, 18500)

The ordered pairs correspond directly to the table values. Often, however, we will write a set of ordered pairs in a list instead of stacked like a table. Here is the same set of ordered pairs in list form.

(2010, -6000), (2011, -2500), (2012, 5700), (2013, 15900), (2014, 12000), (2015, 18500)

When a set of ordered pairs is not tied to a real-world application, we normally use the variables x and y to represent the values. So you will often see the notation (x, y).

Example: Use the following list of ordered pairs (x, y) to fill in the table of values:
(4,15), (-8,12), (5,0), (9,-10), (-6,-1)

x	y

Solution: In each ordered pair, the first number represents a value for the x column and the second number represents the corresponding value in the y column: (4,15), (-8,12), (5,0), (9,-10), (-6,-1)

x	y
4	15
-8	12
5	0
9	-10
-6	-1

STOP Exercise Set - Ordered Pairs

1. The following table gives the number of miles a rental car is driven and the resulting cost. Express the data as a list of ordered pairs.

Miles Driven	Cost ($)
100	57
50	51
340	86
75	54

2. The following table gives the number of cars in the United States over a period of years since 1940. Express the data as a list of ordered pairs.

Years since 1940	Cars (in millions)
0	27.5
20	61.7
40	121.6
53	146.3

3. Use the following set of ordered pairs to fill in the table: $(5,-7),(0,3),(-2,-4),$ and $(8,0)$.

x	y

4. Use the following set of ordered pairs to fill in the table: $(2,2),(-4,11),(1,-8),(0,0)$ and $(-9,15)$.

x	y

The Rectangular Coordinate System

In math, we use graphs to visualize ordered pairs. We have seen this kind of connection already for real-world applications. For example, consider the profit graph at the beginning of this section.

The coordinate system we use to plot generic ordered pairs is just like these line graphs except that they most often include both positive and negative numbers. We still use a horizontal number line and a vertical number line as references. The result is called a *rectangular coordinate system*.

Rectangular Coordinate System

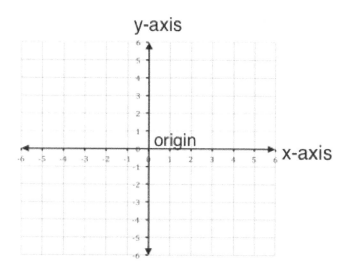

There is some important terminology associated with a coordinate system.

The horizontal number line on a coordinate system is called the **x-axis**.

The vertical number line on a coordinate system is called the **y-axis** (the plural of the word axis is **axes**).

The point where the two number lines intersect is called the **origin**.

Any ordered pair (x, y) can be graphed on the coordinate system.

To Graph (or Plot) an Ordered Pair:

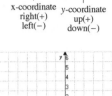

- Begin at the origin and move right/left the number of units given by the **x-coordinate**. Move right if the *x*-coordinate is positive and left if it is negative.
- From there move up or down the of units given by the **y-coordinate**. Move up if the *y*-coordinate is positive and down if it is negative.
- Put a point at that position.

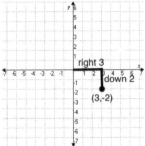

Example: Graph the ordered pairs $(5,3)$, $(-4,2)$, $(3,-3)$, and $(0,-5)$.

Solution: The first coordinate indicates how far left/right to move. The second coordinate indicates how far up/down to move.

(5 , 3)
right 5 up 3

(−4 , 2)
left 4 up 2

(3 , −3)
right 3 down 3

(0 , −5)
none down 5

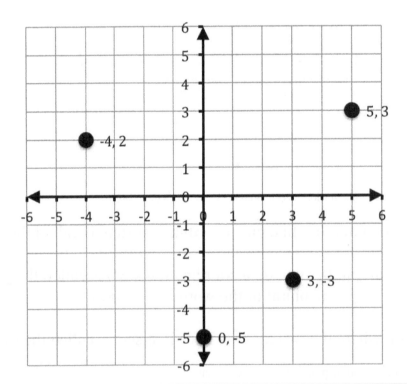

Once you understand how to graph ordered pairs you can also give the ordered pair that corresponds to a given point on the coordinate system. For reference we often label the points with letters.

Example: Find the ordered pairs that correspond to the points given on the coordinate system.

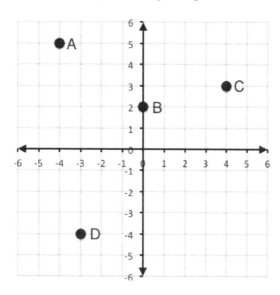

Solution:

Point A was graphed by moving left 4 and up 5, so its coordinates are $(-4,5)$.

Point B was graphed by not moving left/right 4 and up 2, so its coordinates are $(0,2)$.

Point C was graphed by moving right 4 and up 3, so its coordinates are $(4,3)$.

Point D was graphed by moving left 3 and down 4, so its coordinates are $(-3,-4)$.

To summarize all this information we will sometimes see a summary like this:

$A:(-4,5)$, $B:(0,2)$, $C:(4,3)$, $D:(-3,-4)$

STOP Exercise Set - The Rectangular Coordinate System

5. **Fill in the blanks.** To graph the ordered pair $(-6,4)$, begin at the _____ and move six units to the _____. From there, move four units _____.

6. **Fill in the blanks.** To graph the ordered pair $(6,-4)$, begin at the _____ and move six units to the _____. From there, move four units _____.

7. Graph the set of ordered pairs on a coordinate system: $(4,3),(0,-3),(5,4),(-2,-3)$

8. Graph the set of ordered pairs on a coordinate system: $(-3,-1),(3,3)(0,4),(-2,1)$

9. List the ordered pairs that have been graphed on the following coordinate system.

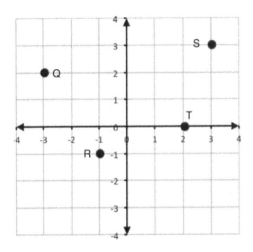

10. List the ordered pairs that have been graphed on the following coordinate system.

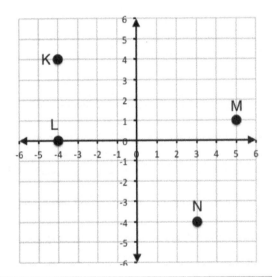

Quadrants

The x and y axes divide the coordinate system into four parts, called *quadrants*.

A quadrant is one of four regions created by the rectangular coordinate system. We use the roman numerals I, II, III, and IV to label the four quadrants.

Notice that all the points in the first quadrant have an x-coordinate that is positive.

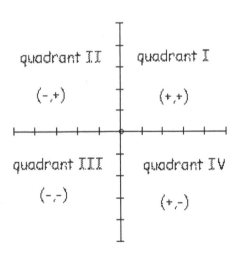

To determine the quadrant in which a given ordered pair will fall, look at the sign of the coordinates:
- An ordered pair that is (+,+) will fall in Quadrant I.
- An ordered pair that is (−,+) will fall in Quadrant II.
- An ordered pair that is (−,−) will fall in Quadrant III.
- An ordered pair that is (+,−) will fall in Quadrant IV.
- An ordered pair for which either the x or y coordinate is 0 does not fall into any quadrant.

Example: Without actually graphing each point, determine which quadrant it will fall into, or indicate that it does not fall into any quadrant.

a) (5,−9) b) (3,15) c) (−8,0)

Solution:
a) (5,−9), Since this ordered pair is (+,−) it will fall in Quadrant IV.
b) (3,15), Since this ordered pair is (+,+) it will fall in Quadrant I.
c) (−8,0), Since this ordered pair has a y-coordinate of 0, it does not fall into any quadrant.

STOP Exercise Set - Quadrants

Without actually graphing each point, determine which quadrant it will fall into, or indicate that it does not fall into any quadrant.
11. (4,-9)
12. (0,7)
13. (4,1)
14. (-13,-25,)
15. (-9,0)
16. (-5,17)

Exercise Set - Putting it ALL Together

Vocabulary Check: Fill in each blank with a word from our Vocabulary Checklist to the right.

Vocabulary Checklist:
ordered pair
x-axis
y-axis
origin
quadrant

17. On a coordinate system, the point where the x-axis and y-axis intersect is called the _____. Its coordinates are (0,0).

18. If we graph the ordered pair (0,5) it does not fall into a quadrant, instead it sits on the _____.

19. The rectangular coordinate system is divided into four _____.

20. An _____ has two coordinates: an x-coordinate and a y-coordinate.

21. What ordered pair is indicated by the following graphing directions?
"Begin at the origin, move to the right twelve units. From there, move down seven units."

22. What ordered pair is indicated by the following graphing directions?
"Begin at the origin, move to the left ten units. From there, move down three units."

23. The following table gives atmospheric carbon dioxide levels over a period of several years. Express the data as a set of ordered pairs.

Years since 2000	CO_2 (parts per million)
0	1.76
3	2.30
6	1.73
9	1.89
Source: www.noaa.gov	

24. The following table gives deforestation levels over time in Brazil. Express the data as a set of ordered pairs.

Years since 2000	Deforestation (in 10000s of sq km)
0	19
5	15
7	12
10	7
Source: www.mongabay.com	

25. Give any three ordered pairs that would fall into the first quadrant.
26. Give any three ordered pairs that would fall into the fourth quadrant.
27. Give any three ordered pairs that would fall into the third quadrant.
28. Give any three ordered pairs that do not fall into any quadrant.
29. Give any two ordered pairs that would fall on the y-axis.
30. Give any two ordered pairs that would fall on the x-axis.

31. Graph the ordered pairs given in the table. What is the pattern?

x	y
-5	-2
-3	0
1	4
-2	1
2	5

32. Graph the ordered pairs given in the table. What is the pattern?

x	y
1	0
-2	3
4	-3
0	1
-3	4

33. Follow these instructions.
    a. Graph the following ordered pairs: (1,4), (1,-2), (-3,4), (-3,-2).
    b. Draw four line segments connecting the following points:
       (1,4) and (1,-2)
       (1,4) and (-3,4)
       (-3,4) and (-3,-2)
       (-3,-2) and (1,-2)

  c. What type of figure have you constructed?

34. Follow these instructions.
  a. Graph the following ordered pairs: (3,1), (3,4), (0,1), (0,4)
  b. Draw four line segments connecting the following points:
      (3,1) and (3,4)
      (3,4) and (0,4)
      (0,4) and (0,1)
      (0,1) and (3,1)
  c. What type of figure have you constructed?

35. For ordered pairs that have very large numbers, we may have to scale the axis differently. Use the scaled coordinate system provided to graph the following ordered pairs:

    (50,150), (75,-100), (-90,130), (190,-100)

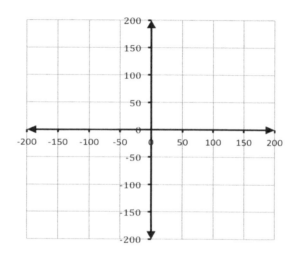

36. For ordered pairs that have very large numbers, we may have to scale the axis differently. Use the scaled coordinate system provided to graph the following ordered pairs:

    (0,-300), (150,200), (-450,225), (300,-475)

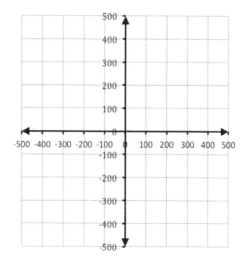

37. The following table gives the pay that a worker will get for working a certain number of hours. Use the coordinate system provided to graph the ordered pairs. Connect the ordered pairs with a line.

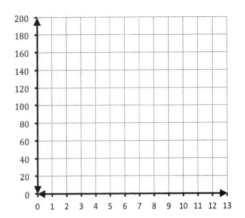

Hours Worked	Pay
2	$30
5	$75
6	$90
9	$135
12	$180

38. The following table gives the distance a marathon runner has gone over several hours. Use the coordinate system provided to graph the ordered pairs. Connect the ordered pairs with a line.

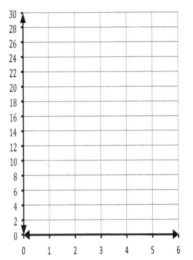

Hours Running	Distance (in miles)
0	0
1	5
2	10
3	15
4	20
5	25

Exercise Set - Cumulative Review

39. Add. $-\dfrac{3}{14}+\left(-\dfrac{6}{21}\right)$

40. Simplify. $-3(x+2y)+2(5x-y)$

41. Convert 45% to fraction notation.

42. Find the area.

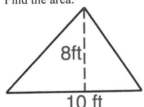

8ft

10 ft

43. Subtract. $-16-(-9)$

9.1 QUIZ YOURSELF:

To make sure you are ready for the EXAM, try these problems without any help. Give yourself about 20 minutes and don't check the answers until you have completely finished.

1. The following ordered pairs give the population (in millions) of San Diego, California over a period of years. Use the ordered pairs to fill in the table.

    (Year, Population)

    (2000, 6.3), (2002, 6.7), (2004, 7.8), (2006, 8.1)

Year	Population

2. List the ordered pairs graphed on the following coordinate system.

    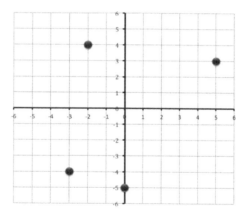

3. Graph the following orderd pairs on a coordinate system: (0,0), (3,5), (-2,5), (-3,-1)

4. Without actually graphing, determine which quadrant the point (-6,-19) would fall into.

Answers to this Quiz Yourself are on page 710.

9.2 Linear Equations and Their Graphs

Topics:

- Ordered Pairs as Solutions to Equations
- Completing Solutions To An Equation
- Graphing Equations: $y = mx + b$
- Graphing Equations: $Ax + By = C$

Are You Ready?

To see if you are ready to understand this section, do the following short quiz.

1. Evaluate the expression $2a + 5b$ for $a = -3$ and $b = 2$.
2. Is $x = -5$ a solution to the equation $3x + 5 = x - 5$?
3. Plot the points (-3,-2), (3,3), and (0,1).

Answers to Are You Ready?

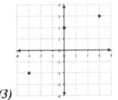

(1) 4   *(2) Yes*   *(3)*

Ordered Pairs as Solutions to Equations

The equations we have solved so far have always had one variable, such as $2x + 9 = 5x$. We now turn our attention to equations with two variables and their solutions.

A **linear equation in two variables** has two general forms:

The first form is $Ax + By = C$ where x and y are variables while A, B, and C are specific numbers.

The second form is $y = mx + b$ where x and y are variables while m and b are specific numbers.

Here are some examples of linear equations in two variables:

$$4x + 2y = 10 \qquad x - 6y = 8$$
These equations
have the form $Ax+By=C$

$$y = 5x + 7 \qquad y = \frac{1}{2}x - 3$$
These equation
have the form $y=mx+b$

We call these equations "linear" because, as we will see, they have an important connection with graphing straight lines. If an equation just has one variable, like $2x+9=5x$ then a solution is just a single value, like $x=3$. But if an equation has two variables, like $x+3y=7$ then there must be two values given to have a solution, like $x=1$ and $y=2$. We use ordered pairs to express solutions to equations with two variables.

A **solution** to a linear equation is an ordered pair (x,y) that satisfies the equation.

To determine if a given ordered pair is a solution, we substitute the given values in for x and y and simplify to see if the equation is true.

Example: Is the ordered pair $(2,6)$ a solution to the equation $x+y=8$?

Solution: Remember that the first coordinate is always x and the second coordinate is always y. So, given the ordered pair $(2,6)$, we substitute $x=2$ and $y=6$ into the equation and see if the result is a true equation.

$$x+y=8$$
$$2+6=8$$
$$8=8 \text{ True}$$

The ordered pair $(2,6)$ is indeed a solution to the equation $x+y=8$.

Example: Is the ordered pair $(-3,5)$ a solution to the equation $2x+3y=10$?

Solution: We substitute in $x=-3$ and $y=5$ into the equation and see if the result is a true equation.

$$2x+3y=10$$
$$2(-3)+3(5)=10$$
$$-6+15=10$$
$$9=10 \text{ False}$$

The ordered pair $(-3,5)$ is *not* a solution to the equation $2x+3y=10$.

While equations with one variable tend to only have one solution, equations in two variables almost always have an infinite number of solutions. It is common to deal with several such solutions in a given exercise.

Example: Of the following ordered pairs, which one(s) are a solution to the equation $y=2x-5$?

$$(3,1) \qquad (0,-5) \qquad (-1,6) \qquad (-2,-9)$$

Solution: In each case we substitute in the values for x and y and simplify to check.

$(3,1)$	$(0,-5)$	$(-1,6)$	$(-2,-9)$
$y = 2x - 5$	$y = 2x - 5$	$y = 2x - 5$	$y = 2x - 5$
$1 = 2(3) - 5$	$-5 = 2(0) - 5$	$6 = 2(-1) - 5$	$-9 = 2(-2) - 5$
$1 = 6 - 5$	$-5 = 0 - 5$	$6 = -2 - 5$	$-9 = -4 - 5$
$1 = 1$ True	$-5 = -5$ True	$6 = -7$ False	$-9 = -9$ True

So, of the ordered pairs given, the ones that are solutions are (3,1), (0,-5), and (-2,-9).

STOP Exercise Set - Ordered Pairs as Solutions to Equations

In each case determine if the given ordered pair is a solution to the equation.

1. $x - y = 4, (9,5)$
2. $2x + y = 5, (2,2)$
3. $y = x - 9, (5,-4)$
4. $5x - 7y = 12, (1,-1)$
5. $y = \dfrac{1}{2}x + 5, (4,-7)$
6. $6x - y = 5, (2,-7)$

7. Of the following ordered pairs, which one(s) are a solution to the equation $x + 3y = 1$.

    $(1,0)$ $(3,-1)$ $(-2,1)$ $(6,-1)$

8. Of the following ordered pairs, which one(s) are a solution to the equation $2x - 5y = 7$.

    $(5,1)$ $(1,-1)$ $(6,1)$ $(4,0)$

Completing Solutions to an Equation

If we are given an equation with two variables and an ordered pair we can determine if the ordered pair is a solution. But we need to work towards being able to find solutions for ourselves. The first step in this is to find the second value for an ordered pair given the first. If only one value of an ordered pair is known we can substitute the given value into the equation and solve to find the other value.

Example: Complete the following ordered pairs so that each one is a solution to the equation $5x - 2y = 6$.

a) $\left(\underline{?}, 2 \right)$ b) $\left(1, \underline{?} \right)$

Solution:

a) $\left(?,2\right)$ The value given is $y = 2$. We substitute this value into the equation.

$$5x - 2y = 6$$
$$5x - 2(2) = 6$$
$$5x - 4 = 6$$

We can now solve the resulting equation for x.
First, add 4 to both sides.

$$5x - 4 = 6$$
$$+4 +4$$
$$5x = 10$$

Divide both sides by 5.

$$\frac{5x}{5} = \frac{10}{5}$$
$$x = 2$$

The corresponding x-value is 2. So the completed ordered pair is $(2,2)$.

b) $\left(1,?\right)$ The value given is $x = 1$. We substitute this value into the equation.

$$5x - 2y = 6$$
$$5(1) - 2y = 6$$
$$5 - 2y = 6$$

We can now solve the resulting equation for y.
First, subtract 5 from both sides.

$$5 - 2y = 6$$
$$-5 -5$$
$$-2y = 1$$

Divide both sides by -2.

$$\frac{-2y}{-2} = \frac{1}{-2}$$
$$y = -\frac{1}{2}$$

The corresponding y-value is $-\dfrac{1}{2}$. So the completed ordered pair is $\left(1, -\dfrac{1}{2}\right)$.

STOP **Exercise Set - Completing Solutions to an Equation**

9. Complete the following ordered pairs so that each one is a solution to the equation $x + y = 7$.
   a. $(3, ?)$
   b. $(?, -3)$

10. Complete the following ordered pairs so that each one is a solution to the equation $6x + 3y = 15$.
    a. $(1, ?)$
    b. $(?, -1)$

11. Complete the following ordered pairs so that each one is a solution to the equation $y = -8x + 5$.
    a. $\left(\dfrac{1}{2}, ?\right)$
    b. $(?, -11)$

12. Complete the following ordered pairs so that each one is a solution to the equation $y = 3x - 5$.

   a. $(\frac{1}{3}, ?)$

   b. $(?, 4)$

Graphing Equations: y=mx+b

We now make the connection between graphing and equations with two variables. Consider the equation $y = -x + 5$. Here are some solutions to the equation:

$$(0,5) \quad (2,3) \quad (7,-2) \quad (1,4) \quad (-3,8)$$

Let's graph these solutions on a coordinate system.

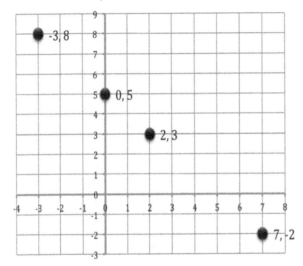

Look at the pattern. All the points lie on the same straight line. In fact, the straight line represents ALL the solutions to the equation $y = -x + 5$.

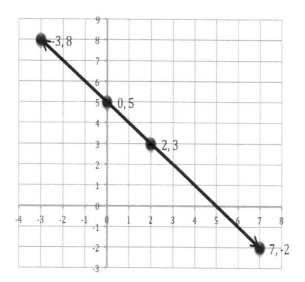

Any ordered pair on the line will be a solution to the equation $y = -x + 5$. Any ordered pair not on the line will not be a solution.

A graph that illustrates all the solutions to an equation is called the **graph of an equation**.

Here are the instructions for graphing a linear equation.

To graph a linear equation of the form $y = mx + b$:

- Find three ordered pairs that are solutions to the equation by picking any three x-values and finding their corresponding y-values.
- Graph the three ordered pairs on a coordinate system.
- Draw a line through the points to draw the graph of the equation.

It takes two points to determine a straight. The third point we find is a check point. If it is on the same straight line as the first two that is a good indication that we our work is correct.

So how do we find three ordered pair solutions to an equation? If the equation has y isolated on one side then an easy way to find ordered pairs is to just choose a value for x and substitute it in to find the corresponding y value.

Example: Graph the linear equation $y = 2x - 1$.

Solution: We will find three ordered pair solutions to graph and draw the straight line that goes through them. We find the ordered pairs by creating a table of values.

We begin the table by selecting three values for x.

x-value	*y*-value	solution
$x = -2$		
$x = 0$		
$x = 2$		

We complete the table by finding the corresponding y-value and writing the ordered pair solution.

x-value	*y*-value	solution
$x = -2$	$y = 2(-2) - 1$ $= -5$	$(-2, -5)$
$x = 0$	$y = 2(0) - 1$ $= -1$	$(0, -1)$
$x = 2$	$y = 2(2) - 1$ $= 3$	$(2, 3)$

We now have the ordered pairs (-2,-5), (0,-1), and (2,3). We plot these on a coordinate system and connect the points to form the graph of the equation.

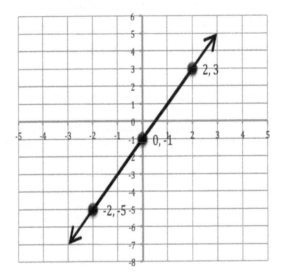

Good Question: In the last example, where did you get the values $x = -2$, $x = 0$, and $x = 2$?

Answer: We could have chosen any three values for x. We chose -2, 0, and 2 simply because they are nice, small numbers that will give points on either side of the y-axis. You can choose any values you want, but generally we choose one positive number, one negative number, and zero.

Example: Graph the linear equation $y = \frac{1}{3}x + 2$.

Solution: When we create our table of values for this equation, we begin by picking x-values. Those x-values will be multiplied by $\frac{1}{3}$, so we should pick values of x that will reduce with a denominator of 3, like -3, 0, and 3.

We begin the table by selecting three values for x.

x-value	y-value	solution
$x = -3$		
$x = 0$		
$x = 3$		

We complete the table by finding the corresponding y-value and writing the ordered pair solution.

x-value	y-value	solution
$x = -3$	$y = \frac{1}{3}(-3) + 2$ $= 1$	$(-3, 1)$
$x = 0$	$y = \frac{1}{3}(0) + 2$ $= 2$	$(0, 2)$
$x = 3$	$y = \frac{1}{3}(3) + 2$ $= 3$	$(3, 3)$

We now have the ordered pairs (-3,1), (0,2), and (3,3). We plot these on a coordinate system and connect the points to form the graph of the equation.

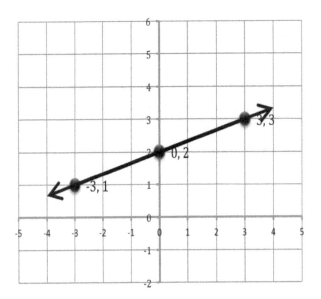

STOP # Exercise Set - Graphing Equations: y=mx+b

Graph each equation.

13. $y = x + 3$

14. $y = x - 2$

15. $y = 2x + 1$

16. $y = 3x - 5$

17. $y = \dfrac{1}{2}x - 4$

18. $y = \dfrac{1}{5}x + 2$

Graphing Equations: Ax+By=C

If an equation does not have the y variable isolated then picking random x-values to create solutions to graph can lead to fractions. We can simplify the process. by relying on intercepts, which always involve a value of 0 for one of the variables.

The **x-intercept** of a graph is the point where graph crosses the x-axis.

An x-intercept always has the form (__,0).

The **y-intercept** of a graph is the point where graph crosses the y-axis.

A y-intercept always has the form (0,__).

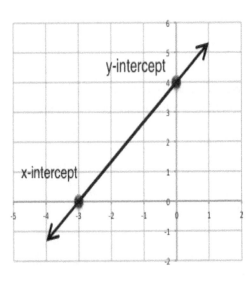

Example: Indicate the intercepts of the graph shown.

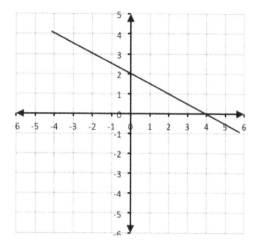

Solution: Looking at the graph we see that the x-intercept occurs at $(4,0)$ and the y-intercept occurs at $(0,2)$.

Because either the x or y coordinate at an intercept is always 0, the intercepts of a graphs are usually easy to find.

To find the *x*-intercept of an equation, substitute 0 for *y* and solve for *x*.

To find the *y*-intercept of an equation, substitute 0 for *x* and solve for *y*.

Looing at a table of values this means that we would be filling in the following table.

x-value	*y*-value	solutions
$x = 0$	?	$(0,?)$
?	$y = 0$	$(?,0)$

We often use the intercepts to graph an equation that has the form $Ax + By = C$.

To graph a linear equation of the form $Ax + By = C$:

- Find the *x* and *y*-intercepts two get two solutions.
- Find a third point as a check point.
- Graph the three ordered pairs on a coordinate system.
- Draw a line through the points to draw the graph of the equation.

Example: Graph the equation $2x + y = 6$ by finding and graphing the x and y-intercepts.

Solution: First we find the x-intercept by substituting in 0 for y.

$$x-\text{intercept: let } y = 0 \qquad\qquad y-\text{intercept: let } x = 0$$
$$2x + y = 6 \qquad\qquad\qquad 2x + y = 6$$
$$2x + 0 = 6 \qquad\qquad\qquad 2(0) + y = 6$$
$$2x = 6 \qquad\qquad\qquad\quad 0 + y = 6$$
$$x = 3 \qquad\qquad\qquad\qquad y = 6$$
$$x-\text{intercept: } (3,0) \qquad\qquad y-\text{intercept: } (0,6)$$

To check our work, we find a third point. All three points, the intercepts and check point, should be on the same straight line. If they are not then we have made a mistake somewhere. To find the check point we a convenient value for x, like $x = 2$, and find the corresponding y-value.

$$\text{Checkpoint: let } x = 2$$
$$2x + y = 6$$
$$2(2) + y = 6$$
$$4 + y = 6$$
$$y = 2$$
$$\text{Checkpoint: } (2,2)$$

Now we graph the intercepts (3,0) and (0,6) along with the checkpoint (2,2) and connect them to graph the line.

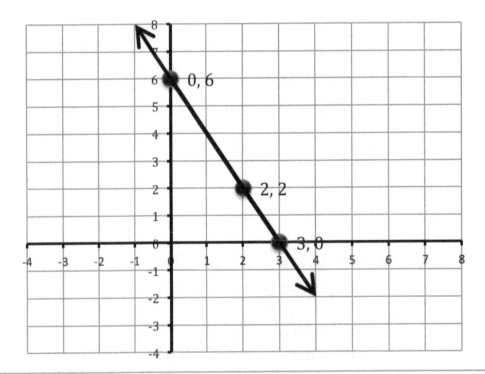

STOP Exercise Set - Graphing Equations: Ax+By=C

Give the x and y intercepts of each graph shown.

19.

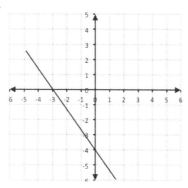

20.

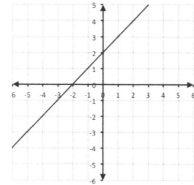

Graph each equation by finding the intercepts and a check point.

21. $x + 3y = 6$

22. $4x + y = 8$

23. $x - y = 3$

24. $x - 2y = 4$

Exercise Set - Putting it ALL Together

Vocabulary Check: Fill in each blank with a word from our Vocabulary Checklist to the right.

25. Equations of the form $Ax + By = C$ or $y = mx + b$ are called

_____. They are called linear because when we graph their solutions we get a straight line.

26. The point where a graph crosses the y-axis is called the

_____ of the graph.

27. A graph that represents all the solutions to an equation is called the _____.

Vocabulary Checklist:
linear equation in two variables
solution
graph of an equation
x-intercept
y-intercept

28. On a straight line, the point (7,0) would be an _____ because it lies on the x-axis.

29. If an equation has two variables then a _____ is an ordered pair that satisfies the equation.

Complete each table of values for the given equation.

30. $4x + 6y = 24$

x-value	y-value	solution
$x = 0$		
	$y = 0$	
$x = 3$		

31. $5x - 6y = 30$

x-value	y-value	solution
$x = 0$		
	$y = 0$	
	$y = 5$	

32. $3x - 7y = 21$

x-value	y-value	solution
$x = 0$		
	$y = 0$	
	$y = 3$	

33. $x + 11y = 22$

x-value	y-value	solution
$x = 0$		
	$y = 0$	
$x = 11$		

Graph each equation using the appropriate method.

34. $y = x + 4$

35. $y = 2x - 4$

36. $x + y = 7$

37. $x - y = 5$

38. $3x - y = 9$

39. $x + 4y = 8$

40. $y = \dfrac{1}{5}x + 2$

41. $y = \dfrac{1}{3}x + 5$

Exercise Set - Cumulative Review

42. Graph the following numbers on a number line using a scale of 25: -15, 79, -50, 145, 10
43. Divide. $\dfrac{15x}{4} \div \dfrac{10x}{11}$
44. Solve. $3(x-5) = x+7$
45. Add without using a calculator. $-9.8 + 7.3$
46. Find the prime factorization of 130.

 # 9.2 QUIZ YOURSELF:

To make sure you are ready for the EXAM, try these problems without any help. Give yourself about 20 minutes and don't check the answers until you have completely finished.

1. Of the following ordered pairs, which one(s) are a solution to the equation $3x - y = 7$?

    (2,1)   (1,-4)   (3,2)   (1,4)

2. Graph the equation $y = x - 3$ using the appropriate method.
3. Graph the equation $x + 2y = 6$ by finding the intercepts and third check point.
4. Fill in the table for the equation $8x + y = 40$.

x-value	y-value	solution
$x = 0$		
	$y = 0$	
$x = 4$		

5. Indicate the x and y-intercepts for the graph below.

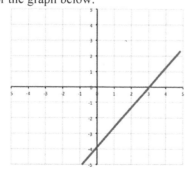

Answers to this Quiz Yourself are on page 710.

Chapter 1: Homework Answers

1.1 Whole Numbers

1. 5,365
2. 26,782
3. 405,000
4. 12,015,942
5. three hundred twelve
6. seven hundred nine
7. two thousand, six hundred one
8. twenty three thousand, nine hundred eighteen
9. three hundred five thousand, two hundred ninety seven
10. one million, eighty eight thousand, five hundred thirteen
11. graph
12. graph
13. graph
14. graph
15. graph
16. graph
17. graph
18. graph
19. 40
20. 600
21. 220,000
22. 4,504,900
23. 894,000
24. 236,000,000
25. 37,000
26. 9,200
27. 15
28. 18
29. May, 25
30. February, 14
31. Toyota, 30
32. Volkswagen, 8
33. 43
34. Ford and Honda
35. 26 lbs.
36. 55 lbs.
37. paper
38. 58 lbs.
39. whole numbers
40. scale
41. place value
42. ten millions
43. hundred thousands
44. 0
45. 5
46. 502
47. 713
48. 13,043
49. 4,705
50. 11,000,076
51. 55,315,000
52. thirty five
53. seventy nine
54. seven hundred forty one
55. three hundred nine
56. forty five thousand, one
57. seven hundred twelve thousand, four hundred eleven
58. four million, eight hundred twenty three thousand, nine hundred fifteen
59. eighteen million, ninety thousand, four hundred twenty three
60. three hundred eighty four thousand, four hundred three
61. one thousand, seven hundred thirty eight
62. six thousand, three hundred seventy one
63. two hundred thirty eight thousand eight hundred fifty seven
64. one billion, seven hundred million, four hundred fifty nine thousand, six hundred fifty
65. one million, six hundred seven thousand, one hundred eighty five
66. 7,800
67. 18,910
68. 713,000
69. 8,010,000
70. 970
71. 35,000,000
72. 54,000
73. 269,000
74. 78,500,000
75. 29,000,000
76. graph
77. graph
78. graph
79. graph

80. graph

81. graph

82. graph

83. graph

84. graph

85. graph

86. about $17 billion

87. about $22 billion

88. publishing, about $37 billion

89. video games, about $7 billion

90. 50 degrees

91. 60 degrees

92. day 6, about 64 degrees

93. day 1, about 42 degrees

1.2 Adding and Subtracting Whole Numbers

1. 148

2. 102

3. 676

4. 1,144

5. 11,805

6. 10,114

7. 1,111

8. 7,147

9. 1800miles; 1729miles

10. $250; $242

11. 26 units

12. 28 units

13. 21 ft.

14. 22 cm.

15. 39 ft.

16. 93 in.

17. 46

18. 52

19. 923

20. 2,969

21. 8,748

22. 148,391

23. about $12,000

24. about $5,000

25. commutative property of addition

26. associative property of addition

27. zero as the identity

28. zero as the identity

29. $(5+15)+9$

30. $99+23$

31. $18+(21+2)$

32. $19+(10+20)$

33. the identity property of zero

34. perimeter

35. addends, sum, total

36. commutative

37. subtraction

38. minuend, subtrahend, difference

39. associative

40. addition

41. 99

42. 9

43. 193

44. 479

45. 4,202

46. 711

47. 43,022

48. 1,316,000

49. 7,089

50. 781

51. 918

52. 1,001

53. 983

54. 1,472

55. 856

56. 93

57. 70

58. 104

59. 240

60. 13,243

61. 4,441

62. 423,508

63. 619,403

64. 55,492

65. 592,112

66. 80,598,397

67. 60

68. 2,600

69. 460

70. 27,000

71. 771,000

72. 18,500,000

73. $93,600

74. 2,053 more miles

75. $5,985

76. $4,693

77. Exact: $1180 Estimate: $1180

78. Exact: $20,329 Estimate: $20,000

79. Exact: $2,860
    Estimate: $3000
80. $729
81. $54,000
82. $41000
83. 60 m
84. 136 cm.
85. 56 ft.
86. 96 in.
87. 32 m
88. 58 ft.
89. 101 mm.

90. 92 cm.
91. 150 ft.
92. 36 ft.
93. California, 2010
94. California, Texas, Washington
95. 943
96. 2,394
97. 207
98. 191
99. 93
100. 111

101. 654
102. 603
103. 3420 for both sums
104. 3903 for both sums
105. 945 for both sums
106. 499 for both sums
107. graph
108. 440
109. 506
110. 5052
111. $(34+26)+77$

1.3 Multiplying and Dividing Whole Numbers

1. 8,451
2. 7,979
3. 539,350
4. 454,572
5. 1,380
6. 760
7. $360
8. $69,160
9. square miles
10. square feet
11. square inches
12. square feet
13. $40 in^2$
14. $120 ft^2$
15. $1,350 yd^2$
16. 945 square yards
17. $21 cm^2$
18. $84 in^2$
19. $312 cm^2$
20. 450 square meters
21. $4,200
22. $3,040

23. 5
24. 4
25. 12
26. 17
27. 31
28. 46 R 2
29. 141 R 9
30. 34 R 1
31. 209 R 21
32. 1834 R 9
33. multiplying by zero
34. commutative property
35. dividing zero
36. one as the identity
37. associative
38. dividing by zero
39. commutative property of multiplication
40. divisor
41. area
42. the identity property of one
43. divisor

44. product, quotient
45. the associative property of multiplication
46. factors
47. $3 \cdot 7, (3)(7)$
48. $\dfrac{154}{2}, 154 \div 2$
49. $5 \cdot 6$
50. $12 \cdot 4$
51. 486
52. 486
53. 112
54. 17
55. 189 R 2
56. 19,946
57. 15
58. 14,760
59. 0
60. 190 R 2
61. 345
62. 490 R 11
63. 1280 R 12
64. 104,995

65. undefined

66. 654

67. 0

68. 3,417,580

69. 6,797,375

70. 1,050

71. 504

72. 1400

73. 0

74. 0

75. 540

76. 5,040

77. 5(7)=35

78. 4(4)=16

79. 1(45)=45

80. 21(7)=147

81. 23(169)=3887

82. 150(236)=35400

83. 54 feet

84. 96 inches

85. 19 servings

86. 29 days

87. $50,000

88. 336 seats

89. 630,000 fans

90. $576

91. 650 terra-bytes per mainframe

92. 1,020 lbs

93. $4450

94. 420,000

95. 280,000

96. $P = 22\,ft., A = 24\,ft^2$

97. $P = 58\,in., A = 210\,in^2$

98. $P = 24\,yd., A = 36\,yd^2$

99. $P = 92\,ft., A = 529\,ft^2$

100. $P = 32\,cm., A = 40\,cm^2$

101. $P = 66\,cm., A = 220\,cm^2$

102. 1,449

103. 4,762

104. 494

105. 602

106. 32,768

107. 29,045

108. 31

109. 562

110. graph

111. 17800

112. 363

113. 30 feet

114. false

1.4 Exponents and The Orders of Operations

1. $(6)^2$

2. $(18)^3$

3. $(21)^4$

4. $(9)^8$

5. $2^2 \cdot 7^3 \cdot 9^2$

6. $6^3 \cdot 7 \cdot 13^4$

7. $8 \cdot 8$

8. $7 \cdot 7 \cdot 7$

9. $5 \cdot 5 \cdot 5 \cdot 5$

10. $17 \cdot 17 \cdot 17 \cdot 17 \cdot 17$

11. $3 \cdot 3 \cdot 3 \cdot 8 \cdot 8$

12. $5 \cdot 5 \cdot 5 \cdot 5 \cdot 5 \cdot 11 \cdot 11 \cdot 11$

13. 16

14. 81

15. 16

16. 27

17. 1296

18. 2197

19. 3200

20. 675

21. $81\,ft^2$

22. $25\,in^2$

23. $196\,in^2$

24. $729\,m^2$

25. $6084\,ft^2$

26. $11881\,in^2$

27. $225\,in^2$

28. $1444\,in^2$

29. 21

30. 12

31. 39

32. 12

33. 48

34. 52

35. 86

36. $4(35) + 5(50)\ /\$390$

37. $65 + 23(50)\ /\$1,215$

38. 131

39. 18

40. 84

41. 141

42. 71

43. 7

44. exponent

45. base

46. 36

47. 1849

48. 16

49. 27

50. 1

51. 1728

52. 196

53. 100

54. 128

55. 900

56. 108

57. 1280

58. 1, 4, 9, 16, 25, 36

59. 1, 8, 27, 64, 125, 216

60. 22

61. 2

62. 24

63. 7

64. 31

65. 13

66. 10

67. 11

68. 148

69. 0

70. 62

71. 199

72. 33

73. 0

74. 80

75. 152

76. 37

77. 253

78. 73

79. 66

80. 163

81. 337

82. 357

83. 243

84. 18

85. 240

86. 62

87. 140

88. 125

89. Mistake: addition before multiplication

$$5 + 3 \cdot 2$$
$$= 5 + 6$$
$$= 11$$

90. Mistake: subtraction before multiplication

$$7 \cdot 8 - 4$$
$$= 56 - 4$$
$$= 52$$

91. Mistake: multiplication before exponents

$$36 \div 9 \cdot 4^2 + 1$$
$$= 36 \div 9 \cdot 16 + 1$$
$$= 4 \cdot 16 + 1$$
$$= 64 + 1$$
$$= 65$$

92. Mistake: subtraction before parenthesis

$$21 - 4(1 + 2)$$
$$= 21 - 4 \cdot 3$$
$$= 21 - 12$$
$$= 9$$

93. Mistake: division before exponents

$$100 \div 5^2 + 6 \cdot 11$$
$$= 100 \div 25 + 6 \cdot 11$$
$$= 4 + 6 \cdot 11$$
$$= 4 + 66$$
$$= 70$$

94. $45 + 14 \cdot 8$, $157

95. $5 \cdot 15 + 12 \cdot 10 + 3 \cdot 25$, $270

96. $10 \cdot 75 - 100$, $650

97. 89

98. 86

99. $118

100. false

101. false

102. false

103. false

104. 12 pages

105. 70 miles

106. 7680

107. 644

108. 160000

109. 705

110. 26

1.5 Factoring

1. yes
2. yes
3. no
4. no
5. true
6. false
7. false
8. false
9. true
10. false
11. $5 \cdot 7$ and $1 \cdot 35$
12. $7 \cdot 7$ and $1 \cdot 45$
13. answers may vary, $8 \cdot 8$ and $2 \cdot 32$
14. not possible
15. answers may vary, $10 \cdot 10$ and $4 \cdot 25$
16. answers may vary, $12 \cdot 12$ and $3 \cdot 48$
17. $2 \cdot 3$
18. $2 \cdot 8$
19. $2 \cdot 12$
20. $4 \cdot 9$
21. 14, 28, 42, 56, 70, 84
22. 25, 50, 75, 100, 125, 150
23. 101, 202, 303, 404, 505, 606
24. 234, 468, 702, 936, 1170, 1404
25. 418
26. 1645
27. prime
28. composite, $3 \cdot 5$
29. composite, $3 \cdot 9$
30. prime
31. composite, $7 \cdot 13$
32. composite, $9 \cdot 9$

33. $2 \cdot 2 \cdot 3 \cdot 3$
34. $2 \cdot 2 \cdot 3 \cdot 7$
35. $2 \cdot 2 \cdot 3 \cdot 11$
36. $5 \cdot 3 \cdot 7$
37. $2 \cdot 2 \cdot 3 \cdot 13$
38. $3 \cdot 3 \cdot 17$
39. $3 \cdot 3 \cdot 19$
40. $2 \cdot 2 \cdot 2 \cdot 5 \cdot 5 \cdot 5$
41. yes
42. yes
43. no
44. no
45. factor (verb)
46. factorization
47. composite number
48. prime factorization
49. prime number
50. divisible
51. multiples
52. factor (noun)
53. composite, $7 \cdot 11$
54. composite, $7 \cdot 13$
55. composite, $2 \cdot 139$
56. prime
57. composite, $2 \cdot 543$
58. composite, $11 \cdot 47$
59. 2, 4
60. 2, 3, 4, 6, 7, 8, 9
61. 2, 3, 4, 5, 6, 7, 9, 10
62. 3, 9
63. 3, 5, 15
64. 2, 3, 4, 12
65. 7, 21
66. 7
67. 5, 11, 55
68. $2 \cdot 2 \cdot 13$
69. $2 \cdot 2 \cdot 2 \cdot 2 \cdot 3$

70. $5 \cdot 31$
71. $2 \cdot 2 \cdot 2 \cdot 3 \cdot 11$
72. $2 \cdot 2 \cdot 2 \cdot 2 \cdot 2 \cdot 11$
73. $5 \cdot 3 \cdot 3 \cdot 13$
74. $5 \cdot 127$
75. $2 \cdot 2 \cdot 2 \cdot 3 \cdot 17$
76. $2 \cdot 2 \cdot 5 \cdot 7 \cdot 7$
77. $3 \cdot 1357$
78. $2 \cdot 5 \cdot 3 \cdot 67$
79. $2 \cdot 2 \cdot 2 \cdot 2 \cdot 2 \cdot 2 \cdot 5 \cdot 19$
80. 248
81. 810
82. 810
83. 513
84. 7623
85. 12672
86. yes
87. yes
88. no
89. yes
90. yes
91. no
92. $3 \cdot 15$
93. $3 \cdot 16$
94. $8 \cdot 9$
95. $3 \cdot 27$
96. $7 \cdot 15$
97. $11 \cdot 12$
98. 4
99. 480
100. $5 \cdot 5 \cdot 5$
101. 10
102. 221

1.6 A Review of Basic Fractions

1. numerator: 3
   denominator: 7
   picture

2. numerator: 9
   denominator: 10
   picture

3. numerator: 3
   denominator: 4
   picture

4. numerator: 5
   denominator: 8
   picture

5. $\dfrac{23}{500}$

6. $\dfrac{22}{25}$

7. $\dfrac{14}{22} = \dfrac{2 \cdot \boxed{7}}{\boxed{2} \cdot 11} = \dfrac{7}{\boxed{11}}$

8. $\dfrac{15}{21} = \dfrac{\boxed{3} \cdot 5}{\boxed{7} \cdot 3} = \dfrac{\boxed{5}}{\boxed{7}}$

9. $\dfrac{3}{4}$

10. $\dfrac{3}{5}$

11. $\dfrac{2}{3}$

12. $\dfrac{3}{8}$

13. $\dfrac{4}{5}$

14. $\dfrac{3}{5}$

15. $\dfrac{6}{7}$

16. $\dfrac{17}{25}$

17. $\dfrac{3}{10}$

18. $\dfrac{7}{24}$

19. $\dfrac{35}{48}$

20. $\dfrac{2}{9}$

21. $\dfrac{3}{2}$

22. $\dfrac{3}{7}$

23. $\dfrac{3}{5}$

24. $\dfrac{5}{9}$

25. $\dfrac{2}{7}$

26. $\dfrac{5}{12}$

27. $\dfrac{2}{15}$

28. $\dfrac{13}{24}$

29. $\dfrac{1}{17}$

30. $\dfrac{2}{5}$

31. $\dfrac{5}{19}$

32. $\dfrac{31}{60}$

33. the fundamental principle of fractions

34. denominator

35. reciprocal

36. equivalent fractions

37. lowest terms, simplifying a fraction

38. numerator

39. fraction

40. $\dfrac{2}{5}$

41. $\dfrac{5}{10}$

42. $\dfrac{2}{3}$ and $\dfrac{8}{12}$

43. $\dfrac{1}{2}, \dfrac{2}{4}, \dfrac{3}{6}, \dfrac{4}{8}$

44. $\dfrac{1}{3}, \dfrac{2}{6}, \dfrac{4}{12}$

45. $\dfrac{3}{9}, \dfrac{2}{6}, \dfrac{1}{3}$

46. $\dfrac{9}{15}$

47. $\dfrac{7}{16}$

48. $\dfrac{1}{2}$

49. $\dfrac{1}{3}$

50. $\dfrac{7}{9}$

51. $\dfrac{1}{3}$

52. $\dfrac{7}{18}$

53. $\dfrac{3}{5}$

54. $\dfrac{12}{13}$

55. $\dfrac{6}{61}$

56. $\dfrac{9}{17}$

57. $\dfrac{5}{17}$

58. $\dfrac{9}{13}$

59. $\dfrac{14}{25}$

60. no

61. no

62. yes

63. yes

64. $\dfrac{8}{15}$

65. $\dfrac{3}{35}$

66. $\dfrac{15}{16}$

67. $\dfrac{8}{21}$

68. $\dfrac{4}{15}$

69. 4

70. $\dfrac{9}{13}$

71. $\dfrac{9}{16}$

72. $\dfrac{4}{5}$

73. $\dfrac{1}{2}$

74. $\dfrac{2}{3}$

75. $\dfrac{1}{2}$

76. $\dfrac{7}{16}$

77. 1

78. 1

79. 1

80. $\dfrac{2}{5}$

81. $\dfrac{1}{10}$

82. $\dfrac{1}{2}$

83. $\dfrac{3}{7}$

84. $\dfrac{31}{47}$

85. $\dfrac{1}{2}$

86. $\dfrac{5}{27}$

87. 1

88. 10

89. 28

90. $\dfrac{1}{6}$

91. draw pictures to show that combining $\dfrac{1}{8}$ and $\dfrac{3}{8}$ gives $\dfrac{4}{8}$, which simplifies to $\dfrac{1}{2}$

92. draw pictures to show that combining $\dfrac{1}{6}$ and $\dfrac{1}{6}$ gives $\dfrac{2}{6}$, which simplifies to $\dfrac{1}{3}$

93. $\dfrac{4}{5}$

94. $\dfrac{11}{13}$

95. a. 50 b. $\dfrac{3}{10}$ c. $\dfrac{11}{25}$

96. a. 98 b. $\dfrac{13}{98}$ c. $\dfrac{12}{49}$

97. false

98. true

99. false

100. true

101. 80

102. 3 and 8

103. $2 \cdot 3^3$

104. 8096

105. 19

1.7 Introduction to Variables, Expressions, and Equations

1. 13
2. 36
3. 25
4. 31
5. 28
6. 133
7. 15
8. 16
9. 25
10. 221
11. 25, 0, 18
12. 1, 4, 7
13. 106
14. 90
15. expression
16. equation
17. equation
18. expression
19. false
20. false
21. false
22. true
23. yes
24. no
25. yes
26. no
27. equation, expression
28. variable
29. evaluate
30. solution to an equation
31. 14
32. 6
33. 6
34. 15
35. 24

36. 11
37. 0
38. 225
39. 90
40. 32
41. 14
42. 26
43. 108
44. 24
45. 907
46. 822638
47. 3
48. 150000
49. 75000
50. 58
51. 11
52. 19
53. 5, 11, 19
54. 4, 5, 40, 173
55. 0, 10, 28
56. 0, 5, 12, 21
57. False
58. True
59. True
60. True
61. False
62. True
63. True
64. True
65. False
66. True
67. False
68. True
69. Yes
70. No
71. No

72. Yes
73. No
74. No
75. No
76. No
77. Yes
78. Yes
79. No
80. No
81. Yes
82. Yes
83. Yes
84. No
85. Yes
86. Yes
87. Yes
88. No
89. No
90. Yes
91. 186
92. 212000
93. answers may vary, $3h + 7$ and $7h^2 + 3h$
94. answers may vary, $h + 3 = 7$ and $7 - h = 3$
95. No
96. Yes
97. $5 \cdot 7$
98. $\dfrac{6}{7}$
99. 3500
100. graph
101. $A = 24 in^2$, P = 26 in.

Quiz Yourself Answers

Section 1.1

1. three hundred five thousand, twenty three
2. 12,000,315
3. 17,900
4. 25,000
5. graph
6. Haywood, 25,809
7. 1997, about 6000 dolphins

Section 1.2

1. 137
2. 4886
3. 2084
4. commutative property of addition
5. 39000
6. 134 ft.
7. 45 employees

Section 1.3

1. 84
2. 11 R 10
3. 425 R 6
4. 32,520
5. 0

6. undefined
7. 93 sheds
8. 3100 miles/minute
9. $P = 36\,ft., A = 65\,ft^2$

Section 1.4

1. 8^3
2. $2 \cdot 2 \cdot 2 \cdot 7 \cdot 7 \cdot 7 \cdot 7$
3. 81
4. 1323
5. 51
6. 144
7. 41
8. 9
9. 850
10. $19 + 13(10) / \$149$

Section 1.5

1. 2, 3, 4, 5, 6, 8, 9, 10
2. 3, 9
3. composite
4. composite
5. answers may vary, $2 \cdot 24$ and $4 \cdot 12$
6. $2 \cdot 2 \cdot 2 \cdot 3 \cdot 7$
7. $5 \cdot 3 \cdot 7 \cdot 11$
8. 378
9. $3 \cdot 8$
10. no

Section 1.6

1. $\frac{4}{11}$, numerator: 4

   denominator: 11
2. $\frac{2}{3}$
3. $\frac{14}{19}$
4. $\frac{1}{7}$
5. $\frac{3}{8}$
6. $\frac{4}{13}$
7. $\frac{1}{15}$

Section 1.7

1. expression
2. 11
3. 40
4. True
5. Yes

ANSWERS TO CHAPTER 1 REVIEW:

1. three thousand six hundred seven	29. 957	58. 2,4,8	83. $\dfrac{8}{11}$
2. 150,000	30. 1	59. 2, 3, 4, 5, 6, 8,10	84. $\dfrac{7}{23}$
3. graph	31. 9,102	60. none	85. $\dfrac{4}{63}$
4. graph	32. 817	61. 3, 5, 9	
5. about 320	33. 0	62. 3^3	86. $\dfrac{1}{2}$
6. 126	34. 639,830	63. $2^3 \cdot 7$	87. $\dfrac{1}{2}$
7. 45,383	35. 51	64. $2 \cdot 3 \cdot 7$	
8. 766	36. 400	65. $2^3 \cdot 3^2$	88. $\dfrac{4}{21}$
9. 400	37. 100,000	66. 3 and 5	89. $\dfrac{7}{2}$
10. 467	38. 117 R 10	67. 4 and 9	
11. 39,574	39. 1347 R 300	68. 27 and 1	90. $\dfrac{10}{33}$
12. 0	40. $1,102	69. 9 and 11	
13. 918	41. 297 dozen with 6 left over.	70. 180	91. $\dfrac{1}{6}$
14. 106,088	42. 27	71. 2,035	92. equation
15. 53,112	43. 32	72. yes	93. expression
16. 200	44. 125	73. yes	94. equation
17. 1,310,000	45. 81	74. picture	95. equation
18. $1,496	46. 9	75. picture	96. 49
19. 264 m.	47. 55	76. picture	97. 10
20. 79cm.	48. 48	77. picture	98. 28
21. 99ft.	49. 0	78. $\dfrac{3}{5}$	99. 40
22. 9	50. 0	79. $\dfrac{7}{9}$	100.51
23. 1,425	51. 126		101.17
24. 0	52. 24	80. $\dfrac{5}{9}$	102.yes
25. undefined	53. 19	81. $\dfrac{1}{13}$	103.no
26. 7	54. 36		104.no
27. 3,638	55. 14	82. $\dfrac{3}{35}$	105.yes
28. 67	56. 19		
	57. 29		

ANSWERS TO CHAPTER 1 TEST YOURSELF:

1. five thousand, six hundred eighty
2. 2, 4, 5, 8 and 10
3. $2 \cdot 7^2$
4. composite
5. 187
6. graph
7. commutative property of addition

8. 62
9. 14338
10. $\dfrac{2}{3}$
11. $\dfrac{27}{28}$
12. 95
13. 162
14. 109
15. 27
16. 616

17. no
18. yes
19. $388
20. 580 ft^2
21. 1254 miles
22. 546 students
23. 80
24. 166 feet of fence

Chapter 2: Integers Homework Answers

2.1 Introduction to Integers

1) -25
2) 52
3) 14
4) -8
5) graph
6) graph
7) graph
8) graph
9) graph
10) graph
11) <
12) >
13) <
14) >
15) <
16) <
17) <
18) <
19) >
20) <
21) Friday
22) Tuesday
23) $-4 > -6$
24) $-6 < 0$
25) -9
26) -4
27) 13
28) 8
29) -4
30) -7
31) 17

32) 5
33) -1
34) -3
35) -3
36) 14
37) -14
38) 3
39) 13
40) 25
41) -14
42) -8
43) 6
44) 23
45) 28
46) 45
47) 16
48) 88
49) 16
50) 4
51) integer
52) opposite
53) absolute value
54) negative number
55) -282
56) -4
57) 10
58) -90
59) $1360
60) -$945

61) May, June, August
62) October, $2680
63) $-760 > -945$
64) $-1240 < 340$
65) $-(17) = -17$
66) $-(80) = -80$
67) $-(-12) = 12$
68) $-(-25) = 25$
69) $|15| = 15$
70) $|-7| = 7$
71) $-|32| = -32$
72) $-|-5| = -5$
73) 9
74) -45
75) 38
76) -8
77) -6
78) -81
79) 96
80) 45
81) =
82) >
83) >
84) >
85) >
86) <

87) >
88) <
89) <
90) <
91) <
92) Always True
93) Always True
94) Sometimes True
95) Never True
96) Always True
97) 7
98) -4
99) 4
100) 11
101) 0
102) -7
103) 3
104) -3
105) 3
106) 8
107) -9
108) 38
109) 4
110) $\dfrac{3}{5}$
111) 10,407
112) 60,000
113) $2^2 \cdot 5^2 \cdot 7$

2.2 Adding Integers

1) c

2) a

3) graph, 5

4) graph, 9

5) graph, 7

6) graph, -4

7) graph, -10

8) graph, -18

9) graph, -7

10) graph, -20

11) 9

12) 38

13) -11

14) -24

15) -63

16) 321

17) 9790

18) -589

19) -46

20) -57

21) -13

22) -$228

23) -4

24) -11

25) 13

26) -20

27) 0

28) 0

29) 44

30) -31

31) -65

32) -248

33) -$63

34) -24 feet

35) -15

36) 12

37) 21

38) -25

39) -1

40) 162

41) -35

42) -1000

43) -62

44) 30

45) -30

46) -1

47) 5

48) -6

49) 77

50) -219

51) -68

52) -51

53) -37

54) 41

55) 62

56) -90

57) 12

58) -15

59) -159

60) 57

61) 776

62) -825

63) 2076

64) -16

65) -20

66) -71

67) -125

68) -15

69) -29

70) -77

71) -1

72) -60

73) $98

74) $222

75) -65 feet

76) -78 feet

77) -140 points

78) 36 points

79) never true

80) always true

81) sometimes true

82) sometimes true

83) -13

84) 0

85) 3

86) 1

87) -12

88) -7

89) 0 5 -2 -8

90) 0 -7 -13 11

91) 5

92) 13

93) <

94) graph

95) $-\lvert -9 \rvert$

96) 7

97) $144\,ft^2$

98) 82

99) $\dfrac{1}{5}$

100)   undefined

2.3 Subtracting Integers

1) subtraction
2) take the opposite of
3) negative number
4) subtraction
5) negative number, subtraction
6) the opposite of, negative number, subtraction
7) $15 + 7 = 22$
8) $23 + 12 = 35$
9) $15 + (-90) = -75$
10) $35 + (-129) = -94$
11) $-13 + (-30) = -43$
12) $-76 + (-35) = -111$
13) $-123 + 67 = -56$
14) $-257 + 57 = -200$
15) $14494 - (-282) = 14494 + 282 = 14776$
16) $535 - (-8) = 535 + 8 = 543$
17) -58
18) 108
19) 159
20) -43

21) -32
22) -10
23) -5
24) -1
25) -73
26) 25
27) -1
28) 5
29) -8
30) 9
31) 6
32) 8
33) -20
34) 26
35) 19
36) 12
37) -8
38) -16
39) 0
40) 0
41) -2
42) 3
43) -75
44) -1020
45) -12
46) 10

47) -29
48) 50
49) 305
50) 12
51) -15
52) -75
53) -1
54) -41
55) 41
56) 2
57) -$270
58) -$16
59) $45
60) $261
61) $14431 - 3350 = 11081$ feet
62) $20320 - (-282) = 20602$
63) Alaska
64) 179 degrees
65) 180 degrees
66) 88 degrees
67) 57 degrees
68) 92 degrees
69) $620, profit
70) -$160, loss

71) -$4940, loss
72) $25,400, profit
73) 2 and -2
74) 12 and 4
75) 12 and -6
76) 16 and 16
77) -18 and 12
78) 13 and 29
79) no
80) no
81) no
82) yes
83) yes
84) no
85) 0
86) <
87) graph
88) -2
89) 14
90) yes
91) $\dfrac{1}{5}$
92) 8
93) 28
94) four hundred fifteen

2.4 Multiplying and Diving Integers

1) -7, 0, 7, 14

2) 3, 0, -3, -6

3) -30

4) -24

5) 36

6) 52

7) 98

8) -42

9) 0

10) -15

11) 360

12) -105

13) 63, -16

14) 30, -11

15) 40, -14

16) 96, -20

17) -10 degrees

18) -24 degrees

19) 4

20) 5

21) 12

22) 12

23) -10

24) -9

25) 9

26) 8

27) 8

28) -2

29) undefined

30) 0

31) 0

32) undefined

33) -$100 per month

34) -$1350 per month

35) -4

36) 7

37) -7

38) 9

39) -14

40) -19

41) 18

42) -13

43) -28

44) undefined

45) -341

46) -42

47) 0

48) -161

49) -155

50) 0

51) 32

52) 0

53) 12

54) 32

55) -504

56) -132

57) -11

58) -1716

59) 510

60) 2938

61) 27

62) -4

63) 12

64) -24

65) -714 feet

66) -855 feet

67) -$480

68) -$920

69) -4 degrees per hour

70) -9 degrees per hour

71) $405 per month

72) $310 per month

73) -10 degrees

74) -24 degrees

75) F

76) F

77) F

78) F

79) T

80) Graph

81) -26

82) -14

83) -17

84) 6, 2

85) 125

86) $2^2 \cdot 17$

87) 41,700

88) 763

89) 7, 14, 21, 28

2.5 Exponents and the Order of Operations

1) Base: -3

   Exponent: 3

   -3 to the 3rd

   power

2) Base: 3

   Exponent: 3

   3 to the 3rd

   power

3) Base: 5

   Exponent: 2

   5 to the 2nd

   power

4) Base: -2

   Exponent: 4

   -2 to the 4th

   power

5) 5^4

6) $(-6)^5$

7) $(-2)^4 \cdot 8^2$

8) $3^3 \cdot (-5)^4$

9) $-4(-4)(-4)$

10) $(-5)(-5)$

11) $3 \cdot 3 \cdot 3 \cdot 3 \cdot 3 \cdot (-7)(-7)(-7)$

12) $(-4)(-4)(-6)(-6)(-6)$

13) -8

14) 9

15) 25

16) -64

17) -9

18) -1

19) -7

20) 4

21) -8

22) 54

23) -100

24) 21

25) -9

26) 7

27) -59

28) 32

29) 81

30) 96

31) 4

32) 8

33) -73

34) -45

35) 2

36) -32

37) 22

38) 21

39) 26

40) 53

41) -6

42) undefined

43) commutative

   property of

   multiplication

44) commutative

   property of

   addition

45) associative

   property of

   addition

46) commutative

   property of

   multiplication

47) 25

48) 49

49) -1

50) -1

51) 1

52) -1

53) 81

54) -49

55) 64

56) -1000

57) 32

58) 48

59) -108

60) -162

61) 1

62) 43

63) 9

64) -9

65) 20

66) 56

67) -7

68) 10

69) -56

70) 31

71) 34

72) -32

73) -11

74) 7

75) 1

76) $\dfrac{20}{7}$

77) 7

78) 13

79) 81, -81

80) 25, -25

81) -8, -8

82) -64, -64

83) $672

84) $6349

85) -3

86) -17

87) 0

88) 3

89) -5 $°C$

90) 6 $°C$

91) -4

92) -15

93) 6155

94) 5

95) 35

96) $\dfrac{2}{9}$

97) 11

98) 500

99) 14,025

100) composite

2.6 Signed Fractions

1) $\dfrac{-3}{5}$ and $\dfrac{3}{-5}$

2) $-\dfrac{4}{7}$ and $\dfrac{4}{-7}$

3) $-\dfrac{2}{3}$

4) $-\dfrac{1}{4}$

5) $-\dfrac{1}{3}$

6) $-\dfrac{8}{9}$

7) $-\dfrac{1}{2}$

8) $-\dfrac{2}{3}$

9) $-\dfrac{3}{4}$

10) $-\dfrac{6}{7}$

11) $-\dfrac{2}{3}$

12) $-\dfrac{3}{4}$

13) $\dfrac{1}{15}$

14) $\dfrac{2}{7}$

15) $-\dfrac{6}{19}$

16) $\dfrac{40}{51}$

17) $-\dfrac{5}{24}$

18) $\dfrac{3}{4}$

19) $-\dfrac{5}{8}$

20) $\dfrac{3}{5}$

21) $\dfrac{1}{2}$

22) $-\dfrac{7}{22}$

23) $-\dfrac{1}{5}$

24) $-\dfrac{1}{7}$

25) $\dfrac{1}{8}$

26) -1

27) $-\dfrac{11}{13}$

28) $\dfrac{7}{12}$

29) $\dfrac{1}{3}$

30) $-\dfrac{3}{4}$

31) $\dfrac{7}{9}$

32) $\dfrac{5}{12}$

33) $\dfrac{3}{7}$

34) $\dfrac{6}{7}$

35) $-\dfrac{5}{7}$

36) $-\dfrac{2}{3}$

37) $-\dfrac{3}{4}$

38) $-\dfrac{6}{11}$

39) $-\dfrac{1}{3}$

40) $-\dfrac{8}{11}$

41) $-\dfrac{1}{5}$

42) $\dfrac{5}{27}$

43) $-\dfrac{5}{9}$

44) $-\dfrac{11}{13}$

45) $\dfrac{1}{3}$

46) $\dfrac{5}{7}$

47) $-\dfrac{6}{11}$

48) $-\dfrac{14}{39}$

49) $-\dfrac{2}{5}$

50) $\dfrac{9}{91}$

51) $\dfrac{7}{9}$

52) $-\dfrac{6}{7}$

53) $\dfrac{10}{9}$

54) -1

55) $-\dfrac{19}{18}$

56) $-\dfrac{1}{9}$

57) False

58) True

59) True

60) False

61) -12, 27

62) 105

63) -3

64) 14

65) 0

66) 17,018

67) $\dfrac{1}{3}$

68) 0

69) 400

70) 60

Chapter 2 Review:

1. 5642
2. -512
3. graph
4. graph
5. 51
6. -3
7. -91
8. 14
9. 345
10. -671
11. 5
12. 102
13. >
14. <
15. >
16. >
17. 115
18. 22
19. -68
20. -25
21. -6
22. 32
23. 275
24. -1791
25. -50
26. -116
27. -3 points
28. -127 feet
29. $465
30. -6
31. -21
32. -124
33. 72
34. 100
35. -118
36. -131
37. -151
38. -78
39. 98
40. 21
41. 3
42. $89
43. yes, -$45

44. 1300 meters
45. -48
46. 0
47. 336
48. -135
49. 714
50. 0
51. 1140
52. 8000
53. -17
54. 36
55. -7
56. 0
57. 49
58. -169
59. undefined
60. -29
61. -$6600
62. -1120 feet
63. $(-5)^3$
64. $(-3)^4 \cdot (-7)^2$
65. $(-9)\cdot(-9)\cdot(-9)\cdot(-9)$
66. $(-4)\cdot(-4)\cdot(-5)\cdot(-5)\cdot(-5)\cdot(-5)$
67. 81
68. -81
69. $-\dfrac{9}{38}$
70. 25
71. 81
72. -125
73. -48
74. 54
75. -15
76. 3
77. -237
78. 75
79. 52
80. 421

81. -20
82. -38
83. -9
84. -5
85. $\dfrac{-3}{5}$
86. $\dfrac{-1}{2}$
87. $\dfrac{-5}{9}$
88. $\dfrac{3}{11}$
89. $\dfrac{11}{15}$
90. $\dfrac{2}{3}$
91. $\dfrac{2}{27}$
92. $\dfrac{49}{32}$
93. $\dfrac{3}{5}$
94. $\dfrac{-5}{18}$
95. $\dfrac{-7}{16}$
96. $\dfrac{-8}{9}$
97. $\dfrac{11}{21}$
98. $\dfrac{-6}{25}$
99. $\dfrac{5}{21}$
100. $\dfrac{-10}{13}$

Chapter 2 Test Yourself:

1. graph
2. -10, -8, -6, -4, -2, 0, 2, 4
3. 17
4. 23
5. 16
6. -141
7. 77
8. -109
9. -54
10. -1281
11. -275
12. -45252
13. 0
14. 108
15. 8
16. -125
17. -16
18. 81
19. undefined
20. 0
21. -45
22. 16
23. 244
24. -2
25. 11
26. $\frac{1}{2}$
27. $\frac{2}{7}$
28. $\frac{-1}{4}$
29. $\frac{25}{8}$
30. $\frac{-21}{16}$
31. -$1670
32. $597
33. $1040
34. $1459
35. $6626
36. 219 rooms

Chapter 2 Cumulative Review:

1. $2^3 \cdot 3^2$
2. $2^2 \cdot 3 \cdot 13$
3. 9 and 2
4. 7 and 8
5. graph
6. graph
7. -15, 19, 0, $\frac{12}{3}$, 87
8. >
9. <
10. 71,300
11. 300,000
12. $\frac{-11}{12}$
13. $\frac{19}{64}$
14. 219
15. 178
16. 30876
17. 0
18. -25
19. undefined
20. 127
21. 57
22. 0
23. $\frac{1}{3}$
24. $\frac{-18}{35}$
25. undefined
26. $\frac{3}{7}$
27. $\frac{-1}{5}$
28. $\frac{26}{51}$
29. $\frac{-5}{4}$
30. 18
31. -11
32. 48
33. 24
34. -19
35. 14
36. -47
37. 16
38. 2
39. 37
40. -21
41. 8
42. $\frac{-5}{8}$
43. 12
44. 64
45. 392
46. 117 minutes
47. $14950
48. -$24500
49. 611 students
50. $-4°$

Section 2.1 Answers to Quiz Yourself.
(1) graph   (2) 46   (3) -56   (4) <   (5) <   (6) $-(-15)$ (7) -105   (8) 11   (9) F

Section 2.2 Answers to Quiz Yourself:
(1) -121   (2) -43   (3) -31 points   (4) -163 feet   (5) -37   (6) -49 feet   (7) -174   (8) T

Section 2.3 Answers to Quiz Yourself:
(1) -22   (2) -84   (3) 123   (4) 0   (5) -304   (6) -17   (7) -5   (8) $551   (9) -$57

Section 2.4 Answers to Quiz Yourself:
(1) 510   (2) -57   (3) undefined   (4) 0   (5) 0   (6) -$1480   (7) $-3°$ per hour   (8) F

Section 2.5 Answers to Quiz Yourself:
(1) -49   (2) 24   (3) 81   (4) -8   (5) -20   (6) -67   (7) 44   (8) -14   (9) divide

Section 2.6 Answers to Quiz Yourself:
(1) $-\frac{1}{3}$ (2) $\frac{1}{12}$ (3) $\frac{2}{51}$ (4) $-\frac{2}{3}$ (5) $\frac{-5}{4}$ (6) $-\frac{1}{3}$ (7) $-\frac{2}{3}$ (8) -1 (9) $-\frac{2}{5}$ (10) $\frac{25}{22}$

Chapter 3: Algebraic Expression and Equations Homework Answers

3.1 More About Algebraic Expressions

1) Terms

2) Coefficient

3) Constant term

4) 3a, 6b, -7a, -9

5) $-x^2$, 4x, -3

6) 2 / 5, -4

7) 3 / 8, -5, 12 / 12

8) 2 / 1, -9

9) 1 / -1

10) 3 / -9, 3, -17 / -17

11) 4 / 5, 7, -1, 16 / 16

12) like terms

13) not like terms

14) not like terms

15) like terms

16) $8x$

17) $-3d$

18) $2a + 8b$

19) $-12x + 25y$

20) $5x + 16y$

21) $12x^2$

22) $23x + 37y$

23) $74c$

24) $15x + 5$

25) $10x - 14$

26) $-4m + 24$

27) -5x - 45

28) $-14y - 42$

29) -6g + 12

30) -4t - 1

31) $5t - 3$

32) $-9x^2 + 13x - 6$

33) $3x^2 - 4x + 15$

34) $-15h^3 + 30h^2 - 55h - 5$

35) $-8g^3 + 16g^2 - 4g + 32$

36) $75t - 150$

37) $7b - 1050$

38) $10x + 13$

39) $21x - 20$

40) $23t - 6$

41) $-24y - 49$

42) $5k - 31$

43) $2d - 32$

44) $-22x + 32$

45) $13p - 16$

46) $11x - 1$

47) $-x + 39$

48) The coefficient is the numerical part of a term.

49) answers may vary / $5x - 3x + 7x$

50) A term is separated by addition or subtraction. A factor is separated by multiplication.

51) distribution and combining like terms, distribution should be done first

52) 81

53) 45

54) -77

55) -36

56) $5k$

57) h^3

58) does not simplify

59) does not simplify

60) $7p$

61) $-7p$

62) 0

63) $14x + 21$

64) $20x^2 - 5$

65) $9x + 5y$

66) $12a + 6$

67) $6y - 19$

68) $-9n + 33$

69) $2m$

70) $g + 12$

71) $-8b - 1$

72) $28t + 9$

73) $-7a - 11$

74) $72 - 56x$

75) $-7x + 16$

76) $60 - 3x$

77) $2500 + 5x$

78) $10750 + 9t$

79) $25h + 675$

80) 3d + 90

81) mistake 1: $-3g + g = -2g$; mistake 2: 13 + (-10) = 3, the student multiplied instead of adding.

82) mistake 1: $-2(4x + 3) = -8x - 6$, distribute negative to both terms; mistake 2: when subtracting a

number from a
negative, you should
add and keep it
negative, not subtract,
so $-7-10=-17$ not -
3.

83) x^2 ; $2x$

84) b^3 ; $4b$

85) y^4 ; $4y$

86) a^2b^4 ; $2a+4b$

87) x^3y^2 ; $3x+2y$

88) $9+5x$; $45x$

89) $40x$; $6+5x$

90) a. 15

b. $2x+9$

c. $6+9=15$

d. same results

91) a. -2

b. $-3b-8$

c. $6-8=-2$

d. same results

92) $\dfrac{-3}{7}$

93) $>$

94) 27 ft.

95) equation

96) yes

3.2 Expressions versus Equations

1) expression
2) expression
3) equation
4) expression
5) equation
6) equation
7) true
8) true
9) false
10) true
11) no
12) no
13) yes
14) yes
15) no
16) no
17) yes
18) no
19) no
20) no
21) 5
22) 13
23) 13
24) 9
25) 18

26) -6
27) a = 2
28) d = 10
29) x = 7
30) f = -7
31) d = 36
32) d = 3
33) When the value is
    substituted into the
    equation, the equation is
    true.
34) A numeric equation only
    has numbers, an
    algebraic equation has
    numbers and variables.
35) An equation has an '='
    sign and an expression
    does not.
36) Substitute in the given
    value and simplify to see
    if the equation is true.
37) Yes
38) No
39) Yes
40) Yes

41) No
42) No
43) 26
44) 53
45) 5
46) -2
47) 14
48) 33
49) 35
50) -44
51) $a = 3$
52) y = -6
53) x = 13
54) y = 22
55) x = 17
56) n = 9
57) x = 108
58) x = 21
59) x = -24
60) x = 10
61) no
62) no
63) $y = -2$
64) x = 2
65) x = -1

66) none of these

67) $3x, x^2$

68) -6t

69) $21g - 35$

70) $5x - 15$

71) $-13b + 4$

72) 11

73) 4582

74) 1

75) -81, 81

76) -66

3.3 The Addition and Subtraction Property

1) $x = 9$

2) $x = 7$

3) $n = -3$

4) $m = -42$

5) $k = 5$

6) $b = 9$

7) $m = -17$

8) $n = -29$

9) $x = \$2135$

10) $n = \$65$ million

11) $a = 7$

12) $b = 3$

13) $x = 24$

14) $y = 8$

15) $h = 57$

16) $b = -3$

17) $y = -119$

18) $k = -180$

19) 13 days

20) 24 inches

21) $x = -10$

22) $x = 9$

23) $x = 3$

24) $x = -45$

25) $x = -59$

26) $h = 13$

27) $a = 26$

28) $d = -12$

29) 75 radios

30) 23 hours

31) subtraction; addition

32) multiplication; division

33) division; multiplication

34) addition; subtraction

35) $n = 18$

36) $m = 91$

37) $n = 8$

38) $m = -2$

39) $x = 44$

40) $x = -35$

41) $x = -24$

42) $x = 90$

43) $y = -3$

44) $k = -23$

45) $m = 55$

46) $h = -221$

47) $x = -24$

48) $y = -60$

49) $y = 10$

50) $a = 17$

51) $b = 10$

52) $x = 33$

53) $x = 3$

54) $x = -7$

55) $x = 68$

56) $t = 11$

57) $x = -1$

58) $p = -3$

59) 28 miles

60) 521 miles

61) 3 hours flying time

62) 7 hours driving time

63) 25 packages

64) 34 bikes

65) Multiplying both sides by zero will make any equation true, even a false one.

66) You must add to both sides of the equation to get the solution.

67) 9ft

68) 8in

69) 3m

70) 9cm

71) $x = 7$

72) $x = 3$

73) $-7d - 33$

74) True

75) $5p, p^5$

76) $8w + 48$

77) no

78) 7

79) five thousand two hundred

80) -2, 0, 2, 4, 6

81) $\left| -3 \right| = 3$

82) -3

3.4 More About Solving Equations

1) $x = 4$

2) $x = 5$

3) $x = 2$

4) $x = -1$

5) $x = 4$

6) $y = 3$

7) $x = 3$

8) $x = 7$

9) $p = 2$

10) $x = -2$

11) $y = 4$

12) $x = 3$

13) $x = 1$

14) $g = 3$

15) $k = 14$

16) $t = 8$

17) $x = 1$

18) $x = 4$

19) $u = 1$

20) $d = -3$

21) $x = \dfrac{78}{29}$

22) $x = \dfrac{55}{6}$

23) $x = \dfrac{-17}{14}$

24) $x = 2$

25) $x = \dfrac{1}{4}$

26) $x = \dfrac{5}{3}$

27) $x = \dfrac{-25}{6}$

28) $x = -2$

29) $x = -4$

30) $x = \dfrac{5}{2}$

31) false

32) false

33) false

34) true

35) $x = 1$

36) $x = 6$

37) $x = -1$

38) $x = -5$

39) $n = 1$

40) $w = 8$

41) $y = \dfrac{-1}{5}$

42) $x = -2$

43) $p = -11$

44) $k = 12$

45) $x = \dfrac{9}{38}$

46) $x = 21$

47) $x = 0$

48) $a = \dfrac{-5}{9}$

49) $x = 10$

50) $x = \dfrac{7}{10}$

51) $x = \dfrac{-46}{11}$

52) $x = 9$

53) $g = \dfrac{45}{12}$

54) $x = \dfrac{15}{11}$

55) 9 movies

56) 36 months

57) 4 bikes

58) $s = 15$ pairs of shoes

59) $x = 125$ miles

60) 33 drinks

61) 13 feet

62) 15 inches

63) yes

64) 60x, 8 + 5x

65) no

66) $r = -18$

67) expression

68) -560

69) 512

70) 10

71) graph

72) <

3.5 Problem Solving

1) n - 6

2) n + 8

3) 3(x + 5)

4) 2n – 7

5) 4x – 5

6) $2x + 16$

7) $5 - n = 28$

8) $21 + x = 12$

9) $x + 12 = 8x$

10) $x - 6 = 14 + 3x$

11) $2(x + 3) = 13$

12) $4(n + 2) = 15$

13) m = movie tickets sold;

    11m

14) d = cost of dinner; 5 + d

15) s = speed you are driving;

$$\frac{456}{s}$$

16) a = price of airline ticket;

a − 45

17) w = number of weeks;

4 + 2w =26

18) m = number of months;

300 + 75m = 2175

19) x = number of chains; 2x

= number of tires; 2x + x

= 214

20) x = number of pull buoys;

x + 15 = number of kick

boards; (x+15) + x = 98

21) −2

22) 3

23) $11 each

24) 12 miles and 16 miles

25) 33 guitars and 45 cases

26) $1210 originally in petty

cash

27) 29° and 61°

28) 32°, 64° and 84°

29) width is 5 feet

30) length is 95/4 feet

31) 6 −x

32) 9 − 2x

33) x − 40

34) 3x − 15

35) n + 7

36) 16 − n = 3

37) 2m − m = 7

38) 3x = 12

39) b + 25 = 45

40) x − 5 = 8

41) x − 6 = 27

42) $\dfrac{5}{x+2}$

43) $\dfrac{4}{m-3}$

44) $2(y+3)+6$

45) 7 − 3(x + 2)

46) $5+\dfrac{x-3}{2x}$

47) 85 + s + 10a

48) 749 + 21c + 50m

49) 244 + 157h +175s

50) $x-12=5;\ x=17$

51) $n+10=20;\ n=10$

52) $2n+4=3;\ n=\dfrac{-1}{2}$

53) $5(x-3)=12;\ x=\dfrac{27}{5}$

54) $x-16=12;\ x=28$

55) $23-x=10;\ x=13$

56) 39 and 54

57) 39 and 117

58) 24 and 30

59) 19 and 12

60) 80° and 100°

61) 29° and 61°

62) 33°, 57° and 90°

63) 36°, 54° and 90°

64) width is 34 ft., length is

68 ft.

65) width is 5 cm, length is 8

cm.

66) 76° and 104°

67) 36° and 54°

68) 80°, 40° and 60°

69) length is 11 cm.

70) length is 51 feet

71) width is 35 feet

72) 70 km and 210 km

73) 110 miles and 220 miles

74) -3

75) w = -15

76) h = 4

77) x = -9

78) 2a + b

79) 0

80) $\dfrac{4}{17}$

81) 3, -3

82) -9

83) 681

3.6 Introduction to Algebraic Fractions

1) 4

2) 18

3) $\dfrac{5}{12}$

4) $\dfrac{8}{13}$

5) 2

6) 10

7) $\dfrac{3}{4}$

8) $\dfrac{3}{2}$

9) $\dfrac{6}{13a}$

10) $\dfrac{2}{3}$

11) $\dfrac{2}{3}$

12) $\dfrac{1}{4x}$

13) $\dfrac{-4y^3}{5}$

14) $-3x$

15) $\dfrac{-5h^8}{2}$

16) $\dfrac{9b^2}{10}$

17) $\dfrac{-6d^4}{5}$

18) $\dfrac{8b^2}{3a}$

19) $\dfrac{4x}{5}$

20) $\dfrac{8a^2}{11}$

21) $3x$

22) $\dfrac{4b^2}{5}$

23) $\dfrac{2}{t^2}$

24) $\dfrac{x}{2}$

25) $\dfrac{-7x}{10}$

26) $\dfrac{10y}{9}$

27) $\dfrac{3x}{2}$

28) $\dfrac{7a^2}{16}$

29) $\dfrac{7x}{9}$

30) $\dfrac{a}{4}$

31) $\dfrac{3ab}{4}$

32) $\dfrac{38x}{25}$

33) $\dfrac{1}{3x}$

34) $\dfrac{2}{3b^2}$

35) $\dfrac{1}{2}$

36) $\dfrac{-3}{2}$

37) 1

38) 6

39) $\dfrac{65}{2}$

40) 13

41) $-2a^3$

42) $6a^2$

43) $2x^4$

44) $-3xy$

45) $\dfrac{7c^3}{d^2}$

46) $\dfrac{-9b^2}{a}$

47) $-2a^3$

48) $6a^2$

49) $\dfrac{4y}{5}$

50) $\dfrac{5a}{14}$

51) $\dfrac{3h}{32}$

52) $\dfrac{15x}{2}$

53) $\dfrac{5}{54x}$

54) $\dfrac{4y^2}{15}$

55) $\dfrac{15b}{17}$

56) x

57) $\dfrac{-a}{9}$

58) $\dfrac{1}{33}$

59) $\dfrac{2}{3x^3}$

60) $\dfrac{14g^2}{15h^2}$

61) $\dfrac{7y^2}{10}$

62) $\dfrac{-3x}{8}$

63) $\dfrac{39xy^2}{40}$

64) $\dfrac{4x^2}{15y}$

65) $\dfrac{a}{3}$

66) $\dfrac{3m}{4}$

67) $\dfrac{-8ab}{19c}$

68) $\dfrac{-x}{2y}$

69) $\dfrac{7mn}{9}$

70) $\dfrac{8x}{11}$

71) $\dfrac{-a^2b}{4}$

72) $\dfrac{2x^3y}{5}$

73) $20 + 4 = 24,\ 4(6) = 24$
    same results

74) yes

75) 2

76) $5 \cdot x + 7 = 22$

77) $h = \dfrac{1}{3}$

78) -13

79) -90

80) $(-8)(-8)(-8)(-8)$

81) -258

82) 45

Quiz Yourself:

3.1

1. a) $-3x^2, 5x, -21$
   b) -3, 5, -21 c) -21

2. $8x + 3y$

3. $6x - 7$

4. $3y + 7$

5. $21x - 47$

6. $-8 + x$

7. $-21h^2 + 12h - 36$

8. $-2x + 41$

3.2

1. expression

2. false

3. no

4. yes

5. $h = 12$

6. $n = -7$

7. $x = 24$

3.3

1. $m = -14$

2. $x = 13$

3. $y = 11$

4. $x = 16$

5. $x = 23$

6. $x = 81$

7. $h = -9$

8. $x = -36$

9. $n = 23$

10. $g = 35$

3.4

1. $x = 5$

2. $x = -2$

3. $x = 0$

4. $x = -1$

5. $x = 30$

6. $x = -1$

7. $x = -2$

8. 36 months

3.5

1) $x + 6 = 12$

2) $2(x + 5)$

3) $5(x - 2) = 4$

4) $\dfrac{n}{7} = -1$

5) $32 - n$

6) 7 and 28

7) 42m, 21m, and 34 m

8) 15 months

9) 57° and 32°

10) 63 couches and 82
    loveseats

3.6

1) 3

2) -5

3) $\dfrac{3x}{4y}$

4) $\dfrac{m^4}{4}$

5) $\dfrac{-3ab^3}{7}$

6) $\dfrac{18x^2}{35}$

7) $\dfrac{-81ab^2}{35}$

8) $\dfrac{7x}{17}$

9) $\dfrac{-12t^2}{35s}$

10) $\dfrac{a^2b}{2}$

Chapter 3 Review:

1) 3 / 16, -3, 451 / 451

2) 4 / -3, 15, 17, 1 / 1

3) a , 2

4) g , 1

5) $22x$

6) $19m$

7) $-52x + 40y$

8) $2a^2 + 14a + 14$

9) $4x - 18$

10) $20x + 5$

11) $-3x + 17$

12) $-9t^3 - 5t^2 + 18$

13) $-35m - 33$

14) $-24x - 20$

15) $35n - 18$

16) $-22b - 22$

17) $16m + 18n - 10$

18) $9y - 48$

19) $38t - 18$

20) $15y + 4$

21) expression

22) equation

23) equation

24) expression

25) yes

26) no

27) yes

28) no

29) 16

30) 9

31) 41

32) 10

33) 56

34) -55

35) $x = 6$

36) $x = 59$

37) $m = 17$

38) $k = -3$

39) $w = -275$

40) $b = -1$

41) $y = 3$

42) $t = -8$

43) $a = -128$

44) $h = -40$

45) $x = -18$

46) $g = -3$

47) $x = 24$

48) $x = -7$

49) $t = 12$ hours

50) $s = 178$ strings

51) $x = \dfrac{17}{5}$

52) $z = -4$

53) $a = \dfrac{14}{5}$

54) $p = 3$

55) $x = 9$

56) $n = -10$

57) $m = -10$

58) $t = \dfrac{-21}{2}$

59) $x = -1$

60) $m = 3$

61) $h = -6$

62) $x = \dfrac{-3}{5}$

63) 15 hours

64) 200 pages

65) $12 - 2x$

66) $4(x + 8)$

67) $12 - 2(x - 4) = 18$

68) $\dfrac{x}{20} = -3$

69) $45 + 12x + 3p$

70) $300 + 55h$

71) 21 and 29

72) $68°$ and $112°$

73) $22°$ and $68°$

74) 35 ft. wide, 42ft. long

75) $\dfrac{2x}{3}$

76) $\dfrac{4}{7m^2}$

77) $\dfrac{-3ab}{4}$

78) $\dfrac{-3g^2h^3}{5}$

79) $\dfrac{3xh}{100}$

80) $\dfrac{19e^2}{21}$

81) $\dfrac{8y^4}{5x}$

82) $\dfrac{9b}{13}$

83) $\dfrac{6}{7m}$

84) $\dfrac{5x^2}{6y^2}$

85) $\dfrac{20ab^3}{49}$

86) $-2x^3$

87) $\dfrac{4st^2}{7}$

88) $\dfrac{15h}{16}$

89) $\dfrac{m^2}{3}$

90) 0

Chapter 3 Test Yourself:

1) 3 / -1, 17, -143 / -143

2) 4 / 15, -31, 16, 16 / 16

3) a, 4

4) x

5) $-6m^2 - 13m + 17$

6) $6x + 41$

7) $-8a + 36$

8) $-18e^3 + 12e^2 - 73$

9) $-19x + 71$

10) $30t + 20$

11) yes

12) x = -2

13) b = 52

14) x = -4

15) x = 56

16) x = 1

17) z = 11

18) $m = \dfrac{58}{7}$

19) y = -3

20) x = -61

21) t = 2

22) 13 bikes

23) x − 5 = 3x

24) 5 (x + 12)

25) 9 and 14

26) 8 hours

27) 27° and 63°

28) 19 ft. wide, 36 ft. long

Cumulative Review 1-3:

1) -14 and -2

2) $2^5 \cdot 3$

3) $\dfrac{-8}{11}$

4) $\dfrac{5x^2 y^6}{2}$

5) 78

6) -34

7) -3

8) 0

9) -913

10) -52

11) -25

12) 37

13) $\dfrac{4}{15}$

14) $\dfrac{2}{3}$

15) $\dfrac{40m}{19}$

16) $\dfrac{9}{10}$

17) $\dfrac{10k}{27}$

18) $\dfrac{13n^2}{17}$

19) $\dfrac{-5m^6}{4e^2}$

20) $\dfrac{15}{22}$

21) 26x

22) -24m + 83

23) 11m + 3

24) $16x^2 + 2x + 10$

25) x = 34

26) x = 7

27) x = 18

28) c = 45

29) k = -72

30) m = -6

31) x = -6

32) y = 9

33) x = 7

34) $b = \dfrac{11}{2}$

35) x = -5

36) x = -17

37) n = -5

38) m = 2

39) -17

40) 1

41) 2

42) 9

43) 2n – 15

44) -12x = -35 + 9

45) 85.5

46) $252

47) 18° and 72°

48) 72°, 36° and 72°

49) 22 and 45

50) Terry - $121, Paulette - $298

Chapter 4: Fractions

4.1 More Fraction Fundamentals

1) $-\dfrac{5}{7}$

2) $\dfrac{4}{5t}$

3) $\dfrac{2}{5}$

4) 4

5) $\dfrac{p}{3}$

6) $\dfrac{2}{5x}$

7) $2b$

8) -1

9) $\dfrac{2}{3}$

10) $\dfrac{5}{14}$

11) proper fraction

12) improper fraction

13) algebraic fraction

14) mixed number

15) improper fraction

16) algebraic fraction

17) $\dfrac{31}{5}$

18) $\dfrac{26}{3}$

19) $4\dfrac{1}{5}$

20) $\dfrac{9}{4x}$

21) $16\dfrac{1}{4}$

22) $-\dfrac{19}{5}$

23) $\dfrac{17t}{6}$

24) $-\dfrac{65}{7}$

25) 1

26) undefined

27) $\dfrac{1}{3}$

28) 3

29) 0

30) 0

31) -9

32) $-\dfrac{1}{14}$

33) undefined

34) 1

35) $d = 0$

36) $y = 0$

37) graph

38) graph

39) graph

40) graph

41) mixed number

42) proper fraction

43) improper fraction

44) $\dfrac{1}{5}$

45) $\dfrac{7}{3}$ and $2\dfrac{1}{3}$

46) $\dfrac{9}{2}$ and $4\dfrac{1}{2}$

47) $\dfrac{6}{7}$

48) diagram

49) diagram

50) diagram

51) diagram

52) $\dfrac{65}{7}$

53) $-\dfrac{68}{5}$

54) $-\dfrac{59}{15}$

55) $\dfrac{76}{29}$

56) $6\dfrac{1}{4}$

57) $-5\dfrac{7}{10}$

58) $-4\dfrac{3}{8}$

59) $2\dfrac{5}{16}$

60) $2\dfrac{1}{3}$

61) $\dfrac{3}{4}$

62) undefined

63) $\dfrac{5}{13}$

64) $6\dfrac{1}{2}$

65) $\dfrac{1}{5}$

66) 5

67) $-\dfrac{10}{9x}$

68) undefined

69) $2\dfrac{1}{3}$

70) $\dfrac{7}{10}$

71) 0

72) $\dfrac{2}{3}$

73) $\dfrac{11t}{12}$

74) 4

75) $\dfrac{39}{100b}$

76) $\dfrac{2}{3}$

77) $\dfrac{8}{15}$

78) $-\dfrac{3}{20}$

79) $\dfrac{2}{3}$

80) 6

81) -1

82) $\dfrac{160}{231}$

83) $\dfrac{3}{17}$

84) $7\dfrac{1}{4}$

85) $-2\dfrac{1}{5}$

86) $14\dfrac{1}{9}$

87) $35\dfrac{1}{5}$

88) $8\dfrac{3}{4}$; 8 complete sets with 3 tires left over.

89) $6\dfrac{1}{2}$; 6 orders of glasses filled with 6 glasses left over.

90) $21\dfrac{2}{3}$; 21 cell phones with two microchips left over.

91) $4\dfrac{3}{4}$; 4 miles with 2 additional laps.

92) graph

93) graph

94) graph

95) graph

96) graph

97) graph

98) $-\dfrac{2}{3}, \dfrac{1}{3}$ and $\dfrac{5}{3}$

99) $-\dfrac{1}{5}, \dfrac{4}{5}$ and $\dfrac{7}{5}$

100) $\dfrac{1}{2}, 1\dfrac{1}{2}, 2\dfrac{1}{2}$ and $3\dfrac{1}{2}$

101) $-1\dfrac{1}{3}, 1\dfrac{2}{3}$ and $3\dfrac{1}{3}$

102) graph

103) graph

104) false

105) true

106) false

107) false

108) A proper fraction represents part of a whole while a mixed number consists of both a whole number and a proper fraction.

109) A proper fraction has a larger denominator than numerator while an improper fraction has a larger numerator than denominator.

110) A numeric fraction contains only numbers while an algebraic fraction is a fraction which contains variables and may also contain numbers.

111) $x = -5$

112) graph

113) $n - 8 = 2n$

114) 2

115) -8

4.2 Multiplying Fractions

1) $\dfrac{1}{2}\cdot\dfrac{3}{10}$

2) $\dfrac{2}{5}\cdot\dfrac{6}{7}$

3) $\dfrac{3}{4}\cdot\dfrac{1}{2}$

4) $\dfrac{2}{3}\cdot\dfrac{1}{11}$

5) $\dfrac{5}{12}$

6) $\dfrac{1}{4}$

7) $\dfrac{1}{3}$

8) $\dfrac{2}{5}$

9) $\dfrac{2}{7}$

10) $\dfrac{8}{35}$

11) $\dfrac{16}{11}$

12) $\dfrac{10}{3}$

13) -45

14) $\dfrac{-2}{5}$

15) $\dfrac{1}{27}$

16) $\dfrac{16c}{25}$

17) $3x$

18) $\dfrac{4b^2}{5}$

19) $\dfrac{6}{5t^2}$

20) $\dfrac{5}{54x}$

21) 29,200 people support the proposition

22) 815 defective microchips

23) $6\dfrac{1}{4}$

24) 3

25) 6

26) $11\dfrac{1}{7}$

27) 45

28) $-45\dfrac{1}{2}$

29) $13\dfrac{10}{11}$

30) -6

31) -21

32) 26

33) $111\dfrac{7}{12}\,ft^2$

34) $24\,ft^2$

35) $x=1\dfrac{10}{11}$

36) $x=\dfrac{2}{5}$

37) $x=\dfrac{-5}{18}$

38) $x=\dfrac{-3}{4}$

39) $x=-21$

40) $y=27$

41) $a=\dfrac{-3}{16}$

42) $g=\dfrac{32}{27}$

43) $\dfrac{1}{2}x=\dfrac{3}{4};\ x=1\dfrac{1}{2}$

44) $\dfrac{5}{6}x=\dfrac{8}{9};\ x=1\dfrac{1}{15}$

45) $\dfrac{11}{15}x=22;\ x=30$

46) $2\dfrac{1}{3}x=\dfrac{6}{7};\ x=\dfrac{18}{49}$

47) -20

48) $\dfrac{13}{116}$

49) $\dfrac{1}{6}$

50) $\dfrac{2}{55}$

51) $\dfrac{4y^2}{15}$

52) $\dfrac{2}{3x^2}$

53) $\dfrac{4y}{5}$

54) $-19\dfrac{1}{2}$

55) 6

56) $\dfrac{1}{33}$

57) $-24\dfrac{4}{5}$

58) $9\dfrac{1}{2}$

59) 5

60) $\dfrac{3h}{32}$

61) $\dfrac{-6}{25}$

62) $\dfrac{8}{45}$

63) $\dfrac{5a}{14}$

64) $\dfrac{15x}{2}$

65) $\dfrac{x}{2}$

66) $\dfrac{15b}{17}$

67) x

68) $\dfrac{2}{63}$

69) $\dfrac{-a}{9}$

70) $x = 12$

71) $x = \dfrac{3}{16}$

72) $k = -\dfrac{1}{10}$

73) $x = 3$

74) $x = \dfrac{5}{42}$

75) $x = -21$

91) $\dfrac{3}{25}$

94) 640

95) 40

96) 120

97) graph

98) 1

76) $1, \dfrac{1}{x}, x$

77) $2, \dfrac{2}{a}, 2a$

78) $-5, -5b, -\dfrac{5}{b}$

79) $2, \dfrac{2}{k}, 2k$

80) top left to bottom

right:
$\dfrac{1}{4}, \dfrac{1}{6}, \dfrac{1}{8}, \dfrac{1}{10},$
$\dfrac{1}{6}, \dfrac{1}{9}, \dfrac{1}{12}, \dfrac{1}{15},$
$\dfrac{1}{8}, \dfrac{1}{12}, \dfrac{1}{16}, \dfrac{1}{20},$
$\dfrac{1}{10}, \dfrac{1}{15}, \dfrac{1}{20}, \dfrac{1}{25}$

81) $103\dfrac{1}{8} in^2$

82) $106\dfrac{7}{8} ft^2$

92) $\dfrac{16}{25}$

99) $1\dfrac{1}{2}$

100) $\dfrac{-6}{0}$

101) $\dfrac{-19}{2}$

102) $3a - 4y$

83) $103\dfrac{1}{2} ft^2$

84) $2\dfrac{31}{32} ft^2$

85) 132 in

86) $2\dfrac{1}{16} cups\ of\ flour$

87) $2\dfrac{1}{2} inches$

88) $553\dfrac{3}{4} miles$

89) $46\dfrac{4}{5} miles$

90) $12\dfrac{1}{3} miles ; 24\dfrac{2}{3} miles$

93) 20

103) $9x - 15$

104) 40

105) 42

106) $<$

4.3 Dividing Fractions

1) $\dfrac{1}{3}$

2) $\dfrac{1}{8}$

3) $\dfrac{4}{27}$

4) $\dfrac{4}{25}$

5) $\dfrac{1}{2}$

6) 2

7) $\dfrac{25}{18}$

8) $\dfrac{5}{2}$

9) 3

10) $-\dfrac{4}{3}$

11) $\dfrac{1}{6}$

12) DNE

13) $1\dfrac{3}{25}$

14) $\dfrac{-4}{5}$

15) $\dfrac{32}{81}$

16) $1\dfrac{1}{3}$

17) $-2\dfrac{5}{8}$

18) $\dfrac{-7}{9}$

19) $\dfrac{-7x}{10}$

20) $\dfrac{10y}{9}$

21) $\dfrac{3x}{2}$

22) $\dfrac{7a^2}{16}$

23) $\dfrac{35}{128}$

24) $8\dfrac{1}{4}$

25) $2\dfrac{2}{15}$

26) $2\dfrac{34}{35}$

27) $\dfrac{14}{15}$

28) $1\dfrac{1}{3}$

29) $-3\dfrac{1}{2}$

30) $\dfrac{-1}{12}$

31) $\dfrac{12}{49}$

32) $2\dfrac{14}{19}$

33) false

34) true

35) true

36) false

37) $\dfrac{1}{14}$

38) $17\dfrac{1}{2}$

39) 0

40) $\dfrac{3}{4}$

41) undefined

42) $\dfrac{2}{25}$

43) $\dfrac{8}{15}$

44) $5\dfrac{1}{16}$

45) $\dfrac{3}{4}$

46) $1\dfrac{5}{9}$

47) -24

48) 36

49) $\dfrac{-1}{121}$

50) 39

51) $\dfrac{-6}{25}$

52) $4\dfrac{10}{17}$

53) $-2\dfrac{22}{57}$

54) $1\dfrac{1}{2}$

55) $\dfrac{1}{4x}$

56) $\dfrac{2y^2}{9}$

57) 0

58) $-2x$

59) $\dfrac{3a^2}{20c^2}$

60) ab^2

61) $\dfrac{1}{x}$

62) undefined

63) $\dfrac{7}{3k}$

64) $\dfrac{9ct}{2}$

65) $\dfrac{7y^2}{10}$

66) $-\dfrac{3x}{8}$

67) $\dfrac{39xy^2}{40}$

68) from top left to bottom

right: $\dfrac{-3}{5}, \dfrac{5}{3}, \dfrac{1}{7}, -7, -8, \dfrac{1}{8}$

69) from top left to bottom

right:

$\dfrac{9}{11}, \dfrac{-11}{9}, -14, \dfrac{1}{14}, \dfrac{-1}{2}, 2$

70) 1

71) 1

72) 1

73) 1

74) 7 desks

75) 4 bushes

76) 45 breadsticks

77) 9 blocks

78) $r = 6\dfrac{3}{65} mph$

79) $r = 6\dfrac{74}{75} mph$

80) $\dfrac{-1}{3}$

81) $\dfrac{-2}{7}$

82) 1

83) $3\dfrac{1}{8}$

84) $\dfrac{7}{5y}$

85) $5 - 3n$

86) -42

87) $x = 1\dfrac{1}{9}$

88) 20 and 20

89) $15 + 4 \cdot 8 = 47$

4.4 LCM and LCD

1) 6, 12, 18

2) 12, 24, 36

3) 45, 90, 135

4) 8, 16, 24

5) 18

6) 36

7) 60

8) 80

9) 36

10) 108

11) $21x^2y$

12) $15a^3b^2$

13) $\dfrac{7}{14}$

14) $\dfrac{16}{24}$

15) $\dfrac{28}{35}$

16) $\dfrac{9}{63}$

17) $\dfrac{63}{72}$

18) $\dfrac{12}{44}$

19) $\dfrac{24x^2}{50x^3}$

20) $\dfrac{39ab}{45b^3c}$

21) $\dfrac{15}{42}, \dfrac{8}{42}$

22) $\dfrac{70}{120}, \dfrac{63}{120}$

23) 45; $\dfrac{12}{45}$; $\dfrac{5}{45}$

24) 48; $\dfrac{39}{48}$; $\dfrac{14}{48}$

25) 15x; $\dfrac{6}{15x}$; $\dfrac{7x}{15x}$

26) 12y; $\dfrac{8y}{12y}$; $\dfrac{7}{12y}$

27) 36; $\dfrac{12}{36}$; $\dfrac{33}{36}$; $\dfrac{26}{36}$

28) 80; $\dfrac{50}{80}$; $\dfrac{75}{80}$; $\dfrac{28}{80}$

29) >

30) >

31) >

32) <

33) LCM

34) multiples

35) LCD

36) 60

37) 70

38) 60

39) 63

40) $102x^2$

41) $286ab^2$

42) 168

43) 468

44) 44; $\dfrac{32}{44}, \dfrac{33}{44}$

45) 60; $\dfrac{36}{60}, \dfrac{35}{60}$

46) 133; $\dfrac{76}{133}, \dfrac{56}{133}$

47) 210; $\dfrac{165}{210}, \dfrac{196}{210}$

48) 252; $\dfrac{91}{252}, \dfrac{174}{252}$

49) 280; $\dfrac{231}{280}, \dfrac{175}{280}$

50) 546; $\dfrac{325}{546}, \dfrac{111}{546}$

51) 1089; $\dfrac{132}{1089}, \dfrac{585}{1089}$

52) 23562; $\dfrac{3773}{23562}, \dfrac{4131}{23562}$

53) 306; $\dfrac{135}{306}, \dfrac{151}{306}$

54) 48xy; $\dfrac{27}{48xy}, \dfrac{35y}{48xy}$

55) 33x; $\dfrac{24}{33x}, \dfrac{15x}{33x}$

56) 152xy; $\dfrac{144y}{152xy}, \dfrac{133x}{152xy}$

57) 132ay; $\dfrac{101y}{132ay}, \dfrac{93a}{132ay}$

58) 60; $\dfrac{48}{60}, \dfrac{35}{60}, \dfrac{17}{60}$

59) 18; $\dfrac{6}{18}, \dfrac{14}{18}, \dfrac{11}{18}$

60) 154; $\dfrac{99}{154}, \dfrac{40}{154}, \dfrac{79}{154}$

61) 204; $\dfrac{51}{204}, \dfrac{120}{204}, \dfrac{75}{204}$

62) 770; $\dfrac{352}{770}, \dfrac{315}{770}, \dfrac{335}{770}$

63) 798; $\dfrac{315}{798}, \dfrac{476}{798}, \dfrac{600}{798}$

64) <

65) =

66) >

67) <

68) <

69) The LCD is the LCM applied to denominators of two fractions.

70) Prime factor each of the numbers, then use this to create a quantity which

has every factor of each
of the numbers. Multiply
these numbers.

71) 0

72) -1

73) $\dfrac{3x^2}{4}$

74) $a = 0$

75) $\dfrac{4}{7}$

76) $46cm$

77) yes

78) $<$

79) 20

80) -3

4.5 Adding and Subtracting

1) 1

2) $\dfrac{5}{4}$

3) $\dfrac{43}{45}$

4) $\dfrac{7}{36}$

5) $\dfrac{-43}{72}$

6) $\dfrac{2}{7}$

7) $\dfrac{27}{68}$

8) $\dfrac{24}{55}$

9) $\dfrac{103}{585}$

10) $\dfrac{-103}{308}$

11) $\dfrac{61a}{44}$

12) $\dfrac{13x}{12}$

13) 12

14) $8\dfrac{3}{5}$

15) $12\dfrac{1}{11}$

16) $5\dfrac{29}{50}$

17) $3\dfrac{10}{27}$

18) $5\dfrac{7}{15}$

19) $4\dfrac{11}{18}$

20) $-7\dfrac{11}{12}$

21) $2\dfrac{19}{20}$

22) $-1\dfrac{1}{4}$

23) $x = 1$

24) $t = \dfrac{1}{15}$

25) $h = -1$

26) $b = \dfrac{7}{11}$

27) $x = -\dfrac{2}{9}$

28) $c = \dfrac{1}{12}$

29) $h = \dfrac{-3}{10}$

30) $x = 1\dfrac{11}{16}$

31) $a = \dfrac{-1}{9}$

32) $x = -5\dfrac{1}{3}$

33) true

34) false

35) false

36) true

37) $\dfrac{7}{12}$

38) $\dfrac{31}{40}$

39) $1\dfrac{2}{21}$

40) $\dfrac{-13}{45}$

41) $38\dfrac{1}{2}$

42) $13\dfrac{1}{8}$

43) $\dfrac{5}{36}$

44) $1\dfrac{40}{63}$

45) $\dfrac{-7}{40}$

46) $14\dfrac{133}{180}$

47) $\dfrac{18}{55}$

48) $15\dfrac{2}{3}$

49) $\dfrac{8}{45}$

50) $8\dfrac{34}{77}$

51) $\dfrac{13}{42}$

52) $\dfrac{31}{150}$

53) $\dfrac{-1}{8}$

54) $\dfrac{8x}{11}$

55) $\dfrac{a}{3}$

56) $\dfrac{1}{2r}$

57) $\dfrac{6b}{5}$

58) $\dfrac{-n}{39}$

59) $\dfrac{-1}{4m}$

60) $\dfrac{5x^2+8}{30x}$

61) $\dfrac{2t+9}{30}$

62) $\dfrac{10+3x^2}{42x}$

63) $-2\dfrac{7}{15}$

64) $\dfrac{3-4x}{36}$

65) $\dfrac{-2}{3}$

66) $\dfrac{33}{50}$

67) $\dfrac{-1}{99}$

68) $2\dfrac{7}{10}$

69) $1\dfrac{13}{15}$

70) $4\dfrac{1}{40}$ yds.

71) $17\dfrac{7}{36}$ yds.

72) $11\dfrac{23}{24}$ ft.

73) $5\dfrac{5}{48}$ ft.

74) $69\dfrac{4}{5}$ in.

75) $50\dfrac{19}{36}$ ft.

76) $40\dfrac{3}{4}$"

77) $12\dfrac{3}{5}$ gallons

78) no

79) no

80) yes

81) no

82) $19\dfrac{2}{5}$ hours

83) $5\dfrac{4}{5}$ hours

84) $15\dfrac{9}{10}$ hours

85) $25\dfrac{1}{5}$ hours

86) $3\dfrac{1}{2}$ hours

87) $\dfrac{1}{5}$ hour

88) $\dfrac{7}{25}$

89) $\dfrac{9}{25}$

90) $\dfrac{7}{50}$

91) $\dfrac{1}{100}$

92) $2\dfrac{3}{4}$

93) $\dfrac{9x^2}{5}$

94) $4\dfrac{1}{11}$

95) $\dfrac{10}{7d}$

96) 9, 18, 27, 36, 45 and 54

97) $3n=n+8, n=4$

98) no

99) graph

100)   -23

101)   37

4.6 Order of Operations

1) $\left(\dfrac{1}{2}\right)^4$

2) $\left(\dfrac{-2}{3}\right)^3$

3) $\left(\dfrac{-4}{5}\right)^5$

4) $-\left(\dfrac{3}{7}\right)^7$

5) $\left(\dfrac{2}{3}\right)\cdot\left(\dfrac{2}{3}\right)$

6) $\left(\dfrac{-4}{5}\right)\cdot\left(\dfrac{-4}{5}\right)\cdot\left(\dfrac{-4}{5}\right)\cdot\left(\dfrac{-4}{5}\right)$

7) $\left(\dfrac{-1}{2}\right)\cdot\left(\dfrac{-1}{2}\right)\cdot\left(\dfrac{-1}{2}\right)\cdot\left(\dfrac{-1}{2}\right)\cdot\left(\dfrac{-1}{2}\right)$

8) $-\left(\dfrac{2}{7}\right)\cdot\left(\dfrac{2}{7}\right)\cdot\left(\dfrac{2}{7}\right)\cdot\left(\dfrac{2}{7}\right)\cdot\left(\dfrac{2}{7}\right)\cdot\left(\dfrac{2}{7}\right)\cdot\left(\dfrac{2}{7}\right)\cdot\left(\dfrac{2}{7}\right)$

9) $\dfrac{1}{16}$

10) $\dfrac{-27}{125}$

11) $-\dfrac{16}{81}$

12) $\dfrac{4x^2}{49y^2}$

13) $\dfrac{8}{27}$ and $\dfrac{8}{3}$

14) $\dfrac{16}{49}$ and $\dfrac{64}{7}$

15) $\dfrac{-2}{5}$

16) $\dfrac{3}{4}$

17) $\dfrac{5}{7}$

18) $\dfrac{86}{15}$

19) $\dfrac{1}{3}$

20) 1

21) $\dfrac{37}{72}$

22) $\dfrac{-9}{20}$

23) $1\dfrac{8}{9}$

24) $1\dfrac{1}{144}$

25) $\dfrac{9}{14}$

26) $2\dfrac{11}{42}$

27) $17\dfrac{1}{2}ft^2$

28) $91cm^2$

29) $\dfrac{3}{70}in^2$

30) $2\dfrac{3}{16}yd^2$

31) $26cm^2$

32) $77\dfrac{1}{2}ft^2$

33) $\dfrac{9}{56}in^2$

34) $7\dfrac{73}{120}yd^2$

35) $17\dfrac{19}{64}ft^2$

36) $147yd^2$

37) $1\dfrac{7}{8}$

38) $\dfrac{7}{12}$

39) $\dfrac{4}{45}$

40) 24

41) $-5\dfrac{1}{2}$

42) $\dfrac{3}{20}$

43) -3

44) $2\dfrac{45}{58}$

45) $\dfrac{56}{171}$

46) False

47) False

48) True

49) $\dfrac{16}{81}$

50) $\dfrac{-1}{125}$

51) $1\dfrac{3}{5}$

52) $\dfrac{-1}{125}$

53) $\dfrac{x^2}{9}$

54) $\dfrac{y^3}{64}$

55) $\dfrac{-11}{12}$

56) $\dfrac{-2}{25}$

57) $\dfrac{-479}{700}$

58) 1

59) $\dfrac{25}{36}$

60) $\dfrac{-3}{125}$

61) $\dfrac{-3}{40}$

62) $\dfrac{9}{20}$

63) $\dfrac{1}{12}$

64) $\dfrac{-2xy+14x}{21y}$

65) $\dfrac{16x}{55}$

66) $\dfrac{-y}{7x}$

67) -2

68) $-1\dfrac{5}{14}$

69) 3

70) -6

71) $2\dfrac{2}{9}$

72) $\dfrac{9}{10}$

73) $\dfrac{7}{12}$

74) $\dfrac{289}{400}$

75) $-5\dfrac{11}{36}$

76) $\dfrac{-37}{48}$

77) $-2\dfrac{5}{12}$

78) $\dfrac{-7}{9}$

79) $8\dfrac{3}{4}\,ft$

80) $45\dfrac{9}{16}\,ft^2$

81) $9\dfrac{139}{240}\,cm$

82) $10\dfrac{4}{9}\,ft^2$

83) $10\,cm^2$

84) $52\dfrac{1}{4}\,m^2$

85) $17\dfrac{37}{60}\,in^2$

86) $24\,yd^2$

87) In $\left(\dfrac{a}{b}\right)^3$ both a and b are cubed. In $\dfrac{a^3}{b}$ only the a is cubed.

88) A fraction with a numerator and/or denominator that is also a fraction.

89) $\dfrac{41}{50}$

90) graph

91) $4\dfrac{4}{17}$

92) $\dfrac{14}{84},\dfrac{63}{84},\dfrac{60}{84}$

93) $d=-1$

94) 6, -9, and 0

95) $m=-65$

96) 6,611

97) 168 square feet

98) $2^3 \cdot 3^2$

Chapter 4 Quiz Yourself Answers

Section 4.1 Quiz Yourself:

(1) $\dfrac{1}{3}$ *(2)* $\dfrac{2}{15}$ *(3)* $\dfrac{7}{9}$ *(4)* $\dfrac{2}{3}$ *(5)* $\dfrac{-25}{7}$

(6) $\dfrac{6}{7}$ *(7)* $\dfrac{-36x}{49y}$ *(8)* 8

Section 4.2 Quiz Yourself:

(1) $\dfrac{8}{21}$ *(2)* $-13\dfrac{1}{2}$ *(3)* 2   *(4)* -48 *(5)* $-27\dfrac{3}{5}$ *(6)* $k = -1$

(7) $n = 1$ *(8)* $1\dfrac{1}{4}$ *cups of peanut butter*   *(9)* $242\dfrac{1}{2}$ *miles*   *(10)* $329\dfrac{3}{5} ft^2$

Section 4.3 Quiz Yourself:

(1) $\dfrac{-17}{5}$ *(2)* $\dfrac{5}{49}$ *(3)* $1\dfrac{3}{26}$ *(4)* $2\dfrac{2}{15}$ *(5)* $-1\dfrac{1}{2}$

(6) $\dfrac{-81ab^2}{35}$ *(7)* $x = \dfrac{17}{24}$ *(8)* $x = -81$ *(9)* $r = 7\dfrac{67}{215} mph$ *(10)* 149 *orange trees*

Section 4.4 Quiz Yourself:

(1) 90, 180, 270   *(2) 156*   *(3)* $102x^4y^2$ *(4)* $\dfrac{42}{105}$ *(5) 195;* $\dfrac{27}{195}; \dfrac{75}{195}$

(6) $462xy^2;$ $\dfrac{336y}{462xy^2}; \dfrac{275x}{462xy^2}$ *(7) 200;* $\dfrac{175}{200}; \dfrac{144}{200}; \dfrac{135}{200}$ *(8)<*

Section 4.5 Quiz Yourself:

(1) $\dfrac{4}{27}$ *(2)* $1\dfrac{5}{22}$ *(3)* $\dfrac{29c}{24}$ *(4)* $2\dfrac{3}{7}$ *(5)* $6\dfrac{1}{12}$ *(6)* $50\dfrac{3}{7}$

(7) $x = 1\dfrac{2}{5}$ *(8)* $h = \dfrac{-11}{27}$ *(9)* $3\dfrac{3}{10}$ *yd. of material.*   *(10)* $57\dfrac{3}{4}$ *ft. of chair rail*

Section 4.6 Quiz Yourself:

(1) $\dfrac{8}{125}$ *(2)* $\dfrac{16x^4y^8}{81}$ *(3)* 1   *(4)* $-\dfrac{27}{43}$ *(5)* $\dfrac{1}{72}$ *(6)* $\dfrac{-44}{45}$

(7) $4\dfrac{1}{5}$ square units

Chapter 4 Review

1) $\dfrac{31}{4}$

2) $\dfrac{-29}{9}$

3) $\dfrac{-41}{5}$

4) $\dfrac{80}{7}$

5) $5\dfrac{3}{4}$

6) $8\dfrac{5}{9}$

7) $-16\dfrac{2}{5}$

8) $-12\dfrac{1}{2}$

9) $\dfrac{-9}{22}$

10) $\dfrac{2b^2}{3}$

11) $\dfrac{7}{12}$

12) $\dfrac{-79}{100}$

13) $\dfrac{-a}{9}$

14) $\dfrac{-6x}{7}$

15) $\dfrac{-18a^2}{35}$

16) $1\dfrac{2}{5}$

17) -4

18) -9

19) $-25\dfrac{1}{3}$

20) $\dfrac{-6}{25b}$

21) $\dfrac{2x^2}{9}$

22) $-4\dfrac{4}{5}$

23) $-11\dfrac{2}{3}$

24) $\dfrac{-3}{4}$

25) $\dfrac{5}{7}$

26) $-27\dfrac{1}{2}$

27) $-2\dfrac{1}{2}$

28) $203\,miles$

29) $3\dfrac{5}{7}\,ft^2$

30) $2\dfrac{2}{3}$

31) $1\dfrac{5}{9}$

32) 24

33) $\dfrac{-5a}{4}$

34) $\dfrac{34x^2}{27}$

35) $-1\dfrac{11}{15}$

36) $-2\dfrac{89}{100}$

37) $\dfrac{14x^3y}{13}$

38) $\dfrac{33a^2b^2}{38}$

39) $-a^2b^2$

40) $\dfrac{15x^2y^3}{14}$

41) 48

42) 210

43) $LCD = 63; \dfrac{35}{63}\,and\,\dfrac{54}{63}$

44) $LCD = 22; \dfrac{6}{22}\,and\,\dfrac{7}{22}$

45) $LCD = 840; \dfrac{320}{840}\,and\,\dfrac{357}{840}$

46) $LCD = 56; \dfrac{32x}{56}\,and\,\dfrac{35}{56}$

47) $LCD = 90x; \dfrac{65}{90x}\,and\,\dfrac{66xy}{90x}$

48) $LCD = 660; \dfrac{108}{660}\,and\,\dfrac{375}{660}$

49) $LCD = 195; \dfrac{117}{195},\dfrac{120}{195}\,and\,\dfrac{171}{195}$

50) $LCD = 1750; \dfrac{1125}{1750},\dfrac{340}{1750}\,and\,\dfrac{791}{1750}$

51) $<$

52) $<$

53) $1\dfrac{4}{45}$

54) $\dfrac{9}{50}$

55) $\dfrac{23}{48}$

56) $-1\dfrac{7}{20}$

57) $\dfrac{-63}{65}$

58) $\dfrac{-181}{1872}$

59) $18\dfrac{5}{36}$

60) $20\dfrac{29}{48}$

61) $x = -1\dfrac{11}{36}$

62) $x = 1\dfrac{1}{15}$

63) $x = 7\dfrac{9}{40}$

64) $x = -4\dfrac{7}{12}$

65) $\dfrac{9}{25}$

66) $\dfrac{-1}{27}$

67) $-2\dfrac{9}{20}$

68) $\dfrac{27}{29}$

69) $\dfrac{1}{36}$

70) $-4\dfrac{5}{12}$

71) 2

72) $-1\dfrac{2}{9}$

73) $\dfrac{9}{14}$

74) $2\dfrac{11}{42}$

75) $47\dfrac{29}{60}m^2$

76) $20\dfrac{3}{7}ft^2$

Chapter 4 Test Yourself

1) $\dfrac{59}{5}$

2) $21\dfrac{6}{7}$

3) $\dfrac{-1}{2}$

4) $LCD = 168x;$
$\dfrac{99}{168x} and \dfrac{35x^2}{168x}$

5) $>$

6) $1\dfrac{7}{45}$

7) $\dfrac{63}{100}$

8) $\dfrac{29}{36}$

9) $\dfrac{-29}{36}$

10) $\dfrac{-905}{1452}$

11) $\dfrac{16bc^2}{105}$

12) $\dfrac{-2}{7}$

13) -9

14) $-1\dfrac{3}{8}$

15) $\dfrac{-8}{75}$

16) $\dfrac{-28}{45}$

17) $n = \dfrac{-34}{63}$

18) $x = 1\dfrac{3}{7}$

19) $x = 1\dfrac{1}{10}$

20) $m = -1$

21) $23\dfrac{5}{6}in^2$

22) $53\dfrac{7}{45}cm^2$

23) $1\dfrac{1}{3}cups$

24) $1,594$ participants

Chapters 1 to 4 Cumulative Review

1) $2^3 \cdot 3 \cdot 13$

2) $-14, 2$

3) seventeen thousand, eight hundred ninety-one

4) 346,000

5) $\dfrac{3^4}{17}$

6) $\dfrac{66}{15}$

7) graph

8) $>$

9) $\dfrac{5}{19}$

10) $-5\dfrac{4}{7}$

11) $\dfrac{9m}{2}$

12) $\dfrac{-5y}{7x}$

13) -32

14) undefined

15) -35

16) 349

17) -5

18) 29

19) 0

20) 0

21) -46

22) $\dfrac{2}{3}$

23) $8\dfrac{3}{35}$

24) $-2\dfrac{5}{6}$

25) $\dfrac{2x^4y^2}{15}$

26) $m = -29$

27) $a = -15$

28) $y = -4$

29) $n = 7$

30) $y = -2$

31) $y = -1\dfrac{1}{2}$

32) $m = -5\dfrac{11}{16}$

33) $x = -6\dfrac{3}{5}$

34) $x = -7\dfrac{6}{7}$

35) $x = \dfrac{-19}{28} \dfrac{-19}{28}$

36) $x = -1\dfrac{1}{4}$

37) $\dfrac{4}{7}$

38) $-5\dfrac{1}{3}$

39) $1\dfrac{8}{9}$

40) $1\dfrac{1}{144}$

41) $n - 11 = 82; n = 93$

42) $A = 29n; A = \$754$

43) $a = 91$

44) $210m^2$

45) $532\,ft^2$

46) $64cm^2$

47) $53\dfrac{5}{8}in^2$

48) $\theta_1 = 48°, \theta_2 = 38°,$ $\theta_3 = 94°$

49) $width = 9\dfrac{1}{4}ft, length = 49\dfrac{1}{4}ft$

50) $455\dfrac{9}{16}ft^2$

Chapter 5:Decimals

5.1 Introduction To Decimals

1) 8

2) 9

3) five and three tenths

4) eighty-seven ten-thousandths

5) negative fifty-one thousandths

6) eight and three thousand four hundred forty-one ten-thousandths

7) 8.5

8) -32.05

9) -11.034

10) 89.0013

11) 0.00187, 0.000005

12) 0.025, 0.00087

13) false

14) false

15) true

16) false

17) <

18) >

19) >

20) <

21) A < B, B weighs more

22) Quarter > yen, US

23) $\dfrac{1}{100}$

24) $\dfrac{49}{10000}$

25) $\dfrac{23}{5}$

26) $\dfrac{69}{20}$

27) $4\dfrac{1}{5}$

28) $8\dfrac{3}{4}$

29) $17\dfrac{163}{2000}$

30) $38\dfrac{114}{125}$

31) $1\dfrac{1}{3}$

32) 3/4

33) ¾ ft wide by 2 4/5ft long

34) $\dfrac{13}{20}$ in. by $\dfrac{81}{200}$ in.

35) 789.3

36) 789.35

37) 789.346

38) 789.34578

39) 3.142

40) 2.718282

41) -$5785.35

42) -$75.41

43) 52.8 ft.

44) -12.8°

45) Eight and seven tenths

46) Negative nine and twenty-five hundredths

47) Seven ten-thousandths

48) Nineteen and four hundredths

49) Eight hundred forty-five thousandths

50) Negative fourteen and eighty-seven hundredths

51) Six hundred and five tenths

52) Eight thousand and nine thousandths

53) 5.6

54) 5.06

55) 5.000006

56) -28.12

57) -113.15

58) 97.503

59) 39.07

60) 3.14

61) 0.005

62) 0.000003

63) 0.0055

64) 0.075

65) $\dfrac{22}{25}$

66) $\dfrac{49}{200}$

67) $\dfrac{-3}{400}$

68) $\dfrac{18}{125}$

69) $17\dfrac{4}{5}$

70) $29\dfrac{7}{20}$

71) $-237\dfrac{34}{125}$

72) $532\dfrac{1}{4}$

73) $\dfrac{53}{60}$

74) $\dfrac{39}{100}$

75) $8\dfrac{37}{100}$

76) $\dfrac{23}{30}$

77) $1\dfrac{41}{75}$

78) $8\dfrac{59}{60}$

79) >

80) >

81) <

82) =

83) >

84) <

85) #2 and #4

86) #1 and #4

87) 1.0

88) 89.46

89) 123.0

90) 23.8

91) 5678.15

92) 1.9236

93) 0.239

94) 14.782

95) $25.39

96) $10.43

97) False

98) True

99) True

100) True

101) False

102) b

103) c

104) 4

105) x = -13

106) 14,600

107) $\dfrac{2}{3}$

108) $2\dfrac{2}{9}$

5.2 Adding and Subtracting Decimals

1) 97.19

2) 18.34345

3) 11.5

4) 393.32

5) 5.656

6) 19.369

7) 2.1x + 10.1

8) 8.55x + 27.03

9) 11.666 − 19.82x

10) 45.6 + 60.13x

11) $1387; $1387.05

12) $2062; $2061.88

13) 56.6

14) -5.28

15) -102.373

16) -477.699

17) -2.93

18) -27.07

19) 107.9

20) 6.56

21) -27.96

22) 13.68

23) $b = -2.9$

24) $a = 33$

25) $p = 29.93$

26) $x = -47$

27) $n = 33.5$

28) $b = -51.05$

29) $x = -31.9$

30) $y = 26.4$

31) $84.58

32) $R = \$5.01$ million

33) 1105.351

34) 44.0055

35) 13.5

36) -59.267

37) -28.26

38) 684.01

39) -3.8a − 9.3

40) 11.89 − 27.9x

41) 17.41 + 1.5w

42) 35.12k − 59.403

43) 93.4 + 38.76q

44) 21.4 − 5.2x

45) No

46) Yes

47) No

48) No

49) x=18.69

50) $g = -14.1$

51) $m = -18.8$

52) $x = 15.677$

53) $p = -28.357$

54) $x = -45.71$

55) $x = 550.385$

56) $y = 615.854$

57) $x = 108.372$

58) $x = -2.2.052$

59) $715.01

60) $395.27

61) $67.33

62) 51.95 inches

63) 61.97 inches

64) 10.07 inches

65) 2.75 inches

66) $1281.991 millions

67) $23.497 millions

68) No

69) 18.7 inches

70) 1.91 ft.

71) 26.2 m

72) 0.38ft.

73) 27 cm.

74) 18 in.

75) -0.13

76) 18.42

77) 0.6

78) 3.6

79) R = $238.8 thousand

80) $10.50 per item

81) markup of $90.59

82) markup of $11.44

83) 4.6295 to 4.6439

84) Megulon: 0.8993 to 1.0363, Pentium: 1.3036 to 1.4406

85) 34.087

86) =

87) 35.015

88) $\dfrac{34}{10} = \dfrac{17}{5}$

89) $\dfrac{6}{1000} = \dfrac{3}{500}$

90) 80

91) $-\dfrac{7}{12}$

92) 31

93) $\dfrac{2}{3x}$

94) 81

5.3 Multiplying Decimals

1) 2.7

2) 0.105

3) -0.234

4) 46.914

5) 0.48

6) -0.0035

7) $7.1x + 2.13$

8) $-2x - 3.6$

9) $-2.5x + 0.85$

10) $-0.16x + 0.93$

11) 29.75 in by 3.85 in.

12) 39.78 in. by 82.62 in.

13) 34.56

14) 982

15) 439000

16) 892000

17) 8.9

18) 1800700

19) 40.019

20) 9214904000

21) 11,400,000

22) 16,000,000

23) 4.41

24) 140.608

25) 0.0196

26) -13.69

27) -25.1001

28) -0.4096

29) 0.00459

30) -0.6889

31) 12π, 37.68 in

32) 0.8π, 2.512 ft.

33) 70.56πcm, 221.5584 cm.

34) 17.64π, 55.3896 ft.

35) $C = 18\pi \approx 56.52$
    $A = 81\pi \approx 254.34$

36) $C = 0.8\pi \approx 2.512$
    $A = 0.16\pi \approx 0.5024$

37) C = 14.13 in.

38) A = 28.26 mi^2

39) 58.8

40) 7.76

41) 0.32

42) 0.045

43) -0.045

44) 0.105

45) -0.00048

46) -2.205

47) 7.675

48) -4517.1

49) 240

50) 700

51) 654.8

52) 76145

53) 1781920

54) 784

55) -0.064

56) -0.81

57) 65.61

58) -0.000343

59) 0.00000001

60) -1.344

61) -0.0243

62) -0.2, 0.3, -1.25

63) 0.81, 0.0036, 2.25

64) 3219.12 ft^2

65) 72 in^2

66) $96

67) $270

68) 92.4 grams of fat

69) 9 grams of saturated fat

70) 1.688 miles

71) 9,750,000

72) 3,900

73) 10,170,000

74) 9,300,000 miles

75) $15152.16

76) $561.48

77) $9420

78) $70

79) $P = 6.4\,ft,\ A = 2.56\,ft^2$

80) $P = 0.32\,in,\ A = 0.0064\,in^2$

81) 37.68 in

82) 31.4 cm

83) 0.17584 ft

84) 52/752 m

85) 12.56 ft^2

86) 314 mm^2

87) 0.581 in^2

88) 9.62 mi^2

89) $C = 18.84\,ft,\ A = 28.26\,ft^2$

90) $C = 628\,cm,\ A = 31400\,cm^2$

91) $C = 5.652\,yd,\ A = 2.5434\,yd^2$

92) $C = 27.004\,mi,\ A = 58.059\,mi^2$

93) $C = 56.52\,in,\ A = 254.34\,in^2$

94) $C = 37.68\,in,\ A = 113.04\,in^2$

95) 3.899 lbs.

96) 7.41 lbs

97) 2.062 lbs.

98) 0.948 lbs.

99) 203.305 lbs.

100)   549.325 lbs.

101)   451.385 yd^2

102)   peanuts: $712.95, chocolate: $812.50, oatmeal: $339.45, sugar: $535

103) $88,762.50

104)   3.52 inches thick

105)   -4.5

106) $k = 0.133$

107)   -6.9

108) $4.2g + 5.3w + 13$

109)   no

110) $3x + 7$

111)   An equation has an '=' sign

112)   -25, 25

113) $\dfrac{y}{5}$

114)   -6

5.4 Dividing Decimals

1)   17.75

2)   25.4

3)   13.65

4)   845

5)   2.53

6)   0.714

7)   49.5

8)   -1.19

9)   3580 cells

10) 72.1875 minutes

11) 78.239

12) 0.93715

13) 0.0567

14) 0.001865

15) 0.984817

16) 0.00064

17) 0.000202

18) 0.000000008

19) $x = 6$

20) $x = -180$

21) $x = -21.07$

22) $x = -0.468$

23) $x = 20.67$

24) $x = -0.7$

25) $x = 477$

26) $x = -7.4$

27) 6 days

28) 58 years old

29) divisor

30) dividend

31) quotient

32) 41033.333

33) 13157

34) -24.4375

35) 28.48

36) 58.97

37) -2.34

38) -0.0089453

39) -9.137

40) $x = 8.523$

41) $x = -49$

42) $x = -305$

43) $x = -6.34$

44) $x = -6$

45) $x = -6.25$

46) $x = -5.22$

47) $x = 32.81$

48) $x = 3.75$

49) $x = -0.425$

50) $x = -23.6$

51) $x = 19.2$

52) $x = 80.8$

53) $x = -58.3$

54) $x = 18.85$

55) $x = -16.01$

56) $x = 8.45$

57) $327.08

58) $243.22

59) 24 gallons

60) 25 drums

61) $8.79

62) $18.59

63) $29.79 for each visit

64) $3.61

65) 23 songs

66) 7.6 decibels each

67) 6.96 mi/sec

68) 36.3 mi/min

69) 5.7 tons

70) $780.40, 15 months, $3041

71) 9.2 MB, 315 MB, 45.5 min

72) 19.5 days

73) 32 sections

74) 0.33375

75) 6.8 ft

76) 8.6 in

77) 2.6 yd

78) 15.8 m

79) 12.6 yrs

80) False

81) True

82) True

83) False

84) True

85) Move decimal to right once in both divisor and dividend and divide 5 into 37.

86) Move decimal to right once in both divisor and dividend and divide to 3 decimal place to round to hundredths.

87) Move decimal to the left one place value

88) Moving decimal places to divide so you are diving by a whole number.

89) -0.00024

90) $462.64

91) 9.5

92) $\dfrac{13}{60}$

93) 7

94) $6 \cdot 6 \cdot 6 \cdot 6$

95) $\dfrac{-5a}{8}$

96) 23

97) -252

5.5 Order Of Operations and Decimals

(Answers rounded to the nearest thousandths place.)

1) 0.5

2) 7.75

3) -2.6

4) -0.375

5) -1.75

6) $-0.91\overline{6}$

7) $2.\overline{3}$

8) $0.\overline{45}$

9) 3.875

10) 5.286

11) no

12) no

13) yes

14) no

15) $\dfrac{13}{20} = 0.65$

16) $\dfrac{2}{14} = 0.148$

17) -10.96

18) -45

19) 3.702

20) 17.07

21) 8.97

22) 2.408

23) $\dfrac{14}{15}$

24) $\dfrac{41}{100}$

25) 0.45 ft.

26) 1.14

27) 22.56

28) -12.36

29) 43.2

30) 3.02

31) 185.18176

32) -55.04

33) 30.8945

34) -0.55

35) 7.45

36) 22.26

37) 5.256

38) false

39) false

40) 7.38

41) 21.135

42) -231.2

43) 68.4

44) -29.792

45) -31.314

46) -0.55

47) -2.68

48) $1\dfrac{11}{100}$

49) $\dfrac{47}{100}$

50) 3.004

51) -5.42

52) -1.125

53) 14.647

54) 1.8

55) 10.35

56) 551.87

57) 37308.838

58) 8.1

59) 41.7

60) 1.5386

61) 116.8394

62) 102.109

63) 0.006

64) 0.0416

65) 139.3875

66) 6.05

67) -21.5

68) 3.14

69) 32.8

70) 32.8

71) 0.130

72) 0.396

73) 0.266

74) 0.337

75) The numerator, 112 is greater than the denominator 105.

76) It isn't since the numerator, 75 is less than the denominator 76.

77) <

78) <

79) <

80) >

81) <

82) =

83) <

84) =

85) $7(1.29) + 3(9.99) + 2(24.59)$

86) $12.65x + 9.45x + 15.95$

87) five and eighty three hundredths

88) 1.7 grams

89) 0.037

90) $4.5t - 2$

91) $x = 5$

92) 0

93) $x = 10$

94) 70,000,000

95) $\dfrac{81}{16} = 5\dfrac{1}{16}$

96) 70

5.6 Statistics: Mean, Median, and Mode

1) 51

2) 19.88

3) 165

4) 2.469

5) $4\frac{107}{180}$

6) $1\frac{1553}{1800}$

7) 48.5

8) 156

9) 19.2

10) 2.85

11) $4\frac{4}{5}$

12) $1\frac{7}{8}$

13) 45

14) 120

15) 23.8

16) no mode

17) $\frac{2}{3}$

18) $4\frac{3}{8}$

19) 88 degrees

20) mean:$3.02

    median:$2.85

21) 9

22) median:10 mode: 10 or

    11

23) mean:68.9 median:75.5

    mode:100 the mode is to

    high

24) mean:67.6 median:85

    mode:0 the mode is too

    low

25) 113

26) 105

27) 110.5

28) 4

29) 6

30) 12 inches

31) 7.8 inches

32) $90.67

33) -1.75

34) x = -11.3

35) $\frac{2}{3}$

36) graph

37) $2 \cdot 3 \cdot 7$

38) 33

39) 2

Chapter 5 Quiz Yourself Answers

Section 5.1 Quiz Yourself:

1) sixty-seven and eight hundred ninety-one thousandths

2) negative thirty four and two hundredths

3) 0.0075

4) 400.035

5) 8.12

6) 2.7183

7) <

8) >

9) $5\frac{3}{4}$

10) $\frac{4}{15}$

Section 5.2 Quiz Yourself:

1) 540.751

2) 133.03

3) -136.328

4) 73.902

5) 7.18x + 78.3

6) -101.4155 + 9.58x

7) x = -276.641

8) x = -759.327

9) $898

10) Revenue = $3.683 million

Section 5.3 Quiz Yourself:

1) 8623.482

2) 78945.02

3) 8.134

4) -0.7921

5) 5.6169

6) 147.6225

7) $1165.36

8) 21.5625 ft²

9) 3,200,000 gaming systems

Section 5.4 Quiz Yourself:

1) 175.908

2) 3.9464

3) -5.632

4) $16\frac{39}{50}$

5) $31.79

6) $15.49 each

7) x = -5.89

8) $x = -62.0\overline{6}$

9) x = 9.6

10) x = 11.858

Section 5.5 Quiz Yourself:

1) 0.875

2) 0.769

3) 21.3

4) 3.79

5) -92.123

6) 1.01

7) 353.073

8) 234.005

9) 280.806 ft²

Section 5.6 Quiz Yourself:

(1) mean: 11, median: 8, mode: 7   (2) mean: 4.2, median: 4.05, mode: none

(3) mean: $\frac{53}{100}$, median: $\frac{1}{2}$, mode: $\frac{4}{5}$ (4) median: 6'11", mode: 7'1"   (5) mean: 1.09 grams

Chapter 5 Summary and Review

1. seventy-five hundredths
2. one and eight tenths
3. seventy-eight and seventeen hundredths
4. nine hundred thirty-two and forty-nine hundredths
5. $\frac{3}{8}$
6. $5\frac{3}{5}$
7. $127\frac{12}{25}$
8. $628\frac{31}{50}$
9. <
10. <
11. >
12. <
13. 1.4
14. 0.098
15. 35.35
16. 62.9
17. 39.9
18. 8.62
19. 152.954
20. -192.55
21. -3.323
22. -52.4863
23. $7.5x + 18.9$
24. $-43.98m + 37.9$
25. $-6.34a - 6.13$
26. $52.83n - 74.17$
27. x = 22.4
28. x = -1.41
29. x = -13.3
30. m = 13.52
31. $489.38

32. $495.36
33. 38.5
34. -703.925
35. -2.68
36. 709.46
37. -358.7
38. 52.275
39. 134.236
40. -0.67
41. 54.872
42. 26.01
43. -1.4641
44. -200.277
45. 32.656 m
46. $227.205 in^2$
47. $28.26 ft^2$
48. 113.668 ft.
49. 15.1
50. -7.18
51. -62.22
52. 15.245
53. 4.5612
54. -0.0090034
55. x = 30.94
56. m = -1241.685
57. x = 26.4
58. x = -4
59. m = 84.7
60. y = -0.9
61. $178.70
62. 10.5 gallons
63. 6.2 min/mile
64. 19.4 miles/hour
65. 0.2
66. 0.65
67. 0.875
68. 0.467
69. 0.833
70. 0.378

71. 7.35
72. -9.78
73. -63.49
74. -50.9
75. 6.16
76. -1.875
77. 24.74
78. -27.375
79. 16.97
80. -8.52
81. 21.8
82. 6.01
83. 1.95
84. 183.72
85. $5301.80; $3844.89
86. 63.5 miles per day on average
87. Mean: 15; Median: 15; Mode: 15
88. Mean: 41; Median: 39.5; Mode: 37
89. Mean: 16.8; Median: 16.2; Mode: 16.2
90. Mean: 36.9; Median: 34.5; Mode: 34.5
91. Mean: $\frac{317}{600}$;
    Median: $\frac{1}{2}$;
    Mode: $\frac{1}{3}$
92. Mean age is 24
93. Median: 20.5; Mode: 19
94. 53
95. Median: 6 feet
96. Mode: 6 feet

Chapter 5 Test

1. Seven thousand, six hundred twenty four and ninety-one thousandths.
2. Thirty-five ten-thousandths
3. 3.05
4. 17,000.000026
5. 3.14
6. 170.146
7. -102.702
8. -5.715

9. -0.2709
10. 0.00064
11. -5288.08
12. -10.95
13. 0.875
14. $0.\overline{45}$
15. $\dfrac{39}{50}$
16. $6\dfrac{11}{4000}$
17. <

18. <
19. >
20. 57.4
21. 3
22. $278.13
23. $3515.04
24. $2680
25. $65.62
26. mean: 13, mode: 15, median: 14

Cumulative Review Chapter 1 to 5

1. 2x + 15
2. 6(x – 7)
3. $2(x+5)=x+12;\; x=2$
4. $\dfrac{3x}{4}=45;\; x=60$
5. $\dfrac{-4}{5}$
6. 0.0016
7. -12
8. 18
9. 225.16
10. $\dfrac{23}{30}$
11. $\dfrac{233}{270}$
12. $11\dfrac{10}{21}$
13. $3\dfrac{14}{15}$
14. $-5\dfrac{23}{24}$
15. $\dfrac{16xy}{15}$
16. $\dfrac{-26x^3}{27y}$
17. 5.87
18. 15
19. -27.25
20. 73
21. 32

22. $\dfrac{6}{7}$
23. 16.2
24. -9.76
25. $54.479 cm^3$
26. x = 37
27. g = -2
28. x = 1
29. m = 3
30. x = -2.1
31. $x=\dfrac{-67}{75}$
32. $b=-9\dfrac{4}{5}$
33. x = -68
34. $x=\dfrac{-15}{2}$
35. LCM = 378
36. $2^2 \cdot 113$
37. 9 and 8
38. LCD = 195, $\dfrac{52}{195}, \dfrac{115}{195}$
39. $0.\overline{63}$
40. $9\dfrac{177}{500}$
41. $319.60
42. $19+4r=64;\; r=11\,\text{rides}$
43. $A=59.5 m^2$
44. $A=14 in^2$
45. $A=56.98\, ft^2$

46. $x+(24+2x)=180$, 52° & 128°
47. 8.78 min/mile
48. 78
49. Mean: $13.89, Median: $13.10, Mode: $8.23
50. Mean: 72; Median: 73; Mode:73

Chapter 6 : Ratios and Proportions

6.1 Introduction To Ratios and Rates

1) $42 to $126; $\dfrac{\$42}{\$126}$

2) 8:44; $\dfrac{8}{44}$

3) 17:35; $\dfrac{17}{35}$

4) 5:14; $\dfrac{5}{14}$

5) 8 to 26; 8:26

6) 10:60; $\dfrac{10}{60}$

7) 9 to 12; $\dfrac{9}{12}$

8) 6:15; $\dfrac{6}{15}$

9) 12:23; 12 to 23

10) 8:6; $\dfrac{8}{6}$

11) $\dfrac{6}{39} = \dfrac{2}{13}$

12) $\dfrac{16}{48} = \dfrac{1}{3}$

13) $\dfrac{35}{95} = \dfrac{7}{19}$

14) $\dfrac{26}{65} = \dfrac{2}{5}$

15) $\dfrac{5/12}{7/20} = \dfrac{20}{21}$

16) $\dfrac{4\,1/6}{1\,3/5} = \dfrac{125}{48}$

17) $\dfrac{3.2}{6.5} = \dfrac{32}{65}$

18) $\dfrac{0.49}{6.3} = \dfrac{7}{90}$

19) $\dfrac{4.8}{3\,1/2} = \dfrac{48}{35}$

20) $\dfrac{5\frac{1}{4}}{4.2} = \dfrac{5}{3}$

21) ratio, units both people

22) rate, units are different

23) rate, units are different

24) ratio, units both $

25) $\dfrac{72\,miles}{5\,hours}$

26) $\dfrac{115\,miles}{2\,hours}$

27) $\dfrac{3\,boxes}{1\,tree}$

28) $\dfrac{2\,cashiers}{19\,customers}$

29) $0.05 per oz.

30) $906 per year

31) $0.90 per package of sports beans

32) 42.1 miles per gallon

33) $0.15 per oz.

34) $6.99 per lb.

35) 48 oz. of cashews for $9.75

36) $59.99 for 700 minutes

37) ratio; $\dfrac{11}{21}$

38) ratio; $\dfrac{8}{7}$

39) ratio; $\dfrac{5}{8}$

40) rate; $\dfrac{1\,foot}{3\,sec\,onds}$

41) rate; $\dfrac{1\,mile}{9\,min.}$

42) ratio; $\dfrac{1}{2}$

43) rate; $\dfrac{13\,rev.}{2\,min.}$

44) ratio; $\dfrac{3}{494}$

45) rate; $\dfrac{\$280}{1\,day}$

46) rate; $\dfrac{\$108}{5\,adjustments}$

47) rate; $\dfrac{100\,miles}{3\,gallons}$

48) 14:3

49) 3:1

50) 3:16

51) 5:12

52) 1:2

53) 1:34

54) 1:112

55) 5:16

56) 139:864

57) 103:228

58) 19:72

59) $\dfrac{\$375000}{2500\,ft^2} = \dfrac{\$150}{ft^2}$

60) $\dfrac{\$154000}{1400\,ft^2} = \dfrac{\$110}{ft^2}$

61) $\dfrac{24326974\,people}{268600\,mi^2} = \dfrac{90.57\,people}{mi^2}$

62) $\dfrac{36756666\,people}{163710\,mi^2} = \dfrac{224.52\,people}{mi^2}$

63) $\dfrac{\$1.29}{8\,oz.} = \dfrac{16c}{oz.}$

64) $\dfrac{\$3.79}{5\,lbs.} = \dfrac{76c}{lb.}$

65) $\dfrac{344\,miles}{2.4\,hours} = \dfrac{143.3\,miles}{hour}$

66) $\dfrac{2384\,miles}{5.8\,hours} = \dfrac{411.03\,miles}{hour}$

67) 120 tablets for $11.25

68) 64 oz jar for $4.99

69) 16oz bottle for $1.29

70) 21 lb. bag for $42.99

71) Jacob's car

72) Tarah

73) $\dfrac{2x}{5}$

74) 8612

75) $<$

76) $\dfrac{2}{5}$

77) yes

6.2 Introduction To Proportions

1) $\dfrac{8}{12} = \dfrac{10}{15}$

2) $\dfrac{24}{90} = \dfrac{140}{525}$

3) $\dfrac{4/5}{7/9} = \dfrac{12/25}{21/45}$

4) $\dfrac{8/9}{5/6} = \dfrac{7.2}{6.75}$

5) $\dfrac{1\,2/3}{3\,1/3} = \dfrac{1}{2}$

6) $\dfrac{4\,5/7}{1\,2/5} = \dfrac{2\,5/14}{7/10}$

7) $\dfrac{4.75}{8.50} = \dfrac{19}{34}$

8) $\dfrac{92.4}{29.4} = \dfrac{22}{7}$

9) false

10) true

11) true

12) false

13) false

14) false

15) true

16) true

17) x = 2.5

18) $a = -13\dfrac{1}{3}$

19) $y = 23\dfrac{1}{3}$

20) $m = 3\dfrac{1}{3}$

21) m = 2.6

22) p = 9.8

23) $b = 2\dfrac{1}{3}$

24) $y = \dfrac{216}{1813}$

25) 221 min.

26) $2\dfrac{1}{3}$ cups.

27) $\dfrac{4}{7} = \dfrac{8}{14}$

28) $\dfrac{9}{12} = \dfrac{51}{68}$

29) $\dfrac{5/8}{1/2} = \dfrac{6.75}{3}$

30) $\dfrac{4\,1/5}{9.4} = \dfrac{5.2}{10\,2/5}$

31) false

32) true

33) true

34) false

35) true

36) true

37) true

38) true

39) x = 15

40) b = 21

41) m = 12

42) $n = 3\dfrac{6}{7}$

43) $y = 1\dfrac{11}{15}$

44) $y = 14\dfrac{2}{3}$

45) x = -8

46) m = 10

47) t = 10.5

48) h = 0.525

49) k = -2.08

50) $x = 5\dfrac{5}{8}$

51) $x = \dfrac{5}{32}$

52) x = 95.12 minutes

53) x = 105.22 minutes

54) $x = 3\dfrac{11}{15}\,cups$

55) $x = 2\dfrac{3}{4}\,cups$

56) b = 404 big brown bats

57) 34.56 hours

58) 5:13, $\dfrac{5}{13}$

59) rate

60) $\dfrac{18}{54} = \dfrac{1}{3}$

61) \$75 per tutor

62) \$14.99 for 10 CDs

63) $\dfrac{3}{5}$

64) -512

65) $\dfrac{3}{4}$

66) $-\left(\dfrac{4}{5}\right)\cdot\left(\dfrac{4}{5}\right)\cdot\left(\dfrac{4}{5}\right)$

67) 14

6.3 More Applications of Proportions

1) $12.50

2) 22 oranges

3) The blade will be 6 inches.

4) The speaker will be 2.5 feet tall.

5) He should use 21.25 oz. of fertilizer.

6) 7.2 liters of concentrated dye.

7) The wall will measure $9\frac{3}{8}$ in. on a blueprint.

8) The second wall will be $14\frac{27}{32}$ feet.

9) It will take the plant 32 seconds.

10) 40,000 gallons in 1 day.

11) 12 lbs will serve about 38 guests.

12) $1\frac{7}{8}$ cups of cheese for 6 people.

13) 362.5 minutes.

14) $101.65

15) $2\frac{2}{9}$ gallons of solution.

16) 219 lbs. of fertilizer.

17) 5.7 milligrams

18) 80.3 oz. of Accelerade

19) 96 grams of protein

20) 7 hours of jogging.

21) 473 minutes of swimming

22) A mortgage of $928.57.

23) A mortgage of $1744.29.

24) 54 problems, yes he will finish.

25) 80.4 minutes

26) $56.25

27) $51.69

28) $2.90

29) $85.82

30) $19.64

31) $22\frac{2}{3}$ minutes

32) 77.5 minutes

33) 629 lbs.

34) 1269 lbs of blubber

35) 4,461 Americans

36) 7,655 Asians

37) $\frac{2}{5}$

38) $\frac{8.4}{5.2} = \frac{21}{13}$

39) $\frac{1.5}{6} = \frac{1.8}{7.2}$

40) $0.08 per copy

41) false

42) 11

43) $\frac{-7}{18}$

44) x =7

45) 3.6

46) 12.6

6.4 Similar Geometric Figures

1. x = 2.5

2. m = 7.5

3. x = 12, y = 18

4. a = 8, b = 15

5. 11.5 feet tall

6. $38\frac{1}{3}$ feet tall

7. x = 21

8. t = 27.5

9. x = 6, y = 8, z = 8.25

10. k = $25\frac{1}{2}$, m = 30, n = $34\frac{2}{3}$

11. k = 12

12. $x = 21\frac{5}{7}$

13. f = 20, b = 7

14. b = 16, c = 42

15. m = 13, p = 14

16. $x = 52\frac{13}{16}$, $y = 25\frac{11}{13}$

17. x = 13.8

18. m = 104

19. a = 4.05, c = 7.8

20. $p = 44\frac{4}{13}$

21. g = 4.2, h = 6

22. a = 1.6, b = 5.5

23. $3\frac{1}{3}$ feet long

24. $55\frac{5}{9}$ feet tall

25. $10\frac{10}{13}$ feet long

26. 200 feet tall

27. 12 feet

28. 20.4 feet

29. $\frac{4}{5}$

30. $\frac{12.5\,miles}{gallon}$

31. $k = 15\frac{1}{9}$

32. true

33. $7.75

34. 0

35. $-\frac{1}{5}$

36. x = -7

37. $A = 78.5cm^2$

38. -48

39. $-5m - 6$

6.5 Square Roots

1. 5 and -5

2. 12 and -12

3. 4

4. 11

5. $-\frac{5}{7}$

6. $-\frac{4}{9}$

7. $17^2 = 289$

8. $512^2 = 262,144$

9. 2.24

10. -3.74

11. 12

12. 63

13. -40

14. -22

15. 16

16. -14

17. $\frac{1}{10}$

18. $1\frac{1}{3}$

19. 5 seconds

20. 12.7 seconds

21. 17 and 13

22. 10 and 14

23. 4 and 8

24. 3 and 1

25. 10

26. 7.9

27. square root

28. radical

29. 9

30. 11

31. 4

32. 14

33. -3

34. -7

35. -12

36. -10

37. 2.4

38. 8.7

39. -6.3

40. -12.5

41. $\frac{4}{7}$

42. $\frac{1}{3}$

43. $\frac{7}{6}$

44. $\frac{10}{11}$

45. $-\frac{3}{4}$

46. $-\frac{3}{8}$

47. $-\frac{2}{5}$

48. 1

49. $\frac{7}{6}$

50. $\frac{13}{20}$

51. 12

52. 14

53. -4

54. -16

55. 37

56. 57

57. 0

58. 0

59. 30

60. 56

61. 30

62. -81

63. 2

64. 1

65. 12

66. 2

67. 6

68. 68

69. 1

70. $\frac{8}{3} = 2\frac{2}{3}$

71. 1 and 3

72. 17 and 13

73. 1

74. 3

75. 40 and 31

76. 10 and -32

77. 1, 1.41, 1.73, 2, 2.24

78. 3.16, 4.47, 5.48,

6.32, 7.07

79. I = 2

80. t = 3

81. S = 20

82. $z = \dfrac{7}{9}$

83. 4

84. 3

85. 19.2 minutes

86. x = 4.5

87. $\dfrac{54\,miles}{12\,min} = \dfrac{9\,miles}{2\,min}$

88. $\dfrac{7\frac{1}{2}}{22\frac{1}{2}} = \dfrac{1}{3}$

89. A = 5 cm

90. 105

91. t = -10

92. graph

93. $\dfrac{8}{15}$

94. 1

Quiz Yourself 6.1

1) 78 defective to 7062

non-defective;

$\dfrac{78}{7062} = \dfrac{13}{1177}$

2) 4:7

3) 22.8 miles per gallon

4) 6.49 minutes per mile

5) $33.79 per hour

6) Jeremy

Quiz Yourself 6.2

1) False

2) x = 16

3) y = 23.7

4) $m = 2\dfrac{1}{7}$

5) $x = 33\dfrac{1}{3}$ grams of

protein.

6) x = 3 hours to hike the

trail.

Quiz Yourself 6.3

1. $110.40

2. 17.1 minute

3. $821.43

4. 438,000

5. 7871 Asian students

Quiz Yourself 6.4

1. h = 20

2. w = 13.6

3. d = 10.8

4. x = 16, y = 18, z = 12

Quiz Yourself 6.5

1. 15

2. $-\dfrac{5}{9}$

3. -2

4. $1\dfrac{9}{10}$

5. -84

6. 5

7. 8.60

Chapter 6 Review

1. rate, $\dfrac{44\,student}{class}$

2. ratio, $\dfrac{9}{13}$

3. rate, $\dfrac{\$4.39}{18oz}$

4. rate, $\dfrac{\$51.20}{12\,gallons}$

5. $\dfrac{2}{18} = \dfrac{1}{9}$

6. 10.08 minutes/mile

7. 70.5 miles/hour

8. $1\dfrac{13}{19}$ tanks per day

9. \$4.29 for 16 oz

10. 3 year 24-hour fitness

11. true

12. false

13. x = 4.8

14. $m = 3\dfrac{1}{3}$

15. y = 9.3

16. $m = 3\dfrac{5}{9}$

17. $y = 2\dfrac{23}{51}$

18. n = 4.1

19. 15 tutors

20. \$298.67

21. \$133.33

22. \$110.45

23. 106 people

24. 778 births

25. \$5.40

26. 148 calories

27. $x = 3\dfrac{1}{3}$

28. x = 6.52

29. y = 5.52

30. z = 2.96

31. y = 2.38

32. 11

33. 10

34. $\dfrac{2}{7}$

35. $-\dfrac{1}{5}$

36. 27

37. -10

38. 95

39. -50

40. 39

41. $\dfrac{1}{3}$

42. 5

43. 59

44. c = 10

45. a = 24

46. b = 8

47. a = 7

48. c = 13.0

49. a = 9.4

50. right

51. right

52. right

53. not right

54. not right

55. right

Chapter 6 Test Yourself

1. $\dfrac{9}{11}$

2. 8

3. 88

4. -2

5. -73

6. -5

7. $5\dfrac{2}{3}$

8. k = 3.6

9. $b = 2\dfrac{1}{9}$

10. \$196.55/square foot of house

11. 8 pack for \$9.79

12. $\dfrac{13.7}{2159}$

13. $32\dfrac{7}{9}$ detonations per year

14. \$19.20 per hour

15. 13.9 earthquakes per hour

16. a. $\dfrac{937613}{1044743}$

   b. $\dfrac{707534}{1300700}$

   c. $\dfrac{1044743}{3990590}$

17. \$4.36

18. 288.4 minutes

19. yes, because it | Pythagorean Thm
     satisfies the | 20. x = 6

Cumulative Review Chapters 1 – 6

1. $2 \cdot 2 \cdot 3 \cdot 61$

2. 576

3. -14 and 4

4. $1\dfrac{49}{200}$

5. -667

6. undefined

7. 0

8. 25

9. 46

10. 105.5

11. -17

12. 30

13. $-4\dfrac{7}{12}$

14. $4\dfrac{35}{48}$

15. $\dfrac{14c^2}{33g}$

16. 45

17. 2

18. -5.278

19. 102.144

20. 0

21. x = 101

22. x = 17

23. x = -7

24. $3\dfrac{8}{35}$

25. m = 11

26. b = 0.49

27. n = 2

28. c = 2.64

29. $u = \dfrac{2}{5}$

30. $64x$

31. $-31m + 46n + 14$

32. -5

33. 63

34. 96

35. 320.76

36. x = 12

37. C = 3 ft.

38. $A = 55.3896\,yd^2$

39. $\dfrac{339\,miles}{4\,hours}$

40. $\dfrac{4}{5}$

41. $99

42. 71.8 average

43. 25°, 65°

44. $692

45. $265.43

46. $10.59

47. $97.45

48. 462.5 calories

49. 15 classes for $154

50. w = 4.125

Chapter 7 Homework Key

7.1 – Introduction to Percents

1. 25%
2. 13%
3. 96%
4. 9%
5. 87%
6. 7%
7. $\frac{13}{20}$
8. $\frac{39}{50}$
9. $\frac{91}{200}$
10. $\frac{1}{8}$
11. $\frac{11}{200}$
12. $\frac{1}{16}$
13. 60%
14. $87\frac{1}{2}\%$
15. 870%
16. 150%
17. $71\frac{3}{7}\%$
18. $8\frac{1}{3}\%$
19. $21\frac{1}{3}\%$
20. $66\frac{2}{3}\%$
21. 0.75
22. 0.23
23. 2.35
24. 6.14
25. 0.00136
26. 0.00083
27. 6%
28. 8.2%
29. 412%
30. 3.5%
31. 15.7%
32. 0.96%
33.

Tax Rate (Decimal Notation)	Tax Rate (Percent Notation)
0.097	9.7%
0.159	15.9%
0	0%
0.0251	2.51%

34.

Account	Interest Rate (Decimal Notation)	Interest Rate (Percent Notation)
Savings	0.0471	4.71%
Checking	0.0308	3.08%
Credit Card	0.1745	17.45%
CD	0.0582	5.82%

35. 4.55
36. 27.98
37. 13.83
38. 0.33
39. 3.36
40. 37
41. 3.52
42. 5.625
43. $806.60
44. 60,0000 elephants
45. 0.25, 25%
46. $\frac{4}{5}$, 80%
47. 0.4, $\frac{2}{5}$
48. .105, $\frac{21}{200}$
49. $\frac{3}{4}$, 75%
50. 0.58, $\frac{29}{50}$
51. 0.6%, $\frac{3}{500}$
52. 80%, 0.8
53. 0.85, $\frac{17}{20}$
54. 1.2, $\frac{6}{5}$
55. 70%, 0.7
56. 125%, $\frac{5}{4}$
57. 12.73
58. 23
59. 50.82
60. 371.79

61. 5.58
62. $58.87
63. $1089.05
64. $5818.75
65. $\frac{17}{25}$, 68%
66. $\frac{27}{41}$, 65.85%
67. $\frac{7}{92}$, 7.61%
68. 38.30%, $\frac{18}{47}$
69. Kansas :0.0625, Texas 7.75%, Nevada: 6.85%, Ohio: 0.05
70. Contador: 0.1155, Armstrong: 4.5%, Cancellera: 0.0385, Gilbert: 8.65%
71. 0.20, $\frac{1}{5}$
72. 0.85, $\frac{17}{20}$
73. 0.50, $\frac{1}{2}$
74. 0.68, $\frac{17}{25}$
75. 0.25, $\frac{1}{4}$
76. 0.30, $\frac{3}{10}$
77. 0.15, $\frac{3}{20}$
78. 0.20, $\frac{1}{5}$
79. 8 students
80. 6 students
81. 6522 visas
82. 5,130,081
83. -35
84. x = 7
85.
86. 9.4 inches
87. 90

7.2 – Solving Percent Statements

1. $0.15(70) = 10.5$
2. $0.38(35) = 13.3$
3. $900 = 0.45(2000)$
4. $120 = 0.75(160)$
5. 7 is 20% of 35;
   $7 = 0.2(35)$
6. 26.2 is 18.63% of 140.6;
   $26.2 = 0.1863(140.6)$
7. $28 = x \cdot 64$
8. $x = 0.18 \cdot 356$
9. $0.16 \cdot x = 49.92$
10. $0.45 \cdot 156 = x$
11. 266
12. 4.8
13. 55%
14. 160
15. $40,000
16. 2114 homes
17. B
18. C
19. C
20. D
21. C
22. B
23. YES
24. NO
25. D

26. B
27. C
28. B
29. B
30. B
31. A
32. D
33. B
34. C
35. A
36. B
37. 5
38. 91
39. 38.5
40. 168
41. 5160
42. 50%
43. 50%
44. 76.67
45. 30.6
46. 30%
47. 146
48. 100%
49. 4.8%
50. $5710.50
51. $12,828.95
52. 61.3%

53. 20%
54. $5500
55. $16,800
56. 18%
57. 80 games
58. 163 games
59. $37,500 per episode
60. $27,000 per episode
61. 20.8% of a day
62. 41.7% of a day
63. 5.6 million US accounts
64. 16 years
65. $\dfrac{27}{200}$
66. 80%
67. 0.352
68. 1570%
69. $15
70. $x = 9\dfrac{3}{5}$
71. -2
72. $\dfrac{29}{36}$
73. -4.816
74. 7

7.3 – Consumer Applications of Percents

1. $7.79
2. $31.16
3. $137.85
4. $321.65
5. $22.25
6. $66.75
7. $27.48
8. $34.50
9. $4119
10. $1495
11. $3.02
12. $70.02
13. $8.51
14. $118.31
15. $2.75
16. $48.60
17. $15.26; $233.26
18. $15,454.80
19. $58.59
20. $148.70
21. $22.50
22. $15
23. $9.5
24. $28.50
25. $31.74

26. $111.09
27. $74.79
28. $288.48
29. $21
30. $46.15
31. $114.60
32. $2043.50
33. $5.23
34. $40.10
35. $15.66
36. $102.68
37. $21.91
38. $131.47
39. $105.49
40. $155.25
41. $251.70
42. $1274.50
43. $15.60
44. $62.40
45. $34.80
46. $313.20
47. $7.16
48. $40.59
49. $399.68
50. $599.52

51. $72.00
52. $215.99
53. $1.41
54. $24.97
55. $9.03
56. $166.03
57. $7.62
58. $105.96
59. $69.84
60. $867.99
61. $4.20
62. $60.20
63. $19.23
64. $167.12
65. $233.75
66. $4908.75
67. $1108.80
68. $54.60
69. $31.2
70. $84.44
71. $137.50, $1387.50
72. $8.46, $97.46
73. $108.75, $115.28
74. $345.87
75. $293.40

76. $34.71
77. $18,853.50
78. $13,822.50
79. $77,727
80. $11,683.50
81. $2.78
82. $6685

83. 72
84. 5%
85. 36%
86. $83\frac{1}{3}\%$
87. 0.105
88. graph

89. y = 7
90. -12
91. $-1\frac{2}{7}$
92. b = 6.5

7.4 – Other Applications of Percents

1. 8 g, 24g
2. 4g, 16g
3. 21 more, 91 total
4. 18,000 more square feet, 63,000 total
5. 32%
6. 8%
7. 4%
8. 38%
9. 14,400 own a cat
10. 160 own a horse
11. 5%
12. 38%
13. 400
14. 660
15. $130, $780
16. $178.50, $416.50
17. 7%
18. 14%
19. 77%
20. 2122%
21. 79%
22. 99.7%
23. 10% off
24. 10% off
25. 15%
26. 114%

27. 28%
28. 26.5%
29. 46.6%
30. 0.6%
31. 1.6%
32. 20.6%
33. 260.236 thousand tons
34. 891.691 thousand tons
35. 11.481 thousand tons
36. 290.852 thousand tons
37. 25%
38. 9%
39. 29%
40. 17%
41. 3850 students exercise
42. 7801 students do nothing
43. 9110 students watch TV, listen to music
44. 729 students clean
45. 7.4%
46. 9.9%

47. 3,164
48. 2,806
49. 55,344
50. 152,595
51. 35%
52. 25%
53. 20%
54. 30%
55. 1,451
56. 251
57. 26.9%
58. $\frac{9}{20}$
59. 5409%
60. $210.94
61. 0.02
62. P = 38 in, A = $84in^2$
63. No
64. $\frac{3}{4x}$
65. $\frac{1}{2}$
66. <

7.5 – Interest

1. $36
2. $100.70
3. $120
4. $3.75
5. $2102.40
6. $1250
7. $3510; $18510
8. $1204.17; $9704.17
9. $541.57
10. $1054.76
11. $13444.23
12. $136,020.56
13. P = 10,000, r = 3.1%, n = 1
14. P = 500, r = 4.7%, n = 12
15. $2840.90

16. $7489.75
17. interest rate
18. principle
19. compound interest
20. interest
21. simple interest
22. $1,920
23. $91.13
24. $180
25. $3,960
26. $9.17
27. $115
28. $478.57
29. $9,56.13
30. $1,576.88
31. $2,859.19
32. $7,136.72

33. $38,082.48
34. $2,527.70, $8,022.70
35. $9,065, $34,965
36. $581.88
37. $1544.23
38. $293,125
39. $745,000
40. $5,254
41. $15,389.81
42. Plan B
43. Plan B
44. 26%
45. $\frac{1}{8}$
46. 40

47. 8.7%   50. $2 \cdot 5 \cdot 13$ 53. $-9a + 3b + 10$
48. $30   51. 10
49. 28   52. $-12y + 27$

7.6 – Introduction to Probability

1. 14.5%, $\dfrac{29}{200}$

2. 46%, 0.46

3. $\dfrac{1}{4}$

4. $\dfrac{1}{4}$

5. $\dfrac{3}{4}$

6. $\dfrac{3}{4}$

7. $\dfrac{2}{3}$

8. $\dfrac{1}{3}$

9. $\dfrac{23}{38}$

10. 0.2

11. {B1, B2, B3, R1, R2, R3, Y1, Y2, Y3}, 9 outcomes

12. {B1, B2, R1, R2, Y1, Y2, G1, G2}, 8 outcomes

13. $\dfrac{3}{13}$

14. $\dfrac{2}{13}$

15. $\dfrac{1}{8}$

16. $\dfrac{1}{6}$

17. $\dfrac{2}{5}$

18. $\dfrac{1}{4}$

19. $\dfrac{1}{2}$

20. $\dfrac{7}{12}$

21. $\dfrac{4}{13}$

22. $\dfrac{9}{13}$

23. $\dfrac{4}{13}$

24. $\dfrac{2}{13}$

25. $\dfrac{1}{4}$

26. $\dfrac{1}{4}$

27. $\dfrac{1}{2}$

28. $\dfrac{3}{4}$

29. $\dfrac{1}{8}$

30. $\dfrac{1}{8}$

31. {1H, 1T, 2H, 2T, 3H, 3T, 4H, 4T}

32. {1H, 1T, 2H, 2T, 3H, 3T, 4H, 4T, 5H, 5T, 6H, 6T, 7H, 7T, 8H, 8T}

33. $\dfrac{1}{8}$

34. $\dfrac{1}{16}$

35. {1H, 1T, 2H, 2T, 3H, 3T}

36. $\dfrac{1}{6}$

37. $\dfrac{1}{6}$

38. $\dfrac{1}{3}$

39. 29.3%

40. $570

41. 32.8%

42. 12.5%

43. $16.88

44. graph

45. 7.95

46. $\dfrac{x}{2}$

47. x = -22

48. $2 \cdot 3 \cdot 7$

49. y = 4.97

Quiz Yourself 7.1

1. 37.5%

2. 7.9%

3. 460%

4. .358

5. $\dfrac{9}{20}$

6. $\dfrac{11}{150}$

7. 15.6

8. 72.345

9. 302 graduates.

Quiz Yourself 7.2

1. 164

2. 134

3. 38.07

4. 36.5%

5. 436

6. 75.2%

7. $42,980

8. c

Quiz Yourself 7.3

1. $543.20

2. 40,507.50

3. $10.47

4. $21.31; $139.69

5. a. $9,945
   b. $39,780

c. $49,725

d. $5,967

Quiz Yourself 7.4

1. 82% increase
2. 3% decrease
3. 35%
4. 10%
5. $516
6. $258
7. $309.60
8. 78%
9. $2012.40

Quiz Yourself 7.5

1. $408
2. $220
3. $658.03
4. $635,800
5. $5490.86

Quiz Yourself 7.6

1. 2.3%
2. $\frac{1}{7}$
3. 0.192
4. 20%
5. $\frac{4}{7}$
6. 12 possible outcomes:

$\{A,1\}\{A,2\}\{A,3\}\{Q,1\}\{Q,2\}\{Q,3\}$
$\{7,1\}\{7,2\}\{7,3\}\{5,1\}\{5,2\}\{5,3\}$

Chapter 7 Review

1. 7.6%
2. 125%
3. 12%
4. 40%
5. $33\frac{1}{3}\%$
6. $34\frac{2}{7}\%$
7. $0.15; \frac{3}{20}$
8. $0.687; \frac{687}{1000}$
9. $0.04; \frac{1}{25}$
10. $0.\bar{6}; \frac{2}{3}$
11. 22%
12. 25%
13. $\frac{37}{40}$, 92.5%
14. $\frac{29}{47}$, 61.7%
15. 11.949
16. 1606.5
17. 44.03
18. 16.65
19. 87.21
20. $42.\bar{2}\%$

21. 19.13%
22. 40
23. 83.58
24. 4,100 visas
25. 47 different types
26. 15
27. 87
28. 30
29. 57.09
30. 13.6
31. $30.66
32. $3355.45
33. $12.09
34. $27,000
35. $35.75, $90.75
36. $67.20, $115.20
37. a. $1173.05
    b. $87.98
    c. $1261.03
38. a. $100   b. $48
    c. $523
39. $90,000
40. $3,850
41. 78.3% increase
42. 57%
43. 24%
44. 13,536%
45. 37.5%
46. 79%
47. 18%
48. 24%

49. 55.44 hours
50. 30.24 hours
51. $1155
52. $576.72
53. $10,001.83
54. $2,977.36
55. $11,188.83
56. $3,120
57. $\frac{1}{2}$
58. $\frac{1}{3}$
59. $\frac{1}{4}$
60. $\frac{3}{13}$
61. $\frac{7}{18}$
62. $\frac{2}{13}$
63. {H1, T1, H2, T2, H3, T3, H4, T4, H5, T5, H6, T6}
64. {HG, TG, HR, TR, HO, TO, HP, TP, HY, TY}

Chapter 7 Test Yourself

1. 65%
2. 380%
3. 37.5%
4. $54\frac{6}{11}\%$
5. 0.28, $\frac{7}{25}$
6. $0.\overline{33}, \frac{100}{3}$
7. 90

8. 29
9. 9
10. 5.728
11. 31.25%
12. 77.14
13. $\frac{37}{40}$, 92.5%
14. $23.88
15. $1,996.06
16. $14.42
17. $17,415

18. a) $431.21   b) $26.95 c) $458.16
19. $\frac{3}{52}$
20. {R1, R2, R3, R4, B1, B2, B3, B4, Y1, Y2, Y3, Y4, G1, G2, G3, G4} 16 outcomes

---

Cumulative Review Chapters 1- 7

1. Composite; $3 \cdot 17$
2. $-15\frac{3}{5}$
3. 12 and 4
4. yes
5. -42
6. -1
7. $\frac{13}{72}$
8. $-7\frac{1}{2}$
9. $\frac{20x^4}{81y^3}$
10. $-2\frac{1}{10}$
11. $5\frac{6}{35}$
12. $-1\frac{2}{3}$
13. $5\frac{13}{24}$
14. 33.915
15. -38.054
16. 776.42
17. $1\frac{4}{45}$
18. 1

19. $x = 24$
20. $x = -136$
21. $\frac{59}{63}$
22. $m = -45.245$
23. $n = -4273.\overline{46}$
24. $x = 8$
25. $x = \frac{-11}{10}$
26. $x = \frac{-27}{2}$
27. 1
28. -33
29. $-3\frac{6}{7}$
30. $\frac{-1}{3}$
31. 25
32. 121
33. $\frac{19}{25}$
34. $0.\overline{8}$
35. $37\frac{1}{2}\%$
36. 0.68
37. $\frac{23}{150}$
38. 136%

39. <
40. >
41. 143
42. 720
43. 16.52
44. 48
45. 400%
46. $45\frac{7}{15} in^2$
47. $616 m^2$
48. $57.776 ft$
49. $2(x+5) = 13 - x; \; x = 1$
50. $1311.11
51. $33°, 66°$, and $81°$
52. $22\frac{1}{2}°, 67\frac{1}{2}°$
53. $2(2+3w) + 2w = 46;$ $w = 5\frac{1}{4} ft. \; l = 17\frac{3}{4} ft$
54. $245.53
55. $232.50
56. 11.2 years
57. $10,997.50
58. $2250

Chapter 8 Answers

8.1 American Measurement

1. $\dfrac{1\,foot}{12\,inches}$, $\dfrac{12\,inches}{1\,foot}$

2. $\dfrac{1760\,yards}{1\,mile}$, $\dfrac{1\,mile}{1760\,yards}$

3. 4 feet
4. 5 yards
5. $4\dfrac{1}{3}$ yards
6. $2\dfrac{1}{4}$ feet
7. 5 yards
8. $\dfrac{25}{96}$ miles
9. $\dfrac{2\,pint}{1\,quart}$, $\dfrac{1\,quart}{2\,pint}$
10. $\dfrac{8\,oz}{1\,cup}$, $\dfrac{1\,cup}{8\,oz}$
11. 28 cups
12. 26 quarts
13. 3 cups
14. $3\dfrac{1}{4}$ gallons
15. $4\dfrac{5}{8}$ gallons
16. $2\dfrac{11}{32}$ quarts
17. $\dfrac{1\,pound}{16\,oz}$, $\dfrac{16\,oz}{1\,pound}$
18. $\dfrac{1\,ton}{2000\,lbs}$, $\dfrac{2000\,lbs}{1\,ton}$
19. 5 tons
20. 1024 oz.
21. $2\dfrac{3}{16}$ lbs.

22. $2\dfrac{7}{20}$ ton
23. 86,400 oz
24. $1\dfrac{1}{8}$ tons
25. 5280
26. 1760
27. 2
28. 12
29. 4
30. 2000
31. 16
32. 8
33. 8 pints
34. 93.6 inches
35. $4\dfrac{11}{16}$ lbs
36. 88 oz
37. 24 yds.
38. $13\dfrac{1}{2}$ cups
39. 13,400 lbs.
40. 18 qts
41. $4\dfrac{1}{2}$ pts.
42. $\dfrac{5}{88}$ miles
43. $2\dfrac{11}{16}$ quarts
44. $3\dfrac{1}{8}$ gallons
45. 17,448 inches
46. 12 tons
47. $12\dfrac{1}{2}$ feet
48. 100,000 lbs
49. 20 gallons
50. 138,336 feet
51. 30 pints
52. $40\dfrac{719}{880}$ miles
53. 144,000,000 lbs

54. $5\dfrac{527}{1056}$ miles
55. $8\dfrac{1}{8}$ lbs
56. 324 inches, 9 yards
57. 198 inches, 16.5 feet
58. 151 feet, $50\dfrac{1}{3}$ yards
59. 2007.6 inches, 55.77 yards
60. P = 56 in = $4\dfrac{2}{3}$ ft,
    A = 180 in^2
    = $1\dfrac{1}{4}$ ft^2
61. P = 36 in = 3 ft,
    A = 72 $in^2 = \dfrac{1}{2}$ ft^2
62. P = 18 yd = 54 ft,
    A = 20 $yd^2 = 2\dfrac{2}{9}$ ft^2
63. P = 29 yd = 87 ft,
    A = 459 ft^2 = 51 yd^2
64. A = 108 $in^2 = \dfrac{3}{4}$ ft^2
65. A = 604.8 ft^2
    = 33.6 yd^2
66. A = 5 ft^2
67. A = 993.6 in^2
68. -0.84
69. false
70. $68 = 2^2 \cdot 17$
71. 0.57
72. $6\dfrac{2}{83}$ tons of steel
73. $54 million

8.2 Metric Measurement

1. b
2. b
3. a
4. c
5. $\dfrac{1kg}{1000g}$
6. $\dfrac{1m}{100cm}$
7. 0.157 m
8. 6,300 g
9. 70 m
10. 0.95 m
11. 0.082 dm
12. 8.19 km
13. 0.0005 daL
14. 800,000 cL
15. 529 dL
16. 0.08750
17. 8.6 dg
18. 6.3 dag
19. 0.065
20. 0.75 dag
21. 13.8 dag = 0.138 dg
22. 75.3 hL = 7.53 kL
23. 8,935 cm = 0.08935 km
24. 13.6 m = 1360 cm
25. 80.5 cg = 805 mg
26. 48.5 kL = 485 hL
27. >
28. <
29. =
30. <

31. d
32. g
33. a
34. h
35. f
36. c
37. e
38. b
39. 600 cg
40. 0.38 g
41. 15,030,000 mL
42. 72 cm
43. 78,200 dg
44. 168 cL
45. 85,000 cg
46. 0.15 km
47. 4,900 m
48. 5 daL
49. 0.0006 daL
50. 40.9 cL
51. 1,405,000,000 mg
52. 7 dL
53. 0.00975 kg
54. 964 cm
55. 0.0823 dm
56. 613 cL
57. 53.4 dm
58. 735 mL
59. 8919.3 dag
60. 84211 mL
61. 14924 mg
62. 5380 dg
63. 284 cm
64. 55.475 L

65. 235 mg
66. 460 mm
67. 13,000,000 m
68. 303,000,000 L
69. 481 m
70. 34 g
71. 3,750 squirts
72. P = 25 m, A = 6 m^2
73. P = 22.5 m, A = 31.5 m^2
74. A = 2 m^2
75. A = 31.5 m^2
76. 0.8 cm = 0.008 m
77. 0.67 L = 0.067 daL
78. 0.0003 km = 300 mm
79. 0.801 dg = 0.00801 dag
80. 78 inches
81. $\dfrac{4quarts}{1gallon}$
82. $\dfrac{19}{80}$
83. 16 fl. oz
84. 40.8 pints of fuel
85. 9 & 2
86. $1416\dfrac{2}{3}$ seconds
87. x = -2
88. 3
89. 5 and -5

8.3 Conversion Between Measurement Systems

1. 1.86 m
2. 18.95 qts
3. 4,583.35 mm
4. $16\dfrac{2}{3}$ lbs
5. 11.4 L
6. 4.095 km
7. 149 °F
8. 181.4 °F
9. 5 °C
10. $44\dfrac{4}{9}$ °C
11. 213.8 °F
12. 98.6 °F
13. 0.31
14. 0.95

15. 1.61
16. 0.45
17. 3.79
18. 29.57
19. 18.95 L
20. 10,290 gallons
21. 112.1 °F
22. 189.5 L
23. 2,638.5 gallons
24. 460 °C
25. 473 °F
26. 182 miles
27. 3.96 kg
28. 556 lbs.
29. 67.4 fl. oz
30. 6.23 feet
31. 11.875 L

32. 2,160 kg
33. 1760
34. $4\dfrac{1}{4}$ gallons
35. $\dfrac{2000lb}{1ton}$
36. 62,000 mm
37. 128 cm^2
38. 2,170
39. 1
40. yes
41. $\dfrac{2}{21}$
42. 3 + 2y

Chapter 8 Review

1. $1\frac{1}{4}$ ft

2. $22\frac{2}{3}$ yd

3. $2\frac{1}{8}$ c

4. $15\frac{1}{2}$ qts

5. $3\frac{7}{16}$ lb

6. 6 gal

7. 576 in

8. 26,928 ft

9. $3\frac{4}{25}$ ton

10. $7\frac{1}{2}$ qts

11. 10,912 yards

12. $6\frac{26}{33}$ miles

13. 5,375 gallons

14. 117 ounces

15. 340 mm

16. 73,000 dg

17. 6,510 cm

18. 89 dm

19. 0.005782

20. 4751.8 hm

21. 0.0993

22. 683,924 cL

23. 113.9 cL

24. 2,117 g

25. 790.3 dL

26. 271.5 cm

27. 5000 m

28. 28,600 g

29. 0.125 grams

30. P = 148 cm, A = 1305 cm^2

31. 22.75 m

32. 4.275 L

33. 2.356 gal

34. 6.75 kg

35. 82.105 pt

36. 304.8 cm

37. 15.53 miles

38. 473.12 mL

39. 39.35 feet

40. $30\frac{5}{9}\,^{\circ}C$

41. $64.4\,^{\circ}F$

42. 124.4 lbs

Chapter 8 Test Yourself

1. $5\frac{1}{3}$ yd

2. 0.00057 hL

3. $1\frac{1}{2}$ lbs

4. $9\frac{3}{4}$ qts

5. 0.678 m

6. 380,000 mm

7. 17.018 dm

8. 180 qts

9. 0.4 km

10. 31.06 miles

11. 1.86 m

12. 99 oz

13. 0.16 grams of caffeine

14. 100 lbs

15. $1076\frac{2}{3}$ yards tall

16. $95\,^{\circ}F$

17. 1,096,000 quarts of ethanol

18. $3,172.50

19. 996.41 mg

20. P = 320 mm, A = 4284 mm^2

Cummulatvie Review Chapters 1 – 8

1. -16 & 3

2. <

3. yes

4. -23

5. $\frac{1}{3}$

6. -6

7. -480

8. $\frac{61}{75}$

9. -140

10. -22.69

11. -0.455

12. $11\frac{7}{9}$

13. $\frac{9x^2}{35y}$

14. $4\frac{13}{30}$

15. $\frac{1}{8}$

16. -2

17. $-5x+9y$

18. $21x^2+112xy-7y^2$

19. $x+28$

20. $10m-19$

21. 32

22. 1

23. 65

24. x = 431

25. $k=\frac{-16}{19}$

26. $x=-3\frac{1}{3}$

27. x = -4.55

28. c = 2

29. $t=-5\frac{2}{7}$

30. 4.5 dm

31. $2\frac{1}{6}$ ft

32. 26 cups

33. 21.091 km

34. $26\frac{2}{3}$ %

35. $\frac{167}{250}$

36. 278.46

37. $59.75, $179.25

38. $8,503,320

39. 0.62, $\frac{31}{50}$

40. $141.33

41. 61.5 grams of carbs

42. 1.17 kg

43. 1648 yards, 20.6 laps

44. -76 $°F$

45. 29.13 cm

46. A = 1886.5 m^2

47. 40°, 140°

48. 20.2%

49. China, 20.6%

50. 4.9%

Quiz Yourself 8.1
1. 5280
2. $\frac{8 ounces}{1 cup}$, $\frac{2 cup}{1 pt}$
3. $2\frac{1}{2}$ feet
4. $\frac{37}{100}$ tons
5. 4 quarts
6. 6 pints
7. A = 155.025 ft^2
   =17.225 yd^2

Quiz Yourself 8.2
1. 100
2. 1500 dg
3. 7000 cm
4. 0.5009 dL
5. 277.5 m
6. 14.4 m^2

Quiz Yourself 8.3
1. 16.91 oz
2. 5.0 L
3. 17.6 m
4. 153 $°F$
5. 232 $°C$

Chapter 9 Answers

9.1 Ordered Pairs and The Rectangular Coordinate System

1. (100,57), (50,51), (340, 86), (75,54)
2. (0,27.5), (20,61.7), (40,121.6), (53,146.3)
3.

x	y
5	-7
0	3
-2	-4
8	0

4.

x	y
2	2
-4	11
1	-8
0	0

5. origin, left, up
6. origin, right, down
7.

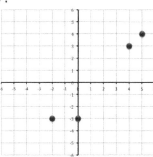

8.

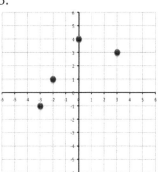

9. Q:(-3,2), R:(-1,-1), S:(3,3), T:(2,0)
10. K:(-4,4), L:(-4,0), M:(5,1), N:(3,-4)
11. IV
12. none
13. I
14. III
15. none
16. II
17. origin
18. y-axis
19. quadrants
20. ordered pair
21. (2,-7)
22. (-10,-3)
23. (0,1.76), (3,2.30), (6,1.73), (9,1.89)
24. (0,19)(5,15)(7,12)(10,7)
25. answers will vary: (+,+)
26. answers will vary: (+,-)
27. answers will vary: (-,-)
28. answers will vary: (0,) or (,0)
29. answers will vary: (0,)
30. answers will vary: (,0)
31. The points all lie on the same straight line.

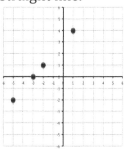

32. The points all lie on the same straight line.

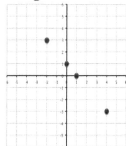

33. The figure is a rectangle.
34. The figure is a square.

35.

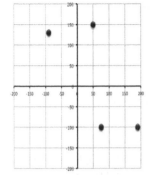

36.

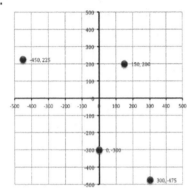

37.

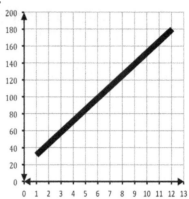

38.

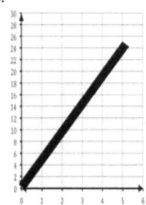

39. $-\dfrac{1}{2}$

40. $7x - 8y$

41. $\dfrac{9}{20}$

42. $40\,ft^2$

43. -7

9.2 Linear Equations and Their Graphs

1. yes
2. no
3. yes
4. yes
5. no
6. no
7. (1,0), (-2,1), (6,-1)
8. (1,-1), (6,1)
9. a.) (3,4) b.) (10,-3)
10. a.) (1,3), b.) (3,-1)
11. a.) $(\frac{1}{2},1)$ b.) (2,-11)
12. a.) $(\frac{1}{3},-4)$ b.) (3,4)
13.

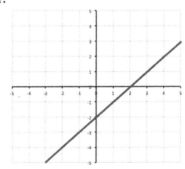

14.

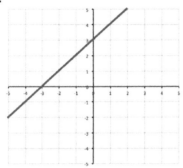

15.

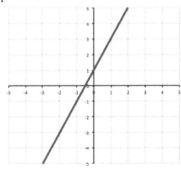

16.

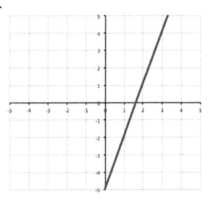

17.

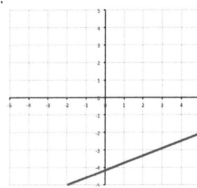

18.

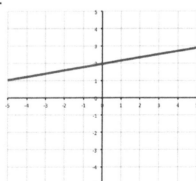

19. x-intercept: (-3,0), y-intercept: (0,-4)
20. x-intercept: (-2,0), y-intercept: (0,2)

21.

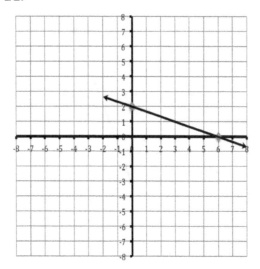

23.

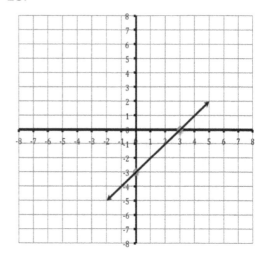

22.

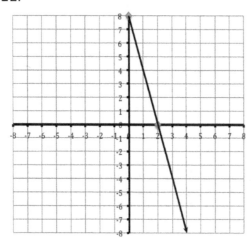

24.

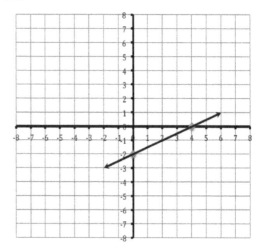

25. linear equations in two variable
26. y-intercept
27. graph of an equation
28. x-intercept
29. solution
30.

x-value	*y*-value	solution
$x = 0$	y = 4	(0,4)
x=6	$y = 0$	(6,0)
$x = 3$	y=2	(3,2)

31.

x-value	y-value	solution
$x = 0$	y=-5	(0,-5)
x=6	$y = 0$	(6,0
x=12	$y = 5$	(12,5)

32.

x-value	y-value	solution
$x = 0$	y=-3	(0,-3)
x=7	$y = 0$	(7,0)
x=14	$y = 3$	(14,3)

33.

x-value	y-value	solution
$x = 0$	y=2	(0,2)
x=22	$y = 0$	(22,0)
$x = 11$	y=1	(11,1)

34.

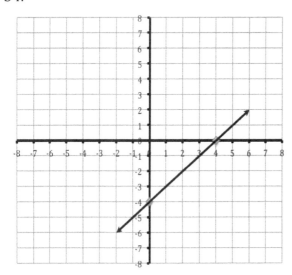

35.

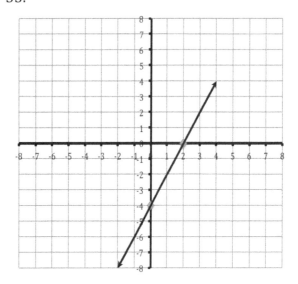

36.

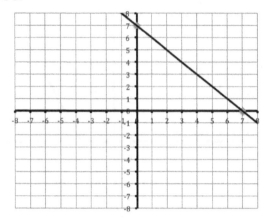

37.

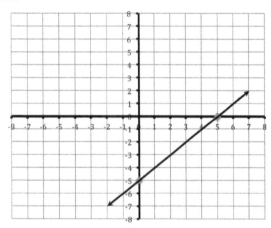

38.

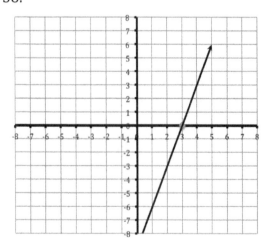

39.

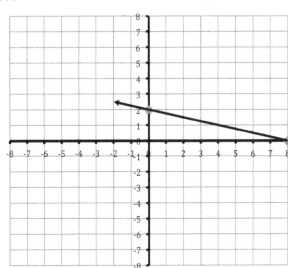

41.

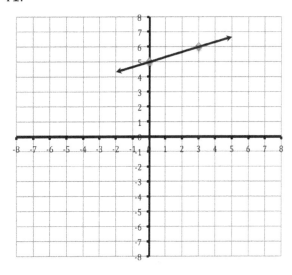

40.

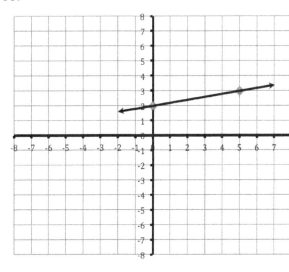

42. graph

43. $\dfrac{33}{8}$

44. $x = 11$

45. -2.5

46. $2 \cdot 5 \cdot 13$

9.1 Quiz Yourself

1.

Year	Population
2000	6.3
2002	6.7
2004	7.8
2006	8.1

2. (-3,-4) (-2,4) (0,-5) (5,3)

3.

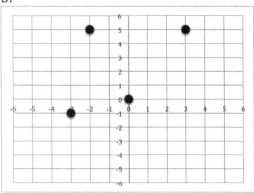

4. III

9.2 Quiz Yourself

1. (1,-4), (3,2)

2.

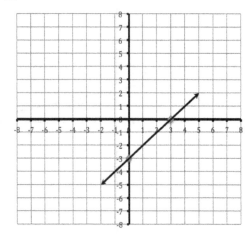

3.

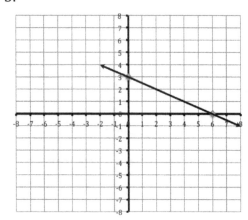

4.

x-value	y-value	solution
$x = 0$	y=40	(0,40)
x=5	$y = 0$	(5,0)
$x = 4$	y=8	(4,8)

5. (3,0) (0,-4)